Note (1) Osilloscope. P 197

") Testing & Mea

ses
P 213

(III) " " "

222

HANDBOOK FOR ELECTRONIC ENGINEERS AND TECHNICIANS

HANDBOOK

FOR ELECTRONIC ENGINEERS AND TECHNICIANS

Harry E. Thomas

CONSULTING ENGINEER

PRENTICE-HALL, INC.

ENGLEWOOD CLIFFS, N.J.

PRENTICE-HALL INTERNATIONAL, INC.   *London*

PRENTICE-HALL OF AUSTRALIA, PTY., LTD.   *Sydney*

PRENTICE-HALL OF CANADA, LTD.   *Toronto*

PRENTICE-HALL OF INDIA (PRIVATE), LTD.   *New Delhi*

PRENTICE-HALL OF JAPAN, INC.   *Tokyo*

**Handbook
for Electronic Engineers
and Technicians**

by Harry E. Thomas

© 1965 by
Prentice-Hall, Inc.
Englewood Cliffs, New Jersey

Library of Congress Catalog Card Number: 65-22188

PRINTED IN THE UNITED STATES OF AMERICA
37729-C

Preface

The era of post-war technology produced a tremendous expansion in the country's electronic design laboratories and in production facilities for military hardware. Missile, aircraft, communication, and radar equipment were all operated by and supported with tremendous electronic complexes. This whole trend heightened the need for printed data on theory, design, and application.

This complexity and the requirements for condensed but explicit information (particularly to meet military specifications) prompted the need for technical handbooks which were oriented toward design, production, and application of electronic hardware.

The aim of *Handbook for Electronic Engineers and Technicians* is to present, in concentrated form, those areas of theory, design, test, and operation pertaining to electronic hardware. It is intended for the design and operating engineer and his supporting technicians, and it follows the progressive steps they encounter in producing a piece of hardware. This arrangement saves time in looking up details of materials, metalworking, components, specifications, circuitry construction, manufacturing, and testing.

The first six chapters cover the essentials of drafting systems and techniques, sheet-metal working tools and shop practices, electronic component parts and their handling, and wiring and chassis assembly. As a prelude to testing and measurement, Chapter 7 provides the simpler facts of arithmetic, algebra, logarithms, trigonometry, binary numbers, and the use of slide rule.

The next eight chapters cover the techniques and tools of measurement necessary to develop and process the assembled hardware at the component and circuit level. This includes basic measurement circuits, general techniques, simple indicating meters, and adaptations of electronic voltmeters, frequency meters, and oscilloscopes.

The last six chapters concern equipment measurement and crystallize techniques and circuitry of major electronic hardware areas. Using brief functional analysis by text and block diagram, the material summarizes the measurements to be conducted, the instruments to be used, and the procedure to be followed. In covering microwaves, receivers, transmitters, radar, servomechanisms, and power supplies, a full cross section of military hardware is exposed.

The appendices supplement the text with ready usable data in the form of tables, curves, and procedures in addition to detailed glossaries and lists of frequently used formulas and symbols. The six appendices provide the essential data used in general electronics, components, mechanical and shop work, microwave maintenance, design, and mathematics for electronics.

This book is intended for the working engineers and laboratory technicians. As a group, they form the backbone of the personnel employed in our modern electronic laboratories and undoubtedly contribute more to our scientific and engineering effort than any other group in the electronic industry. Their excellence determines the basic quality of a laboratory's output, for it is they who deliver the actual, operating missile guidance system, the fighter plane communication system, or the submarine navigational mechanism.

HARRY E. THOMAS

Acknowledgments

Appreciation is expressed to the following companies for permission to use the indicated materials:

The Admiral Corporation, Chicago, Ill.   Fig. 1-2(c).
Allen-Bradley Co., Milwaukee, Wis.   Fig. 5-4(a).
Alvin and Co., Windsor, Conn.   Fig. 2-7.
The Amperite Co., Union City, N. J.   Fig. 5-6.
Amphenol-Borg Electronics Co., Chicago, Ill.   Fig. 5-35.
Ballantine Laboratories, Inc., Boonton, N. J.   Fig. 9-10.
The Billings and Spencer Co., Hartford, Conn.   Fig. 4-3.
Boonton Radio Co., Div. of Hewlett-Packard Co., Rockaway, N. J.   Fig. 9-11.
Brown and Sharpe Mfg. Co., Providence, R. I.   Figs. 3-13, 3-17, 3-18(b, c), 4-17.
Charles Bruning Co., Inc., Mount Prospect, Ill.   Figs. 2-6, 2-7, 7-1(a).
Bussmann Mfg. Div., McGraw-Edison Co., St. Louis, Mo.   Fig. 5-6, App. B-10.
Cambridge Thermionic Corp., Cambridge, Mass.   Fig. 5-16.
Cannon Electric Co., Los Angeles, Calif.   Fig. 5-35.
Chicago Rivet and Machine Co., Chicago, Ill.   Fig. 4-34.
Clarostat Mfg. Co., Chicago, Ill.   Fig. 5-5(a, b).
The Cleveland Twist Drill Co., Cleveland, O.   Figs. 4-17, 4-23.
The Coes Co., Hartford, Conn.   Fig. 4-3(a).
Continental Connector Corp., Woodside, N. Y.   Fig. 5-35.
Corning Glass Works, Corning, N.Y.   Figs. 5-13, 6-4(b).
Dale Electronics Inc., Columbus, Neb.   Fig. 5-5(d).
The Daven Co., Livingston, N. J.   Fig. 5-4(c).
Daystrom Inc., Transicoil Div., Worcester, Pa.   Fig. 5-33; App. E-9.
Dialight Corp., Brooklyn, N. Y.   App. B-12.
Electro-Motive Mfg. Co., Willimantic, Conn.   Fig. 5-8(b).
Electronic Design, *Hayden Publ. Co., N. Y., N. Y.   App. B-13.*
The Electronic Industries Association.   App. A-10.
Electronic Industries, *a Chilton Publication, Philadelphia, Pa.   Figs. 21-10, 21-11.*
Engineered Electronics Co., Santa Ana, Calif.   Fig. 3-1.
Erie Resistor Corp., Erie, Pa.   Fig. 5-12.
Famco Machine Co., Kenosha, Wis.   Fig. 4-21.
Federal Electric Corp., a Subsidiary of International Telephone and Telegraph Corp., Paramus, N. J.   Figs. 1-5, 1-14, 6-1; App. D-3.
Federal Telecommunications Laboratories, a Subsidiary of International Telephone and Telegraph Corp., Nutley, N. J.   Figs. 3-1, 6-5(c).
GC Electronics Co., Div. of Textron Electronics, Inc., Rockford, Ill.   Fig. 6-16(a).
General Electric Co., Schenectady, N. Y.   Figs. 5-29, 15-12, 15-13, 15-14, 21-1, 21-4; Tables 15-4, 15-5; Apps. B-3, B-5, B-6, B-7, B-11.

General Radio Co., Cambridge, Mass.   Fig. 5-19; App. A-7.
Greenfield Tap and Die Co., Greenfield, Mass.   Figs. 4-26, 4-27.
Greenlee Tool Co., Div. of Greenlee Bros. and Co., Rockford, Ill.   Fig. 4-21.
G-V Controls Inc., Livingston, N. J.   Fig. 5-31.
The Hammarlund Mfg. Co., New York, N. Y.   Fig. 5-9.
Hartmann und Braun AG, Frankfort, Germany, (Epic Inc., N. Y.)   Fig. 10-8.
Heath Co., Benton Harbor, Mich.   Fig. 11-12.
Heineman Electric Co., Trenton, N. J.   Fig. 5-37.
Hewlett-Packard Co., Palo Alto, Calif.   Fig. 11-1; App. D-4.
Hunter Tool Div., Hunter Industries, Santa Fe Springs, Calif.   Fig. 4-39.
IERC Div., International Electronics Research Corp., Burbank, Calif.   Fig. 6-9.
International Resistance Co., Philadelphia, Pa.   Fig. 5-4(e).
Jennings Radio Mfg. Corp., San Jose, Calif.   Fig. 5-14(c).
E.F. Johnson Co., Waseca, Minn.   Fig. 5-20.
Keuffel and Esser Co., Hoboken, N. J.   Fig. 2-5.
L-R Mfg. Co., Torrington, Conn.   Fig. 5-32.
Malco Mfg. Co., Chicago, Ill.   Fig. 6-7.
P. R. Mallory and Co., Inc., Indianapolis, Ind.   Figs. 5-11, 5-35.
MicroSwitch Div., Minneapolis-Honeywell Regulator Co., Freeport, Ill.   Fig. 5-34.
The Motorola Corp., Chicago, Ill.   Figs. 15-13, 15-14, 15-15, 15-16, 15-17.
Nicholson File Co., Providence, R. I.   Figs. 4-11, 412.
Non-Linear Systems Inc., Del Mar, Calif.   Fig. 10-9.
Norton Co., Worcester, Mass.   Fig. 4-37.
Oak Mfg. Co., Crystal Lake, Ill.   Fig. 5-34.
Ohmite Mfg. Co., Skokie, Ill.   Fig. 5-2; Apps. E-4, E-6.
The Peck, Stowe, and Wilcox Co., Southington, Conn.   Figs. 4-8, 4-21.
Pel-Electronics Co., Ridgewood, N. J.   Fig. 12-12.
Price Electric Co., Frederick, Md.   Fig. 5-30.
Radio Corp. of America, N. Y., N. Y.   Figs. 5-22, 5-23, 11-2(c); Apps. B-4, F-10.
Sheldon Machine Co., Inc., Chicago, Ill.   Fig. 4-38.
Silicon Transistor Corp., Carle Place, L. I., N. Y.   Fig. 5-27.
Simpson Electric Co., Chicago, Ill.   Fig. 11-1.
The Singer Co., Metrics Div., Bridgeport, Conn.   Fig. 10-7.
South Bend Lathe Inc., South Bend, Ind.   Fig. 4-35.
Southern Screw Co., Statesville, N. C.   Fig. 4-31; App. C-5.
Sperry Microwave Electronics Co., Div. of Sperry Rand Corp., Clearwater, Fla.
    App. D-5.
Sprague Elec. Co., N. Adams, Mass.   Figs. 5-4(b,d), 5-8(a,c), 5-10, 5-14(a), 11-12.
Stancor Electronics Inc., Chicago, Ill.   Fig. 5-17.
Stanley Tools Div., The Stanley Works, New Britain, Conn.   Figs. 3-6, 3-12, 3-16,
    4-5, 4-14, 4-36.
The L. S. Starrett Co., Athol, Mass.   Figs. 3-6, 3-7(b), 3-8(a), 3-9(a), 3-10(a),
    3-11, 3-14, 3-18(a, d), 3-19, 4-25.
Tektronix Inc., Beaverton, Ore.   Figs. 13-11, 13-12, 13-13, 13-14, 13-15.
Triplett Electrical Instruments Co., Bluffton, O.   Fig. 10-11.
Tungsol Electric Inc., Newark, N. J.   Apps. B-1, B-2.
Universal Toroid Coil Winding Co., Irvington, N. J.   Fig. 5-18.
Vitramon Inc., Bridgeport, Conn.   Fig. 5-14(b).
Ward Leonard Electric Co., Mount Vernon, N. Y.   Fig. 5-5(c).
Western Gear Corp., Pasadena, Calif.   Fig. 5-32.
Weston Instrument Co., Newark, N. J.   Fig. 10-10(b).
Whitehead Metal Products, New York, N. Y.   Tables 3-2, 3-3.

Contents

Appendix **F** Mathematical Tables and Formulas, 410

HANDBOOK FOR ELECTRONIC ENGINEERS AND TECHNICIANS

Prints and Drawings

1

BASIC DRAWINGS

In the modern electronics laboratory, standardized, uniform drawings and prints of drawings are the basic method of recording mechanical and electrical engineering information. They are necessary to guide the building, assembling, wiring, or testing of any piece of electronic gear, Any engineer, technician, planning clerk, or shop foreman must have complete printed and/or drafted information before starting work on any hardware project.

A complete collection of such working documents is known as a *set of drawings*. One set usually applies specifically to one chassis or piece of equipment. When several chassis constitute a piece of gear, each chassis has its own set of drawings; an overall collection, or a *set of sets* of drawings, is compiled. Hardware drawing sets, instruction books, repair manuals, together with the mechanical drawings describing racks, mountings, interconnecting cables, accessories, specifications, packing, labels, and so forth, constitute the most complete kind of printed drafting information, known as overall documentation. Figure 1-1 is a block-tabular representation of these drawings. Note that, in addition to the three main drawing divisions, the group labeled "accessory" drawings are merely aids to the overall operation. In the laboratory these are rarely used. However, in planning, testing, or manufacturing electronic equipment, the additional information they yield is necessary.

The operating engineer, and particularly his supporting technicians, require four key drawings before all others within a set of drawings: (1) *a chassis assembly drawing or photograph*, (2) *a mechanical parts list*, (3) *electrical parts and accessory lists*, and (4) *a schematic wiring diagram*. A technician should be familiar with these drawings and their associated subdrawings, lists, and sheets, not only to enlarge his background in drafting, but because they constitute the basic information he needs for general guidance in construction and overall handling of electronic hardware. They

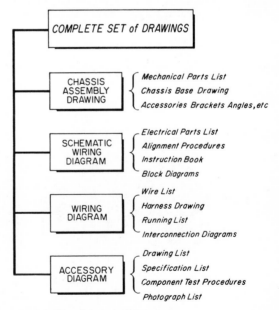

FIG. 1-1 Complete set of drawings

will lead him to other drawings necessary for specific portions of the job with which he must be familiar. (See Chapter 6 on assembly and wiring.)

THE CHASSIS ASSEMBLY DRAWING

A number of assembly drawings are shown in Fig. 1–2. They may be three-dimensional, exploded views, or conventional two-dimensional drawings, of the electrical and mechanical components making up a unit of equipment, as arranged and fastened together in final operational form. Main dimensions are sometimes shown on this type of drawing although they are not always necessary, since the idea of the drawing is to show only the relationship of parts. Each electrical part is usually shown with its schematic designation letter and number, or located is by a reference number.

A SERVICE CHASSIS ASSEMBLY PHOTOGRAPH is very much like an assembly drawing (see Fig. 1–3). Such photographs are used extensively in the television and service industries and are simple to prepare. Production assembly drawings, however, have the advantage of being more precise because they give complete details and provide the opportunity to show assembly sequences and, if necessary, key dimensions. An assembly drawing can also include a complete listing and location of parts. A photograph, on the other hand, has three-dimensional and perspective qualities sometimes not possessed by a drawing, and many manufacturers superimpose location reference information upon photographs.

FIG. 1-2 Chassis assembly drawings

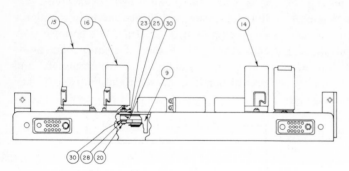

Two-dimensional

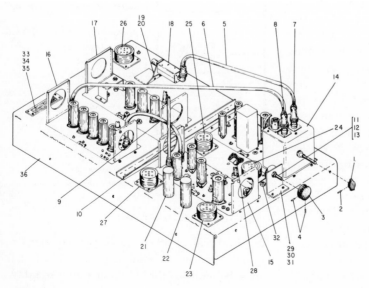

Exploded

Three-dimensional

PRODUCTION ASSEMBLY DRAWINGS (not shown because of space limitations) are an absolute necessity for fabrication, assembly, and wiring shops because they include all dimensions, sizes, shapes, fastenings, and arrangements, detailed according to standardized drafting techniques, plus identification captions, location numbers, "balloons," and other printed information which can not be shown on a photograph. These drawings also include subsidiary information on extra lists, groupings, and so forth.

THE MECHANICAL PARTS LIST OR LIST OF MATERIAL

Separate tabulation of chassis assembly parts is called a mechanical parts list or list of material even though it contains electrical component parts (sometimes called piece parts) together with some of their electrical characteristics in the printed description. These parts are tabulated directly on the main assembly drawing or listed on separate $8\frac{1}{2}'' \times 11''$ parts sheets. Physical location of the individual piece parts on the assembly drawing is linked to listed items by placing the item number of each part (as given on the parts list) within a circle or "balloon" and locating the balloon over or alongside the actual position of the part on the main drawing and connecting the two by an arrow. Figure 1–4 shows an assembly drawing with its accompanying parts list.

ELECTRICAL PARTS AND ACCESSORY LISTS

The electrical parts lists shown in Fig. 1–5 are quite different from mechanical parts lists, and are printed on a different form. They are useful in a manufacturing firm, not only to engineers and technicians, but to many others, including purchasing agents, planning clerks, specification engineers, and component testing personnel, since they contain a more detailed description of electrical components than given on the mechanical parts list. These lists are useful to the technician and engineer since their information, together with the schematic drawing, may often be enough to serve as a guide to construction without the assembly drawing.

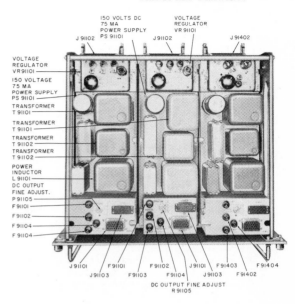

FIG. 1-3 Service chassis assembly photogragh

FIG. 1-4 Mechanical parts list

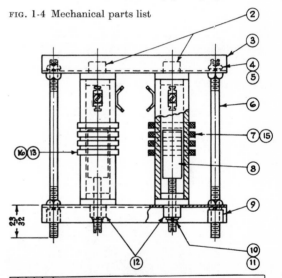

QTY	QTY	QTY	ITEM	REFERENCE	PART OR GROUP	FIN.	DESCRIPTION	MATERIAL
	X	X	1			O	ASSEMBLY	
1	2	2	2	K-829306	1	O	BUSHING	
2	2	2	3	K-829305	1	O	CHANNEL	
4	4	4	4	K-59048	60	010	LOCKWASHER (#8)	(BRONZE)
6	6	6	5	K-57435	55	099	HEX. NUT (#8-32)	(BRASS)
2	2	2	6	K-69275	4	099	STUD	
1			7	M-413204	502	O	COIL ASSEMBLY	
1	2	2	8	K-829302	501	O	CORE AND STUD ASSEMBLY	
2	2	2	9	K-77841	26	099	SPACER	
1	2	2	10	K-59048	59	010	LOCKWASHER (#6)	(BRONZE)
1	2	2	11	K-57435	74	099	HEX. NUT (#6-32)	(BRASS)
1	2	2	12	K-829306	2	O	BUSHING	
		1	13	M-413204	501	O	COIL ASSEMBLY	
X		X	14	K-85221		O	COIL SPECIFICATIONS	
		1	15	M-413204	503	O	COIL ASSEMBLY	
		1	16	M-413204	504	O	COIL ASSEMBLY	
		X	17	K-85222		O	COIL SPECIFICATIONS	

LIST OF PARTS — COIL ASSEMBLY M (LOOP LOAD)

Drafting systems usually have a number of accessory lists, such as drawing lists, specification lists, voltage-resistance data, and wire lists. (See Fig. 1–5.) Most of these are typewritten on $8\frac{1}{2}'' \times 11''$ sheets. A drawing list, for instance, tabulates all types of drawings connected with an assembly, such as the schematic block diagrams, wiring diagrams, or manufacturing flow charts. A wire list gives lengths and types of wire used on an assembly. These lists carry identifying prefixes and the number of the main assembly to which they belong. Army Ordinance drawings, for instance, use the following prefixes:

DL = Drawing List   CL = Combined List
PL = Parts List   EL = Electrical List
SL = Specification List PH = Photograph

FIG. 1-5 Accessory lists

A schematic wiring diagram (or schematic) for a piece of electronic gear shows the electrical components designated in symbolic form, numbered properly, arranged, and interconnected according to their correct operational and functional sequence. Figure 1–6 illustrates a typical circuit.

A schematic diagram and an accompanying electrical parts list often give the experienced technician all the *electrical* information he needs to build a chassis. It may or may not give him complete *mechanical* information, such as the exact placement of all parts when assembling the equipment. An experienced man, however, can often do an entirely acceptable job without additional mechanical information.

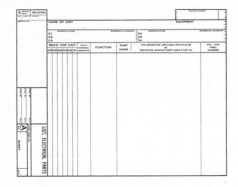

Electrical parts list

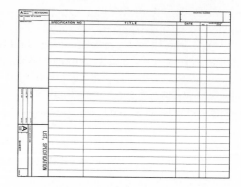

Specification list

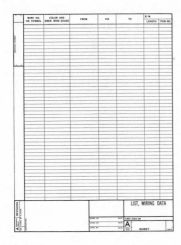

Wiring data list

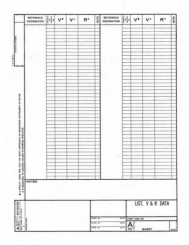

Voltage and resistance list

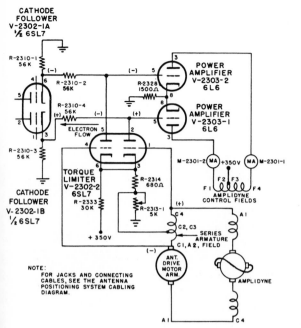

FIG. 1-6 Schematic wiring diagram for a typical circuit

In design and testing the schematic is of prime importance since it is a functional road map of signal voltages, contains useful information about d-c currents and voltages, and gives many other operating characteristics. Both quiescent and dynamic values of voltage and current, as well as waveforms, are marked directly on some schematics.

THE MILITARY DRAFTING SYSTEM

Descriptive drafting information in this volume is specifically slanted toward the present MIL-STD (military standards, previously JAN—Joint Army Navy) standardized drafting system required by all military services and generally used throughout the electronic industry. Although a number of different numbering, lettering, and drafting systems are used by manufacturing firms within the MIL-STD system, and specialized drafting techniques may be used in such areas as building construction, plumbing, and electrical wiring, the greater part of drafted information on electronic hardware follows the basic military specifications listed in Table 1-1.

Table 1-1 Military standards

JAN-STD-1	Standard for general drawing practice
MIL-STD-2	Drawing sizes
MIL-STD-3	Format for production drawings
MIL-STD-8	Dimensioning and tolerancing
MIL-STD-10	Surface roughness, waviness, and lay
MIL-STD-12	Abbreviations for use on drawings
MIL-STD-15	Electrical and electronic symbols
MIL-STD-16	Electrical and electronic reference designations
MIL-STD-17	Mechanical symbols
MIL-STD-18	Structural symbols
JAN-STD-19	Welding symbols
MIL-STD-20	Welding terms and definitions
MIL-STD-23	Nondestructive testing symbols
MIL-STD-24	Revisions of drawings
MIL-STD-27	Designations for electric switchgear and control devices

TYPES OF DRAWINGS

Drawings may be categorized according to function as *detail drawings*, *assembly drawings*, *block and flow diagrams*, *interconnection diagrams*, *waveform diagrams*, *schematic diagrams*, *picture drawings*, and *wiring diagrams*. Detailed description of each of these (except schematic and assembly drawings, described earlier) follows:

DETAIL DRAWINGS, as their name implies, give specific views, sections, and mechanical dimensions pertaining to single pieces and parts making up an assembly. Figure 1-7 is a detail drawing showing positional tolerances on a small piece.

FIG. 1-7 Detail drawing of positional tolerances

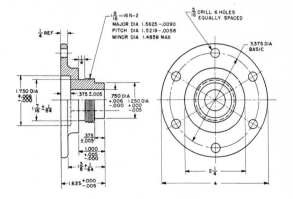

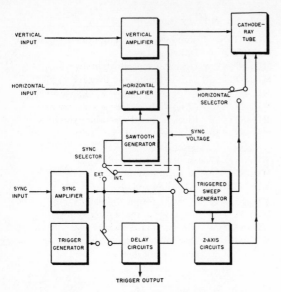

FIG. 1-8 Electronic layout of a synchroscope

BLOCK AND FLOW DIAGRAMS, consisting of labeled and interconnected rectangular enclosures, give general functional descriptions which simplify complicated drawings by show-

ing broad steps of divisions in construction, flow of motion, current, cabling, authority, or other functions. Figure 1–8 shows the electronic layout of a synchroscope.

INTERCONNECTION DIAGRAMS simplify the network of cable and plug connections between subchassis of a multichassis assembly. Figure 1–9 shows multiwired cables between the sections of an azimuth tracking unit.

PICTURE DRAWINGS, usually drawn in perspective, or in isometric projection, aim to give lifelike positioning and to clarify hidden or functional operation without going into extra views or drawings. See Fig. 1–2(c) where an isometric, "exploded" view of a television tuner mechanism is shown.

WIRING DIAGRAMS show the specific physical interconnections between the component parts in an assembly as directed by the schematic diagram. A wiring diagram illustrating details for wiring individual component parts on a small phase-shifter subchassis is shown in

FIG. 1-9 Interconnection diagram of azimuth tracking unit

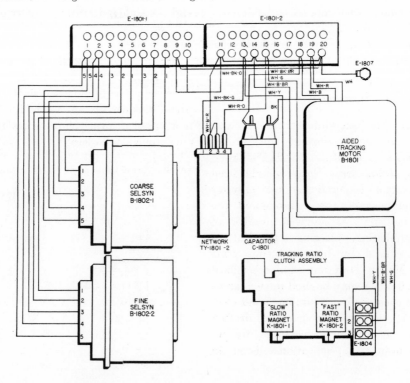

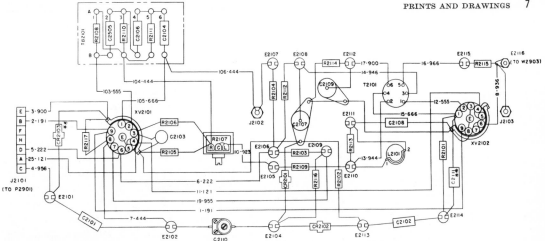

FIG. 1-10 A wiring diagram

Fig. 1–10. A wiring harness pictures all wires, their ends, and their breakaway points as they appear when they are bound or cabled together ready for fitting into a chassis. This type of wiring assembly allows the interconnection of a number of components to be preplanned in the drafting room for fabrication to a chassis externally. When completed, the harness arrangement automatically places the ends of the individual wires to be soldered adjacent to their intended terminals. Lists in Chapter 6 show the lengths and specific types of wires used in chassis wiring, along with specific descriptions.

WAVEFORM DIAGRAMS show contours of amplitude, time spacing, and shape of alternating currents and pulses occurring throughout operating electronic circuitry. They are many times indispensable in the measurement and operational testing of a piece of gear. Figure 1–11 shows typical waveforms in a radar azimuth timing system.

DRAWING FORMAT

Drawings for electronic equipment come under the category of *production drawings*. That is, they are intended for hardware or articles produced in quantity. These must be suitable for manufacture, inspection, installation, operation, and maintenance operations. The well-versed engineer or technician must be familiar with the terminology, techniques,

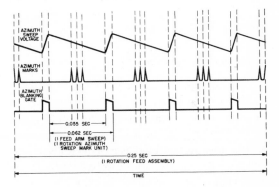

FIG. 1-11 Waveform diagram of radar azimuth timing system

and language. Production drawings must adhere to a given *format*. This includes (1) *size*, (2) *number and spacing of blocks containing printed information*, (3) *types of lettering*, (4) *weight of lines*, (5) *zoning*, (6) *columnar headings*, and (7) *space identification*. Details of these requirements appear in MIL-STD-3A.

DRAWING SHEET SIZES

Drawing sheet sizes are referred to by letters ranging from A ($8\frac{1}{2}'' \times 11''$) to K($40'' \times 50''$). The dimensions are chosen so that the larger sizes may be folded to reduce to the size of the smallest sheet ($8\frac{1}{2} \times 11$). A pile of drawings of various sizes may then be folded and punched so that all sizes may be mounted in a three-ring, $8\frac{1}{2} \times 11$ binder. When folding is inconvenient the three larger sizes may be rolled along their long dimension. Sometimes a 4-inch margin is added to drawings to protect them in handling. (See Fig. 1–12.)

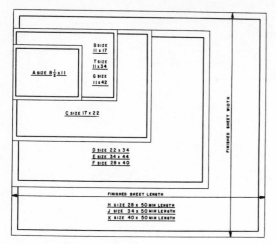

FIG. 1-12 Drawing sheet sizes

DRAWING IDENTIFICATIONS

The basic items of information describing a drawing are located in a number of blocks or enclosures at the lower right-hand corner of the drawing. With a glance at this corner of the drawing, an engineer or technician can tell its size, nature, the approximate date it was made, what changes were made on it, and many other facts about the drawing. These blocks vary in size depending upon the importance of the information they contain and often have subdivisions containing additional information pertinent to the main block. Listed in order of importance of the data (with letter designations referring to Fig. 1–14), the main blocks contain: (A) *the drawing number*, (B) *description or title*, (C) *organization or issuing agency*, (D) *signature and dates*, (E) *application of reference*, (F) *tolerances*, (G) *materials and finishes*, and (H) *supplementary information*.

DRAWING NUMBERS AND LETTERS (See Fig. 1-13.)

THE BASIC NUMBER, assigned and recorded when a drawing is generated, serves for master referencing and filing throughout the useful life of the drawing. It is found, as noted earlier, in the extreme lower right-hand corner of the drawing (see Block A, Fig. 1–14) and contains the most important fact concerning

a drawing. In its most complicated form, the basic drawing number may have associated with it one or more prefix letters, one suffix letter, and a sheet number.

THE DRAWING SIZE LETTER is the first single prefix, located in a square to the left of the basic number. For example, A-2004863 and D-842682 are two drawings of A and D sizes.

DRAWING TYPE LETTERS, when used, are prefixes written along with the main drawing number. They serve to indicate the size of the drawing and whether a sheet is some type of list, such as a parts list (PL), a drawing list (DL), a specification list (SL), or some other type. When such prefixes indicate a list, it is unnecessary to use the drawing size letter since most lists are made on the A size sheet. A parts list would be designated as PL 8,973,246, or its accompanying drawing list as DL 8,973,246, regardless of the size of the main drawing.

DRAWING ISSUE LETTERS are located in a sub-block to the right of the last numeral and usually denote the *change issue* (a revision) of a particular drawing. The issue letter is necessary because a drawing, over a period of years, may be revised several times, and all reference to changes, including the latest revision, must be catalogued. Details of the issue changes are printed in one of the supplementary blocks. In B-8672324-C and F-9276324-E, the C and E suffixes denote the

FIG. 1-13 Drawing numbers and letters

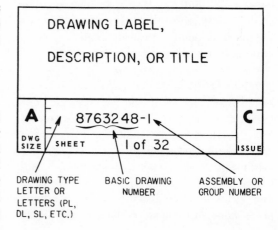

last issue, or major change, that was made on these particular drawings. If for any reason it is necessary to insert a group number or any other letter or number between the issue number and the main drawing number, print the word "*Issue*," followed by the issue letter. (See Fig. 1–13.)

ASSEMBLY OR GROUP NUMBERS are used to denote slight differences in the listing of parts making up assembly drawings. These numbers follow the main number, separated from it by a hyphen. They are not to be confused with the sheet number or the issue letter. To avoid confusion when group numbers are used, the complete numbering information for the assembly drawing should be written out. For instance, in C-3246821–3 Issue H Sheet 1, the numeral 3 stands for a particular group. Some systems may write C-3246821-G3 Issue H-1. Since the collection of parts would be slightly different in each group of a main assembly, there would be columns on the accompanying parts list, numbered by groups.

DRAWING SHEET NUMBERS are used on an assembly drawing or on a series of lists when there is additional drafting information tabulated on a number of supplementary A size sheets. The main drawing is labeled *Sheet #1* in the small block provided directly below the main basic drawing number. Each additional sheet has in this block its own sheet number along with the total number of sheets in the series of drawings. For example, the original drawing would be labeled sheet 1 of 16; other drawings might be sheet 2 of 16, sheet 7 of 16, and so forth. As discussed previously, multiple sheet drawing numbers most often apply to collections of A size or $8\frac{1}{2}'' \times 11''$ drawings, upon which are printed lists of parts covering any items not conveniently listed or handled on one larger size drawing.

To summarize, we conventionally label a drawing by listing its prefix size letter, its main numerals, its group number, its issue letter, and the sheet number. Since the sheet number is the least important, it is usually placed last in listing a drawing. Thus, T-

8187342–6 Issue F sheet 11 is a T size drawing, numbered 8187342, covering the sixth group of this particular assembly, in its sixth or F issue.

MAIN DESCRIPTIVE BLOCKS (With Letter Designations Referring to Fig. 1-14) are:

TITLE (B) is written in large print to define and label the drawing. Many titles give the type of drawing, together with brief explanatory captions. For instance, the title may say "Cable Assembly, Special Purpose, Electrical," or "Filter, Band Pass, ABC Receiver, Mounting Socket Assembly." Within this block there may be subdivisions concerning the drafting scale, the material, the weight, or the finish.

ORGANIZATION OR ISSUING AGENCY (C) indicates the company or branch of the military which issues the drawing. Many times an address is given, such as "ORDNANCE CORPS—Redstone Arsenal," or "JUMBO RESISTOR CO.—Alvis, N.Y." Often a statement of ownership by the originating company appears in this block.

SIGNATURE AND DATES (D) is composed of a number of subdivisions, including the date of completion and the numerous approval signatures of personnel concerned with the design, such as the supervising engineer, the designer, the draftsman, and the detailer or drafting checker.

APPLICATION AND REFERENCES (E) also contains a number of subdivisions, listing related drawings, an actual assembly in the case of detail drawings, associated bills of material, source of the part, or where it was first used, and group numberings and tabulation.

DRAFTING TOLERANCES (F) has subdivisions listing the tolerances which apply to all dimensions throughout the drawings. This device saves drafting time when standard or noncritical dimensions are applied to measured distances. The tolerances, which vary with

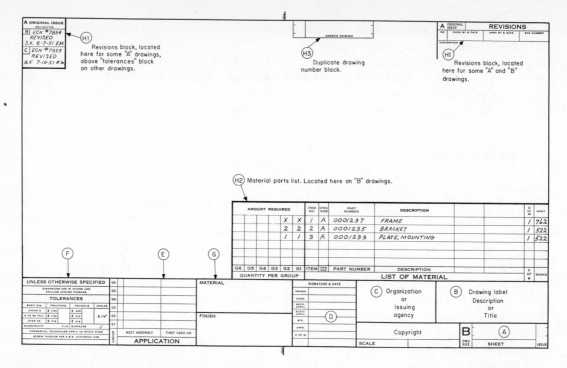

FIG. 1-14 Drawing and identification blocks

the magnitude of the dimensions, are grouped into lengths up to 6 in., between 6 in. and 24 in., and over 24 in.

MATERIAL AND FINISH (G) may be included within the title area or alongside it in some drafting formats. In assembly drawings, where the information may be more complicated, this block may adjoin the application block. As we shall see later, there are numerous types, hardnesses, and tempers which apply to steel, while several similar details apply to brass, aluminum, and other metals. Finishes may be described in a great many ways, all of which have specifications pertaining to color, protective characteristics, and other attributes. In many cases, for simplicity, code numbers are used to describe a finish.

SUPPLEMENTARY INFORMATION (H) may include a number of additional areas existing within the confines of a drawing. Their arrangement is usually at the option of the issuing company. Chief among these is the *revision block* (H-1), which is usually keyed into the main drawing number by one of its suffixes. Information in this block describes the revi-

sion sequence and gives condensed details concerning its date and nature. *A material or parts list* (H-2) may also be included on an assembly drawing. Sometimes small blocks are reserved along the margins of a drawing for inserting duplicates of the main drawing number (H-3). These blocks make it easier to locate and tabulate a large drawing when it is folded. Additional space blocks located at various points within a drawing area may contain other information, such as government, company, patent numbers, or other references.

The printed information contained in the blocks described above may vary slightly among drafting departments of different companies. Most industries, however, follow similar plans. The format for preparing drawings for military services is prescribed by the government specification MIL-STD-3A. The rules for execution of these drawings, such as the means of presentation, the weight of line, and other exact drafting details are found in Military Standard Spec. JAN-STD-1. Many other rules, guide lines, and variations in procedure occur throughout government specifications, as shown in Table 1–1.

Drafting Equipment and Techniques 2

EQUIPMENT

To produce the graphic material necessary in engineering, the engineer or technician must have suitable equipment and instruments. A minimum set of the conventional tools will serve the technician since he is not expected to produce drawings of the excellence of those drawn by trained draftsmen. But he can not ignore the conventional drafting techniques since he may be called upon to do simple drafting. Familiarity with the basic techniques will also enable him to better understand the drawings he uses.

Tools essential to the production of a moderate-quality drawing include: drafting instruments, the drawing board, T-square, 30° × 60° triangle, 45° triangle, French curves, triangular or flat scales, protractors, and an erasing shield. The use of these basic tools will be discussed briefly later in this chapter. Some common drafting accessories are: pencils (6H through 2H leads), pencil pointer (mechanical file or sandpaper pad), lettering pens, erasers (for pencil lines, for cleaning, for inklines), and a pen holder, wiper, and guide.

PAPER used for drawings may be medium grain, cream-colored paper (to reduce eye strain), thin white unglazed tracing paper, or thin transparent tracing cloth which is coated with a special starch or plastic.

DRAFTING BOARDS should be smooth and warp-proof. They may be laid across a desk or mounted on an adjustable tilt-top table.

T-SQUARES are placed across the drawing board so that they may slide along one of the vertical edges of the drawing board. The straight horizontal edges of the T-square may then be used to draw parallel lines, or as a horizontal basis for such implements as triangles and protractors. T-squares are sometimes made with steel heads and blades, which may be adjustable to angles varying from the horizontal, or they may have fixed wooden heads and a hardwood blade with transparent celluloid edges. Figure 2–1 shows a drafting board with a T-square and triangles in position.

TRIANGLES, usually made of transparent plastic, are necessary for drawing vertical and

FIG. 2-1 Drafting board with T-square and triangles

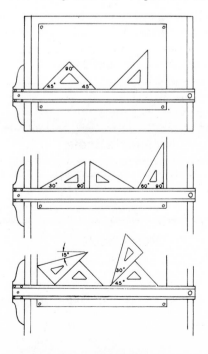

11

inclined lines unless a drafting machine is used. There are two common types. Both are right triangles. One has a 30° and a 60° angle, while the other has two 45° angles. Many sizes of triangles may be used, varying according to the size of the figures to be drawn. Adjustable triangles are sometimes added to these basic types. For positioning of the 30° × 60° and 45° triangles to obtain many commonly used angles, see Fig. 2–1.

PROTRACTORS are used when it is necessary to measure angles directly, or to lay off angles that can not be obtained by using the triangles. (See Fig. 2–2.)

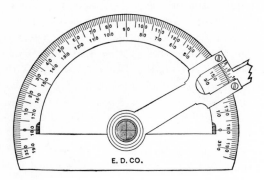

FIG. 2-2 Protractor

SCALES are used for laying off measured distances, and may be classified according to their function as architects' and engineers' and metric scales. (See Fig. 2–3.)

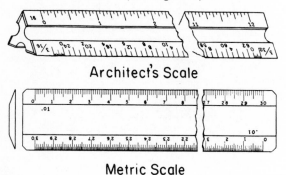

Architect's Scale

Metric Scale

FIG. 2-3 Scales

FRENCH CURVES are plastic drawing templates used as mechanical guides when draw-

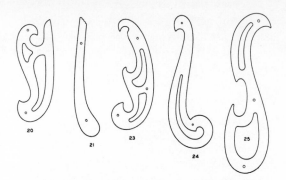

FIG. 2-4 French curves

ing curves other than circles or circle segments. (See Fig. 2–4.)

ERASING SHIELDS are thin metal templates, used to prevent wrinkling the drawing paper or to mask unaltered lines when an erasure is being made.

DRAFTING MACHINES may be used in the place of a T-square, angles, and protractor. (See Fig. 2–5.) This mechanism, which may

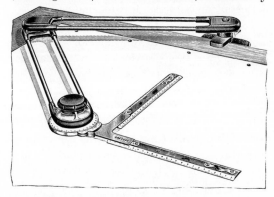

FIG. 2-5 Drafting machine

be attached to the drafting board, is arranged so that its bottom blade slides to any T-square position, while its vertical blade may be adjusted to assume vertical or angular positions. Both blades have linear scales scribed on them and may be adjusted to any angular position, as indicated on the protractor-marked adjustment knob. The device provides a convenient means of performing the basic drafting operations with a minimum of drafting tools.

DRAWING INSTRUMENTS usually come in sets as shown in Fig. 2–6. These sets include: *dividers*, used to divide curved or straight lines into equal parts, or for measuring and transferring distances. These may be of the large type or the finely adjusted bow-type. *Compasses* are used to draw circles or circle arcs. In addi-

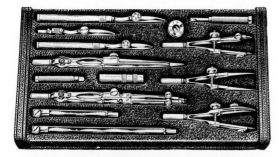

FIG. 2-6 Set of drawing instruments

tion to pencil-tipped compasses, detachable ink pen-tipped compasses may be used. The large, small, and bow-types of these are suitable for most circle drawing. *The beam compass* is used for drawing larger circles than it would be possible to draw with the conventional divider compass. Long and short extension legs may be used to lengthen compass or divider legs for measures beyond the normal capacity of the instrument. Large or small *ruling pens* may be used, depending on the width of line that is to be inked. (See Fig. 2–7.)

TECHNIQUES

The techniques for drawing horizontal lines, measuring, and for drawing circles and arcs, are shown in Fig. 2–8. Vertical and angular lines are drawn with triangles positioned as in Fig. 2–1. Special training courses would be necessary for instruction in the techniques of using pencils and pens, the straight edge, compasses, and other instruments. The control of line widths, scale reading, care of instruments, and inking of lines are also techniques which are important to the drawing process, but can only be indicated graphically within this volume. However, all drawings are first made in pencilled lines which may or may not be inked over, depending upon the type of paper

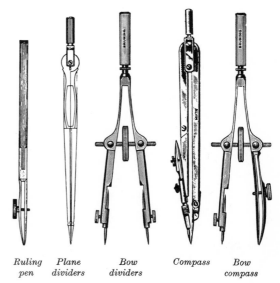

| Ruling pen | Plane dividers | Bow dividers | Compass | Bow compass |

Beam compass

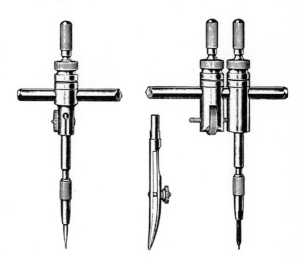

FIG. 2-7 Drawing instruments

used or the requirements of printing and reproduction.

TYPES OF LINES

For purposes of drafting clarity, and in order to differentiate between hidden surfaces, center lines, dimension lines, sections, and other parts of the drawing, it is necessary to use many types of solid, broken, and dotted lines. Lines also vary in width or heaviness. Drafting departments throughout industry use standardized relative widths and character of line to indicate specific parts of a drawing. Drafting lines may be divided into four weights or widths: thin, medium, thick, and extra thick, as shown in Fig. 2–9. These

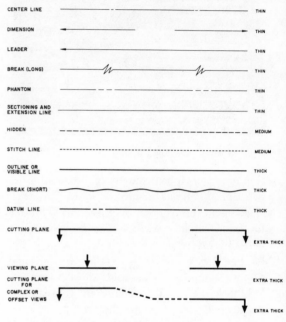

FIG. 2-9 Weights of drafting lines

widths are relative to the size of the drawing and in absolute measurement may vary tremendously. For instance, a thin line on a detailed $8\frac{1}{2}'' \times 11''$ sketch would be much thinner by actual measure than a thin line on a 20-foot drawing of an airplane fuselage. The lines would have similar meanings, though, in both drawings. In other words, the *ratio* of line width should remain the same no matter what the drawing size. The ratio from thin, to medium, to thick, to extra thick lines should be roughly $1:2:4:6$. Definitions of the various symbolic lines shown in Fig. 2–9 are given below. An example of their use is shown in Fig. 2–10.

CENTER LINES are thin lines alternating evenly spaced long and short dashes, with a long dash at each end of the line.

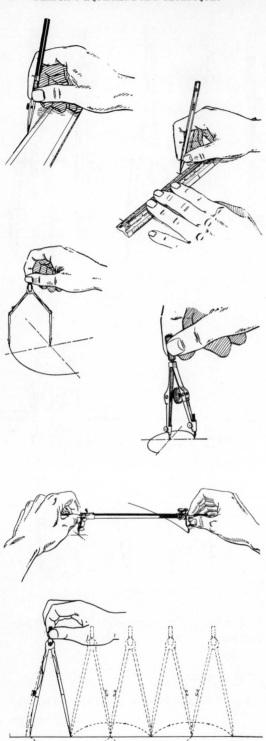

FIG. 2-8 Drawing techniques

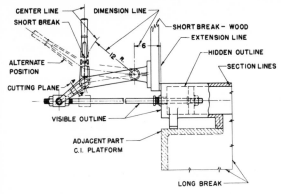

CENTER LINE
SHORT BREAK

DIMENSION LINE

SHORT BREAK — WOOD
EXTENSION LINE

ALTERNATE
POSITION

HIDDEN OUTLINE

SECTION LINES

CUTTING PLANE

VISIBLE OUTLINE

ADJACENT PART
C.I. PLATFORM

LONG BREAK

FIG. 2-10 Use of symbolic lines

indicate the extent of a dimension. They should never touch the outline of the drawing.

DATUM LINES are similar to phantom lines (one long dash plus two short ones) except that they are drawn in the thick width. They are used as reference lines in special drawings where center line techniques are not employed. A datum line might show the floor line of a building, for example, or the base of a complicated metal casing.

OUTLINES OF VISIBLE LINES are thick solid lines representing all edges and surfaces perpendicular to and visible from the viewing plane.

DIMENSION LINES are thin unbroken lines which terminate at each end in arrowheads.

HIDDEN LINES are short, evenly spaced dashes (medium weight) showing edges which cannot be seen from the view in question, such as back surfaces, rear holes, and recesses.

LEADER LINES are thin lines which terminate at one end in an arrowhead. They indicate a portion of a drawing that refers to a note, number, or reference. The leader line begins in a line approximately $\frac{1}{8}''$ long, parallel to the lettering of the note, and centered on the first line of the note.

BREAK LINES are thin lines indicating a midway break or discontinuity in the drawing of an object. They may be drawn freehand or with instruments as zig-zag, wavy, or parallel curved lines which show each edge of the discontinuity.

PHANTOM LINES are thin lines composed of one long and two short dashes, evenly spaced, with a long dash at each end. They indicate alternate positions and missing or suggested outlines.

EXTENSION LINES are thin lines used to

CUTTING-PLANE OR VIEWING-PLANE LINES are solid extra-thick lines, usually accompanied by some lettering to indicate the direction of view.

SECTIONING LINES are used to shade an exposed sectional area and are made up of parallel unbroken thin lines which cover the area. When two sectional surfaces adjoin each other, the lines in one sectional view should be drawn at a 90° angle to those in the other. (See Fig. 2–11.) When it is necessary to indicate different materials, the sectional

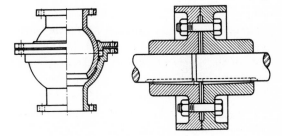

FIG. 2-11 Use of sectioning lines

lines are changed to varied combinations of line thickness and spacing, dot and dash sequences or various stipplings may be used. (See Fig. 2–12.) These symbolic sectional patterns are specified for government drawings in JAN-STD-1. They are commonly used throughout industrial drafting.

PROJECTION OF VIEWS

Mechanical drawings picture an object by

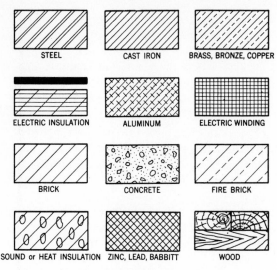

STEEL CAST IRON BRASS, BRONZE, COPPER

ELECTRIC INSULATION ALUMINUM ELECTRIC WINDING

BRICK CONCRETE FIRE BRICK

SOUND or HEAT INSULATION ZINC, LEAD, BABBITT WOOD

FIG. 2-12 Types of symbolic sectional patterns

means of projected views. These give a full graphic description of the shape of the object, with actual sizes given by dimensions printed on the drawing.

The drafted picture may be imagined as projected onto a transparent vertical picture plane, located directly in front of the viewer. The picture may be compared to the image which would result if the object were being illuminated by an intense, uniform light located directly behind it. Details of the front side of the object are shown in the drawing of the picture plane view just as if they too were illuminated by reflected light or by rays passing straight through the object toward the viewer.

Types of drawings are defined by the kind of projection system that is used. In perspective projection the picture is drawn as if rays of light passing through the picture plane converge at the viewer's eye. In orthographic projection, the type most frequently used for mechanical drawings, the object is shown as if these imaginary light lines reach the viewer by perpendicular passage through the viewing plane. Orthographic projection assumes that the front or flat face of the pictured object is parallel to the viewing plane so that in a rectangular object, only one side (the front) would be visible. When the object is

drawn as if it had been angularly displaced, so that two sides are visible simultaneously, we have what is known as isometric or oblique projection.

ORTHOGRAPHIC PROJECTION

Flat, head-on views are used in most drafting systems to show selected sides of the piece or object being drafted. Since an orthographic projection shows only the surface of the drawn object which faces the viewing plane, it is often necessary to draw additional views to indicate depth. When three views are shown the drawing is called a third angle projection. These three views should include: a top or *plan view*, drawn as if looking from overhead at the outline of the object as it might be projected onto a horizontal glass coverpiece;

FIG. 2-13 Orthographic projection

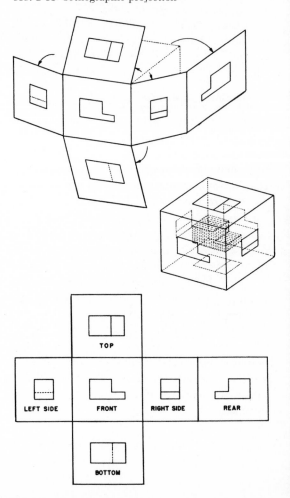

TOP

LEFT SIDE FRONT RIGHT SIDE REAR

BOTTOM

a *front view*, or the outline of the object drawn as if projected onto a vertical glass door directly in front of the object; a side or profile view, drawn as if outlined on a glass panel directly parallel to the side plane of the object.

Figure 2–13 shows views of an object as if projected onto six of these glass planes (one additional side view and back and bottom views). The projected drawings appear as we would see them from the mutually perpendicular sides of the glass box made up of these six glass planes. For most three-dimensional and symmetrical objects, the first three views mentioned give enough information to describe the piece being drawn since some parts of each view correspond to parts shown in an adjoining view. Height and length in the front view would correspond, for example, to height and depth in the profile view. Bottom and back views are used only when they are necessary to show something that might not appear in other views.

SINGLE VIEW DRAWINGS are sometimes made of simple objects such as cylinders, nuts, collars, or flat pieces (see Fig. 2–14(a)), where the diameter, dimensions, or notes give sufficient information to indicate unpictured dimensions.

DOUBLE VIEW DRAWINGS may suffice in many cases where the object is symmetrical or purely rectangular. A double view drawing of a rivet is shown in Fig. 2–14(b).

FIG. 2-14 Single and double view drawings

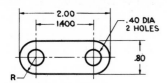

(a) *Single view drawing*

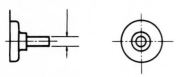

(b) *Double view drawing*

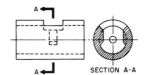

(a) *Full sectional view*

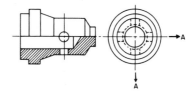

(b) *Half sectional view*

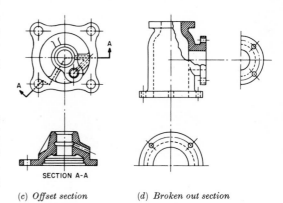

(c) *Offset section*   (d) *Broken out section*

FIG. 2-15 Cross sections

SECTIONAL OR CUTAWAY VIEWS, commonly called sections or cross-sections, are used when the interior or hidden construction of a piece cannot be shown clearly by external views. The sectional view, whether half section or full section, is a part of a drawing which exposes the interior features of an object just as if a portion of the object between the viewer and the previously hidden feature had been cut away by passing an imaginary plane through the object. The material exposed by the cutting-plane line represents an edge view taken at the cutting plane. Reference letters show where the cutting-plane axis crosses the object being sectioned. In Fig. 2–15(a) Section *AA* denotes a full-section view as if the cutting edge went across the full diameter of the piece. At *AA* in Fig. 2–15(b), only half of the view is sectioned. Note that the interior sections are shown in *sectional lines* or crosshatching. Figure 2–15(c) shows sectioning through webs and ribs of a flange, while Fig. 2–15(d) shows a specific "broken out" section.

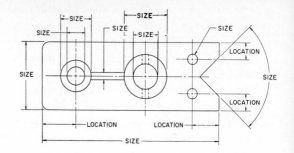

ISOMETRIC OR ANGULAR PROJECTION

This type of projection shows two sides of an object in one view. It is used in drafting practice where simplification in drawing is desired without sacrificing clear dimensioning of the part. Figure 2–16 shows a simple example of this "picture" type of drafting. Single or double auxiliary views of isometric drawings may be added for clarifying special details.

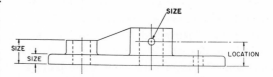

FIG. 2-17 Typical dimensioning procedures

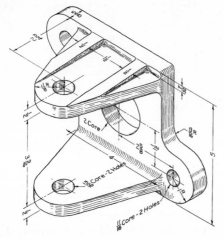

FIG. 2-16 Isometric projection

DIMENSIONING AND TOLERANCES

The purpose of dimensioning a drawing is to give physical sizes of an object so that the piece may be manufactured or fitted into an assembly. There are two types of dimensions required to describe an object, *size dimensions* and *location dimensions*. The size dimension describes the width, length, diameter, as well as other geometric characteristics, such as ledges, cutaways, or diagonals. Location dimensions specify the position relationships of one feature of an object with respect to

another, such as center-to-center distances, surface-to-surface, and center-to-surface distances. Datum-line or reference-plane positions may be included in location dimensions. Figure 2–17 shows typical dimension procedures which use the recommended types of lines.

FORMAT FOR DIMENSION LINES is standard in all drafting, with main dimension lines, extension lines, center lines, and leaders spaced at least $\frac{1}{8}''$ apart when running parallel to each other. They should be arranged neatly for clarity and should avoid unnecessary duplication.

ARRANGEMENT OF NUMBERS for dimensions can be important to the clarity of a drawing. Wherever practicable, dimensions should always be placed on the outside of the view being described. Over-all figures should be located above and to the right of the principal view, and when surfaces are shown in profile, they are preferably placed between views. They should be arranged to read in order of size from the bottom of the drawing upward. That is, the largest dimensions should be at the bottom with successively smaller dimension figures progressing upward. Vertical dimensioning should read from left to right with the largest dimension on the outside. (See Fig. 2–18.) A line should represent the

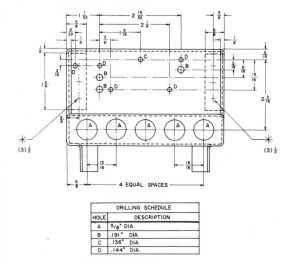

DRILLING SCHEDULE	
HOLE	DESCRIPTION
A	5/8" DIA.
B	.191" DIA.
C	.136" DIA.
D	.144" DIA.

FIG. 2-18 Format for dimension lines

true length of the object from which it is drawn, and the view should allow for as clear and uncrowded an arrangement of dimensions as possible. The front view is usually the best for over-all major dimensions, while the side view lends itself best to detail dimensions. Dimension lines should never cross each other. This condition may be avoided by properly grouping related dimensions and by observing the bottom-to-top and left-to-right reading rule. Sometimes a number of dimensions can be both staggered to improve clarity and shown in reference to a center line. Figure 2-18 shows how to dimension from one edge and how to stagger the figures. Techniques and practices recommended for military drawings are spelled out in government specification MIL-STD-8.

UNITS OF MEASUREMENT used to dimension drawings in common industrial practice are whole and decimal inches, with the figures centered in a break near the center of the dimension line. The inch symbol (″) may be used to indicate dimension units, and in larger drawings the foot symbol (′) is used. Although fractional dimension figures may be used, decimal numbers are preferred. Where a very fine tolerance of a particular dimension must be given in addition to the tolerances listed in the description area, it is printed in plus and minus figures alongside the main

figure in a form similar to that used in writing a fraction. A thousandth of an inch tolerance in an inch dimension, for example, should be written $1'' \pm .001/.001$. See also the hole dimensions in Fig. 2–18.

SPECIAL DIMENSIONING designations are used whenever they are more convenient or clear. It is sometimes more convenient, for instance, to dimension a piece in angular measure rather than by the rectangular method of length, width, and height. Figure 2–19 shows two views of the same piece, one dimensioned in angular measure, the other by the linear system.

Another designation which simplifies dimensioning may be used on a piece having a number of holes of the same size. If all similar holes are labeled with a common letter, a printed tabulation of the various hole sizes and their diameters may be added in some free space on the drawing, as in Fig. 2–18.

FIG. 2-19 Dimensioning by angular and linear systems

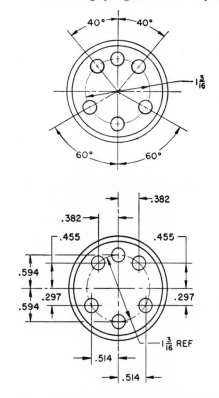

Diameter dimensioning of each individual hole is then eliminated.

Curved-surface dimensions should be shown in views perpendicular to the curvature with a caption of "Dia" (for diameter) or "Rad" (for radius) inserted on the dimension line. The center of the dimensioning circle should, of course, be located with reference to some plane or surface on the drawing. (See Fig. 1–7.)

LETTERING, PRINTING, AND SYMBOLS

When there is additional explanation needed on the various parts of a drawing, such as notes or references which cannot be expressed by drafting methods, the information must be printed. If the notes are detailed and voluminous they may be typewritten on available vacant space. Additional typewritten sheets may accompany the drawing (they are referred to by appropriate notes on the drawing itself), or the printing may be hand lettered. In mechanical drawings the lettering is usually done using standard types and sizes of lettering. Most drafting systems use vertical upper-case commercial gothic style lettering, following the size and format shown in Fig. 2–20, as recommended by the American Standards Association in their specification ASA X14: 2–1957. Mechanical aids such as Wrico pens and templates or the Leroy letter-

FIG. 2-20 Commercial gothic style lettering

TYPE 1
ABCDEFGHIJKLMNOP
QRSTUVWXYZ&
1234567890 $\frac{1}{2}\frac{3}{4}\frac{5}{8}$
TITLES & DRAWING NUMBERS

TYPE 2
FOR SUB-TITLES OR MAIN TITLES
ON SMALL DRAWINGS

TYPE 3
ABCDEFGHIJKLMNOPQRSTUVWXYZ&
1234567890 $\frac{1}{2}\frac{3}{4}\frac{5}{8}\frac{9}{32}$
FOR HEADINGS AND PROMINENT NOTES

TYPE 4
ABCDEFGHIJKLMNOPQRSTUVWXYZ&
1234567890 $\frac{1}{2}\frac{3}{4}\frac{5}{8}\frac{9}{32}$
FOR BILLS OF MATERIAL, DIMENSIONS & GENERAL NOTES

ing device may also be used to insure unformity of lettering on drawings.

BLUEPRINT READING

While the making of a mechanical drawing or the drafting of a piece part is a technique which requires considerable knowledge and skill, the technique of *reading a print* may be acquired without knowing how to do the drafting. The knowledge of how to *make* a mechanical drawing, however, covers all of the necessary facts for correct blueprint reading. The preceding material on the tools and techniques of drafting should serve to familiarize the technician with print reading, as well as to instruct him in the fundamentals of drafting. Many times the well-trained technician may also be called upon to make reasonably well-executed sketches in the conventional drafting style.

TECHNIQUE OF READING BLUEPRINTS

After understanding the general nature of a print from the printed information in the lower right-hand corner, the technician must interpret the drafted or graphic details so that he understands the physical form they specify for the finished object. Since most drawings, with the exception of diagrams and lists, are mechanical drawings, he must obtain a mental concept of the physical ideas that the designer or engineer aims graphically to convey. These ideas cover: the exact *shape* of the object, its precise *size* in complete detail, and the *description for manufacture*, with details as to the material used, fabricating methods, plating, assembly, or other processing.

Specifically, these ideas require that two important skills be acquired by the technician in order to read a print. He must know and understand the meaning of lines, signs, symbols, and graphic projection methods used by the engineer or draftsman. These are the basis of the language of *mechanical drawing*. He must also be able to *visualize* the size, shape, and mechanical features of the object being described by these drafting conventions.

Note that the visualization process applies only to drawings of objects which require several views to describe their specific details and dimensions. An entirely different approach is used in block diagrams, schematics, wiring diagrams, lists, and accessory drawings. Symbols are used in these to describe parts, pieces, and operation.

The basic steps in blueprint reading are as follows:

1. *Reading and understanding the description box* reveals such general ideas as the approximate size of the part, the scale, the material, and important facts such as whether it is a part of an assembly or a detail drawing.

2. *Analyzing and understanding the size and number of component parts* helps to visualize how the individual parts are arranged, and how they are mechanically attached to each other or to the main frame. On a piece part each of the three views should be studied, one by one, to understand how the actual piece must look from all angles. This helps to fix in mind the main physical facts concerning size, weight, color, and function.

3. *Establishing the key dimensions, critical hole locations, and important large surfaces* helps to locate important configurations which will govern tool operations in fabricating the piece, to act as a guide to its inspection after it is completed, or to simplify assembly if it must fit with other parts.

4. *Studying the details of minor holes, bends, lengths,* and *finishes* will aid in visualizing them with respect to the main dimensions.

5. *Understanding how the part finally fits* with its associated parts, if it is part of an assembly, and how it would be used by itself if it is not, should be the last step in interpretation.

When he has a knowledge of drafting techniques, the technician should be able to comprehend any print given to him well enough to construct or physically assemble the piece in question with the other mechanical components making up an electrical apparatus. In addition to this, his drafting knowledge should enable him to interpret complicated piece parts, such as fine mechanisms, gear assemblies, or instruments, even though their construction is beyond his scope. Critical features of such parts are usually explained to the technician first by a mechanical engineer or by a highly trained machinist.

3 Preparing Material For Chassis Construction

The chassis base serves as the skeleton for assembling electrical and mechanical components in equipment drawers. Together these elements compose the basic unit for electronic systems. The electronic technician may often be required to fabricate a chassis base for a system from the flat sheet metal, guided by a working drawing or photograph, as described in Chapter 1. After the technician has mastered the techniques of reading engineering drawings, and before he can proceed to the actual construction of the electronic chassis, he must be able to transfer the dimensional and descriptive specifications of the drawing onto the material he will use to build the chassis. Since this material is usually metal, and dimensions must be precise, special tools are used for marking and measuring the chassis layout.

In order to construct a complete chassis base the technician must concern himself with three aspects of construction. He must: (1) be acquainted with the materials from which chassis are built; (2) know how to measure and lay out the working dimensions for the equipment, employing commonly used markings, tools, and techniques; and (3) be able to utilize the skills necessary for fabricating the chassis from the metal or other material. Materials for chassis construction, layout of the chassis plan onto this material, and the tools used for measuring and marking the layout comprise the material of this chapter; metalworking skills and chassis fabrication will be covered in Chapter 4.

TYPES OF CHASSIS

The chassis commonly used as the base for military or commercial electronic apparatus is a boxlike metal framework, sometimes called a "pan." The construction of this pan has the variations described below. (Illustrations of each type are shown in Fig. 3–1.)

THE "LAY-DOWN" CHASSIS is built so that tubes are mounted perpendicular to the horizontal base. If long enough, this chassis may be mounted on a rack. Smaller versions are inserted into radio or high fidelity cabinets.

THE "STAND-UP" CHASSIS is built for tubes to be mounted standing along the top of the vertical base. In operation this unit is usually mounted alongside other vertical chassis and each unit in the group is then plugged into a panel.

PRINTED CIRCUIT CHASSIS, or subassembly boards, are made of fiberboard and used to mount and wire all components, including tubes, within labeled conductive areas. These components are mounted directly onto the metal framework, parallel to it, so that the entire unit remains flat. The chassis is designed to be plugged into a panel, as in the case of the "stand-up" chassis.

COMPONENT PART BOARDS are fiber chasses, shaped and drilled to hold piece parts between riveted terminals. The board provides insulated support for mounting the component parts. Since such boards may be mounted at various

"Lay-down" chassis

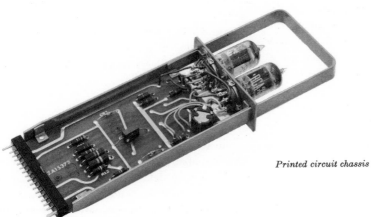

Printed circuit chassis

Component part board

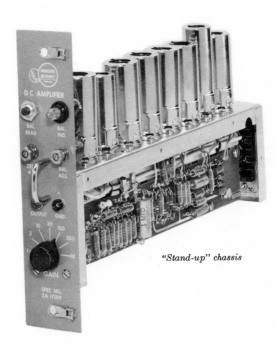

"Stand-up" chassis

FIG. 3-1 Types of chassis

angles to the circuitry which they accompany and raised ledges are usually built on them so that tubes may be set parallel to the chassis base. This helps to relieve crowding against other elements of the apparatus.

CHASSIS BASE DRAWINGS

Chassis base drawings are mechanical drawings describing metal frameworks made from flat plate or sheet metal. Punched or drilled holes and openings for insertion and mounting of sockets, transformers, and capacitors are also indicated. The base drawings follow the conventions described in Chapter 1 and give enough cutting, bending, and drilling information to completely build the metal framework. (See Fig. 3–2.) Assembly and wiring according to the chassis assembly drawing will be discussed in Chapter 4.

FIG. 3-2 Chassis base drawing

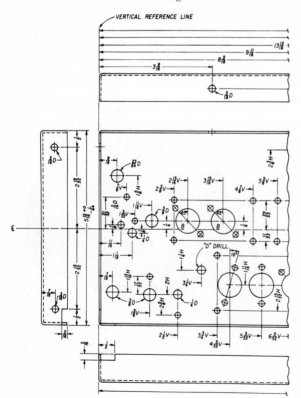

Before the metal work on a sheet-metal chassis base is started, the technician may often find it convenient to draft what is known as a development sketch. This drawing is a picture "in the flat" of the exact area of metal that must be cut from the sheet stock so that it will bend to conform to the desired dimensions of the chassis base. (See Fig. 3–3(a).) Figure 3–3(b) shows the development drawing for a drilled metal cylinder.

Development drawings are dimensioned to include the amount of material consumed in bending and any extra metal required for such special shapes as notches, cutouts, or lips in their equivalent flattened-out shape. Many times it is convenient to spot and drill most of the required holes before the flat material is bent.

CHASSIS MATERIALS

The choice of material for building chassis depends upon the required strength, ease of fabrication, weight, cost, ability to accept plating, ability to conduct electric current, and several other factors. If the equipment is for the armed services there may be additional specifications. These factors are decided upon by the mechanical design engineer responsible for layout on the job and are not within the technicians province. A knowledge of the physical and mechanical characteristics of a material and its governing specifications definitely adds to his appreciation of the job, though. Such information is found in physical and chemical engineering handbooks.

FLAT STOCK

In starting to build a complete chassis base, the first consideration is the kind of material indicated on the chassis base print. In most cases the material called for is either sheet aluminum or steel, which is often called steel plate or flat stock. Infrequently, copper, magnesium, or alloys are also used.

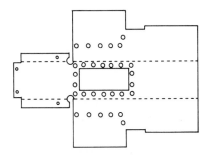

(a) Development sketch for chassis base

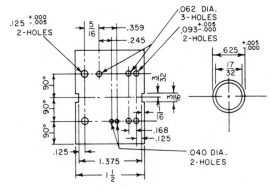

(b) Development of drilled metal cylinder

FIG. 3-3 Developmental drawings

FLAT STEEL STOCK, commonly known as cold rolled sheet steel, is the most frequently used material for chassis bases. It comes in a number of thicknesses and is easily cut, bent, drilled, formed, or otherwise manipulated into the desired shapes for chassis bases and their associated metal parts. Flat steel stock may also be made to have spring or temper and is made in several stainless varieties. Cold rolling makes steel stock soft in temper, suitable for bending and stamping, and gives it a fairly smooth finish suitable for plating or finishing (in contrast to having temper and the dark scaly finish of hot rolled plates). The small metalworking shop usually carries such stock in various size sheets with the thicknesses and gauges listed in Table 3–1. A list of the commonly used stainless steel gauges and their equivalent thicknesses is given in Table 3–2.

Table 3-1 Cold rolled steel sheets

Gauge and size, inches	Est. weight per sheet, lb.
3/16 × 24 × 96	120.0
36 × 120	225.0
No. 11 × 36 × 96	120.0
36 × 120	150.0
48 × 120	200.0
No. 12 × 24 × 96	70.0
30 × 96	87.5
36 × 120	131.3
48 × 120	175.0
48 × 144	210.0
No. 13 × 24 × 96	60.0
36 × 120	112.5
No. 14 × 30 × 96	62.5
36 × 96	75.0
36 × 120	93.8
48 × 120	125.0
60 × 120	156.3
No. 16 × 24 × 96	40.0
30 × 96	50.0
36 × 96	60.0
36 × 120	75.0
48 × 96	80.0
48 × 120	100.0
60 × 120	125.0
No. 18 × 24 × 96	32.0
30 × 96	40.0
36 × 96	48.0
36 × 120	60.0
48 × 96	64.0
48 × 120	80.0
No. 19 × 24 × 96	28.0
36 × 120	52.5
No. 20 × 24 × 96	24.0
30 × 96	30.0
*36 × 96	36.0
No. 20 × *36 × 120	45.0
*48 × 96	48.0
*48 × 120	60.0
48 × 144	72.0
No. 21 × 24 × 96	22.0
36 × 120	42.0
No. 22 × 24 × 96	20.0
30 × 96	25.0
*36 × 96	30.0
*36 × 120	37.5
*48 × 96	40.0
*48 × 120	50.0
No. 24 × 24 × 96	16.0
30 × 96	20.0
36 × 96	24.0
*36 × 120	30.0
No. 26 × 30 × 96	15.0
36 × 96	18.0

Table 3-2 Stainless steel sheets

Size, U.S.S. Gauge	Est. weight per sheet, lb.
No. 10 (.141″) × 36 × 120	177.2
48 × 120	236.2
No. 11 (.125″) × 36 × 120	157.5
No. 12 (.109″) × 30 × 120	114.8
36 × 96	110.2
36 × 120	137.8
48 × 120	183.7
No. 14 (.078″) × 30 × 120	82.0
36 × 96	78.7
36 × 120	98.4
48 × 120	131.2
No. 16 (.063″) × 30 × 96	52.5
30 × 120	65.6
36 × 96	63.0
36 × 120	78.8
48 × 96	84.0
48 × 120	105.0
No. 18 (.050″) × 30 × 120	52.5
36 × 96	50.4
36 × 120	63.0
48 × 96	67.2
48 × 120	84.0
No. 20 (.038″) × 30 × 96	31.5
30 × 120	39.4
36 × 96	37.8
36 × 120	47.3
48 × 96	50.4
48 × 120	63.0
No. 22 (.031″) × 30 × 96	26.3
36 × 96	31.5
36 × 120	39.4
48 × 120	52.5
No. 24 (.025″) × 24 × 96	16.8
30 × 96	21.0
30 × 120	26.3
36 × 96	25.2
36 × 120	31.5
48 × 96	33.6
48 × 120	42.0
No. 26 (.019″) × 24 × 96	12.6
24 × 120	15.8
30 × 96	15.8
30 × 120	19.7
36 × 96	18.9
36 × 120	23.6

ALLOY SHEETS, such as aluminum, brass, bronze, copper, and nickel-silver come in several weights, hardnesses, and thicknesses, as listed in Table 3–3. In addition to being easier to work than steel, each of these has advantages permitting its use in special applications. Flat aluminum sheet is used extensively in place of sheet steel in aircraft and missile electronic gear, where weight is an important factor. A comparison of metal gauges is shown in Table 3–4.

SPECIAL MATERIALS in sheet stock, such as bakelite, formica, hard rubber, and phenolic plastic, also used for chassis, are listed in material handbooks in detail beyond that warranted for inclusion in this volume.

OTHER STRUCTURAL MATERIALS include rectangular, square, or hexagonal bar stock, rods, tubes, strips, angles, channels, I-beams, and many other material configurations which may be procured in the various steels and alloy metals. A listing of these is beyond the scope of this book, but the commoner types are carried by most metal-shop stock rooms. The particular type of metal stock necessary to make any part is called for in the material block on the piece-part drawing.

CHASSIS CONSTRUCTION LAYOUT

Making a metal chassis base first requires *layout*, or transfer of the basic drawing measurements onto the selected flat or unbent piece of stock. The first step in layout is the development, or the marking of measurement lines and locations on the flat piece to establish a certain number of bending, cutting, and drilling points. The layout of holes is usually done on the flat development piece after cutting. Or it may be done on the chassis in its bent form if it is not inconvenient. The layout, measurement, and marking of a metal chassis or development piece may require very accurate measurements for the location of holes, shafts, and the like, even to thousandths of an inch.

LAYOUT AND MEASUREMENT TOOLS

The measuring and marking of straight and curved lines on a metal surface require the following implements: (1) hard pencils, (2) scribers, (3) steel scales, (4) center and prick

Table 3-3 Special sheet metals
(by fractional inch thicknesses)
(in pounds per square foot)

| Thickness in inches | | Metals | | | | | | | | |
Frac.	Decimal	2S Aluminum	Brass	Commercial bronze	Copper	18% Nickel Silver	Monel	*Nickel-clad Steel	Lead	Zinc
1/16″	.0625	.880	2.754	2.862	2.898	2.844	2.87	....	4.0	2.35
1/8 ″	.125	1.760	5.508	5.724	5.796	5.688	5.75	....	8.0	4.70
3/16″	.1875	2.641	8.262	8.586	8.694	8.532	8.62	7.75	12.0	7.05
1/4 ″	.250	3.521	11.02	11.45	11.59	11.38	11.49	10.33	16.0	9.40
5/16″	.3125	4.401	13.77	14.31	14.49	14.22	14.35	12.91	20.0	11.75
3/8 ″	.375	5.282	16.52	17.17	17.39	17.06	17.25	15.49	24.0	14.10
7/16″	.4375	6.162	19.28	19.94	20.29	19.91	20.09	18.08	28.0	16.45
1/2 ″	.500	7.043	22.03	22.90	23.18	22.75	22.98	20.66	32.0	18.80
9/16″	.5625	7.923	24.79	25.76	26.08	25.60	25.83	23.24	36.0	21.15
5/8 ″	.625	8.803	27.54	28.62	28.98	28.44	28.75	25.82	40.0	23.50
11/16″	.6875	9.684	30.29	31.48	31.88	31.28	31.57	28.40	44.0	25.85
3/4 ″	.750	10.564	33.05	34.35	34.78	34.13	34.47	30.99	48.0	28.80
13/16″	.8125	11.444	35.80	37.21	37.67	36.97	37.31	....	52.0	30.55
7/8 ″	.875	12.325	38.56	40.07	40.57	39.82	40.25	36.15	56.0	32.90
15/16″	.9375	13.205	41.31	42.93	43.47	42.66	42.95	....	60.0	35.25
1 ″	1.000	14.086	44.06	45.80	46.37	45.50	45.96	41.31	64.0	37.60
1 1/16″	1.0625	14.966	46.82	48.66	49.27	48.35	48.83	....	68.0	39.95
1 1/8 ″	1.125	15.846	49.57	51.52	52.16	51.19	51.71	....	72.0	42.30
1 3/16″	1.1875	16.727	52.33	54.27	55.06	54.04	54.58	....	76.0	44.65
1 1/4 ″	1.250	17.607	55.08	57.25	57.96	56.88	57.45	....	80.0	47.00
1 5/16″	1.315	18.487	57.83	60.11	60.86	59.72	60.31	....	84.0	49.25
1 3/8 ″	1.375	19.368	60.59	62.87	63.76	62.57	63.03	....	88.0	51.70
1 7/16″	1.4375	20.248	63.34	65.74	66.65	65.41	66.05	....	92.0	54.05
1 1/2 ″	1.500	21.129	66.10	67.70	69.55	68.26	68.94	61.97	96.0	56.40
1 9/16″	1.5625	22.009	68.85	71.56	72.45	71.10	71.79	....	100.0	58.75
1 5/8 ″	1.625	22.889	71.60	74.42	75.35	73.94	74.71	....	104.0	61.10
1 11/16″	1.6875	23.770	74.36	77.28	78.25	76.79	77.58	....	108.0	63.45
1 3/4 ″	1.750	24.650	77.11	80.15	81.14	79.63	80.43	....	112.0	65.80
1 13/16″	1.8125	25.530	79.87	83.01	84.04	82.48	83.27	....	116.0	68.15
1 7/8 ″	1.875	26.411	82.62	85.87	86.94	85.32	86.71	....	120.0	70.50
1 15/16″	1.9375	27.291	85.37	88.73	89.84	88.16	89.05	....	124.0	72.85
2 ″	2.000	28.172	88.13	91.60	92.74	91.01	91.92	82.62	128.0	75.20

*10% Nickel-Cladding (15% and 20% Cladding slightly heavier).

punches, (5) a machinist's hammer, (6) dividers and calipers, (7) beam compass or trammel, (8) toolmaker's clamp, (9) toolmaker's vise, (10) surface gauge, (11) surface plates, (12) V-blocks, (13) angle blocks, and a combination set which includes a (14) steel square, (15) center head, (16) bevel protractor, and (17) spirit level. A description of these tools and brief examples of their use will be given in illustrations to follow. These descriptions, together with other notes and information, will serve to explain the marking and layout process. The tools required for sheet-metal layout and measurement are often used in final fabrication, also. Particularly necessary in much. shop work are precision tools, such as calipers and gauges, having extreme accuracy. These are generally called micrometer tools, the most common of which is the machinist's micrometer or outside caliper. It is commonly called a "mike" and used to measure diameters of shafts, collars, strips, or other pieces requiring precise fits or construction. The various types of micrometer tools will be covered in more detail later in this chapter since they require more detailed description of the special skills and handling for correct operation.

MARKING THE CHASSIS MATERIAL

In marking a flat metal surface, the common practice is to coat it with some layout fluid. Bluing fluid is most commonly used, although a surface may be sprayed with zinc chromate solution or, in the case of a polished steel surface, with a copper sulphide solution.

A HARD PENCIL with a chisel-sharpened point is the best tool for marking a polished surface where scratch marks can not be tolerated. In marking a sharp line, the narrow side of the pencil's chisel point should bear against and run parallel to the side of whatever straightedge is used.

THE STEEL SCRIBER is made of hardened steel (see Fig. 3–4) and has sharp needle-

Table 3-4 Comparison of sheet metal gauges (by fractional inch thicknesses)

Gauge No.	American or Brown & Sharpe	United States Standard	Birmingham or Stubs
0000000	....	.500	....
000000	.5800	.46875	....
00000	.5165	.4375	....
0000	.4600	.40625	.454
000	.4096	.375	.425
00	.3648	.34375	.380
0	.3249	.3125	.340
1	.2893	.28125	.300
2	.2576	.265625	.284
3	.2294	.25	.259
4	.2043	.234375	.238
5	.1819	.21875	.220
6	.1620	.203125	.203
7	.1443	.1875	.180
8	.1285	.171875	.165
9	.1144	.15625	.148
10	.1019	.140625	.134
11	.90074	.125	.120
12	.08081	.109375	.109
13	.07196	.09375	.095
14	.06408	.078125	.083
15	.05707	.0703125	.072
16	.05082	.0625	.065
17	.04526	.05625	.058
18	.04030	.05	.049
19	.03589	.04375	.042
20	.03196	.0375	.035
21	.02846	.034375	.032
22	.02535	.03125	.028
23	.02257	.028125	.025
24	.02010	.025	.022
25	.01790	.021875	.020
26	.01594	.01875	.018
27	.01420	.0171875	.016
28	.01264	.015625	.014
29	.01126	.0140625	.013
30	.01003	.0125	.012
31	.008928	.0109375	.010
32	.007950	.01015625	.009
33	.007080	.009375	.008
34	.006305	.00859375	.007
35	.005615	.0078125	.005
36	.005000	.00703125	.004
37	.004453	.006640625	....
38	.003965	.00625	....
39	.003531	....	....
40	.003145	....	....

[1] Used for aluminum, copper, brass and nonferrous alloy sheets, wire and rods.

[2] Used for iron, steel, nickel and ferrous alloy sheets, wire and rods.

[3] Used for seamless tubes; also by some manufacturers for copper and brass.

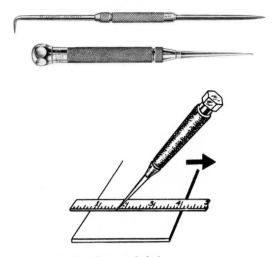

FIG. 3-4 Steel scribers and their use

pointed ends which will scratch fine lines on metal when the tool is used as a pencil and run along a straightedge. One type shown has a removable point. The hook-edged type enables scratching lines where the straight end cannot reach.

STEEL SCALES, often called steel rules, or machinist's rules, are made in many thicknesses, widths, and lengths. They should be protected from being nicked and worn, for they are accurately divided into parts of an inch by fine lines or divisions scribed along each edge. These divisions or gradations may be as fine as 1/64 or 1/100 of an inch, with the number of gradations per inch usually marked near one end of the scale. (See Fig. 3–5.) Flexible steel scales are used for measur-

ing along a curved surface. A hook scale uses an end step to hook over an edge for convenience in measurement. The steel rule 12 inches long and one inch wide may accommodate sliding attachments to become part of a combination set. Other scales, such as the folding model or the holder and fractional inch scale assembly, are used in special applications.

PRICK PUNCHES AND CENTER PUNCHES, as shown in Fig. 3–6, differ slightly in size and in the shape of their points. A prick punch is usually smaller than a center punch and has a sharper point. When drilling a hole, the wider point of the center punch allows a drill point to slip into the indentation and automatically to center itself. Automatic center punches are available for rapid location work. These punches release a spring-driven marking point which delivers a sharp blow from a mechanism within the body of the instrument. The act of pressing the punch with increasing force against a location point first cocks the mechanism and then releases it so that the blow is delivered. The use of a hammer is thus eliminated and greater accuracy obtained.

THE MACHINIST'S HAMMER, used in layout work, usually weighs between 2 and 6 ounces, since only light blows are necessary in marking work. The hardened flat face and the rounded peen are described in the later sections on hand tools. (See Fig. 3–7(a).) In marking a

FIG. 3-5 Steel scales

Steel rule

Tape rule

Steel tape

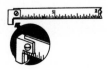

Hook rule

Folding rule

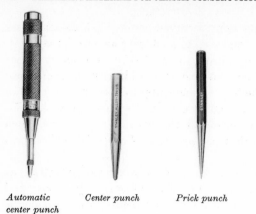

*Automatic
center punch*   *Center punch*   *Prick punch*

FIG. 3-6 Metalworking punches

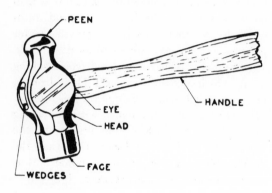

(a) *Machinist's hammer*

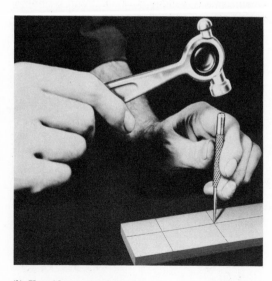

(b) *Use of hammer and punch*

FIG. 3-7 Machinist's hammer

location or making a center hole, the punch should be held directly perpendicular when striking a blow with the machinist's hammer. (See Fig. 3–7(b).) In locating a point at the intersection of two scribed lines, the point of the punch is run along the groove made by the scriber during the marking of one line until the point strikes the burr made by the other intersecting line.

DIVIDERS AND CALIPERS are used for transferring distances. The divider is a two-legged device similar to a compass. (See Fig. 3–8.) The sharpened, hardened points open as shown and may be used to divide a distance or to measure lengths for transfer from one point to another. The divider can be used as a compass to scribe the circumference of a circle with one point while the other remains fixed at the circle's center. A beam compass and trammel points (see Fig. 3–9) is a type of

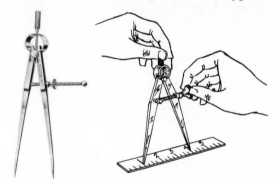

(a) *Shop dividers*   (b) *Transcribing distances*

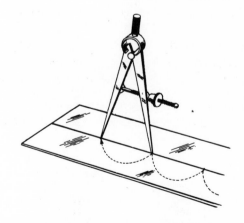

(c) *Dividing a line into equal parts*

FIG. 3-8 Common shop dividers

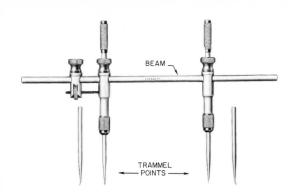

(a) *Beam compass and trammel points*

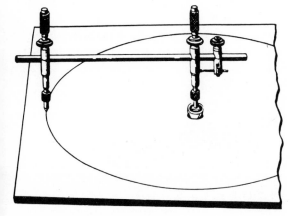

(b) *Use of trammel with ball point*

FIG. 3-9 Beam compass

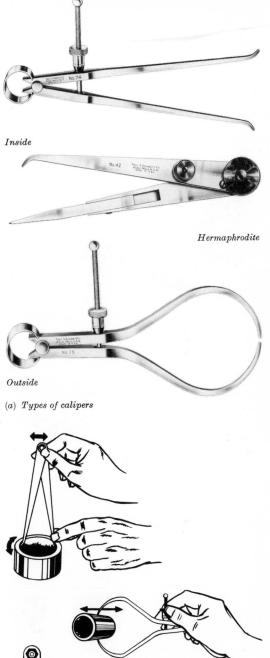

Inside

Hermaphrodite

Outside

(a) *Types of calipers*

(b) *Use of calipers*

FIG. 3-10 Calipers and their use

divider where the points, which are actually scribers, are suspended from a horizontal holding bar or beam, so that relatively wide distances may be measured and marked.

Calipers have three categories—inside, outside, and hermaphrodite, as shown in Fig. 3–10. They are used, respectively, to measure or transfer outside distances, to measure or transfer inside dimensions, or to simultaneously mark and measure a distance. The hermaphrodite caliper, used for these operations, is half divider and half caliper.

A STEEL SQUARE is a scale or ruler with an accurate right-angle bend in it. It is used to scribe lines at 90° to a reference edge, to establish lines parallel to the edge, or to serve as a guide or reference edge for other instruments. Figure 3–11 shows a solid square, a steel square with a blade and movable beam, and a combination set, which transforms a

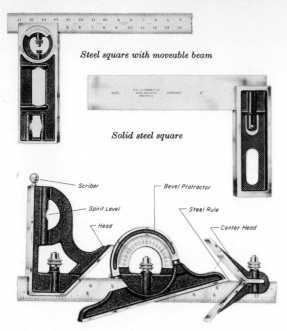

Steel square with moveable beam

Solid steel square

Combination set

steel rule into a square and guide which have many uses.

The parts to a combination set, in addition to the rule, are the center head, a square head, a spirit level, and a protractor head. Figure 3–12 shows the many uses to which this tool may be applied on edges or angularly located surfaces.

SURFACE PLATES AND SPIRIT LEVELS are required for precise workmanship. (See Figs. 3–13 and 3–14.) Such plates afford a flat level surface for squaring, measuring, and leveling accurately. These plates should be exactly horizontal when used on a bench set up as determined by a master precision level.

FIG. 3-13 Surface plate

FIG. 3-14 Machinist's level

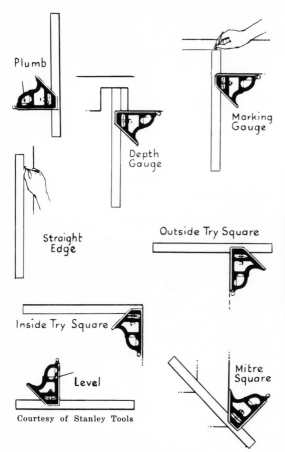

Courtesy of Stanley Tools

FIG. 3-12 Uses of combination set

Angle block giving vertical alignment

V-Block holding metal rod

FIG. 3-15 Use of the angle block and V-block

32

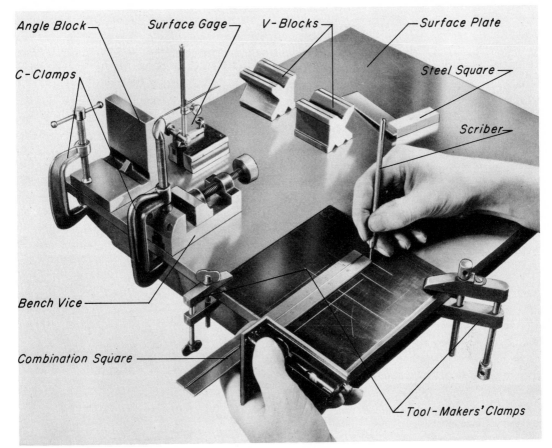

Angle Block — Surface Gage — V-Blocks — Surface Plate

C-Clamps — Steel Square

Scriber

Bench Vice

Combination Square

Tool-Makers' Clamps

FIG. 3-16 Use of layout tools

V-BLOCKS and angle blocks allow correct alignment and a firm level base when working on round stock. (See Fig. 3–15.) An angle block serves to obtain an accurate vertical measurement from a surface-plate reference.

THE BENCH VISE, C-CLAMPS, AND TOOL-MAKER'S CLAMPS may be used to hold pieces being worked on. Figure 3–16 shows all of these tools being used in typical layout work.

THE SURFACE GAUGE, when used on a surface plate, gives accurate height measurements. (See Fig. 3–17.)

MICROMETER INSTRUMENTS

The most common form of this type of tool is the micrometer caliper, or "mike." It is a calibrated outside caliper capable of meas-

uring lengths accurate to thousandths of an inch. The *outside micrometer* is used to make precise measurements across critical outside surfaces such as shaft diameters, widths, and thicknesses. This instrument is made in sizes ranging from one to twenty-four inches. The *inside micrometer* is used mainly to measure the diameters of holes. To determine depths of holes, grooves, or slots, the *depth micrometer* may be used. The *screw micrometer* is used to obtain accurate measurements of screw threads. (See Fig. 3–18.)

From Fig. 3–19, we see that a micrometer has a frame, a hub, a rotating sleeve, an adjustable spindle connected through an internal screw to the sleeve, an anvil or base upon which the measured piece rests, and a ratchet. The general procedure for manipulating the micrometer is to screw in the sleeve so that the end of the spindle lightly touches one side of the shaft or object whose opposite side

33

rests upon the anvil. Distances from the anvil to the face of the spindle are then directly read in thousandths of an inch on the scale markings at that particular position on the hub where the edge of the sleeve has stopped. The various types of micrometer instruments come in a number of one-inch ranges measuring, with proper attachments in the case of most types, up to as much as 24 inches. For example: A 1″ mike measures from 0″ to 1″, A 2″ mike measures from 1″ to 2″, and so on up the scale.

In holding a micrometer when making a measurement, the curved part of the frame should be held between the meaty or fat part of the heel of the hand and the fourth or little finger. This leaves the thumb, middle, and forefinger free to turn the sleeve. (See Fig. 3–18(d).) Turning the ratchet stop nut at the end of the sleeve after the spindle has touched the piece being measured causes the ratchet clutch to slip and to maintain a uniform pressure between the spindle and anvil so that all measurements will be alike.

TO READ THE MICROMETER at any setting, we must first read off and then add the sum of three figures as they appear on the two micrometer scales. Two of the three figures are obtained from the first, or hub scale, which has a baseline running lengthwise along the hub, in the direction of measurement. The third is obtained from the hub which has two kinds of index lines (Fig. 3–20): (1) long index lines spaced 1/10 of an inch apart which are labeled from 1 to 10 and yield the first set of figures in tenths of inches; (2) short index lines located at evenly spaced intermediate positions between the long index markings to indicate each 25 thousandths of an inch (.025″, or 1/40″).

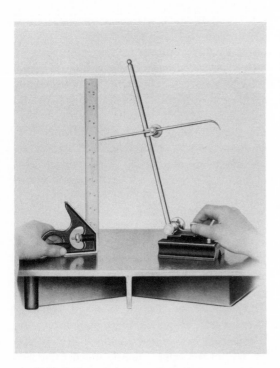

FIG. 3-17 Surface gauge

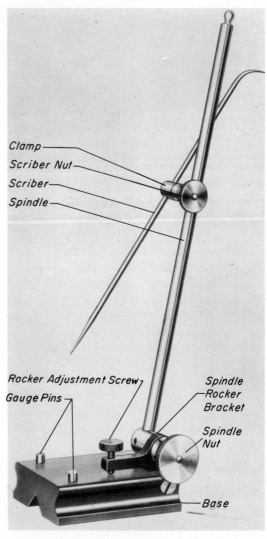

Clamp

Scriber Nut

Scriber

Spindle

Rocker Adjustment Screw

Gauge Pins

Spindle
Rocker
Bracket

Spindle
Nut

Base

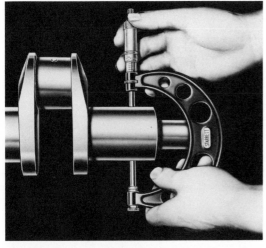

(a) Outside micrometer

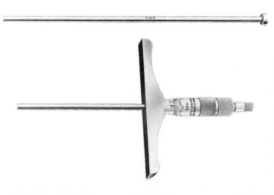

(c) Depth micrometer

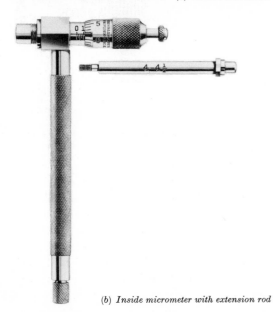

(b) Inside micrometer with extension rod

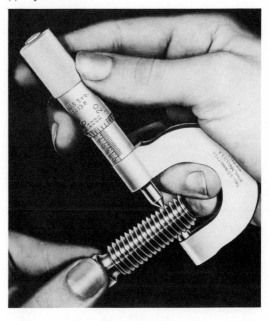

(d) Screw micrometer

FIG. 3-18 Micrometer instruments

As the edge of the thimble sleeve is rotated to assume various positions parallel to the index lines, the particular hub marking across which the sleeve edge finally rests represents a distance measurement between the anvil and the spindle, since turning the sleeve moves the spindle.

The edge of the rotating sleeve has 25 evenly spaced index marks scribed around it, providing another movable scale which runs at right angles to the hub scale and gives the third of the figures necessary to make a measurement. Every fifth of these marks is labeled from 0 to 25 around the thimble-sleeve circumference, so that the distance between each index mark represents one-thousandth of an inch. As we turn the thimble sleeve and its edge moves along between each of the small lines on the hub scale (which, as explained previously, are 25 thousandths of an inch apart) it measures a dimension of one-thousandth of an inch each time a thimble sleeve mark crosses the baseline, since there are 25 marks along the entire circumference.

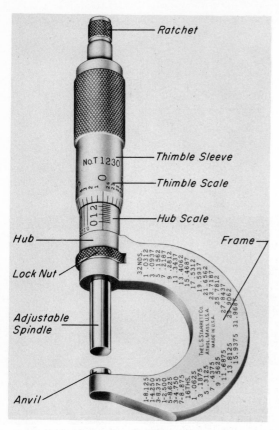

FIG. 3-19 A micrometer caliper

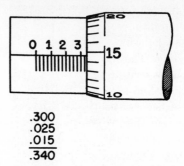

$$\begin{array}{r} .300 \\ .025 \\ .015 \\ \hline .340 \end{array}$$

FIG. 3-21 Procedure for reading the micrometer scale

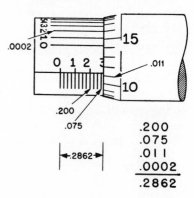

$$\begin{array}{r} .200 \\ .075 \\ .011 \\ .0002 \\ \hline .2862 \end{array}$$

FIG. 3-22 Reading the Vernier scale

The procedure in arriving at a measurement for any thimble position consists of adding, as shown in Fig. 3–21, the three basic figures described above: (1) the total number of tenths of inches along the hub markings from zero on up to the sleeve—in this case 3: $3 \times .1 = .3''$; (2) the number of $25/1,000''$ or small intermediate hub divisions from the last tenth-inch division to the sleeve—in this case $1 \times .025 = .025''$; (3) the number of thousandths showing on the circular thimble scale at the hub base line—in this case almost fifteen.

Setting (1) three $1/10''$ divisions .... = .300
Setting (2) one $25/1,000''$ divisions = .025
Setting (3) 15-$1/1,000''$ divisions ... = .015
　　　　　　Add for total .... .340

THE VERNIER SCALE CALIPER

Some micrometers and other measuring instruments and gauges are graduated in *ten-thousandths* of an inch. They are used like the conventional instruments graduated in

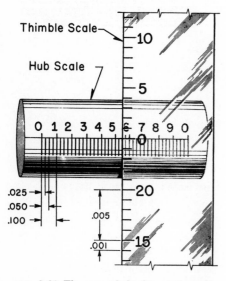

FIG. 3-20 The expanded micrometer scale

thousandths of an inch, except that an additional reading in ten-thousandths is obtained from a Vernier scale, which is added to the thousandths reading. The Vernier scale consists of ten divisions scribed on the hub just beyond the tenth-of-an-inch numbers. (See Fig. 3–22.) These occupy the same space as nine divisions on the thimble. Therefore, the difference between the width of one of the *ten* spaces on the Vernier and one of the *nine* spaces on the thimble is one-tenth of a division on the thimble, or one-tenth of one-thousandth which is one ten-thousandth of an inch.

To read a ten-thousandth micrometer, first obtain the thousandths reading, then see which of the lines on the Vernier *coincide* with a line on the thimble. If it is a Vernier line marked 1, add one ten-thousandth; if it is

a Vernier line marked 2, add two ten-thousandths, etc.

EXAMPLE: (Refer to Fig. 3–22.)

(a) The 2 line on the sleeve is visible beyond the edge of the thimble, representing .200″

(b) Three additional lines are visible, each representing .025″....3 × .025″ ...075″

(c) The hub scale baseline coincides with the longitudinal line on the sleeve at the eleven mark so that there are 11 added thousandths ....011″

(d) The *first* Vernier division that aligns with *any* thimble mark is 2. (In this case matching up with thimble mark 16.) .0002

Add for total   .2862

4 Sheet Metalworking On Electronic Chassis

BASIC SHEET METALWORKING OPERATIONS

The fabrication of a metal chassis base after marking has been completed on the developed flat stock calls for a number of working operations. These procedures involve basic hand tools and usually do not require the use of the larger power tools such as engine lathes, power punches, motor-driven band saws, or milling machines. The basic sheet metalworking operations on a chassis and the tools used for them will be described in this chapter. The basic operations are (1) cutting the flat stock to size and cutting any additional holes that cannot be drilled within the outlines of the chassis base; (2) drilling or punching socket mounting or fastening holes, usually while the chassis is still in its flat state; (3) bending the chassis flanges or other parts to the three-dimensional shape called for on the chassis print; (4) filing, reaming, or tapping operations to modify existing holes or add any other alterations that are necessary; (5) fastening and assembling the various mechanical accessories to the base or to each other by screws, rivets, clamps, welding, or some other means. The accessories are usually independent of the components and include brackets, gussets, castings, bearings, or miscellaneous pieces that can be identified on the material parts list. Component mountings are usually simple bolt-and-screw arrangements which operate in ways that may be seen by inspection of the components.

USE OF BASIC METALWORKING HAND TOOLS

The fabrication of a complete chassis requires a set of hand tools, most of which are generally recognized by people who do technical work. These tools will be listed according to type, size, and the special functions they perform. The component sections and parts of each tool are described, as well as the application of the tool in the basic metalworking operations.

HAMMERS commonly used for most metal forming or bending are the machinists' ball peen, cross peen, or straight peen hammers, shown in Fig. 4–1. The common claw hammer is not used in the machine shop. Peen hammer operations using the flat face consist of the usual driving and flattening procedures. The peen end of a hammer is used for rounding

FIG. 4-1 Machinists' hammers; ball peen hammer is center

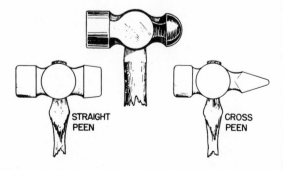

STRAIGHT PEEN CROSS PEEN

over, riveting, or driving operations in positions where the flat face will not reach. Special riveting and welding hammers often have soft faces made of rawhide, copper, or plastic in order to prevent marring of a hammered surface. Machinist's hammers used in metalworking are in general heavier than those used in chassis layout described in Chapter 3. (See Fig. 3–7.)

SCREWDRIVERS may be of almost any length or blade size. Two general categories are screwdrivers with straight blades and those fitting Phillips, or recessed-head screws. Figure 4–2 shows the parts of a screwdriver, the regular and Phillips type blade, and offset and ratchet types. The proper size of straight-blade screwdriver should always be used, so that the blade fits snugly into the slot on the head of the screw. The blade weight and strength, and the force applied to the screw which it fits, are then in correct proportion, and the screw slot will not be injured under normal pressure. The Phillips screwdriver has the advantage that any size blade will fit a smaller screw than that which the blade is constructed to fit.

WRENCHES are used to grip or hold a bolt head or a nut, and may be generally categorized as fixed or adjustable. Fixed wrenches may be either the open-end or the closed or socket type. Figure 4–3 shows the conventional monkey wrench, the adjustable end wrench, the Stillson, box, socket, and open end wrenches. Stillson or pipe wrenches have teeth on both jaw faces, with the additional

feature of a slight play between the adjustable jaws. This play enables the teeth of the wrench to grip round pieces of stock or pipe. Spanner wrenches are fixed wrenches specially designed to fit into specific indentations, notches, or holes in a threaded plate or piece. Figure 4–4 shows three of the most common types. Set screw wrenches are really screwdrivers used to turn headless set

FIG. 4-3 Wrenches

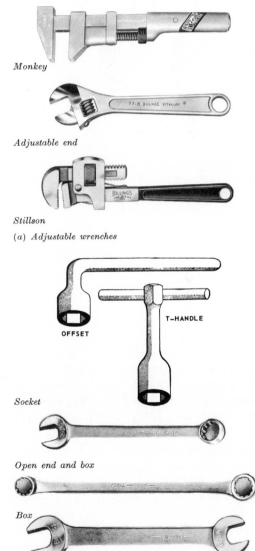

Monkey

Adjustable end

Stillson

(a) *Adjustable wrenches*

OFFSET

T–HANDLE

Socket

Open end and box

Box

Double open end

(b) *Fixed wrenches*

FIG. 4-2 Types of screw drivers and proper fit of blade

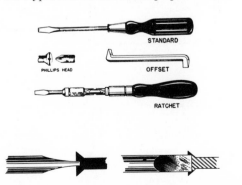

STANDARD

PHILLIPS HEAD

OFFSET

RATCHET

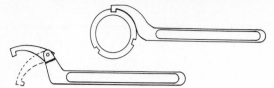

Hook spanner wrench and adjustable hook spanner

Pin face spanner wrench and its use

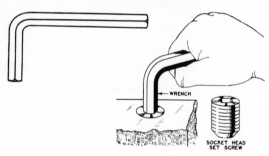

WRENCH

SOCKET HEAD
SET SCREW

Set screw wrench and its use

FIG. 4-4 Specialized wrenches

screws. The body of the wrench is hexagonally contoured to fit into a hollowed-out portion of the set screw. The most common of these is the Allen type shown in Fig. 4–4.

VISES AND CLAMPS (see Fig. 3–16) are almost indispensable for holding metal parts that are being hammered, bent, cut, or drilled. The machinist's vise has a solid or swivel base and movable jaws, as contrasted to the C-clamp and the toolmaker's clamp, which do not need to be fastened down.

THE HACK SAW is a metal-cutting tool with a removable metal blade mounted in an adjustable metal frame. (See Fig. 4–5.) Hack saw blades, available in 8-inch, 10-inch, and 12-inch lengths, have hardened teeth for cutting efficiency and soft springy bodies to reduce breakage. Coping and jeweler's saws are variations in the basic type of hack saw. Figure 4–6 shows the correct technique for cutting with a hack saw. Downward and forward pressure is applied by holding the saw at both ends of the frame. The cutting stroke should be on the forward and down blade movement, and the saw should be lifted on the return strokes to avoid wearing out the blade by rubbing. Best efficiency is obtained by long steady strokes. Deep cuts near the edge of material can be made with the saw blade turned at right angles to the frame. Cutting should be done on pieces firmly held in a vise with as short a distance as possible between the holding grip and the cutting line in order to eliminate vibrating, springing, or chattering. Very thin metal, thinner than the space between saw teeth, should be clamped in a vise between two boards and the cut made through both the metal and the boards.

SHEARS AND CUTTERS of various kinds are used for cutting sheet or chassis base metal,

FIG. 4-5 The hack saw and its variants

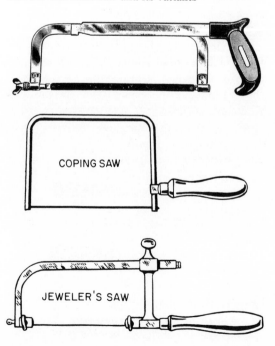

COPING SAW

JEWELER'S SAW

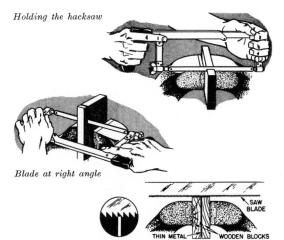

Holding the hacksaw

Blade at right angle

Cutting metal thinner than tooth spacing

FIG. 4-6 Using the hacksaw

Hand snips   Using bench shears

FIG. 4-7 Metal cutting shears

Foot-operated squaring shear

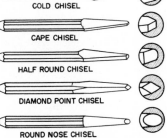

Lever shear

FIG. 4-8 Squaring and lever shears

FIG. 4-9 Types of chisels

COLD CHISEL

CAPE CHISEL

HALF ROUND CHISEL

DIAMOND POINT CHISEL

ROUND NOSE CHISEL

depending upon its thickness. Commonly called snips, these are all large, heavy versions of the common household scissor, designed to cut light metal. For small cutting operations, cutting pliers may be used. Figure 4–7 shows two common types of shears. For larger chassis bases where a straight cut of 12 inches or more is needed, the foot-operated bench, or squaring shear, is sometimes used. For notches, corners, thicker stock, and small rods, the lever shear is used. (See Fig. 4–8.)

THE CHISEL is the simplest metal-cutting tool. It has many applications, especially where the piece to be cut is smaller than the width of the chisel cutting blade. Chisels are made of hardened steel and vary in size from 3/8 to 1 inch in diameter and from 6 to 8 inches, in length. Because of the temper of their metal, chisels are commonly referred to as "cold." They are identified by the shape of the cutting edge as the flat chisel, cape chisel, diamond chisel, or half and full round nose chisel, as shown in Fig. 4–9. Some of the cutting, grooving, and shearing techniques for using the various chisel types are shown in Fig. 4–10.

FILES are surface-cutting tools. They are hardened pieces of bar steel with various cross-sectional shapes. Slanting parallel rows of teeth or cutting edges are forged on their various outside surfaces. The main character-

Shearing

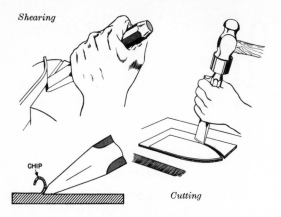

Chipping

Cutting

FIG. 4-10 Using the flat chisel on sheet metal

istics, or toothed surfaces, are described in terms of the "cut." *Single-cut files* have a single set of teeth cut at an angle of from 60° to 80° to the center line of the tool. *Double-cut files* have two sets of teeth crossing one another. *Rasp-cut files* have no groove or surface connection between individual teeth. *Curved-tooth files* have circular cutting edges. The spacing between the cutting teeth determines the coarseness of a file and increases with the file's length. Spacings are designated as rough, coarse, bastard, second-cut, smooth, or dead smooth. (See Fig. 4–11.)

Figure 4–12 shows the various parts of a file. For filing operations, a wooden handle is usually forced on the *tang* in order to obtain a firm grip. Most commercially available files come in 6, 8, 10, and 12 inch lengths. They may have hundreds of shapes, described according to the cross-section of the blade. Most of the commonly used files, listed by their cross-sectional areas, are shown in Fig. 4–12. One manufacturer advertises over 5,000 different sizes, shapes, and cuts of files.

THE FILING OPERATION can be performed on all metals except hardened steel. The work to be filed should be held firmly in a vise. Slow forward strokes should be made with moderate pressure while holding the file by its handle with the right hand, and guiding it with the left. (See Fig. 4–13.) As in the case of a hack saw, the forward stroke should always be the cutting stroke. Rapid rubbing, slipping, or sliding of a file will wear off the points on its teeth and make it dull. Heavy filing should be done with a full, firm grasp and a forward stroke as shown in Fig. 4–13. When finer finish is desired, "draw" filing is performed. Almost any shape hole can be filed in a flat piece of stock by using one of the various file sizes and cross-sectional shapes. Keyhole files, needle files, or jeweler's files are miniature in size but have cross-sectional areas similar to those of the standard files shown in Fig. 4–12. A useful adjunct to filing work is the combination file card and brush (see Fig. 4–13), whose stiff metal bristles enable particles to be easily removed and then brushed away from between file teeth after working soft material.

DRILLS for metalworking are shown in Fig. 4–14. The word drill is used to describe both

FIG. 4-11 File cuts and tooth spacings

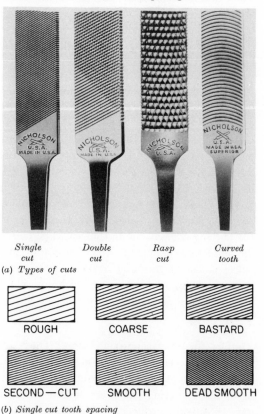

Single cut   *Double cut*   *Rasp cut*   *Curved tooth*

(a) *Types of cuts*

ROUGH   COARSE   BASTARD

SECOND—CUT   SMOOTH   DEAD SMOOTH

(b) *Single cut tooth spacing*

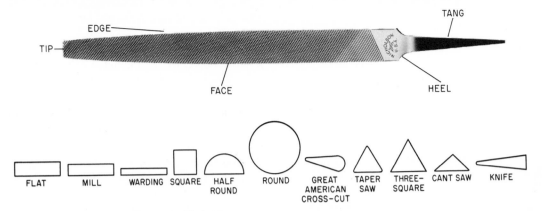

FIG. 4-12 File parts and cross-sectional shapes

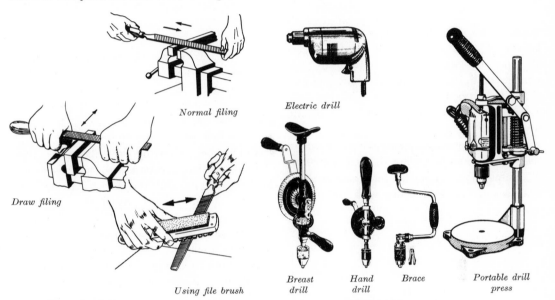

Normal filing

Draw filing

Using file brush

FIG. 4-13 Using the file

Electric drill

Breast drill

Hand drill

Brace

Portable drill press

FIG. 4-14 Drilling machines

FIG. 4-15 Drill construction

FIG. 4-16 Types of drills

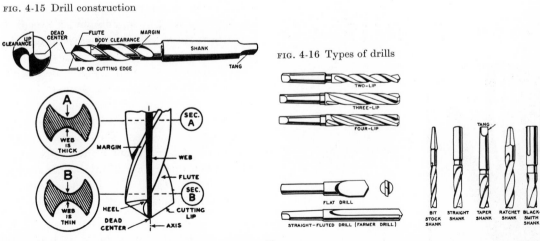

43

the *twist drill* or *drill point* and the *drilling machines* used to hold and to apply rotary motion and pressure to the drill point. Common drilling machines include the hand drill, the breast drill, the portable electric drill, the bit brace, and the portable drill press.

Twist drill parts and general construction are shown in the layout of Fig. 4–15; actual cuttings done by the drill lip. Common twist drill points are made of carbon steel or of high speed steel. The latter may be run approximately twice as fast as ordinary carbon steel drills and are usually marked H.S. on the body of the drill. The flat drill can be made in the shop. The farmer's drill is used for copper, brass, or other soft metals. Several types of twist drills described by the number of lips and shanks are shown in Fig. 4–16. The various shanks for twist drills are designed to fit the chucks of different drilling machines.

Small drills are usually kept in sets where they are stacked according to their diameter. A common type of holder for a set of drills is shown in Fig. 4–17, along with a standard

FIG. 4-17 Drill holder and gauge

Drill gauge

A set of drills

drill gauge. Holders and gauges have correct size holes marked corresponding to the drill which fits the hole snugly. Drill holders are necessary because many drills lose the stamped identification of their diameter and because it is impossible to stamp a number on a very small drill. Drill diameters and their corresponding gauge numbers (see Table 4–1) run from number 80 drill (.0135 inch diameter) up to number 1 (.228 inch diameter). Letters A to Z are used to denote drill sizes larger than number 1, but not multiples of $\frac{1}{64}$ inch. These diameters range from .234 to .413 inches. Drill diameters from number Z up to 1 inch in diameter come in sizes graduated evenly each $\frac{1}{64}$ inch.

IN FOLLOWING CORRECT DRILLING PRACTICE the first consideration (after selecting the drill point and the hole location) is the means of holding the piece to be drilled. In some cases pliers or wrenches are adequate. In other cases, a drill press provides several devices for clamping or for resting the drilled piece. (See Fig. 4–18.) The C-clamp, the parallel or toolmaker's clamp, and the bench vise are examples of these. Drill press clamps and step blocks make use of T-slot bolts in the drill press base to tighten the clamp and the piece which it holds. V-blocks, angle plates, and parallel blocks also may be used to hold pieces in place at the proper angle while drilling.

The final drilling operation should be guided by the allowable running speed of the drill. This depends upon the size of the drill and the type of material being drilled. Table 4–2 shows safe drill speeds under specified conditions. Most drill presses have adjustable speeds made available by selections of driver pulley diameters. Note that high speed drills can be run twice as fast as carbon steel drills and that some type of lubricant should be used to coat the cutting surfaces, especially if high speed is selected. The lubricant should be run in a steady stream on the area being drilled when operations of any length are being performed. Table 4–3 lists the types of lubricant for drilling and other operations.

THE SHARPENING OF A DRILL is necessary periodically and should bring the cutting

Table 4–1 Twist drill sizes

Size	Decimal equivalents	Size	Decimal equivalents
1/2	.5000	13	.1850
31/64	.4844	14	.1820
15/32	.4687	15	.1800
29/64	.4531	16	.1770
7/16	.4375	17	.1730
27/64	.4219	11/64	.1719
Z	.4130	18	.1695
13/32	.4062	19	.1660
Y	.4040	20	.1610
X	.3970	21	.1590
25/64	.3906	22	.1570
W	.3860	5/32	.1562
V	.3770	23	.1540
3/8	.3750	24	.1520
U	.3680	25	.1495
23/64	.3594	26	.1470
T	.3580	27	.1440
S	.3480	9/64	.1406
11/32	.3437	28	.1405
R	.3390	29	.1360
Q	.3320	30	.1285
21/64	.3281	1/8	.1250
P	.3230	31	.1200
O	.3160	32	.1160
5/16	.3125	33	.1130
N	.3020	34	.1110
19/64	.2969	35	.1100
M	.2950	7/64	.1094
L	.2900	36	.1065
9/32	.2812	37	.1040
K	.2810	38	.1015
J	.2770	39	.0995
I	.2720	40	.0980
H	.2660	41	.0960
17/64	.2656	3/32	.0937
G	.2610	42	.0935
F	.2570	43	.0890
E 1/4	.2500	44	.0860
D	.2460	45	.0820
C	.2420	46	.0810
B	.2380	47	.0785
15/64	.2344	5/64	.0781
A	.2340	48	.0760
No. 1	.2280	49	.0730
2	.2210	50	.0700
7/32	.2187	51	.0670
3	.2130	52	.0635
4	.2090	1/16	.0625
5	.2055	53	.0595
6	.2040	54	.0550
13/64	.2031	55	.0520
7	.2010	3/64	.0469
8	.1990	56	.0465
9	.1960	57	.0430
10	.1935	58	.0420
11	.1910	59	.0410
12	.1890	60	.0400
3/16	.1875		

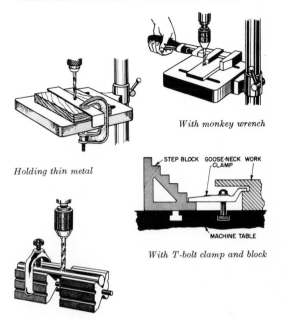

With monkey wrench

Holding thin metal

STEP BLOCK GOOSE-NECK WORK CLAMP

MACHINE TABLE

With T-bolt clamp and block

In V-blocks

FIG. 4-18 Holding work to be drilled

edges and other dimensions back to correct proportions. The lengths of the lips of a drill (see Fig. 4–19 (a)) should be equal and their angles with the center line of the drill should be equal. In regular drills this angle is 59°, and in flat point drills it is 67.5°; the lips should also be beveled at respective angles of 8° to 12°, and 6° to 9°. The lip clearance angle is particularly important and should be preserved when sharpening the drill to obtain best cutting efficiency. Drill point sharpening is done on an abrasive grinding wheel (Fig. 4–19(b)), using some kind of a rest or gauge to maintain the correct lip angles as the drill is held against the wheel. A drill grinding gauge should be used in checking the finished results, as shown in Fig. 4–19 (c).

PUNCHES

In moderately thin flat stock, holes up to $1\frac{1}{2}$ inches may be punched by hand-operated tools. The center punch, the hollow punch, and other hand punches (see Fig. 4–20) are suitable for flat-stock punching where the thickness does not exceed $\frac{1}{8}$ inch. Using small punches on thin stock, backed by a lead plate, one

Table 4–2   Maximum Drill speeds in revolutions per minute

Diameter of drill, inches	Cast iron		Steel		Brass		Feed per revolution, inches
	Carbon steel drill	High speed steel drill	Carbon steel drill	High speed steel drill	Carbon steel drill	High speed steel drill	
	35 ft. per min.	70 ft. per min.	30 ft. per min.	60 ft. per min.	100 ft. per min.	200 ft. per min.	
1/4	535	1,070	458	917	1,528	3,056	0.005
1/2	268	535	229	458	764	1,528	0.008
3/4	178	357	153	306	509	1,018	0.010
1	134	267	115	229	382	764	0.012

Table 4–3   Lubricants for drilling, cutting, threading or tapping

Metals	Sawing with power saw	Drilling	Reaming	Threading with die	Tapping	Knurling (on lathe)
Cast iron	Dry	Dry	Dry	Dry	Dry or Lard oil	Lard oil
Wrought iron	Soda water	Soda water or lard oil	Lard oil	Lard oil	Lard oil	Lard oil
Steel	Soda water	Soda water or lard oil	Lard oil	Lard oil	Lard oil	Lard oil
Copper		Kerosene or dry	Lard oil or kerosene	Lard oil or dry	Lard oil	Lard oil
Brass		Dry	Dry	Dry	Dry or lard oil	Lard oil
Bronze		Dry or soluble oil	Dry	Dry		Lard oil
Aluminum		Kerosene or turpentine	Kerosene or turpentine	Kerosene or turpentine	Kerosene	Kerosene or turpentine
Babbitt		Dry or lard oil	Dry	Lard oil	Dry	Dry
(Glass)		Turpentine or kerosene	Turpentine or kerosene			

FIG. 4-19 Drill point sharpening

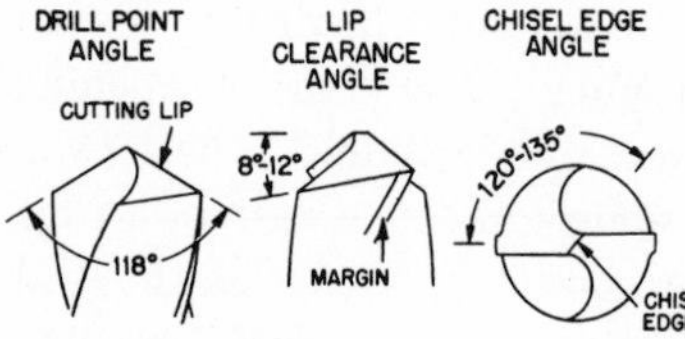

FIG. 4-20 Hand punches

(a) Cutting edge angles

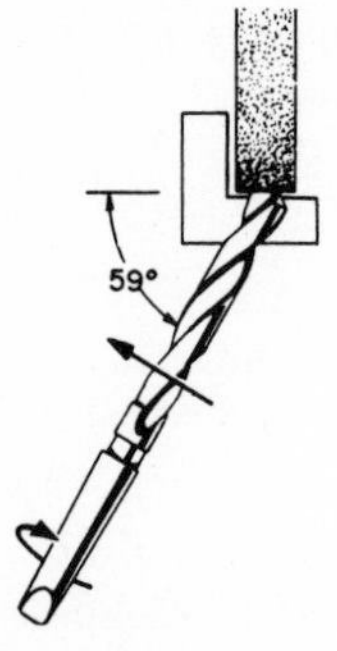

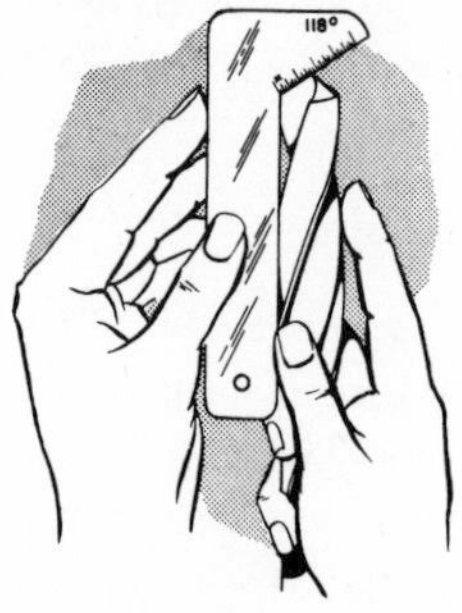

(b) The grinding operation   (c) Drill grinding guage

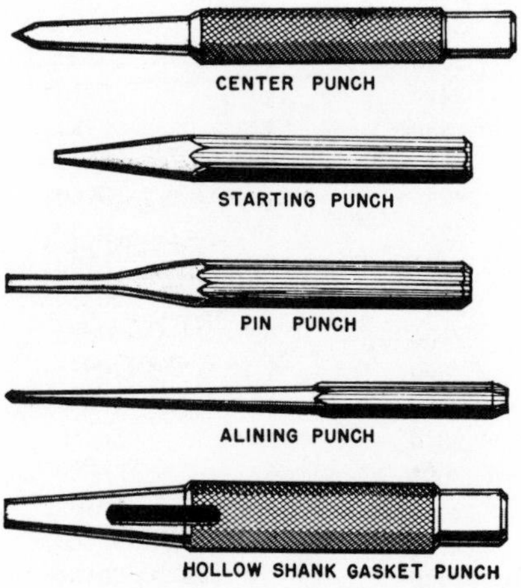

merely drives a hole through the flat stock by striking the punch with a hammer. For thicker stock and holes of larger diameter, punches may be inserted into a hand or arbor press (see Fig. 4–21) where powerful leverage may be obtained to exert pressure against the punch. Figure 4–21 also shows a small power-operated punch press which produces holes up to 1 inch in diameter. A more commonly used tool is the Greenlee knockput punch set. This unit clamps over a pilot hole through the metal to be punched and uses the cutting and pressing action of the top section of the assembly, which is turned by a wrench.

REAMERS, COUNTERSINKS, COUNTERBORES

REAMERS (see Fig. 4–22) are used to enlarge holes that have been drilled in order to bring them to exact size. In effect, the reamer is a circular scraping tool utilizing fluted cutting edges running lengthwise along its sides. When it is rotated after being forced within a drilled hole, the flutes finish the inside of the hole by scraping it to exactly the outside diameter of the fluted cutting edges.

THE COUNTERSINK (see Fig. 4–23) is a flattened or foreshortened drill which is used to enlarge only the top of a drilled hole to enable the head of a flat-head screw to sink down into the material so that it does not protrude above the surface.

THE COUNTERBORE combines a drill and countersink of different diameters on one shaft. It is used when filister-head or round-head screws must be sunk into a material.

FIG. 4-21 Machine punches

Arbor punch press

Greenlee knockout punch set

Power punch press

Hand-operated press

FIG. 4-22 Reamers and their use

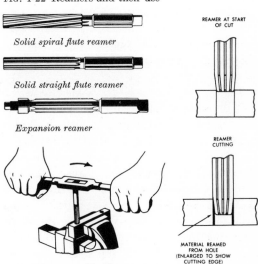

Solid spiral flute reamer

Solid straight flute reamer

Expansion reamer

Use of tap wrench with reamer

(See Fig. 4–24(a)). The counterbore first drills a hole into a surface to the depth of the smaller drill. Then the larger diameter drill starts to cut and makes a wider hole, while the smaller drill continues to cut deeper, making a pilot hole for the screw. (Fig. 4–24(b)). The hole made with this tool allows space for a screw head to be sunk below the surface of the piece being worked on. Various sizes of cap and machine screws are given in Table 4–4. Table 4–5 lists tolerances that need to be allowed when cutting threads in holes.

TAPS

A TAP is a hardened, slightly tapered screw-like tool with recessed spaces or flutes running perpendicular to its cutting threads. Cutting edges are formed along the edges of the flutes at the start of each section of thread. When the tap is turned in a hole just slightly smaller than its thread, it cuts threads along the inside of the hole. The basic types include the taper, plug, bottoming, and machine screw taps. Figure 4–25 shows these and the tapping operation. Straight or chuck-handle wrenches may be used to turn the tap by hand. Machine tapping is done by inserting the tap into the chuck of a drill press.

THE TAPPING OPERATION must be performed very carefully since taps, being of hard steel and somewhat brittle, break off very easily if they cannot run truly parallel to the axis of the hole.

The tap itself must be the same size as the bolt or screw intended for the tapped hole. This means that the hole which is drilled must be smaller than the final hole in order for the tap to cut away enough metal to form threads. This relationship is given in Table 4–6 for all sizes of screw threads, their corresponding tap size, and the size of the tapping drill to be used. The operation should be started with a tapered tap and the work should be clamped so that the tap hole is vertical. During the final running-in when using a plug

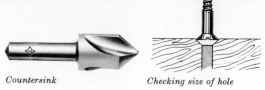

Countersink   Checking size of hole

FIG. 4-23 Countersinks

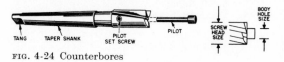

FIG. 4-24 Counterbores

Table 4–4   Screw thread sizes

Diameter		Threads per inch			
No.	Inch	Decimal equivalent	NC (U.S.S.)	NF (S.A.E.)	EF (extra fine)
0	...	.0600	...	80	...
1	...	.0730	64	72	...
2	...	.0860	56	64	...
3	...	.0990	48	56	...
4	...	.1120	40	48	...
5	1/8	.1250	40	44	...
6	...	.1380	32	40	...
8	...	.1640	32	36	...
10	...	.1900	24	32	40
12	...	.2160	24	28	...
...	1/4	.2500	20	28	36
...	5/16	.3125	18	24	32
...	3/8	.3750	16	24	32
...	7/16	.4375	14	20	28
...	1/2	.5000	13	20	28
...	9/16	.5625	12	18	24
...	5/8	.6250	11	18	24
...	3/4	.7500	10	16	20
...	7/8	.8750	9	14	20
...	1	1.0000	8	14	20

tap, the shank of the tool should be checked for squareness to the surface in which the hole has been drilled.

BROKEN TAPS may also be caused by: (1) an undersized drill hole, which requires more pressure and strain than the tap can stand; (2) a lopsided tap; (3) a skewed tap wrench, which acts like a lever; (4) lack of lubricating oil; (5) failure to periodically back the tap up and out of the hole to remove chips; (6) turning the tap after the bottom of the hole is reached. In blind holes (holes which do not go through the metal) a bottoming tap should be used.

Table 4–5   Tolerances to be allowed in cutting threads

Class	Nominal diameters	Up to 1/2″	9/16″ — 1″	1 1/16″ — 2″	2 1/16″ — 3″	3 1/16″ — 4″	4 1/16″ — 5″
				Tolerances in standard holes*			
A	High limit	+0.0002	+0.0005	+0.0007	+0.0010	+0.0010	+0.0010
	Low limit	−0.0002	−0.0002	−0.0002	−0.0005	−0.0005	−0.0005
	Tolerance	0.0004	0.0007	0.0009	0.0015	0.0015	0.0015
B	High limit	+0.0005	+0.0007	+0.0010	+0.0012	+0.0015	+0.0017
	Low limit	−0.0005	−0.0005	−0.0005	−0.0007	−0.0007	−0.0007
	Tolerance	0.0010	0.0012	0.0015	0.0019	0.0022	0.0024
				Allowances for forced fits			
F	High limit	+0.0010	+0.0020	+0.0040	+0.0060	+0.0080	+0.0100
	Low limit	+0.0005	+0.0015	+0.0030	+0.0045	+0.0060	+0.0080
	Tolerance	0.0005	0.0005	0.0010	0.0015	0.0020	0.0020
				Allowances for driving fits			
D	High limit	+0.0005	+0.0010	+0.0015	+0.0025	+0.0030	+0.0035
	Low limit	+0.0002	+0.0007	+0.0010	+0.0015	+0.0020	+0.0025
	Tolerance	0.0003	0.0003	0.0005	0.0010	0.0010	0.0010
				Allowances for push fits			
P	High limit	−0.0002	−0.0002	−0.0002	−0.0005	−0.0005	−0.0005
	Low limit	−0.0007	−0.0007	−0.0007	−0.0010	−0.0010	−0.0010
	Tolerance	0.0005	0.0005	0.0005	0.0005	0.0005	0.0005
				Allowances for running fits†			
X	High limit	−0.0010	−0.0012	−0.0017	−0.0020	−0.0025	−0.0030
	Low limit	−0.0020	−0.0027	−0.0035	−0.0042	−0.0050	−0.0057
	Tolerance	0.0010	0.0015	0.0018	0.0022	0.0025	0.0027
Y	High limit	−0.0007	−0.0010	−0.0012	−0.0015	−0.0020	−0.0022
	Low limit	−0.0012	−0.0020	−0.0025	−0.0030	−0.0035	−0.0040
	Tolerance	0.0005	0.0010	0.0013	0.0015	0.0015	0.0018
Z	High limit	−0.0005	−0.0007	−0.0007	−0.0010	−0.0010	−0.0012
	Low limit	−0.0007	−0.0012	−0.0015	−0.0020	−0.0022	−0.0025
	Tolerance	0.0002	0.0005	0.0008	0.0010	0.0012	0.0013

* Tolerance is provided for holes, which ordinary standard reamers can produce, in two grades, Classes A and B, the selection of which is a question for the user's decision and dependent upon the quality of the work required; some prefer to use Class A as working limits and Class B as inspection limits.

† Running fits, which are the most commonly required, are divided into three grades: Class X for engine and other work where easy fits are wanted; Class Y for high speeds and good average machine work; Class Z for fine tool work.

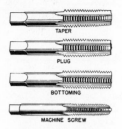

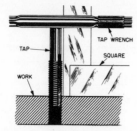

Kinds of taps   *Aligning the tap*

Tapping a hole

FIG. 4-25 Taps and the tapping operation

To remove a broken tap, a hole is drilled in the body of the tap and a screw extractor is forced into the tap, reversing the rotation with respect to the original tapping operation. (See Fig. 4–26.) The screw extractor is also used to remove broken-off screws.

THREADING DIES

In order to cut threads on rods, round stock, or pipes, a *threading die* is used. It is a round, nutlike, square block of hardened steel containing a slightly tapered and threaded hole which has flutes running perpendicular to the cutting thread. The flutes form the forward cutting edges of each section of cutting thread so that outside threads can be cut on a rod in the same way as a nut might if it were forced to cut its own threads when screwed onto an unthreaded piece.

Figure 4–27 shows a typical round die with an adjustable feature created by a split in the die body. A tapered set screw adjusted within this slit allows the die to cut threads over a small range of outside diameters. A set of taps and dies are also shown, together with the *die stock*, or die holder, used to hold the die while rotating it around the threaded piece.

Most dies have stamped upon their faces the size and the number of threads per inch that the die will cut. These markings show what outside diameter the thread being cut will have, plus the corresponding thread dimensions as given in Table 4–4.

THE THREADING OPERATION should always be performed on metals softer than the die itself. The end of the stock should be beveled

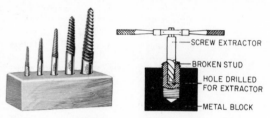

Set of screw extractors   *Using screw extractor*

FIG. 4-26 Screw extractors

FIG. 4-27 Threading dies

A: *adjusting screw*
B: *block screw*
C: *cutting threads*
D: *retaining shoulder*
E: *die stock handle*

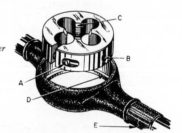

Cutting die and die stock

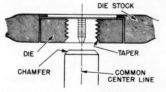

Fitting the die to the stock

Combined threading and tapping set

Table 4–6 Tap and clearance drills

Size of tap		Outside diameter (inches)	Size of tap drill (size of hole)				Clearance drill		Clearance (inches)
NC (U.S.S.)	NF (S.A.E.)		Number drills	Letter drills	Fractional drills	Decimal equivalent	Size	Decimal equivalent	
	#0–80	0.0600			3/64	0.0469	#51	0.0670	0.0070
#1–64		0.0730	53			0.0595	#47	0.0785	0.0055
	#1–72	0.0730	53			0.0595	#47	0.0785	0.0055
#2–56		0.0860	50			0.0700	#42	0.0935	0.0075
	#2–64	0.0860	50			0.0700	#42	0.0935	0.0075
#3–48		0.0990	47			0.0785	#36	0.1065	0.0075
	#3–56	0.0990	45			0.0820	#36	0.1065	0.0075
#4–40		0.1120	43			0.0890	#31	0.1200	0.0080
	#4–48	0.1120	42			0.0935	#31	0.1200	0.0080
#5–40		0.1250	38			0.1015	#29	0.1360	0.0110
	#5–44	0.1250	37			0.1040	#29	0.1360	0.0110
#6–32		0.1380	36			0.1065	#25	0.1495	0.0115
	#6–40	0.1380	33			0.1130	#25	0.1495	0.0115
#8–32		0.1640	29			0.1360	#16	0.1770	0.0130
	#8–36	0.1640	29			0.1360	#16	0.1770	0.0130
#10–24		0.1900	25			0.1495	13/64	0.2031	0.0131
	#10–32	0.1900	21			0.1590	13/64	0.2031	0.0131
#12–24		0.2160	16			0.1770	7/32	0.2187	0.0027
	#12–28	0.2160	14			0.1820	7/32	0.2187	0.0027
1/4″–20		0.2500	7			0.2010	17/64	0.2656	0.0156
	1/4″–28	0.2500	3			0.2130	17/64	0.2656	0.0156
5/16″–18		0.3125		F		0.2570	21/64	0.3281	0.0156
	5/16″–24	0.3125		I		0.2720	21/64	0.3281	0.0156
3/8″–16		0.3750			5/16	0.3125	25/64	0.3906	0.0156
	3/8″–24	0.3750		Q		0.3320	25/64	0.3906	0.0156
7/16″–14		0.4375		U		0.3680	29/64	0.4531	0.0156
	7/16″–20	0.4375			25/64	0.3906	29/64	0.4531	0.0156
1/2″–13		0.5000			27/64	0.4219	33/64	0.5156	0.0156
	1/2″–20	0.5000			29/64	0.4531	33/64	0.5156	0.0156
9/16″–12		0.5625			31/64	0.4844	37/64	0.5781	0.0156
	9/16″–18	0.5625			33/64	0.5156	37/64	0.5781	0.0156
5/8″–11		0.6250			17/32	0.5312	41/64	0.6406	0.0156
	5/8″–18	0.6250			37/64	0.5781	41/64	0.6406	0.0156
3/4″–10		0.7500			21/32	0.6562	49/64	0.7656	0.0156
	3/4″–16	0.7500			11/16	0.6875	49/64	0.7656	0.0156
7/8″– 9		0.8750			49/64	0.7656	57/64	0.8906	0.0156
	7/8″–14	0.8750			13/16	0.8125	57/64	0.8906	0.0156
1″– 8		1.0000			7/8	0.8750	1 1/64	1.0156	0.0156
	1″–14	1.0000			15/16	0.9375	1 1/64	1.0156	0.0156

or chamfered by filing at the proper angle around its outside edge. (See Fig. 4–27(b).) When threading is started, the die should be turned while being kept squarely perpendicular to the common center line of the piece being threaded. A mixture of white lead and lubricating lard oil should be used on the die, and the die should be backed up every quarter turn in order to clear out accumulated chips. Threading and tapping tools are often kept together as a set for convenience.

BENDING TOOLS

Bending operations, even on a simple chassis, are done best on a bar folder (see Fig. 4–28) although crude bends may be made with hand tools by holding the work in a vise with extended jaws and hammering over the desired bend with a suitable block.

It should be pointed out that the bending of a metal piece requires an overall flat dimension greater than that equal to the sum of the sides being bent. Allowance for this is made in the dimensions of the development drawing for the chassis. Table 4–7 gives amounts of chassis material consumed in 90° bends of various thicknesses of stock. Experience will show that extra-hard stock, such as number 2 aluminum or steel, can not be bent successfully without cracking the material at the corner bend.

SCREW THREAD FASTENINGS

Screw or thread fastening of metal pieces is the most flexible and widely used fastening method. Other methods include riveting, welding, stapling, brazing, or crimping. Since these special methods involve complex techniques, this volume will be restricted to a thorough treatment of various screw fastenings. A picture summary of the many types of bolts, screws, nuts, and washers is given in Fig. 4–29.

SCREWS are generally named according to the shape of head, which is determined by the kind of service for which the screw is intended. They may be made from brass, aluminum, or steel and may be finished in black anodizing or cadmium for rough steel screws, or in nickle, brass, or copper plating for brass screws. The type of finish depends on the degree of rust or corrosion protection needed. The following description will apply to steel screws since brass and aluminum types are used only in special applications.

Numerically, a screw is described by two figures: (1) its size as given by its body diameter, and (2) its body length in inches, a dimension which does not include the head (except in the case of flat head screws). Screw sizes are listed in $\frac{1}{16}$ inch steps starting with number 0. (See Table 4–4.) Below that diameter they are made in gauge numbers running from number 0 (.06 inches in diameter) up to number 12 (.216 inches in diameter).

Almost all screws are single-threaded, and the thread designation is given in terms of the number of threads per inch for this particular type unless the screw is specifically listed otherwise as double, triple, or quadruple. Double, triple, quadruple, and left-hand threads are not commonly used on screws.

A screw, exclusive of its finishing and material, would thus be listed in terms of its length, head type, diameter (or gauge) and number of threads per inch.

Thus: $\frac{7}{8}$ inch flat head, $\frac{1}{4}$ inch $\times$ 20, would mean a $\frac{7}{8}$ inch long flat-head screw $\frac{1}{4}$ inch in diameter, having 20 threads per inch. $1\frac{1}{2}$ inch round head, $\frac{1}{2}$ inch $\times$ 13, means a $1\frac{1}{2}$ inch long, round-head screw of $\frac{1}{2}$ inch diameter

FIG. 4-28 Bar folder

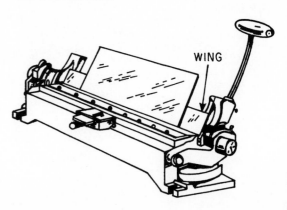

Table 4–7   Length corrections for metal to be bent 90°

Length correction for inside to inside dimensions

Thickness	Dutch bend 180° 0	Inside radius of bend													
		0	1/64	1/32	1/16	3/32	1/8	5/32	3/16	7/32	1/4	5/16	3/8	7/16	1/2
.031	.0324 1/32	.0162 1/64	.0095 1/64	.0028 0	.0106 1/64	.0240 1/32	.0374 1/32	.0508 3/64	.0642 1/16						
.037	.0388 1/32	.0194 1/64	.0127 1/64	.0060 0	.0074 0	.0209 1/64	.0343 1/32	.0477 3/64	.0611 1/16						
.044	.0450 3/64	.0225 1/64	.0156 1/64	.0091 1/64	.0043 0	.0177 1/64	.0310 1/32	.0445 3/64	.0579 1/16						
.050	.0524 3/64	.0262 1/32	.0195 1/64	.0128 1/64	.0006 0	.0141 1/64	.0275 1/32	.0409 3/64	.0543 3/64			Minus	values		
.0625	.0654 1/16	.0327 1/32	.0262 1/32	.0193 1/64	.0059 0	.0075 0	.0209 1/64	.0343 1/32	.0478 3/64						
.078	.0816 5/64	.0408 3/64	.0341 1/32	.0274 1/32	.0140 1/64	.0006 0	.0128 1/64	.0262 1/32	.0396 1/32						
.093	.0982 3/32	.0491 3/64	.0424 3/64	.0357 1/32	.0223 1/32	.0089 1/64	.0046 0	.0180 1/64	.0314 1/32						
.125	.133 1/8	.0665 1/16	.0587 1/16	.0520 3/64	.0386 1/32	.0252 1/32	.0118 1/64	.0016 0	.015 1/64						
.156							.048 3/64	.035 1/32	.021 1/64	.008 0	.005 0	.032 1/32	.058 1/16	.085 5/64	.111 7/64
.1875			Plus				.069 1/16	.055 3/64	.042 3/64	.029 1/32	.016 1/64	.011 1/64	.036 1/32	.065 1/16	.090 3/32
.218			values				.089 5/64	.075 5/64	.061 1/16	.049 3/64	.036 1/32	.009 0	.017 1/64	.044 3/64	.070 5/64
.250							.109 7/64	.095 3/32	.081 5/64	.069 1/16	.056 1/16	.032 1/32	.005 0	.025 1/32	.051 3/64
.281							.130 1/8	.116 7/64	.102 7/64	.089 3/32	.078 5/64	.050 3/64	.021 1/64	.005 0	.031 1/32
.3125							.015 5/32	.137 9/64	.123 1/8	.111 7/64	.097 3/32	.070 5/64	.045 3/64	.016 1/64	.010 1/64

Figures shown in table are applicable when figuring developed lengths of parts to be formed on power brakes or power presses with V-dies, and excludes all forming in which wiping action takes place.

Fractions are the correction factors used for ordinary production.

Decimal figures are the more exact evaluations of correction factor.

Figures to the left of heavy line are plus (+) values, and the amount indicated is added to the calculation.

Figures to the right of heavy line are minus (−) values, and should be subtracted from the calculation.

Example: To find the developed length of example, add the two inside dimensions ($1\frac{1}{4}$ and 1). The radius is $\frac{1}{8}$ and the correction factor for this radius in .0625 stock is minus $\frac{1}{64}$.

$$\text{DEV. LENGTH} = \left(1\frac{1}{4} + 1\right) - \frac{1}{64} = 2\frac{15}{64}$$

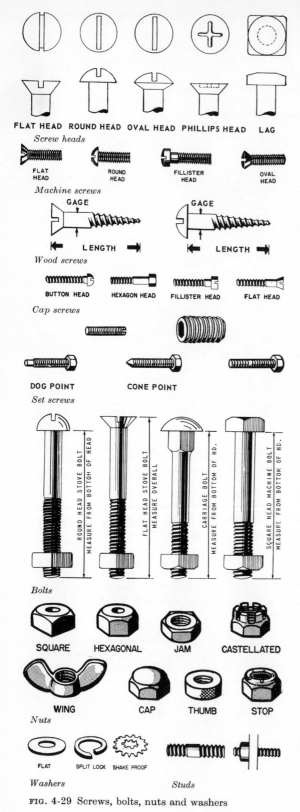

FLAT HEAD   ROUND HEAD   OVAL HEAD   PHILLIPS HEAD   LAG

Screw heads

FLAT HEAD   ROUND HEAD   FILLISTER HEAD   OVAL HEAD

Machine screws

GAGE   GAGE
LENGTH   LENGTH

Wood screws

BUTTON HEAD   HEXAGON HEAD   FILLISTER HEAD   FLAT HEAD

Cap screws

DOG POINT   CONE POINT

Set screws

ROUND HEAD STOVE BOLT MEASURE FROM BOTTOM OF HEAD   FLAT HEAD STOVE BOLT MEASURE OVERALL   CARRIAGE BOLT MEASURE FROM BOTTOM OF HD.   SQUARE HEAD MACHINE BOLT MEASURE FROM BOTTOM OF HD.

Bolts

SQUARE   HEXAGONAL   JAM   CASTELLATED

WING   CAP   THUMB   STOP

Nuts

FLAT   SPLIT LOCK   SHAKE PROOF

Washers   *Studs*

FIG. 4-29 Screws, bolts, nuts and washers

having 13 threads per inch. $\frac{1}{4}$ inch filister head, number 4–40, means a $\frac{1}{4}$ inch long filister-head screw of number 4 gauge with 40 threads per inch.

SCREW THREADS are used in three common styles: (1) national coarse (NC), which were formerly called United States Standard (USS); (2) national fine (NF), which was formerly SAE* thread; and (3) extra fine threads (EF), used in special autmobile applications. Table 4–4 gives these screw threads by number, diameter, and their corresponding NC, NF, and EF numbers.

FITS FOR SCREWS AND NUTS in assembly work are divided into four classes. Class 1, or loose fit, applies to threaded parts that can be put together quickly and easily by hand even when the threads are slightly bruised or dirty. Class 2, or free fit, designates freely fitting threaded parts which can be put together with only the fingers. (Most screw threads are made to fall in this category.) Class 3, or medium fit, covers threaded metal parts of a higher grade than can normally be put together by fingers alone, but which fit more tightly than those in class 2. Class 4, or close fit, is for the finest threaded work where very little shake or looseness may be permitted. A screw driver or wrench may be necessary to fit these parts together.

DIAMETER ALLOWANCE FOR DIFFERENT CLASSES OF FITS expresses the closeness of a fit in an actual measured hole or on a pitch diameter according to assigned tolerances. Table 4–5 gives upper and lower diameter tolerances for fitting pins or shafts which run, or which are forced, driven, or pushed into a hole.

SCREW THREAD MEASUREMENTS must occasionally be made on screws to determine the number of teeth per inch, or the pitch or pitch diameter. Where a count of threads per inch is desired, an ordinary steel rule may be used. Screw pitch measurements require a screw pitch gauge (see Fig. 4–30), which

*SAE = Society of Automotive Engineers.

54

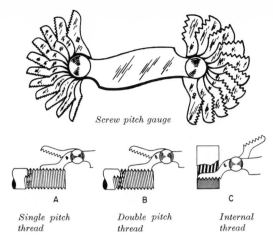

Screw pitch gauge

A	B	C
Single pitch thread	*Double pitch thread*	*Internal thread*

Gauging single, double, and internal threads

FIG. 4-30 Screw pitch gauge and its use

consists of a set of thin leaves on the edge of which teeth are cut with contours that correspond to standard thread sections. Pitch is determined when a certain leaf exactly fits the screw thread contour. The individual leaves of such a gauge are stamped to show the pitch of the thread and also the double depth of the thread in inches. This information is helpful in selecting the right diameter drill to use before tapping holes.

Because the inside and outside diameters of threaded pieces vary, depending upon the sharpness or fullness of the thread, measurement must be made at the pitch line to find the pitch diameter. The pitch diameter is equivalent to the full diameter less the depth of one thread. To measure this accurately, we use a screw thread micrometer (see Fig. 3–18(b)), which has a pointed spindle and a V-shaped anvil. In order to make a true pitch diameter measurement, the point of the spindle and the face of the anvil are designed so that contact is made only on one side of the thread.

SELF-TAPPING SCREWS, a type of hardened metal screw with threads similar to wood screws, have become popular in recent years. With the proper diameter of drilled holes, these screws can be driven through moderately thick metal, thus forming or cutting their own threads. Figure 4–31 shows a number of typical self-tapping screws with slotted, fillister, round, Phillips, or hexagonal heads. Sizes generally do not exceed number 14.

RIVETS

Rivets are short metal pins that look like bolts without threads. Solid-shank rivets are available with several types of heads, as shown in Fig. 4–32(a). The required length or grip of a rivet is determined by the combined thickness of the pieces of metal it must hold together plus the amount of the end of the shank which must be turned over to form another head. For general dimensions see Fig. 4–32(b). The riveting operation is simple, since the shank of a rivet protruding beyond the metals being fastened together may be rounded over with a ball peen hammer. Some types of hollow rivets are shown in Fig. 4–33. A rivet head may also be formed by using a rivet set tool or a power-driven rivet machine, as shown in Fig. 4–34. The protruding length of a hollow rivet is somewhat more easily turned over by an internally fitted riveting tool, which

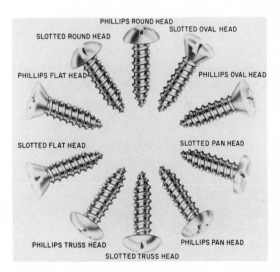

FIG. 4-31 Typical self-tapping screws

FIG. 4-32 Solid rivets and their dimensions

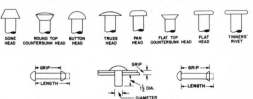

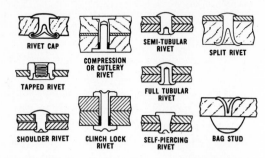

FIG. 4-33 Types of hollow rivets

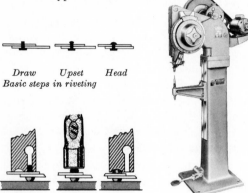

Draw   Upset   Head
Basic steps in riveting

Draw   Upset   Head
Using the riveting tool   *Power riveting machine*

FIG. 4-34 Riveting

adapts to rapid machine operations but is not used extensively in the metalworking shop.

WELDING, BRAZING, SWEATING, OR SOLDERING

Metal pieces may be fastened together by any of these fusing processes, all of which are similar in that they require external heat. Either the surfaces are melted enough to join and hold themselves together by fusion of the metal itself, or they are held together by some type of metal alloy or solder which is applied in melted form to fasten the pieces together.

The process known as welding requires considerably higher temperatures than soldering. Brazing, sweating, and soldering may all be classed as soldering processes. Brazing, for instance, applies generally to nonferrous metals, while sweating is the actual process of soldering.

In all three processes, the surfaces of the joined metals must be cleaned and smoothed before applying heat. In *welding* the heat may be created by an oxy-acetyline torch or by electric currents sent through the joint from a spot welding machine while the points are being pressed together.

Before soldering or brazing, the surfaces are usually chemically cleaned by *flux* liquid or paste. The uses of different types of flux are given in Table 4–8. The solder itself may be either soft or hard solder. Soft solder is an alloy of lead and tin with proportions running from 50 percent of each up to 70 percent tin. The individual mixtures depend on the temperature at which the soldering is to be done. Soft soldering is done at a temperature below red heat of the joining surfaces.

Hard soldering is done with higher melting solders and is used in brazing and in the fastening together of copper, silver, gold, or metal work where greater mechanical strength

Table 4–8   Flux chart for soldering or brazing

Base metal or applied coating	Plain rosin	Activated rosin	Zinc-ammonium chloride
Hot tin dipped	Yes	Yes	Yes
Hot solder dipped	Yes	Yes	Yes
Electrotin	Note 1	Yes	Yes
Silver plate	Note 2	Note 2	Yes
Cadmium plate	Note 3	Note 3	Yes
Nickel plate	No	Fair	Yes
Galvanized steel	No	No	Note 4
Copper	Note 2	Yes	Yes
Brass	Note 2	Yes	Yes
Phosphor bronze	Note 2	Yes	Yes
Beryllium copper	No	Note 2	Yes
Aluminum bronze	No	No	Note 5
Silicon bronze	No	No	Yes
Zinc & zinc plate	No	Note 4	Note 4
Monel	No	Fair	Yes
Nichrome	No	No	Note 4
Steel	No	No	Yes
Stainless	No	No	Note 4

NOTE 1: Variable with age, residue, etc. Hot palm oil is sometimes used.

NOTE 2: For clean surfaces.

NOTE 3: Use with *thin platings* or over aluminum (less than 0.0002 m) *not recommended*.

NOTE 4: Addition of free muriatic helps; final washing is necessary.

NOTE 5: 85% orthophosphoric acid may be used.

is needed soft solder provides. These solders may be partly silver and are then called silver solder.

Soldering for the laboratory technician is usually confined to making joints of copper wire wrapped around some form of terminal which is usually "tinned" by being plated with tin, silver, or some other metal easily susceptible to the flow of solder. These techniques and those covering the use of a soldering iron in wiring are described in Chapter 6. Welding, brazing, the fabrication of seams and joints, and other techniques are more properly placed in a specialized machine shop which is equipped to do sheet-metal work.

FINISHING

The surface of a fabricated chassis must finally have a finish or some type of electroplating before the electronic components are assembled. Cadmium, copper, and nickel are the usual plated finishes used to protect a structure from rust and corrosion and to give it a final covering that is neat and uniform. In addition to protecting against rust or corrosion, plating in most cases provides a low-resistance conductive ground path for common chassis currents. Most a-c filament circuits operate with one side grounded to the chassis base while many signal circuits operate with grounded cathodes. In some commercial cases where electrical grounding is not a factor, the outside of the chassis may be painted over the plating in order to match up with the color scheme of the case or other items of the overall equipment.

The type of finishing specified for a piece part is noted in the appropriate description space on the part's drawing. Since there are a number of different types of plating, some with one type superimposed upon another, and since there is an infinite variety of paints from the standpoints of color and protective and chemical properties, finishes are most often referred to on the assembly drawing by code numbers or by short descriptive phrases or commercial names. Detailed description of the paint and techniques of applying it may then be obtained from the referenced specification sheets. Table 4–9 is a list of typical paint and plating references used on military equipment.

In general, the plating on a chassis depends on the material of the chassis itself, upon general adherence, electrolytic interaction between two dissimilar metals, durability, and ease of accepting solder. For aluminum, the plating is restricted to two types, cadmium and silver. Brass and copper may be plated with silver or cadmium. In some cases, the cadmium may be superimposed on the silver.

OTHER MACHINE-SHOP OPERATIONS

Beyond the sheet-metal operations which constitute the basis of chassis fabrication by means of hand-operated tools, the average machine shop has many other metalworking devices which are mainly power operated. In making accessories to electronic equipment, there may be parts such as shafts, collars, gears, blocks, or supports. Machining these parts may require the following machine-shop tools.

THE ENGINE LATHE is the most widely used machine in modern machine shops. Used with attachments, it may be called a toolmaker's lathe. Mounted on a bench, it is called a bench lathe, and in various sizes and versions it may have other names, such as a wheel lathe, jeweler's lathe, axle lathe, pulley lathe, or turret lathe. For round stock or cylindrical pieces, this machine is probably the most versatile piece of equipment in a shop, for it is used to perform drilling, turning, boring, grooving, finishing, cutting, or threading of cylindrical metal pieces.

The main parts of a lathe are shown in Fig. 4–35. They are: (1) the *bed*, which is the main framework and may or may not rest on legs or on a bench, (2) the *headstock*, fixed on the left-hand end of the bed, and which serves to hold the stock upon which work is being done. The headstock is rotated by the driving power pulleys and may use its *face plate* or a *jaw chuck* attached to the plate

Table 4–9   Frequently used chassis finishes

Anodize—Dichromate seal
Anodize—Hot water seal
Black alumilite
Black—Chemical for iron and steel
Black—Gloss lacquer
Black—Optical—Synthetic
Black oxidize
Black wrinkle—Regular
Blue-green hammeroid
Blue-green metalustre enamel
Cadmium plate (.0002″)
Cadmium plate—For screws
Cadmium plate—Heavy (.0005″)
Chromium—Polished (.0005″)
Chromium—Polished—For screws
Chromium—Satin (.0005″)
Chromium—Satin—For screws
Chromium—Second grade (.0005″)
Clear baking synthetic
Clear lacquer
Clear synthetic
Clear water dip
Copper flash (.00005″)
Copper plate (.0002″)
Copper plate—Heavy (.0005″)
Dark cobalt lacquer
Flock—Black—Rayon
Flock—Havana brown—Rayon
Gray—Cobalt—Enamel
Gray—Dark industrial—Hammeroid
Gray—Deep umber—Enamel—Second grade
Gray—Lacquer—dark
Gray—Light cobalt—Lacquer

Gray—Light industrial—Hammeroid
Gray—Low gloss—Smoky—Enamel
Gray—Silver—Metalustre enamel
Gray—Silver—Metalustre lacquer
Gray—Smoky enamel
Gray—Trim cobalt—Enamel
Gray—Trim umber—Enamel
Gray wrinkle—Dark—Special
Green—Marine Corps lustreless enamel
Ivory enamel
Maroon lacquer
Moisture and fungus resistant treatment for
   equipment
Nickel—Black (.0003″)
Nickel—Black—For screws
Nickel—White (.0005″)
Olive drab—Lustreless enamel
Red—Lacquer
Rust preventative—Temporary
Satin dip—Aluminum
Stain dip and clear water dip
Silver plate and clear water dip (.0002″)
Tan lacquer
Taupe—Light—Metalustre lacquer
Tin plate
Tin plate and wax dip
White lacquer
White synthetic enamel
Zinc chromate primer
Zinc plate—for screws
Zinc plate—Heavy (.0005″)
Zinc plate—Heavy and iridite—Olive drab
Zinc plate—Light (.0002″)

FIG. 4-35 The engine lathe and its parts

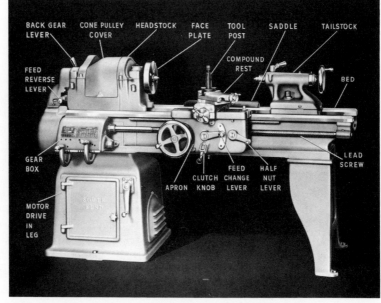

to support or hold the piece being driven, (3) the *tail stock*, which may be used to: (a) support the other end of a rotating piece, (b) hold a drill or other end of a rotating piece, (c) hold a drill or other cutting implement when the work is being supported and rotated by the headstock. (4) The *compound slide rest* which rides on tracks (called "ways") on the bed between the head and tail stocks while holding cutting implements which will bear against and cut the rotating work. Figure 4–35 shows the operating positions of lathe parts when performing the turning operation.

GRINDERS may be simple rotating wheels like those used for sharpening tools, or complicated multi-element wheels for precise and high speed finishing. They consist of some type of abrasive wheel made of emery, carborundum, alundam, alexite, crystalon, or carbolite. The abrasive is mixed with a binding material in amounts and compositions which determine whether the wheel surface will be termed hard or soft.

The index number of a wheel, which indicates the nature of its grinding action, is determined by the number of meshes per square inch on the sieve through which the constituent abrasive has been passed. Lower numbers indicate coarser wheels, while large numbers refer to fine wheels.

Except for its usefulness in tool sharpening, the grinding wheel is not important to the fabrication of a piece of electronic gear unless there are complicated mechanical parts requiring finishing more precise than can be accomplished with a lathe. The lab technician will probably not use the grinder except to sharpen tools or make small cuts on chassis accessories.

Figure 4–36 shows a power-operated bench grinder. Its use requires certain precautionary measures. The operator should use a safety hood and eye goggles, and apply only moderate pressure to the work, holding the piece usually at less than right angles to the rotation of the wheel so that the wheel will not "grab" against the piece, causing it to slip and become jammed between the wheel and the tool rest.

Since a piece being ground gets hot, many grinders are equipped with a small pot of water in which the piece may be cooled for quick handling after the operation is completed.

The grinding wheel may also be used to identify different types of ferrous metals. This test is made by merely holding a sample against the rotating surface and inspecting the spark stream of red-hot particles which are being torn off.

Figure 4–37 identifies typical spark streams from commonly used metals. Note the various characteristics of the spark stream—the shaft, the sprinklers on the shaft, springs from the sparklers, and the breaks in the shaft stream.

PLANER, SHAPER, AND MILLING MACHINES

Planer and shaper machines perform the same operations on flat or plane surfaces that the lathe does on cylindrical surfaces. They are usually fairly massive machines designed to periodically move a cutting tool lengthwise back and forth along a bed which holds the piece being worked. The cuts made are longitudinal, as contrasted with the circular cuts made by a lathe. Their use in chassis fabrication is very slight.

Milling machines utilize a rotating cutter in place of the fixed cutting tool used in a

FIG. 4-36 A power-operated bench grinder

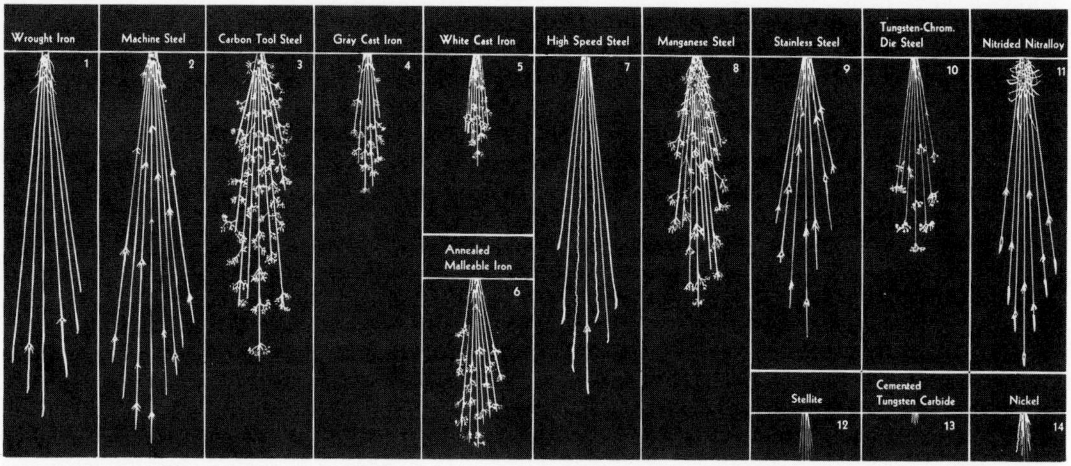

Metal	Volume of stream	Relative length of stream, inches†	Color of stream close to wheel	Color of streaks near end of stream	Quantity of spurts	Nature of spurts
1. Wrought iron	Large	65	Straw	White	Very few	Forked
2. Machine steel (AISI 1020)	Large	70	White	White	Few	Forked
3. Carbon tool steel	Moderately large	55	White	White	Very many	Fine, repeating
4. Gray cast iron	Small	25	Red	Straw	Many	Fine, repeating
5. White cast iron	Very small	20	Red	Straw	Few	Fine, repeating
6. Annealed mall. iron	Moderate	30	Red	Straw	Many	Fine, repeating
7. High speed steel (18–4–1)	Small	60	Red	Straw	Extremely few	Forked
8. Austenitic manganese steel	Moderately large	45	White	White	Many	Fine, repeating
9. Stainless steel (Type 410)	Moderate	50	Straw	White	Moderate	Forked
10. Tungsten-chromium die steel	Small	35	Red	Straw*	Many	Fine, repeating*
11. Nitrided Nitralloy	Large (curved)	55	White	White	Moderate	Forked
12. Stellite	Very small	10	Orange	Orange	None	
13. Cemented tungsten carbide	Extremely small	2	Light orange	Light orange	None	
14. Nickel	Very small**	10	Orange	Orange	None	
15. Copper, brass, aluminum	None				None	

† Figures obtained with 12″ wheel on bench stand and are relative only. Actual length in each instance will vary with grinding wheel, pressure, etc.

* Blue-white spurts.

** Some wavy streaks.

FIG. 4-37 Typical spark streams from commonly used metals

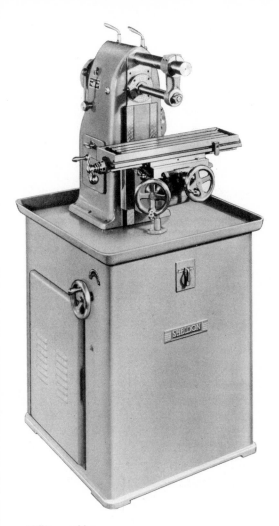

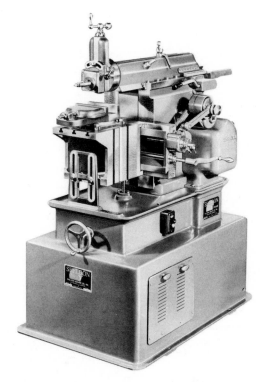

Milling machine   *Shaping machine*

FIG. 4-38 Typical milling and shaping machines

planer. Figure 4–38 shows typical machines of these types.

WIRING AND SOLDERING TOOLS

In wiring a chassis the technician uses a collection of special hand tools, some of which deserve special attention. These include various sizes of long-nose pliers, cutting pliers, blunt-nosed or electricians' pliers (sometimes called "gas pliers"), small and large soldering irons (depending upon the work to be done), a pick and hook tool, a stiff glue brush, a wire stripper, one or more sets of socket wrenches, various small screwdrivers, a dental mirror, miscellaneous files, and tapered hand

reamers for holes up to $\frac{1}{2}$ inch in diameter.

Figure 4–39 shows the basic types of pliers, cutters, and hex-nut socket wrenches. The other tools listed are more frequently used in wiring than in chassis assembly, and are described and illustrated in Chapter 6.

The standard 100-watt soldering iron (see Fig. 4–40) has a working point, a heating element, a handle, and a stand. The removable working point comes in several sizes and shapes, depending on the fineness needed for the work being done. The point is solid copper and periodically should be taken out of the heating element to scrape off the scale which usually accumulates with age and which reduces heating efficiency. The working part of the point should be repeatedly wiped off on fine steel wool or rough cloth during continuous soldering operations. Keeping it shiny bright provides for the best flow of solder. Filing of the point to brightness each day while it is warming up is recommended, along with the application of solder during the filing operation.

Solder for wiring is most commonly supplied in rolls of hollow wire. The core or hole in the solder is filled with rosin, or flux, which keeps the solder flowing easily when it is being heated. Solders made up of varying amounts of tin and zinc, to be used for different soldering purposes, are described in Chapter 6. Each type is best for a certain kind of work, as recommended by the supplier of the solder. Silver solder, for instance, is used frequently on silver-plated surfaces, while aluminum alloy solder is best for joining pieces of aluminum.

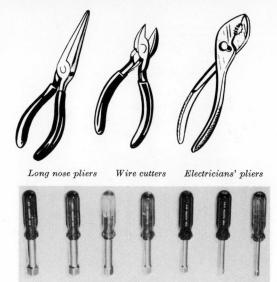

Long nose pliers   *Wire cutters*   *Electricians' pliers*

Hex-nut socket wrenches

FIG. 4-39 Pliers, cutters, and hex-nut socket wrenches

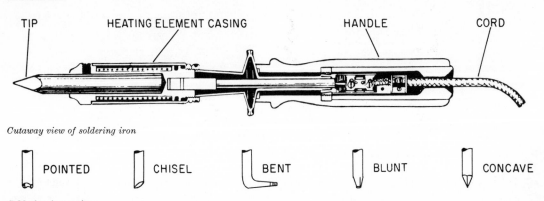

TIP   HEATING ELEMENT CASING   HANDLE   CORD

Cutaway view of soldering iron

POINTED   CHISEL   BENT   BLUNT   CONCAVE

Soldering iron points

FIG. 4-40 Soldering iron

Electronic Component Parts 5

COMPONENTS

To assemble and wire a complete chassis the technician must know the size, shape, and electrical characteristics of all component parts. Some of these may be partially identified from the labels which they bear and from their location markings on the assembly drawing and wiring diagram. Others can be located by electrical means from the schematic wiring diagram.

This information, however, is not enough. A technician must be familiar with component part drawings, color coding, specifications, and mounting. This chapter supplies such detailed physical and electrical information; testing and many other special features pertaining to piece parts are described in Chaps. 13 and 14.

Specifically, it does cover the basic types of tubes, transistors, resistors, capacitors, and inductors, as well as special devices used in electronic gear, which of necessity include some electrical functional characteristics.

The basic component parts for all electronic apparatus may be classified under the following categories: resistors, capacitors, inductors, tubes, semiconductor devices, electromagnetic devices, electron magnetic devices, and hybrid and special devices, including combinations of these groups. See Fig. 5-1.

Reference designations, color coding, and symbols, as discussed in this chapter, will closely follow those employed in the armed services since military gear constitutes a major portion of our electronics industry. These also coincide, in general, with the specifications issued by the Electronics Industries Association (EIA). Identifying information, usage, applications, and important electrical characteristics which relate directly to the assembly mounting or physical placement of the components will be discussed even though they are covered more thoroughly under electronic component testing in Chapter 14. This information includes such factors as resistor heat dissipation, mechanical clearance for voltage breakdown between capacitor terminals, and shielding or grounding of coils. A general breakdown of basic electronic component parts and their symbols is shown in Table 5-1.

ELECTRONIC COMPONENT SYMBOLS

Every component may be described in three ways.

1. Drawings or pictures may be used by themselves or on associated assembly drawings. Here the description can not be too specific since there are so many standardized components which are almost physically indistinguishable from one another.

2. Graphic symbols are used on schematic wiring diagrams as labels both on the part itself, and on the picture of the part on the wiring diagram. Electrical and electronic symbols for government drawings are fully

Table 5–1 Electronic component breakdown

	Symbol	Designation	Type and construction		Electronic application	Physical nature
Resistors		R	Composition Wirewound Film		Dissipative	Homogeneous conductors
Capacitors		C	Paper-air Mica-glass Deposited film Ceramic Electrolytic film	Passive	Storage	Dielectric insulated Plates
Inductors		L	Coiled conductor with or without ferrous core Audio, P.S. or high frequency		Storage	Self-inductive impedance
Vacuum tubes		V	Light emissive Photo-generative Receiver Transmitter		Amplifier Detector Oscillator Display Photo-transducer	Electrodes in vacuum
Transistors		Q	Silicon Germanium Low signal Power circuits Computer	Active	Amplifier Detector Oscillator Switching Photo-transducer	Solid-state double junctions
Diodes		CR	Germanium-silicon Low signal Power Computer Tunnel Depletion layer Photo-emmissive	Passive	Detector Power rectifier Power switching Signal switching Parametric effect	Solid-state single junction
Crystal diodes		CR	Piezo-electric Quartz Rochelle salt	Active	Oscillator Frequency standard Physical transducer	Metal plate crystal sandwich

Appendix A-1 is a condensed and simplified list of these symbols taken from the American Standards Association publication Y32.2–1954.

3. Designation letters or abbreviations, such as R for resistors, or C for capacitors, may also be used to identify components. These letters appear alongside a component's symbol on a schematic wiring diagram or parts list, followed by a hyphen and by the parts list number of the component in a particular assembly. A resistor listed as part number 242 would be identified as R-242, while C-8196 would indicate a capacitor listed as number 8196 on the parts list. Complete reference designations for some twenty-five commonly used component parts are shown in Table 5–2, which is taken from MIL-STD-16A. Appendix B-9 summarizes the preferred value system for resistors and capacitors and also describes the general color-coding procedures that apply to these components.

RESISTORS

A resistor is composed of some form of electrically conductive material (other than interconnecting wire) concentrated or encased as a component unit, having terminals or leads, between which there exists a definite marked value of ohmic electrical resistance. Resistors have a symbolic circuit designation identifying them on schematic drawings (see Appendix A-1) and the letter designation R (see Table 5–1). Examples of resistor designations are R-4, R-82, and R-91A. Designation of types, as specified by military documents or by EIA, are expressed by using an additional letter: RC for carbon, or RW for wirewound, for example. These two-letter designations do not appear, however, on schematic diagrams.

Resistors are usually described in terms of: (1) their electrical resistance (in ohms), (2) their heat-radiating capabilities or wattage, (3) their chemical or physical makeup (whether wirewound, composition, or film), (4) their functional makeup (whether they are fixed, semifixed or tapped, adjustably tapped, or

completely variable), (5) the tolerance in their ohmic value. A certain resistor might be described, then, as an 820-ohm, fixed, 5-watt, wirewound unit with a 10 percent tolerance. Another resistor may be identified as a variable 50-ohm, 2-watt, composition type (with tolerance omitted because unit is variable). Still another may be a 50-megohm, 10 percent tolerance, high-voltage, fixed, metallic-film type capable of dissipating 10 watts while having impressed across it 20,000 volts. A chart of the various types of resistors, grouped according to their respective categories, specifications, and general characteristics, is shown in Table 5–3. Descriptions of these specification categories follow.

SIZE AND WATTAGE SPECIFICATIONS

The foregoing information tells nothing about the physical size of a resistor. It is possible, however, from the listed ohmic value, the type, and the wattage to estimate how large the resistor must be. The wattage figure for instance indicates how many sq. in. of external surface area the unit must have to dissipate the heat generated within itself before it deteriorates. In larger resistor sizes manufacturers arrange to have the wattage rating stamped on the unit alongside the resistor's ohmic and tolerance value.

Figures 5–1 and 5–2 show the wattage ratings of several types of fixed and adjustable units and illustrate the relationship of size to wattage. Although the material from which a resistor is made and its heat-resistant protective coating determine to some degree how much power it can dissipate before it becomes too hot and deteriorates, we follow the rule: *a resistor must occupy a free space of one cubic inch for each five watts of dissipation.*

In resistor designs this rule converts to an allowable operating-temperature rise of between 100 and 200 degrees centigrade when normally operating in a surrounding atmosphere temperature of 40°C and in a reasonably ventilated location. In recent years the ceramic

Table 5–2   Component designation letters
(from MIL-STD-16A)

AT	Attenuator, pad, resistive termination
B	Blower, fan, motor, prime vomer, resolver, synchro
BT	Battery
C	Capacitor. capacitance bushing
CB	Circuit breaker
CP	Coupling (aperture, loop, or probe), coaxial or waveguide junction (tee or wye)
CR	Crystal detector, crystal diode, crystal unit, crystal contact or metallic rectifier, selenium cell, varistor (asymmetrical)
D	Dynamotor, converter, inverter
DC	Directional coupler
DL	Delay line
DP	Diaphragm
DS	Miscellaneous illuminating or indicating device (except meter or thermometer) such as: alarm, annunciator, audible or visual signalling device, bell, buzzer, drop, flasher, pilot (illuminating or signal lamp), telephone set ringer, telegraph sounder, vibrator (indicating)
EQ	Equalizer
F	Fuse, fuse cutout
FL	Filter
G	Exciter, generator, magneto, rotating amplifier, vibrator (interrupting)
HR	Heater (element for thermostats, oven, etc.), heating lamp
HS	Handset
HT	Telephone receiver (not part of handset), headset, hearing aid
HY	Hybrid coil, hybrid junction
J	Electrical connector, fixed (mounted on a bulkhead, equipment, wall, chassis, rigid conduit, or panel), jack, receptacle
K	Relay (electrically operated contactor or switch)
L	Choke, inductor, loading coil, relay operating coil, retardation coil, solenoid, tuning coil, winding
LS	Loudspeaker, horn, howler, siren, speaker

M	Meter, clock, counter (indicating device), elapsed-time recorder, gauge, instrument, message register, oscillograph, oscilloscope, thermometer
MG	Motor generator
MK	Microphone, telephone transmitter
MT	Mode transducer
P	Electrical connector, movable (affixed to the end of a cable, flexible conduit, coaxial line, cord or wire), plug
PS	Power supply, source of power
PU	Pickup, erasing head, recording head, reproducing head
Q	Transistor
R	Potentiometer, resistor, rheostat, shunt
RE	Radio receiver, receiver
RP	Repeater (telephone usage)
RT	Ballast lamp, resistance lamp, thermistor
RV	Symmetrical varistor
S	Switch (mechanically or thermally operated), contactor, disconnecting device, dial (circuit interrupter), electrical safety interlock, governor switch, interlock, speed regulator, telegraph key, thermal cutout, thermostat
T	Transformer, autotransformer, IF transformer, repaeting coil (telephone usage), transformer, waveguide or coaxial taper, induction coil (telephone usage)
TB	Terminal board, connecting block, group of individual terminals on its own mounting, terminal strip, test block
TC	Thermocouple
TR	Radio transmitter, transmitter
V	Electron tube, barrier photocell, blocking layer cell, light-sensitive cell, photoemissive cell, phototube
VR	Voltage regulator (except an electron tube)
W	Cable, cable assembly, coaxial cable, guided transmission path, waveguide, wire, wire assembly
X	Socket, fuseholder
Y	Oscillator (excluding electron tube used in an oscillator), piezoelectric crystal, magnetostriction oscillator

materials used to coat the outside of power resistors have been improved, so that resistors may somewhat exceed the temperature rise noted above without suffering any loss of life expectancy. Figure 5–2 is a chart for estimating wirewound resistor wattage ratings under abnormal conditions or under intermittent usage. In reliability design calculations a resistor may be rated according to this table.

Under high-voltage operation, resistors are subject to limitations depending upon the material from which they are made; they also must have sufficient distance between their terminals to avoid direct voltage breakdown because of surface dust or moisture. In half-watt composition or carbon resistors, for instance, the maximum allowable voltage is 500.

Table 5–3 Resistors

Type	Construction and size	Range of power ratings (watts)	Resistor range (ohms)	Other Characteristics	Applications	Military specifications
COMPOSITION	Cylindrical	1/10–2	$3 - 10^7$	100°C Max. temp.	General use	MIL-R-11A
Insulated	.5 × 2″	1/10–2				
Noninsulated	.2 × 4″ Diam.			5–201°C tolerance		
WIREWOUND						
Power-insulated	Cyl., flat, disk	2–200	$.1 - 10^6$	800°C Max. temp.	Motor control circuits	MIL-R-26B
Noninsulated	Cyl., 2 × 15″	125–1,200	.03–800	300°C Max. temp.	Standards, high precision acts	MIL-R-93A
Precision	Cyl., .5 × 1″	.1–4	$.1–20 × 10^6$			MIL-R-10683A
FILM						
Deposited carbon	Cyl., .3 × 1″	.1–2	$10–5 × 10^6$	100°C Max. temp.	Stable	
Metal	Cyl., .4 × 1″	.1–2	$25–10^7$	180°C Max. temp.	Stable at high temp.	MIL-R-10509A
High voltage	Cyl., 1 × 20″	0–10	$1 Meg–10^7$	200°C Max. temp.	Power supply divider	JAN-R-29
VARIABLE						
Composition	Toroidal element	0–2	0–4 Meg	120°C Max. temp.	General use	MIL-R-94A
Wirewound–precision	wiping arm	0–1	0–20,000	0–300°C	Instr., precise circuits	JAN-R-19
Wirewound–power		0–1,000	0–10,000	350°C Max.	Power control circuits	MIL-R-22A
SPECIAL						
Ballast tubes	Glass envelope	.5–5	—	Automatic	Regulators	
Vacuum type	Up to ST-19 bulb			Variable		
Semiconductors:	Solid-state	—	—	Specialized	Instrumentation	—
Thermistors	transistor-type	—	—			—
Varistor	mounting	—	—			
Binistor						

FIG. 5-1 Wattage rating versus temperature

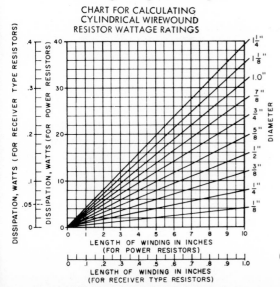

CHART FOR CALCULATING
CYLINDRICAL WIREWOUND
RESISTOR WATTAGE RATINGS

Temperature Rise Factor Divide the resistor wattage by these factors under the conditions listed.

	Factor Temperature Rise	
	250°C (450°F)	100°C (212°F)
Continuous Duty		
Free ventilation and 12″ clearance . .5		1.35
Reduced ventilation and clearance. .2.5		.67
Cramped locations. 1.25		.34

Intermittent Duty Factor

	Factor
On 15 seconds in 4 minutes 3	
On 30 seconds in 4 minutes 2	
On 60 seconds in 4 minutes 1.5	
On 1 ½ minutes in 4 minutes. 1.3	
On 2 minutes in 4 minutes 1.2	

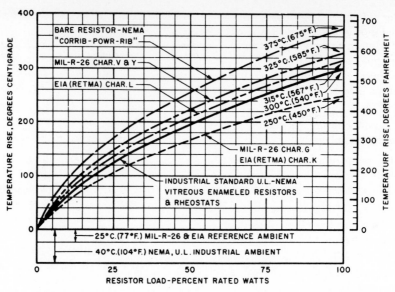

Temperature rise of resistor in free air for various specifications

Specification	Standard ambient		Degrees rise		Temperature attained		Approx. watt rating compared compared to commercial	Type of resistor
	C	F	C	F	C	F		
MIL-R-26 Char. F X G EIA (RETMA)[1] Char. K	25°	77°	250°	450°	275°	527°	75%	Coated
Industrial-commercial- U.L.[3] & NEMA[4] [2]	40°	104°	300°	540°	340°	644°	100%	Coated
EIA (RETMA) Char. L	25°	77°	315°	567°	340°	644°	100%	Coated
MIL-R-26 Char. V & Y	25°	77°	325°	585°	350°	662°	115%	Coated
Industrial U.L. X NEMA	40°	104°	375°	675°	415°	779°	180%	Open wound

[1] Electronic Industries Association (formerly Radio Electronic Television Manufacturers Association).

[2] This rating also applies to rheostats per U.L. and NEMA standards.

[3] Underwriter' Laboratories Inc.

[4] National Electrical Manufacturers Association.

FIG. 5-2 Resistor temperature and wattage requirements

MILITARY SPECIFICATIONS for resistors use a standardized lettering and numbering system which has been generally accepted by commercial industry. An example of how this system specifies composition resistor characteristics symbolically and sequentially, together with pertinent construction and design information, appears in Fig. 5–3. Table 5–4 lists common resistor types with their individual designations and governing military specifications.

FIXED RESISTORS

Resistors can be grouped into three basic classes: composition, high-stability film, or wirewound. Table 5–4 shows the applicable military specification covering government use of these resistors, the subscript used in tabulating them according to type, and the maximum permissible voltage that may be applied across composition resistors of various wattage ratings.

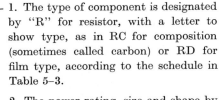

1. The type of component is designated by "R" for resistor, with a letter to show type, as in RC for composition (sometimes called carbon) or RD for film type, according to the schedule in Table 5–3.

2. The power rating, size and shape by a two-digit number.

3. The temperature characteristic, a two-letter symbol identifying the temperature characteristic.

4. The ohmic resistance in ohms, by three digits: the first and second significant figures followed a multiplier showing the number of zeros.

5. The tolerance letter denoting tolerance in percent.

RC   20   BF   122   K

EXAMPLE: the resistor coding RC 20 BF 122K, shown here, would be interpreted to mean a $\frac{1}{2}$-watt, 10 percent tolerance, 1200-ohm composition unit with a BF temperature characteristic.

FIG. 5-3 Breakdown of typical military specification for a composition resistor

COMPOSITION RESISTORS, as the name implies, are molded rods made from a powdered and electrically conductive mixture of graphite and an inert plastic binder. Wire terminal leads are affixed axially to each end of the conductive rod, and then the whole assembly (leads and rod) is molded again, for insulating purposes, within a bakelite case. The final step in packaging is to stamp the appropriate color bands on the case for convenient identification value and tolerance. Figure 5–4(a) shows typical composition resistors with ratings ranging from $\frac{1}{10}$ watt up to 2 watts.

The power rating, resistance value, and shape as described by the digits in the second part of the basic designation scheme described in Fig. 5–3 can be extended, in the case of carbon resistors, to various wattage ratings as shown below.

Style	Rating (Watts)
RC 09	1/2
RC 20	1/2
RC 30	1
RC 32	1
RC 41	2
RC 42	2

POWER TYPE WIREWOUND RESISTORS consist of a wire or metallic ribbon wrapped around a supporting ceramic form; Fig. 5–4(b) shows several types and wattages in fixed, tapped, and adjustable construction and with various terminals and mounting provisions. The wire generally used is an alloy of two or more elements such as copper, iron, nickel, chromium, zinc, or manganese. It can stand relatively high temperatures and is usually protectively coated with some ceramic material.

Power type, fixed wirewound resistors have a number of subscripts corresponding to their basic RW military and EIA designation and indicating the different types of terminals. The following table gives the range of numerical subscripts for the different types.

Terminal	Style	Power, watts
Ferrule	RW 10 through 16	15–200
Tab (flat)	RW 20 through 24	15–100
Tab (tubular)	RW 29 through 47	8–200
Axial	RW 50 through 56	5–15

PRECISION TYPE WIREWOUND RESISTORS are shown in Figure 5–4(c). Their extreme accuracy results from their construction of fine, accurately controlled wire which remains stable under changing operating temperatures. This type seldom operates with more than 5 watts, dissipation. Stud mounting, axial leads, or sealed units are available.

THE FILM TYPE RESISTOR is composed of a resistive film of carbon or metal deposited on or inside an insulating cylinder or filament. Figure 5–4(d) shows typical constructions in

Table 5–4 Resistor types covered by coordinated military specifications

Description of resistor	Component designation	Range		Specification
		Min. ohms	Max. ohms	
Fixed, composition (insulated)	RC	2.0	30 Meg	MIL-R-11A
Fixed, (composition film, very high frequency)	RF	2.0	1 Meg	MIL-R-10683A
Fixed, film (high stability)	RN	1.0	10 Meg	MIL-R-10509A
Fixed, wirewound (accurate)	RF	2.0	1 Meg	MIL-R-93A
Fixed, wirewound (low power)	RU	.2	2 K	JAN-R-184
Fixed, wirewound (power type)	RW	0	200 K	MIL-R-26B
Variable, composition	RV	100	6 Meg	MIL-R-94-A
Variable, wirewound (low operating temperature)	PA	4.	12 K	JAN-R-19
Variable (wirewound power type)	RP	3.	10 K	MIL-R-22A

various resistance values and wattages and in sealed and unsealed packaging. Film type resistors have exceptionally good stability at high frequencies or under changes of voltage or temperature, but they are expensive, fragile, and subject to mechanical damage.

Film type resistors have a number of sub-types under their basic RN designation used by the armed forces and by EIA. These subtypes are:

Style	Rating (watts)
RN 10	1/4
RN 15	1/2
RN 20	1/2
RN 25	1
RN 30	2

Since it is generally impracticable to make high-voltage, high-ohmic-value resistors of composition, such units (20 megohms and upwards) are made by applying a continuous ribbon of carbon-graphite or thin metallic film in coil-like fashion over a glass tube. Terminals, fused to the conductive strip and to the glass, are thus separated by a long conductive path and can withstand high voltages. Figure 5–4(e) shows a typical group of high-voltage resistors.

VARIABLE RESISTORS

Continuously variable resistors, as distinguished from tapped or adjustable types,
may be either composition or wirewound types. Whether metallic or composition, their resistive elements are toroidal or annular and are so constructed that a wiping or sliding contact is made between them and the terminal common to the central shaft. Adjustment is by a knob, handle, or through a screwdriver slot on the end of the control shaft. (See Fig. 5–5). In higher-powered, wirewound types they are more often called *rheostats*, and in smaller-wattage units they are called *volume controls* or *potentiometers* ("pot" for short). Strictly speaking, however, a rheostat, regardless of size or wattage, is a two-terminal device, while a potentiometer has three connecting leads—the arm and two ends.

COMPOSITION TYPE VARIABLE RESISTORS are seldom made larger than with a 2-watt rating. In the typical sizes pictured in Fig. 5–5(a) they range in diameters from $\frac{3}{4}''$ up to $1\frac{1}{2}''$ and may be grouped in up to three units, tandem mounted on a single shaft.

The military and EIA subscripts designations denoting power rating applying to the RV type variable composition resistors are as follows:

Style	Power rating (watts)
RV 1	1/5
RV 1	1/4
RV 4	2
RV 5	1/2
RV 6	1/3

(a) Composition resistors

(a) Composition type variable resistors

(b) Power type wirewound resistors

(b) Precision wirewound variable resistor

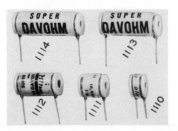

(c) Precision type wirewound resistors

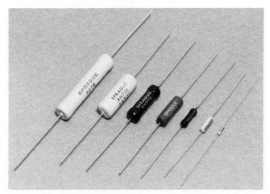

(d) Film type resistors

(c) Power type variable resistor

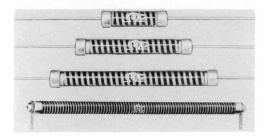

(e) High-voltage resistors

FIG. 5-4 Types of fixed resistors

(d) Miniature type variable resistor

FIG. 5-5 Types of variable resistors

A PRECISION WIREWOUND VARIABLE RESISTOR is pictured in Fig. 5–6(b). Precision types are usually potentiometers and are constructed of wirewound elements, allowing extreme accuracy in manufacture and more stable operation than can be obtained from the composition types. On variable wirewound resistors of the RA designation the subscripts show power ratings as follows:

Style	Power rating (watts)
RA 20	2
RA 25	3
RA 30	4

POWER TYPE VARIABLE RESISTORS are used in electronic gear; they range from 5 watts up to 50 watts. The resistance elements are wound on ceramic cores and the construction is generally rugged and heat resistant. (See Fig. 5–5(c).) Subscripts and power ratings correspond as follows:

Style	Power rating (watts)
RP 10	25
RP 11	12.5
RP 15	50
RP 16	25
RP 20	75
RP 25	100
RP 30	150
RP 35	225
RP 40	300
RP 45	500
RP 50	750
RP 55	1000

MINIATURE VARIABLE TYPES are shown in Fig. 5–6(d). Their resistive element is wound on a solenoid so that the center arm contact runs lengthwise on the element, actuated by a 25-turn screwdriver adjustment.

THE BALLAST RESISTOR is an electronic, automatically variable type of resistor sometimes used in electronic circuitry. (See Fig. 5–6.) Its wirewound resistance element is

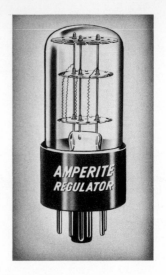

FIG. 5-6 Ballast resistor

encased in a glass vacuum tube envelope filled with an inert gas. When current through the resistance element increases, the temperature of the wire rises, which in turn increases its resistance and reduces current. Thus, the ballast resistor regulates or limits changes in current. Glass envelope sizes for this unit range from subminiature to seven pin glass.

MOUNTING METHODS

On the chassis assembly photo, Fig. 1–3, we see several examples of the mounting and assembly of resistor units. In general, the assembly technique depends upon the size of the individual unit. Small fixed resistors are usually self-supported or mounted on a terminal board, while variable resistors are usually mounted with their shafts protruding through a hole provided in the chassis frame or through a hole in a support bracket. Wirewound and power resistors may have mounting feet or stand-off mounting spacers. Heavy-duty units, variable or fixed, may require special brackets or sockets.

COLOR CODING

An industry-wide, eight-unit color code indicating size, type, and description, has been established to identify the resistance characteristics of fixed nonmetallic resistors. (Wire-wound and variable units have values and characteristics stamped upon each unit.) To completely spell out an individual resistance value the system uses sets of three of the eight available colors and locates them in a cluster of bands at one end of the resistor body. A voltage-indicating color band is located beyond the three value bands.

The *value* of individual resistors is thus established by the sequence of colored bands or dots reading from the end toward the center. The color-number sequence for resistance for each band is translated by decoding the color-band markings into resistance values using the color-number coding list in Appendix B-10 (Black = 0, Brown = 1, Red = 2, etc.).

Figure 5–7 illustrates the conventional marking and decoding system:

1. The end band color represents the first digit of the resistance value—a blue band, say, means 6.

2. The next band represents the second digit of resistance value—a red band thus means 2.

3. The third band represents a decimal-multiplier factor, or number of zeros to the right or decimal places to the left, of the first two digits—a third yellow band means 4 zeros taken from the decimal-multiplier column in Appendix B-9.

Thus far we have, reading the bands from left to right, a blue, red, and yellow banded resistor whose value is 620,000 ohms. If the third band had been black, the number of zeros would have been zero; the final digit in the overall value would have been interpreted as no zeros or a multiplier equal to 1. Thus, the value of our blue, red, and black banded

resistor would have been 62.0 ohms; with a silver band the value would be 0.62 ohms.

For resistor tolerance a fourth color band is used beyond the last color bar, generally spaced a small distance so as to be more legible. This code uses

A gold band – 5 percent tolerance
A silver band – 10 percent tolerance
No band – 20 percent tolerance

One and two percent tolerance resistors (not common except in precision units) respectively use brown and red dots. In our 620,000-ohm example, if there were no color bar beyond the yellow one, the resistor would be assumed to be of 20 percent tolerance; it could vary anywhere between 50,000 and 74,000 ohms. A 5 percent tolerance resistor (with a gold band) could vary between 589,000 and 651,000 ohms.

CAPACITORS

A fixed capacitor is an encased component consisting of two electrodes or sets of metallic plates insulated from each other by a non-conducting or dielectric material and brought out to terminals external to the case. (Variable air capacitors whose plates are mechanically actuated with respect to one another will be discussed later.)

Schematically, a capacitor is designated by its own particular symbol (see Fig. 5–1), its letter designation or "C" number, and a notation showing its electrical value and the voltage at which it works—for example, C-81, .01 MF, 4000 V; or C-6619, .003 MF, 500 V, etc. This notation usually appears on the schematic alongside the capacitor's symbol, thereby physically describing it in a general way to one familiar with capacitors, since size is directly proportional to a unit's electrical capacity and to the voltage it can withstand. Details of construction, however, vary widely between identical values of the same type, and can not be inferred from the capacitor symbol, which simply shows two plates or electrodes separated by open space. In actual construction, capacitors actually may have many pairs of parallel connected

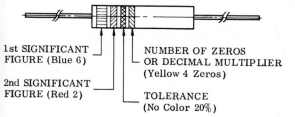

1st SIGNIFICANT FIGURE (Blue 6)

2nd SIGNIFICANT FIGURE (Red 2)

NUMBER OF ZEROS OR DECIMAL MULTIPLIER (Yellow 4 Zeros)

TOLERANCE (No Color 20%)

FIG. 5-7 Conventional marking and decoding system for resistors

plates, and the open space shown on the symbol may represent many types of dielectric material.

To completely describe a capacitor we speak in terms of: (1) Its electrical size in microfarads —μf, mf, or MF (millionth of a farad); or in micromicrofarads—$\mu\mu$f, mmf, or MMF (one millionth of a microfarad). (2) The d-c working or operating voltage, DCWV. (3) The type of dielectric used between its electrode plates. (4) Whether the capacitance is fixed or variable. Table 5–5 gives an overall summary of capacitor types versus their pertinent characteristics, specifications, etc.

TYPES OF DIELECTRIC

The dielectric used in a capacitor can not be determined from the schematic symbol, since its physical size, shape, mounting shield,

Table 5–5 Fixed capacitor characteristics

Dielectric classification	Capacity range (MF)	Voltage range	Leads, mounting
PAPER:			
Tubular	.0005–6.0	200–400	Axial
Plastic film		200–600	
Special:			
bathtub, rectangular case	.1–2.0	100–12,500	Terminals
MICA:			
Molded	.00001–.015	300–3000	Axial
Potted plastic (ceramic case)	.00005–.1	250–5000	Terminals, ears, stud mounting
Button	.00001–.0039	300	Tab and mounting stud
CERAMIC:			
Tubular	.00001–.03	0 to 500 or 600	Radial or parallel wire
Disc			
Special:			
standoff	0–.00001		Body or stud mounting
feedthrough	0–.00005		
compensating			
high voltage	.0005	10,000–20,000	Stud and terminal mounting
ELECTROLYTIC:			
Tubular	0–100	150–450	Axial leads
Aluminum foil (plug-in)	6–2000		
Non-polarized (screw)		6–500	End mounting
Wet or dry (base)	450–50		
Cylindrical (twist, prong)			
Tantalum:			
foil	.5–60	.5–150.0	Lead mounting
tubular slug	7–300	.5–600.0	Body mounting
GLASS:			
Rectangular	.00005–.005	0–300	Axial
VITREOUS ENAMEL:			
Rectangular	.00001–.01	0–300	Axial
SPECIAL:			
Vacuum	.0001–.0005	0–50KV	Terminals
Gas	.00001–.00005		Terminals

cover, or any other accessories are not spelled out. If we need details for purposes of mounting we must refer to the electrical parts list or to the assembly drawing parts list. In the description of various classifications that follows, the variable types will be covered along with the fixed, since only three classes have variable versions. It should be noted that the various capacitor types designated and classified dielectrically in Table 5–5 can be also listed according to their applicable military specification, in their various ranges, working voltage, and style. (See Table 5–6.)

The various dielectric categories are as follows:

MICA DIELECTRIC CAPACITORS

Mica dielectric capacitors are usually sealed in rectangular plastic cases (Fig. 5–8(a)). The

Operating temp. range (°C)	Application frequency and range	Designation	Marking	Applicable MIL specification
−55−+150	General purpose, up to 1 MC	CN CP	EIA standard color-coded bands	MIL-C-25A
			Direct MIL-STD labelling	MIL-C-91A
−60−+85	General purpose, up to 10 KMC	CM CB	EIA or MIL-STD color-dot coding	MIL-C-5A MIL-C-1095A
	General purpose, 50–1000 MC	CK		MIL-C-11015A
−55−+125	UHF bypass, critically tuned circuits, 50–1000 MC	CC—for compensating	EIA or MIL-STD color-dot or band marking	JAN-C-20A for compensating type
	High-voltage TV filter 0–20 KC	none	MMF stamped on body	Commercial only
		CE	Body stamping	MIL-C-62A
0−+65	0–20 KC		Body stamping or	MIL-C-62A
		CJ (polarized)	coded indentations	MIL-C-3871
−55−+85 55−+200		CE	Body stamping	MIL-C-18,211 MIL-C-25,102 MIL-C-14,006
−60−+200	0–100 MC	CY	EIA color-dot	MIL-C-1172A
−60−+200	0–100 MC	none	EIA color-dot	None
−60−+400	Blocking and decoupling	none	Body stamping	None
−60−+200	Blocking and decoupling	none	Name plate	None

smaller types are often called postage-stamp capacitors (from their size and shape) and vary in common electronic equipment from 50 MMF up to several thousand MMF.

The variable "book" type or mica-compression trimmer capacitor has only moderate use because of size and stability limitations. Multiplate units for transmitter usage likewise have proportionately larger plastic cases. (See Fig. 5–8(b).)

The molded mica type capacitor is manufactured in accordance with MIL-C-5A military specifications and EIA specification RS-153. All capacitors are color coded in accordance with MIL-C-5A unless otherwise specified. (See Fig. 5–8(c).)

(a) *Postage-stamp capacitor*

(b) *Mica-compression trimmer capacitor*

(c) *Molded mica type capacitor*

FIG. 5-8 Types of mica dielectric capacitors

MOLDED MICA CAPACITOR DESIGNATION MARKING AND COLOR CODING

Standard military designation for this type has nine characters and contains complete specification for the part. A typical part might be designated CM20D471J—illustrating the military system of numbering, which in general carries over into commercial practice.

The designation is broken down and explained as follows:

CM	20	D	471	J
Type designation	Case size	Character-istic	Capacity value	Tolerance

In discussing details of the above designation, we can apply the same descriptive format to other capacitor types since the various items are in general similar.

Table 5–6 Military designation, specifications, and capacitor ratings

Description	Military style designation	Capacity range		Max working volts	Applicable MIL specification
		Min	Max		
Paper	CN	1,000 MMF	2 MF	1,000	MIL-C-91A
Paper	CP	0.001 MF	20 MF	12,500	MIL-C-25A
Mica	CB	10 MMF	3,900 MMF	300	MIL-C-10950A
Mica	CM	5 MMF	0.1 MF	35,000	MIL-C-5A
Ceramic	CV	1.5 MMF	125 MMF	500	JAN-C-81
Ceramic	CC	0.5 MMF	1,300 MMF	500	JAN-C-20A
Ceramic	CK	100 MMF	10,000 MMF	500	MIL-C-11015A
Glass	CY	5 MMF	5,100 MMF	500	MIL-C-11272A
Air	CT	3.5 MMF	143 MMF	†	JAN-C-92
Tantalum	CW	0.5 MF	320 MF	630	[1]MIL-C-18211
Electrolytic, AC Aluminum,	CJ	21 MF	552 MF	125	[2]MIL-C-25102 [3]MIL-C-14006
Electrolytic	CE	4 MF	2,000 MF	450	JAN-C-62
	*	0.01 MF	0.25 MF	†	
	♯	0.01 MF	2.0 MF	†	

* Paper, high-voltage, suppression. † Not specified. [2] USAF.
♯ Paper, feed-through, suppression. [1] Navy. [3] Sig. Corps.

CASE SIZE. Two digits designate the case
size of the capacitors. Most molded capacitors
are available in MIL-C-5A with case sizes
CM15, CM20, CM25, CM30, CM35, and CM40.
In addition, there are two sizes not mentioned
in either MIL or EIA specifications: CM19
and CM42. The CM19 is technically also a
CM20 case size, since it falls within the same
size limits. The CM19 was developed after
the CM20 to provide a size saving where
required. Both CM19 and CM20 meet all
MIL and EIA specifications for CM20. The
CM42 is a relatively special size whose use
is limited.

CHARACTERISTIC. This letter designates temperature performance requirements by specifying temperature coefficient and capacity
drift. The former is the rate of change of
capacity as temperature is varied; the latter
represents the deviation of capacity value
from original value after temperature cycling.
Table 5–7 lists available characteristics. De-

Table 5–7 Temperature characteristic for
molded mica capacitors

Letter	Temperature coefficient, ppm/°C*	Capacitance drift
A	EIA: ±1,000 Mil—not specified	±(5% + 1 MMF)
B	EIA ±500 Mil—not specified	±(3% + 1 MMF)
C	−200 to +200	±0.5%
D	−100 to +100	±0.3%
E	−20 to +100	±(0.1% + 0.1 mmf)
F	0 to +70	±(0.05% + 0.1 mmf)

* ppm = parts per million.

spite the designation as molded mica capacitors, specifications under "A" and "B"
characteristics call for foil mica construction;
such capacitors can be identified by their
yellow case. However, the silver mica may
also be supplied (red case) instead of foil.
Characteristics "C," "D," "E," and "F" can
be obtained in silver mica only.

CAPACITANCE. The three exemplary digits
"471" represent the nominal capacity value.
This figure plus tolerance specified will provide
the exact capacity range within which the
value of the component lies. The first two
figures (4, 7) are the significant ones; the
third is the decimal multiplier. This is the
power of ten by which the significant figures
must be multiplied, or simply the number of
decimal places or zeros to be added to the
significant figure. In this example the decimal
multiplier is "1," so the significant figure is
multiplied by ten, thus moving the decimal
point one place or adding zero to give the
specified nominal capacity value of 470 MMF.
If the third digit had been a zero, there would
have been no movement of the decimal and
the value would have been 47 MMF. If the
third number had been two, then the capacity
value would have been 4,700.

Sometimes, but only when absolutely necessary, three significant figures are given to
specify capacity value. In this case the total
number of digits is expanded to four, and
the first coding dot occupies the upper left-
hand position. The first three digits are then
the significant figures and the last digit remains as the decimal multiplier. For example,
3,350 MMF would appear in the designation
as "3351," the "335" being the significant
figures and the "1" being the decimal multiplier.

TOLERANCE. The last letter of the part
number indicates the tolerance. The tolerance
is the allowable percent variation from the
nominal capacity value. The smaller the
tolerance, the narrower the range within
which the actual capacity value must fall.
The letters used to designate tolerance are
as follows:

M................20%
K................10%
J................ 5%
H................ 3%
G................ 2%
F................ 1%

COLOR CODING. Mica capacitors employ either a six-dot or a three-dot color code following the generalized color-coding system illustrated in Fig. 5–7. Other capacitor types use colored bands, as in resistor coding, or use colored dots. Table 5–8 illustrates six-dot color coding. The units of electrical capacitance can be translated into and read by means of the painted dots located lengthwise along the capacitor body. In addition, the shape, size, and color of the body plus the color of the upper left-hand dot identify the case size.

When the capacitor marking is being decoded, the direction indicator (an arrow on the body or a pointed oval color dot) should point to the right of the reader. The dots are read from *left* to *right* across the top row and from *right* to *left* along the bottom row in that order. We have designated the sequence of reading by numbering the dots 1 through 6 in the illustration.

Table 5–8   Reading the six-dot mica capacitor code

Dot 1   Identification of dielectric. For mica, the MIL-C-5A color is black. The EIA color is white.
Dot 2   First significant figure of capacity value.
Dot 3   Second significant figure of capacity value.
Dot 4   Decimal multiplier of capacity value.
Dot 5   Tolerance.
Dot 6   Characteristic.

The only exception that may be made occurs when three significant figures are to be found in the part number. In this case dots 1, 2, and 3 represent the three significant figures. The identification color is eliminated. The colors and their values are tabulated as follows (MIL and EIA color codes are identical except as noted).

Color	Dots 2 & 3	Dot 4	Dot 5	Dot 6
Black	0	1	±20% (M)	A EIA only
Brown	1	10	±1% (F)	B
Red	2	100	±2% (G)	C
Orange	3	1,000	±3% (H)	D
Yellow	4			E
Green	5		±5% (J) EIA only	F
Blue	6			
Purple	7			
Gray	8			
White	9			
Gold		.1	±5% (J) MIL only	
			MIL only	
Silver		.01	±10% (K)	

AIR DIELECTRIC CAPACITORS

Most capacitors of this class are variable by virtue of the adjustable amount of engagement between the sets of plates; Fig. 5–9 shows two models used for circuit adjustment. A very common type is the tuning control unit in a radio receiver. They run from fractional MMF values up to several hundred MMF's. Some types have widely spread plates to prevent voltage breakdown and are used in the tuning of transmitter oscillator circuits.

FIG. 5-9 Air dielectric capacitors used for circuit adjustment

The standard military part numbers or characters giving specifications for this type are shown below. Their governing specification is JAN-C-92.

CT	1	B	010
Capacitor trimmer	Class	Characteristic	Capacitance (MMF)

These units are not color coded; the characteristic describes the type of shaft and torque characteristics.

PAPER DIELECTRIC FIXED CAPACITORS: TUBULAR AND OIL FILLED

Most units of this type are called *tubular capacitors* from the shape of their cylindrical

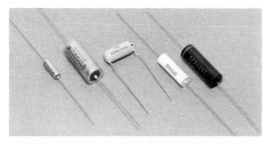

(a) Tubular capacitors

(b) Oil filled capacitors

FIG. 5-10 Paper dielectric fixed capacitors

metal or plastic containers as shown in Fig. 5–10(a). They may run from a few thousand MMF up to 1 MF in value and operate up to 600 volts.

In transmitter, high-voltage usage, paper capacitor units are immersed in insulating oil and may be mounted in a wide range of cylindrical and rectangular cases with appropriately insulated terminals (Fig. 5–10(b)).

The military designations for tubular plastic-cased units are:

CN	22	A	E	202	N
Capacitor, paper— nonmetallic case	Shape and dimensions	Characteristic	Voltage	Capacitance	Capacitance tolerance

Color coding follows the scheme used in plastic-cased mica capacitors.

For the metal-cased tubular versions, the designations are:

CP04	A	1	E	B	333	K
Style	Terminal	Circuit	Characteristic	Voltage	Capacitance	Capacitance tolerance

The capacitance and voltage ratings of these capacitors are usually stamped directly on each case.

ELECTROLYTIC FILM OR FIXED ELECTROLYTIC CAPACITORS

Low-capacitance units are generally provided in tubular cases; larger values come in cylindrical metal cases. Both types are larger than paper or mica capacitors and vary in d-c operating voltages from one or two volts to a top of 450 volts. (See Fig. 5–11.)

Although the descriptive words aluminum and film are not usually employed in describing them, electrolytic capacitors derive their capacitance from the dielectric properties of an aluminum film on the positive electrode. The film is chemically formed by the particular electrolyte used and is in the form of a paste; thus, these units are called "dry" electrolytic capacitors in distinction to early units which were filled with a liquid hydroxide. Single units may run from full microfarad values to several hundred MF, and multiple-section units of several capacitors contained in one case are common. Since most electrolytics are polarized they must have the proper terminal markings to indicate the positive and negative voltages which should be used across them.

The military designation for polarized electrolytic units follows MIL-C-62-A and bears

FIG. 5-11 Fixed electrolytic capacitors

Table 5-9 Type designation and identification for JAN-C-62 electrolytic capacitors

CE 31 A 101 E

Component	Container types—mounting		Temperature characteristics		Capacitance	D-c working volts and surge volts		
Electrolytic capacitor (d-c polarized)	31, 32, and 33	single, double, and triple universal mounting	Designation	Working temp. range	first two digits capacity, MF third digit multiplier (no zeros)	Desig- nation	Working volts	Surge volts
	41 and 42	single and dual stud mtg.	A	0 — +85°C		E	15	20
	51, 52, and 53	single, dual, and triple plug-in mtg.	B	−20 — +85	*Example:* 040 = 4 MFD	F	25	40
	61, 62, 63, and 64	single section bathtub can	C	−40 — +85	100 = 10 MFD	G	50	75
			D	0 — +65	200 = 20 MFD	H	100	150
			E	−20 — +65	161 = 160 MFD	J	150	200
			F	−40 — +65	202 = 2000 MFD	K	200	250
					(Capacity tolerance = 10% ± 1.50%)	M	250	300
						N	300	350
						P	350	400
						Q	400	450
						R	450	500

All multiple section units have equal capacity and equal voltage.

the label, DC, Dry, Aluminum, Polarized. Capacitance markings are stamped on the body.

CE	31	C	101	E
Capacitor, dry, polarized electrolytic	Case and mounting style	Characteristic	Capacitance	Voltage (15, 150, 450)

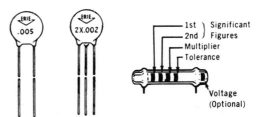

An expansion of the above coding schedule is shown in Table 5–7.

Nonpolarized units which operate in a-c circuits come under MIL-C-3871. Their designation is:

CJ	62	A	025	C	M
Capacitor, dry, nonpolarized electrolytic	Style, shape, dimension	Characteristic	Capacitance	Voltage	Case

Schematic symbol markings show polarization connections, and capacitance values are stamped on the body.

CERAMIC DIELECTRIC CAPACITORS

This class encompasses a wide variety of fixed and variable types. The fixed types include the following:

CERAMIC DISC CAPACITORS (Fig. 5–12(a)) range from hundreds of MMF up to .01 MF. These are for general usage and are predominantly used as by-pass units. They are easy to install, small, and inexpensive.

Ceramic disk capacitors are designated under MIL-C-11015 as follows:

CK	22	W	101	Z
Ceramic capacitor	Shape and dimension	Characteristic	Capacitance	Tolerance

Marking is by color-coded dots.

CERAMIC TUBULAR CAPACITORS resemble resistors in size and shape. They may be

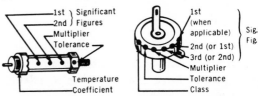

(a) Ceramic disc capacitors   (b) Ceramic tubular capacitors

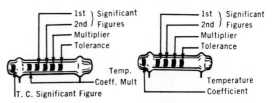

(c) Ceramic stand-off and feed-through capacitors   (d) Ceramic button capacitors

(e) Ceramic trimmer capacitors   (f) Ceramic trimmer capacitor using the piston principle

FIG. 5-12 Ceramic dielectric capacitors

for general usage or for temperature compensating. Capacity is obtained between metallic films on the inside and outside of ceramic tubes; Fig. 5–12(b) shows the construction. They are available in insulated and uninsulated types, range from 20 MMF to 1,500 MMF, and are particularly stable under varying temperature and humidity conditions. Under general usage these capacitors come under MIL-C-11005-A and utilize generalized color-band coding. For the temperature-compensated type they fall under JAN-C-20 and are specified as follows (also, see detailed JAN-C-20A marking schedules Table 5–10):

CC	25	U	K	10C	G
Ceramic capacitor	Shape and size	TC	TTC	Capacitance	Capacitance tolerance
		TC characteristic			

CERAMIC STAND-OFF AND FEED-THROUGH CAPACITORS (Fig. 5–12(c)) are modifications of the tubular type in which mounting rings and bushings have been added, so that in passing a connection through a metal base or attaching a lead to one terminal the lead, by proximity, becomes automatically by-passed to ground or to the base metal. They run from 500 up to 1,500 MMF. There is no general military specification governing these units. Color coding is by dots.

CERAMIC BUTTON CAPACITORS are shown in Fig. 5–12(d). This construction, mostly used in by-pass units, aims to provide a maximum of concentrated capacity in a minimum space with a short, low-inductance lead path, provided by the case and mounting. These units come under MIL-C-10950A. Color-dot coding is used.

CB	11	N	B	101	K
Button-style mica	Shape and dimension	Terminal assembly	Characteristic	Capacitance	Capacitance tolerance

CERAMIC TRIMMER CAPACITORS are shown in Fig. 5–12(e) in several types. First is the flat, screwdriver-adjusted type in which a sector of a metal-film coated rotor rides against a portion of the base which has a film-coated area on its rear side. Capacitance is developed between the coated areas on the rotor and base, the body material acting as the dielectric between the electrodes. This capacitor is designated under MIL-C-81A. The numbering and lettering system is:

CV	11	A	070
Ceramic Trimmer	Style	Characteristic	Capacitance

Color-dot coding is used.

A type of ceramic tubular trimmer capacitor shown in Fig. 5–12(f) uses the piston principle; variable capacity is developed by movement from a metallic piston-like slug within the body as it moves with respect to a metallic-coated area on the outside of the capacitor body.

GLASS DIELECTRIC FIXED CAPACITORS (Fig. 5–13(a)) are similar in size and shape to mica capacitors.

Table 5–10 Marking schedule for JAN-C-20A capacitors

Style	Temperature characteristic		T.C. tolerance, ppm./25–85°C		Capacity, MMF	Capacity tolerance		
JAN	JAN	Color code	Tolerance	JAN letter		If capacity is 10 MMF or less	JAN letter	Color code
20	A	Gold	± 30	G	Color code‡	± .25 MMF	C	Gray
21	B	Gray	± 60	H	0 Black	± .5 MMF	D	Green
25	C	Black	±120	J	1 Brown	±1.0 MMF	F	White
26	H	Brown	±250	K	2 Red	±2.0 MMF	G	Black
30	L	Red	±500†	L	3 Orange			
	P	Orange			4 Yellow	If capacity is greater than 10 MMF	JAN letter	Color code
32	R	Yellow			5 Green			
35	S	Green			6 Blue			
36	T	Blue			7 Violet	± 1%	F	Brown
	U	Violet			8 Gray	± 2%	G	Red
45	SL*	White			9 White	± 5%	J	Green
						±10%	K	White
						±20%	M	Black

* If dielectric used falls within SL characteristic, this color is white.

† T.C. tolerance "L" is used on N330 only and means that any nominal between P120 and N750 (inclusive) may be supplied.

‡ First digit = first significant figure; second digit = second significant figure; third digit = number of zeros that follow the first two digits. If capacity is expressed in a decimal fraction, the decimal point is indicated by an "R." Thus 1R5 is 1.5 MMF.

(a) *Typical glass dielectric fixed capacitors*

(b) *Variable, piston glass type trimmer capacitors*

FIG. 5-13 Glass dielectric fixed capacitors

CY	20	C	561	K
Glass dielectric capacitor	Shape and dimension	Characteristic	Capacitance	Tolerance

Variable, piston glass type trimmer capacitors (see Fig. 5–13(b)) develop capacity between the outside metal film on the capacitor's tubular body and a movable internal "piston" or grounded electrode. Color-dot coding is used.

SPECIAL CAPACITORS

PLASTIC FILM CAPACITORS most commonly use Teflon, Mylar, Amplifilm, or polystyrene dielectric films. These dielectrics make possible higher voltage ratings. Typical Teflon and Mylar capacitors are in most cases physically identical with paper dielectric tubular types (Fig. 5–10(a)), since they often use the same case or container.

TANTALUM ELECTROLYTIC CAPACITORS use an insulating oxide film of tantalum instead of an oxide of aluminum. This film has a very high dielectric constant, so these units can be physically very small for their developed capacitance. The electrolyte may be wet, using foil electrodes, or dry, using "slug" construction. They operate relatively well at low temperatures and have comparatively low leakage. Figure 5–14(a) shows a number of types for both high- and low-voltage transistorized equipment, where this type has its greatest size and weight advantage. These units are specified under MIL-C-3965; values are usually designated by body stamping.

VITREOUS ENAMEL CAPACITORS are used as an equivalent to glass capacitors; they operate well at high temperatures compared to mica capacitors. (See Fig. 5–14(b).) Color-dot coding usually applies.

VACUUM CAPACITORS use the dielectric space of an air capacitor by evacuating it so as to maintain a high vacuum between the plated surfaces. These units will withstand as high as 50,000 volts, but have low space efficiency and are seldom made in sizes above .001 MF. Figure 5–14(c) shows fixed and variable types.

CAPACITOR MOUNTING

The method of mounting capacitors for wiring is usually made obvious by the con-

(a) *Tantalum electrolytic capacitors*

(b) *Vitreous enamel capacitors*

(c) *Vacuum capacitors*

FIG. 5-14 Special capacitors

struction and location of the studs, mounting holes, brackets, etc., that accompany each unit. Location should follow good electrical practices. By-pass units should be mounted close to the source of interference and in places where interconnecting leads are as short as practicably possible.

BODY-BAND COLOR CODING

The color coding identifying tubular plastic-case or ceramic capacitors uses the same basic color-number relationships employed on resistors—that is, black = 0, brown = 1, red = 2, etc. (See Table 5–8.) The coded capacitance values are in micromicrofarads (MMF), and the coding is usually extended by using additional colors to denote voltage rating and the capacity temperature coefficient, thus making the most commonly used code a five-color affair. Small cylindrical capacitors use color bands, but for convenience colored dots are used on rectangular-cased capacitors and other types whose shape does not permit the use of bands, as in the case of mica capacitors.

An example of the most complicated banding that would be used on a unit of the tubular type is shown in Fig. 5–15(a). Here, of the seven bands encircling the capacitor body from left to right, we use two for significant figures, one as the multiplier band, and one as the tolerance band. The fifth denotes voltage rating, the sixth, temperature co-

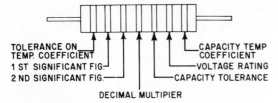

TOLERANCE ON TEMP. COEFFICIENT
1 ST SIGNIFICANT FIG.
2 ND SIGNIFICANT FIG.
DECIMAL MULTIPIER
CAPACITY TEMP COEFFICIENT
VOLTAGE RATING
CAPACITY TOLERANCE

(a) *Example of the most complicated banding used on a tubular type unit*

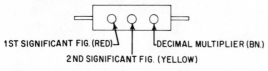

1ST SIGNIFICANT FIG. (RED)
2 ND SIGNIFICANT FIG. (YELLOW)
DECIMAL MULTIPLIER (BN.)

(b) *Example of the three-dot system used on a 240-MMF capacitor*

FIG. 5-15 Body-band color coding for capacitors

efficient, and the seventh, temperature coefficient tolerance.

In the case of button, feed-through, disk, and stand-off types, the coding dots are located around the outside rim of the unit or within a convenient area.

The simplest capacitor code (usually applied to small mica capacitances) is a three-dot code reading from left to right; Fig. 5–15(b) shows an example of the three-dot system used on a 240-MMF capacitor. It is employed where the capacitor's working voltage is under 500 volts, and where the tolerance is more than 20 percent.

MILITARY TYPE AND SIZE DESIGNATIONS

It can be seen from previous details that the government-specified lettering and numbering system for capacitors is similar to that used for resistors. As we have noted, capacitors require more than electrical description; in some cases the coding sequence may cover as many as eight items besides information about mounting.

The common and applicable JAN or MIL specification appears together with capacitor designation in Table 5–5. Table 5–6 elaborates on additional features such as case type, terminals, circuit, mounting, etc.

INDUCTANCES (CHOKES)

An inductance (inductor, choke) is the electrical name for a coil of wire wound on a supporting form or core. A coil is described schematically and has a letter designation "L" as shown on the basic list of component symbols in Table 5–1. Thus we may have L-18, L-92, L-95A, and so on. Between its terminals there exists a definite electrical value of inductance in henries (H) or submultiple units such as millihenries (MH) or microhenries (μH). This value is usually listed along with the "L" number; it may be supplemented by notations on the schematic, by information on the electrical parts list, or by specifically detailed information on a separate drawing.

Inductances may be classified in general as (1) low-frequency iron-core units or (2) high-

(a) Low-frequency iron-core unit
(b) High-frequency air-core unit
(c) High-frequency unit in which coil form provides means
      of incorporating mounting feet or brackets and encloses
      assembly in metal assembly or can

FIG. 5-16 Inductances

frequency air-core units. The former category implies relatively large closed magnetic-circuit inductances existing in power, audio, and TV sound equipment. The presence of iron within a coil is indicated symbolically by parallel lines alongside the loops representing the coil winding.

Low-inductance coils are most often open-ended air-core windings (called solenoids), although they sometimes use a powdered iron movable slug within the winding (Fig. 5–16 (a)). Note that air-core coils must have some support for the winding and are accordingly wound on a fiber, ceramic, or plastic form. The coil form also provides a means of incorporating mounting feet or brackets and in some cases provides the framework for enclosing the assembly in a metal shield or cam. (See Fig. 5–16(b).) The electrical significance of the iron core, and the size and configuration of winding in both types, will be covered in Chapter 7.

Higher-frequency open-ended solenoid inductors for use above about 50 kc have either an air core or a cylindrical core of powdered iron. Most variable open-ended inductors coils use a movable iron core allowing adjustment of their inductance for tuning a resonant circuit. Variable air inductors may use a movable copper slug or a movable section of winding. To denote inductor variability note the slanting arrow superimposed on the basic symbol. See Fig. 5–16(c).

Two or more coil windings or inductances schematically indicated as being combined or magnetically coupled in single assembly is known as a *transformer*, which is given a schematic symbol as shown in Appendix A-1 plus a "T" number—for example, T-6, T-74, T-81A. Since a transformer may have several windings it must have a number of corresponding terminals as shown in Fig. 5–17. Also, certain coils, such as those in relays, motors, generators, or vibrators produce motion electromechanically, and their symbols are modified to show physical movement.

Air-core inductances range from tenths up through hundredths of microhenries, while iron-core coils go as high as 50 to 100 henries.

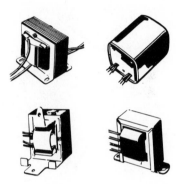

FIG. 5-17 Typical transformers

Iron-core coils, depending upon how much direct current flows through the coils, may in some cases require rather heavy wire which will increase their physical size. The fact that a coil carries current is often noted on a schematic alongside its inductance value, together with an arrow or $+$ and $-$ signs indicating polarity; the current value also gives some hint as to its physical size.

The iron cores used in power transformers, audio transformers, and choke coils are arranged in magnetically closed circuits and more or less encase the winding. (See Fig. 5–17.)

Another variation in audio inductances is the use of *toroids*, or doughnut-shaped coils (Fig. 5–18); this type of winding gives a maximum of inductance for a given core size.

Although most low-frequency power or audio coils are fixed, they may include adjustable taps on their windings. Special,

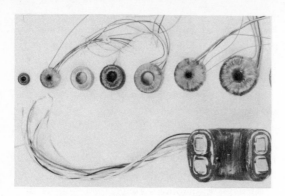

FIG. 5-18 Toroids

FIG. 5-19 Variacs, or powerstats

FIG. 5-20 Variable, high-power, high-frequency coils

continuously variable power transformers using a sliding tap and known as *variacs* or *powerstats* may occasionally be encountered in equipment where manual voltage regulation is necessary. (See Fig. 5-19.)

Figure 5-20 shows variable, high-power, high-frequency coils.

Mounting of coils, chokes, and transformers is usually by conventional feet, brackets, or, in the case of small RF coils, by threaded bushings which are part of the coil form. Color coding is seldom used to denote the inductance of audio- and power-frequency inductors; electrical values are usually stamped on each unit. Most inductors do, however, have their leads identified by color coding. Several schedules covering the color coding of various windings used in audio transformers, power transformers, loudspeakers, IF transformers, and field coils are given in Fig. 5–21. These codes are fairly similar, one being specified by the EIA for commercial use while the others originate with the MIL-STD-122 specification used in government equipment.

ELECTRON TUBES AND BASE PIN LAYOUTS

Electron tubes are active components; all common types are described by type number, physically and electrically, in Appendix B-2. On schematics, parts lists, and technical descriptions they bear a "V" number designation—V301, V22, V81A, etc.—rather than the type number given in handbook listing.

The basic physical facts about a tube are its envelope size and base pin layout; these, together with the symbol which is an electrical schematic of its internal elements, allow it to be fitted to an appropriate socket and then electrically connected to associated circuitry.

The remainder of this chapter will discuss tube base pin layouts in detail after a brief consideration of general tube classifications, which provides a basis for the more detailed description in Chapter 14, on tube testing.

TUBE CLASSIFICATIONS

In general, electron tubes are classified in tube listings by function as receiving tubes; transmitter tubes; picture-display tubes; thyratrons, ignitions, and glow-discharge tubes; photo-sensitive tubes; miscellaneous types.

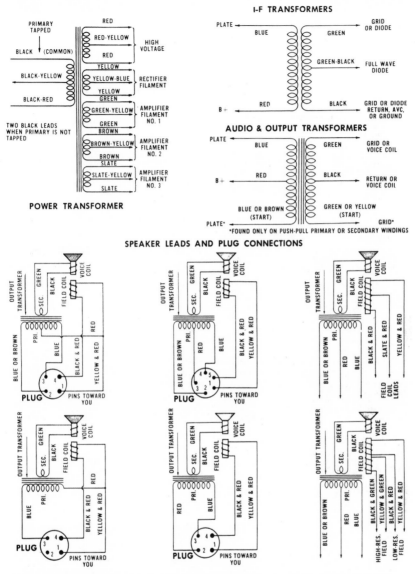

FIG. 5-21 Schedules for the color coding of windings used in audio transformers, power transformers, loudspeakers, IF transformers, and field coils

Receiving tubes constitute the numerically largest group of those listed above. Figure 5–22 shows a representative collection which may be roughly categorized in terms of their envelopes as subminiature, miniature, glass, or metal. Subminiature tubes are used in aircraft gear or other situations where size and weight are important. Miniature, regular glass and metal types form the preponderant majority of all other tubes used. Diodes and power rectifiers used in receiver-type equip-

ment are classified as such in tube listings.

Transmitter tubes (including rectifiers), as distinguished from receiver tubes, are classified more closely as to size and the amount of dissipated power. Their most common application is in transmitters, although many rectifiers in this category are used in relatively heavy power supplies regardless of classification. Transmitter tubes range in sizes from the receiving types up to units several feet high and a foot or two in diameter. (See Fig.

FIG. 5-22 Commonly used receiving tubes

FIG. 5-23 Typical transmitter tubes

5-23.) Transmitter tube construction varies much more radically among manufacturers than does that of receiver types, and two transmitters with essentially the same power output may have tubes that differ in size, basic construction, in sockets and mounting mechanisms, in cooling methods, and in operating techniques. Such variations are beyond the immediate scope of this book.

The early method of labeling receiving tubes with a first number corresponding to the heater voltage is still in general use.

This procedure gives a general clue to the type of service in which a tube is used, and in some cases indicates whether its design is of old or new style. For those familiar with tube types, the base pin and filament designation—especially the former—very often define the type of envelope and socket that must be used. See Table 5–12.

TUBE SYMBOLS AND BASE PIN LAYOUT CHART

When one is electrically interconnecting tube elements by means of their pin and socket connections, he must have some knowledge of the internal structure and its relation to basic electronic functioning. This is particularly valuable when operating or testing and measuring the voltages or currents exist-

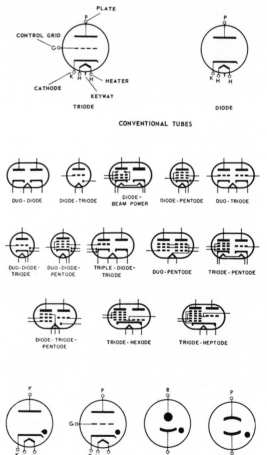

FIG. 5-24 Common tube type symbols

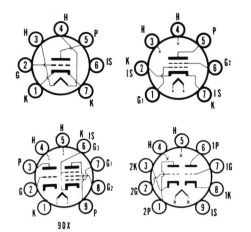

90X

FIG. 5-25 Basing diagrams

Common tube base configurations depend upon the style, size, type, functions, and usage of a particular tube; older style tubes differed materially from modern miniature types. (See Table 5–11.)

Table 5–11   Kinds of tube base pin layouts

Subminiature	– Pinch base pins (leads brought out alongside each other)
Subminiature	– Flexible leads
Subminiature	– Subminor 8 pin base
Miniature	– 7 prong
Miniature	– 9 prong
Glass	– Octal base (8 pin)
Glass	– Locktal base (7 pin)
Metal	– Octal base
Glass	– 7 pin base
Metal	– 7 pin base
Glass	– 6 pin base
Glass	– 5 pin base
Glass	– 4 pin base
Acorn	– Radial 5 pin base
Acorn	– Radial 7 pin base
Magnal	– 11 pin for cathode-ray tubes
Duodical	– 12 pin for cathode-ray tubes
Diheptal	– 14 pin for special tubes

ing on a particular tube element. Figure 5–24 shows common tube type symbols; they are schematically pictured with functional lettering which shows the physical positioning of grid, plate, cathode, and heater electrodes within the internal structure of basic tube types. This allows them to be related to corresponding base pin connections, more commonly known as a basing diagram (Fig. 5–25). Such basing diagrams tell by inspection whether a tube is a diode, triode, pentode, etc., plus the relative electronic location of the grid, plate, cathode, etc. In addition other manufacturers even letter the tube element functionally alongside the pin number.

The tube basing diagrams appearing in Appendix B-2 show views when looking at the bottom of a tube socket. Every tube has a distinctive base pin layout, arranged so that the pin numbering sequence proceeds clockwise from the keyway in each socket. When no keyway exists, the index position from which numbering starts is midway between the only two widely spaced pins. This space is clearly identified on miniature 7- and 9-pin tubes. On older tubes (where no difference in spacing was used) the index point is mid-way between the only pair of large-diameter base pins, which are usually the filament pins.

USE OF TUBE INDEX AND MASTER BASE AND SOCKET CHART

In selecting a tube from the master index list we can find its base pin layout by referring to a letter corresponding to its coded base pin arrangement which is listed following the index number. This layout physically locates all base pins for a selected tube. From the base pin designation letters and their socket connections we can, as noted above, identify the internal tube elements from the diagram.

This index together with the base diagrams covers all receiver and special tubes; transmitter tubes are omitted because of their special nature. It is continually kept up to date by the EIA (formerly RETMA) by whom it is issued.

EXAMPLE 1.

From the index we see that the 1B3 tube has a 3C base pin code. Looking up this code layout we see that the tube has an 8-pin base with an external cap. Only two of the internal elements are used—the filament winding, which requires two terminals (2) and (7), and the external plate at the top of the tube.

EXAMPLE 2

The type 117N7 tube has a base pin code number 8 AV. From basing diagram 8 AV we see it uses an octal base (note the keyway) and is a dual-unit tube consisting of a rectifier diode and a pentode. The rectifier section's cathode is pin (8) and its plate is pin (7). The pentode section has a cathode as pin (6), grid as pin (5), screen as pin (4), plates as pin (3). The filament is across pins (2) and (7), the latter also being connected to the power rectifier cathode. Pin (1) has no connection.

TUBE SOCKETS (Fig. 5-26)

In assembling a chassis, the tube sockets are a technician's first concern because the base pins of each tube must fit the socket he selects, which must in turn be correctly mounted to the chassis along with the other sockets. In a completely engineered chassis assembly he will find that the socket types are specified on the material parts list and that the chassis has been correctly punched and drilled to allow insertion of the sockets and their mounting lugs. Fastening to the frame is either by machine screws and nuts, by self-tapping screws, or by rivets.

With an accompanying wiring diagram the orientation of the socket lugs for convenient wiring and best proximity to associated components has been spelled out; the assembly process merely follows the drafted instructions. (See also Chapter 6.)

If, however, the chassis must be wired from the schematic, the socket style, size, and mounting must be obtained by reference to the tubes being used. Here one must refer to the tube's size and base pin arrangement and must pick a socket to correspond. Figure 5–26 shows the common sockets used in modern chassis assembly. Basically, the socket

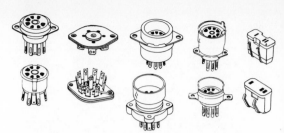

(a) Molded (b) Wafer   (c) Ceramic (d) Shielded (e) Transistor

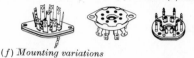

(f) Mounting variations

FIG. 5-26 Common styles of sockets used in modern chassis assembly

type is determined by the number, size, and layout of the pins on its mating tube. The style depends upon the material used, the mounting requirements, and the government specification under which it must operate.

Various socket styles are listed below:

1. Molded, using bakelite, plastic, or phenolic base material to hold the socket pin terminals (Fig. 5–26(a)).

2. Wafer, using laminated fiber or bakelite to hold the terminals (Fig. 5–26(b)).

3. Ceramic, using steatite or other material impervious to moisture and heat. This type lends itself to high-voltage construction (Fig. 5–26(c)).

4. Shielded, base with provision for complete metal enclosure (Fig. 5–26(d)).

5. Transistor sockets (Fig. 5–26(e)) generally use molded construction.

6. Mounting variations (Fig. 5–26(f)):

(a) Saddle mounting—two diametrically located screws.

(b) Ring mounting—using a crimped retainer ring.

(c) Chassis clinch—using specially punched chassis holes.

(d) Full floating—nonmounting type with provision for shielding and bringing out of leads.

TRANSISTORS AND SOCKET PIN LAYOUT

The transistor is a semiconductor device, electrically similar to two junction rectifiers assembled back to back, whose electrical characteristics approximate those of a vacuum tube. Transistors can be made to amplify, oscillate, rectify, or act as an electronic switch. See Chapter 15.

Physically speaking, most switching and low-power amplifier types are minute, beadlike assemblies of small bits of fused semiconductor material mounted within small thimble-shaped plastic or metal cases comparable to the end of a pencil. Fine, stiff wire connector leads extend from the bottom of the case and are suitable for direct soldering to other circuit elements, or for insertion in special sockets. (See Fig. 5–26(e) and Appendix B-4.)

Power transistors are larger, disc-like assemblies, an inch or two in diameter and up to an inch in height, and with a metal cover. The cover contains the unit and attaches to a heat-radiating base. (See Fig. 5–27.) External connections are through stiff terminal wires coming through the insulated base.

The two basic transistor circuit symbols, PNP and NPN, are given in Table 5–1; their designation letter(s) is "Q." Thus we have Q-221, Q-19A, etc. Attempts have been made to standardize base connections and case sizes. The Joint Electronic Device Engineering Council (JEDEC) has assigned basing arrangements and case outline dimensions, which appear in Appendix B-4. However, many manufacturers have not yet been able to conform to JEDEC specifications.

Transistors are electrically made in two basic types, PNP and NPN, depending upon

FIG. 5-27 Power transistors

the arrangement of the different electrode materials from which they are made. Letters denoting the three internal electrodes—the emitter (E) and base (B) and the collector (C)—are stamped opposite the respective connecting leads or are indicated on the JEDEC outline.

Functionally, transistors are categorized into AF, RF, computer switching, and power switching groups. Subcategories in these groups are as follows (they are further broken down into specific types in Chapter 14 on transistor testing):

AF	RF	Computer switching	Power switching
Small signal	VHF amplifier	Delay (μ sec)	Dissipation:
Driver	HF amplifier	300	Up to 5 W
Large signal	IF amplifier	100–300	5 to 50 W
Power amplifier	Mixer	30–100	Over 50 W
0–5 W	Oscillator		
5–50 W	Converter	10–30	
Over 50 W		5–10	

The wiring and assembly of transistors follow the same procedures used for vacuum tubes. The type selected refers, on the master index (Appendixes B-3 and B-4), to the basing diagram from which physical mounting and wiring data can be used.

DIODES AND SEMICONDUCTOR RECTIFIERS

These components are individual or stacked arrays of single-junction diodes developing rectifier action by electron and other atomic reactions between molecular structures at the junction of the two dissimilar metals being used. In simple terms this means that diodes pass current in only one direction across a semiconductor junction. In general, they may be classified as either power or nonpower units. Older power rectifier units use aluminum, copper oxide, or selenium alloys, while modern designs are confined mostly to junctions of silicon and germanium. Diode symbols appear in Fig. 5–28; their designation letter is CR.

Figure 5–29(a) shows a variety of low-signal

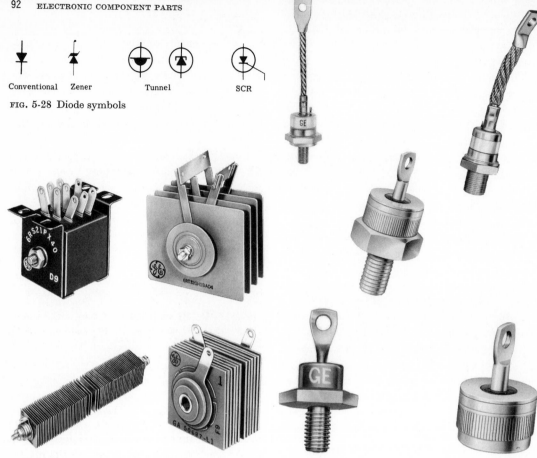

Conventional   Zener   Tunnel   SCR

FIG. 5-28 Diode symbols

(a) *Low-signal and stacked-disc power diodes*   (b) *Power-type silicon rectifier diodes*

FIG. 5-29 Low-signal diodes

diodes plus a number of the older-style copper oxide and selenium power rectifier units using stacked series of disc assemblies, arranged so that a number of junctions is held together and mounted by simple studs and brackets. The protruding fins between the stacked disc junctions provide heat conduction to outer surfaces where air cooling takes place. Modern silicon rectifiers of equally high power are much smaller, since most use single junctions and operate quite successfully at high temperatures without cooling fins. (See Fig. 5–29(b).) One type uses a third electrode to control the rectification process.

Low-power junction diodes used in signal or other electronic circuitry comprise the majority of units used in modern equipment. Typical varieties are pictured in Fig. 5–29(a). Their size, in general, permits soldering and

mounting techniques like those used with small resistors and capacitors. Their varieties and styles warrant the following discussion.

FUNCTIONAL CATEGORIES

Small-signal, low-power diodes may be categorized functionally as (1) detector diodes, (2) zener diodes, (3) tunnel diodes, (4) special diodes. Physically, any of these types may be provided in single- or double-ended sealed glass, plastic, or ceramic packages. (See Fig. 5–29(a)). They are in general mounted like capacitors or resistors of equal size and shape. Schematically, they must be wired in the correct polarity as stamped on the cathode terminal. Symbols and designations are shown in Fig. 5–28. Polarities, physical sizes, operating characteristics, and other complete technical information in all categories and sub-categories is given in Appendix B-5, which is reviewed in Chapter 15 along with transistor testing and measurement.

For further clarification, each of the above basic functional categories has the following subdivisions.

DETECTOR AND LOW-POWER DIODES may, in addition to normal usage, be classified under microwave diodes or switching diodes with electrical characteristics to correspond.

ZENER DIODES are essentially variable forward-impendance rectifiers used in voltage-regulator circuits, where they may run to ratings as high as 50 watts. Low-power zener diodes with special construction and circuitry are also used as precision reference-voltage sources.

TUNNEL DIODES are single PN-junction rectifiers possessing a negative resistance when correctly forward-biased. Characteristics, testing methods, and other details of their application in working circuitry appear in Chapter 15.

SPECIAL RECTIFIERS are manufactured to perform many functions. The following have appeared commercially:

1. Silicon-controlled rectifier (SCR). This NPNP negative-resistance device operates as a highly efficient d-c switch. (Also called a thyrode.)

2. High-voltage silicon rectifier stacks. These have markedly improved characteristics over old-style selenium units.

3. Voltage-variable capacitor diodes or var-actors. These have many applications in devices where tuning control must be remote, non-magnetic, or nonmechanical.

4. Photo diodes.

HYBRID COMPONENTS

Components serving some function other than a purely electronic one, whether it be mechanical, optical, chemical, magnetic, or otherwise, will, for convenience, be called hybrid components; they are summarized in

Table 5–12. Electrical symbols and the designation letters for hybrid components are listed in Appendix A-1.

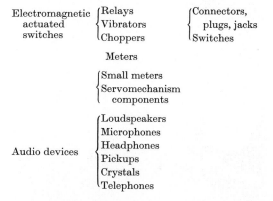

Table 5–12   Summary of hybrid components

Electromagnetic actuated switches	Relays Vibrators Choppers	Connectors, plugs, jacks Switches
	Meters	
	Small meters Servomechanism components	
Audio devices	Loudspeakers Microphones Headphones Pickups Crystals Telephones	

Among the great variety of hybrid components, the following types are used almost as frequently as basic electronic components. The discussion includes purely mechanical items such as switches, plugs, meters, servos, audio devices, etc., since they, too, appear as symbols and are an important part of any wiring operation.

RELAYS, VIBRATORS, AND CHOPPERS

Relays function fundamentally as switches and in their many forms are widely employed in electronic circuitry; vibrators are used mainly in battery-driven power supplies, and choppers are precision vibrators used to convert d-c signals to a-c. Table 5-13 summarizes relay types; several are also illustrated

Table 5–13   Relay classifications (a-c or d-c)

Size	Power transfer Sensitive Miniature Midget	Style	Telephone Rotary Latching Stopping Balanced armature
Function	Coaxial Time delay (a) Thermal (b) Synchronous	Service	General purpose Sealed Multipole High-shock High-voltage High-current

FIG. 5-30 Types of relays

in Figure 5–30. Except in the case of thermal relays, they are remote solenoid-controlled switches with a magnetically actuated movable armature controlled by the passage of current through the solenoid coil. Their description and their ratings cover first the power and sensitivities of their solenoid actuating mechanism in watts and, second, the current and voltage capabilities of their contacts. Relays may also be categorized according to the type of their magnetic action, thermal action, mechanical movement, or multiplicity of contacts. Details of relay operation, the common parts, and the language of operation and design appear in Appendix B-9.

CHOPPERS

These devices, as the name implies, convert, for amplification purposes, d-c or small analog voltages into square waves by alternately switching them rapidly on or off or alternately above or below a center voltage reference level. The various types are: (1) mechanical choppers, which are merely vibrators, similar to those used in mobile power

supplies; (2) solid-state or transistor circuit choppers, which accomplish the analog voltage switching in self-oscillating switcher circuits; (3) magnetic modulator choppers, which use self-saturating inductive elements for the switching; (4) photo-conducting-cell choppers, which perform by using the periodic illumination of photo resistors or photo transistors. Choppers are also called contact modulators, interrupters, or synchronous modulators. Mechanical models usually consist of a contact-carrying ferrous reed positioned between fixed contacts and actuated by an alternating-current-carrying coil. This type takes the physical form of a plug-in cylindrical unit similar to a mobile vibrator.

THERMAL RELAYS

Many special relays are used in electronic equipment, and some are too detailed in construction and operation for description here. These may include sealed relays, high-voltage types, coaxial line switching relays, and miniature types—all of which are actuated electromagnetically by an energizing current.

A different approach to relay design appears in the special type known as the thermal relay. In it the load contacts open or close in response to the heating effect of the energizing current, as distinguished from the electromagnetic effect. The thermal relay finds its chief use as a time-delay device, utilizing the time interval between the start of energizing current flow and the instant that load contacts touch each other, owing to the heating effect on the expanding element which actuated them. This delay is adjustable and serves many purposes in situations where certain circuits must be turned on sometime after power application to the main supply.

Figure 5–31 shows a typical unit with details of the differential expanding thermal element and the load contacts.

METERS

Common meter symbols cover a number of variations which are described in Appendix

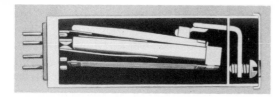

FIG. 5-31 Typical thermal relay unit

A-1. Many types of meters used in the laboratory find no place in operating equipment, where panel-mounted types are more commonly used. Meter mountings are usually through flanges in the instrument panel; connections are usually to terminals provided on the back of the meter. Figure 10–11 is a photograph of commonly used meters of various sizes used in military portable and rack-mounted equipment.

MOTORS, GENERATORS, AND DYNAMOTORS

A selected number of symbols appear in the section of Appendix A-1 covering direct-current machines. They are usually designated as shunt or series machines with separately, self-, or compositely excited field systems. A-c induction, squirrel-cage, and synchronous motors and generators appear in the same section.

They are most commonly used in laboratory apparatus as blowers for ventilating fans, as drive motors for multicontact switches, and as dynamotors for plate-voltage supplies in aircraft transmitters and receivers. Figure 5-32 shows two small-to-medium blower types.

FIG. 5-32 Two small-to-medium blower types

SERVO DEVICES—SYNCHROS

Servomotors, generators, and control transformers (occasionally including fixed synchro capacitors) are rotating inductances used chiefly for accurately controlling the rotational movement in electronic gear. They are the electromechanical components making up the heart of industrial and military servomechanisms. Physically, they are small power devices having windings, fields, shafts, etc., and may be accompanied in overall equipment by electronic amplifiers and extensive mechanical adjuncts in order to deliver angular positioning, or to rotate certain devices, such as radar dishes or gun turrets. They are many times called synchros and have been classified as magnesyns, telegrons, autosyns, or selsyns. A detailed discussion concerning their use, testing, and measurement appears in Chapter 20.

FIG. 5-33 Typical servo devices of various sizes

The different servo devices are physically very much alike. The basic types, accompanied by their respective electronic symbol designattions, are: the regular motor, M; the regular generator, G; the differential motor, DM; the differential generator, DG; the control transformer, CT. Figure 5–33 shows a collection of typical servo devices of various sizes.

AUDIO DEVICES

Audio devices, including loudspeakers, earphones, microphones, pickups, and cartridges,

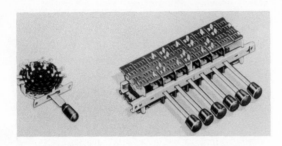

FIG. 5-34 Major varieties of switches

may be classed as *electro-acoustical accessories*, and are most often associated with commercial sound equipment. In this area they are usually called accessories and may or may not be strictly classified as components depending upon the type of equipment with which they are associated. Mountings, connections, speaker enclosures, turntables, and so on, are covered more specifically in another phase of electronic construction and do not apply importantly to military equipment.

MECHANICAL WIRING ACCESSORIES

SWITCHES. The simple switch symbols appearing on the master symbol chart, Appendix A-1, apply to a multitude of designs. Major varieties have been pictured in Fig. 5–34.

We see that, physically, switch sizes are governed by the voltage they will withstand and the current they will carry, and in signal-carrying circuits sometimes by the inherent built-in inductance and capacitance. In primary battery or transformer circuits large contact areas are necessary, and in secondary high-voltage units the contacts must be separated far enough before switching to prevent leakage or voltage breakdown. Low-capacity, low-contact-resistance switches are used in multiple switching of complicated high-frequency circuits such as those in the tuner circuits of some television receivers.

With respect to their control shafts or linkage, switches may be of many types: knife-blade, toggle, rotary wiping, sensitive or snap-action, vacuum, mercury, and several other kinds.

Terminals on switches are usually accessible for wiring or for testing; mountings are made to fit their particular application.

CONNECTORS, PLUGS, AND JACKS. Almost as many types of connectors are commonly used as there are types and sizes of wire (see Fig. 5–35), since the current flowing through either

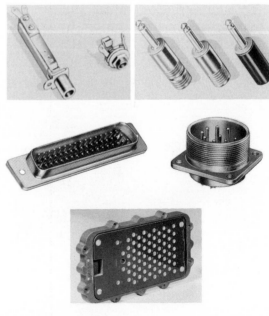

FIG. 5-35 Connectors

a wire or in its associated connector is common to both. Voltage must also be considered, specifically in terms of the separation required between contacts on a plug in order to eliminate voltage brakdown.

MISCELLANEOUS ACCESSORIES

FUSES

A fuse is a special, easily melted conductor mounted or contained in some replaceable holder. It serves as a protective device in circuits that must be instantly relieved of overload current. The entire assembly is usually called a fuse holder and consists of the mounting lugs, holders, and the other accessories in addition to the meltable link. The accessories make possible easily insertion or replacement in the circuit. Figure 5–36 shows a number of sizes and types of fuses used in electronic equipment, together with their accompanying fuse holders.

COLOR CODING OF FUSES. In the common types of push-in or screw-in panel fuses it is customary to indicate the amperage by inserting colored washers between the mounting collar and the front panel. The coding indicates amperage as follows:

FIG. 5-36 Typical fuses and holders

FIG. 5-37 Smaller types of circuit breakers

Amps	Color	Amps	Color
1/16	Yellow	2	Buff
1/4	Lavender	3	Orange
1/2	Blue	5	Brown
3/4	White	10	Grey
1	Red	15	Green

Fuse action in opening a supply circuit depends upon the fuse link's melting point and is determined by the current passed through it. Other factors enter the design of a fuse, such as whether it is of the "slow-blow" variety, whether it is replaceable from the front or rear panel, whether it is in a low- or a high-current circuit, etc.

In high-current circuits a circuit breaker is sometimes used instead of a fuse.

CIRCUIT BREAKERS

A circuit breaker is an electromechanical device that breaks a circuit under overload current conditions. It differs from a fuse in that it does not destroy itself but merely needs resetting after being tripped as overloaded. Figure 5–37 shows a number of smaller types; the size and weight of circuit breakers preclude their use in most electronic equipment except possibly in moderate- to high-power transmitters where size and weight are no handicap and where quick and repeated replacement may be necessary.

LAMPS

Pilot-light or indicator-light assemblies and their associated bezels are selected for visibility, serviceability, and size. The usual design includes a bracket, socket, and bezel of the selected color plus its particular lamp. Special models include miniature push-button-contained lamps, neon bulbs which take a minimum of power, alarm bulbs which light when trouble occurs, flashing lamps which periodically illuminate at designated times, and many others. (See Appendix B-8).

Bulbs for indicator lights, or for illuminating panels in general, are supplied in four sizes and with seven variations of screw or bayonet type bases. They are made also in various filament voltages. Appendix B-12 illustrates the more common types, tabulated according to their respective filament voltages and the identifying color beads supporting the filament.

MICROWAVE COMPONENTS

Although the symbols for microwave components appear on master symbol charts, details of their physical characteristics are not given in this chapter. Chapter 18 will tabulate and describe common microwave components and discuss their physical and electrical manipulation.

Chassis Assembly and Wiring 6

Assembly and wiring are the two main processes required to complete the construction of an electronic chassis after the chassis base has been built. The chassis assembly process includes collecting the necessary electronic and mechanical parts, arranging them in their designated locations, and fastening them to the chassis base or frame. The wiring process consists of electrically interconnecting the component parts so that the equipment functions properly.

These operations are performed according to information given in a set of key drawings. In addition to acquiring detailed knowledge about component parts (see Chapter 5) and familiarity with chassis base construction (see Chapter 4), the technician must know how to read and interpret the information included in this set of key drawings.

The eight kinds of drawings or lists which serve as guides to chassis assembly and wiring are the: (1) chassis assembly drawing, (2) mechanical or material parts list, (3) chassis wiring diagram, (4) schematic wiring diagram, (5) electrical parts list, (6) wiring data and cutting list, (7) wiring harness drawing, and (8) wiring hardware list. The first five of these are shown and described in Chapter 1. The following summary of the function of each of these drawings outlines their applications to the wiring process.

THE CHASSIS ASSEMBLY DRAWING (see Fig. 1–2) shows the proper location, or layout, for mounting the component parts in relation to each other in the chassis base. The main chassis base drawing is included.

A MATERIAL OR MECHANICAL PARTS LIST (see Fig. 1–3) gives a physical description in tabular form of the electrical components and of the mechanical parts to be mounted on the chassis. This parts list, as explained in Chapter 1, is sometimes printed directly on the chassis assembly drawing (see Fig. 1–2) and is intended to be chiefly mechanical in nature since the electrical characteristics and the symbolic description of the components are given in electrical parts lists.

A CHASSIS WIRING DIAGRAM (see Fig. 1–1) shows the arrangement of components with particular emphasis on interconnecting wires. Figure 6–5 shows similar interconnections on a printed circuit board.

THE SCHEMATIC WIRING DIAGRAM (see Fig. 1–5) shows the electrical circuitry of the apparatus and fills in gaps in the wiring diagram, which can not show every interconnection between all components.

AN ELECTRICAL PARTS LIST (see Fig. 1–5) lists labels, and describes in words and, as far as practicable, gives the characteristics of all the electrical components called for on the schematic. (This list is described in Chapter 1.) It sometimes overlaps or is combined with the chassis assembly list of mechanical parts, because some components are both electrical and mechanical.

THE WIRING DATA AND CUTTING LIST (see Fig. 6–1) enumerates and describes all the wires shown geographically in the wiring diagram. It lists the size, color coding, and length of each piece and at the same time keys each item into the wiring diagram.

A WIRING HARNESS (see Fig. 6–2) results when the main wires are combined by being laced or bound together. This device is used as a time-saver when a number of common wires travel parallel routes throughout the chassis. Although all wires in a complete apparatus are not included in the wiring harness, the grouping of common wires makes possible their prefabrication outside

of the chassis. In making a harness the conductors are cut, laid out, and bent to shape around pins driven in a wooden board. They are then laced together with string and placed back in the chassis among the components which they interconnect.

THE WIRING HARDWARE LIST describes the wiring accessories used in running, cabling, tying, or clamping the wires. (These accessory parts will be discussed later on.) Many manufacturers do not supply this list, leaving the actual requisitioning of the parts to the discretion of the technician-wireman.

ASSEMBLY PROCEDURE

Assembly, the final step in mechanical construction, starts with: (1) *Collecting* the components and mechanical items according to the material parts list. (2) *Locating* them in their correct position on the chassis frame,

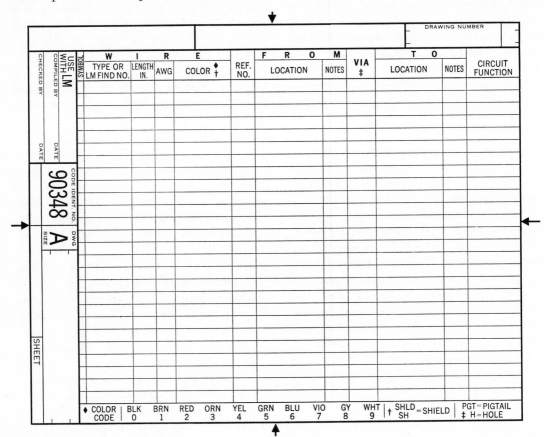

FIG. 6-1 Wiring data and cutting lists

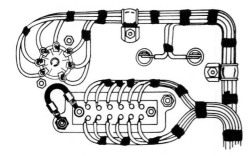

FIG. 6-2 Wiring harness

as shown on the assembly drawing. (3) *Fastening* the parts upon the frame.

Physical location is more or less defined and described by the reference "balloons" on the assembly drawing which give the location of the components and mechanical accessories and key them to the parts list. Expanded and auxiliary views make their physical positions clearer and show some details of mounting. Note that the assembly drawing labels each component with its electrical designation letter and number, relating it to the symbols on the schematic, on the wiring diagram, and on the electrical parts list.

Mounting of the components requires *fastening* by means of screws, nuts, washers, brackets, rivets, or whatever may be indicated on the assembly drawing. Most of these mechanical devices and methods are described on the assembly drawing (and have been described in Chapter 3) or become obvious when holes, lips, or brackets on the individual components are inspected with regard to their positioning as shown by the assembly drawing. Figure 6–3 illustrates a number of tongue, snap, and clinch fastening methods, as differentiated from methods involving screws, nuts, and washers.

The exact mechanical technique of the assembly is acquired only through experience since many unforeseen conditions arise. There

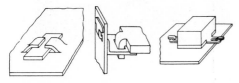

FIG. 6-3 Fastening methods

will, for instance, be misfits where redrilling, filing, or reaming must be done on the mounting base; there will be mistakes in the drawings which must be corrected; and the technician will employ certain obvious short cuts or improvements on individual chassis as he sees fit. Above all, the job must be done neatly and securely, with no damage to parts or chassis and with as close adherence as possible to the specified assembly drawing.

ASSEMBLY PROCEDURE PRECAUTIONS

A number of the more important assembly details and precautions will aid the technician:

1. Assemble the more inaccessible components first; overlapping and easily wired components should be mounted last.

2. Assemble and mount the smaller components next (and wire some of them if possible), the larger components later. This saves handling.

3. Orient all terminals in the best possible position insofar as predictable from an electrical and physical standpoint in order to make the shortest, most direct arrangement of leads.

4. Protect all components having finished cases or holders by covering them with paper tape and keeping in place any protective covers or lids through which dirt might fall.

In general, chassis assembly layouts either physically follow the path of the signal in a circuit or are arranged in a definite operational sequence which electronically follows the basic electrical schematic. In an amplifier, for instance, the output tube is placed near the output terminals and next to the amplifier tube electrically preceding it, which in turn follows the tube from which it receives input. This is particularly true for electrical reasons in high-frequency amplifiers where the length of leads between an amplifier plate and the grid of the next tube must be as short as possible and where output-signal wires must be as far as possible from input-signal component parts. A typical example of this layout exists in a chain of radar IF amplifier tubes. (See Chapter 18.) Other considerations such as weight, strength, size, and fit also influence chassis layout.

Serviceability and ease of testing and manufacture many times dictate the scheme of a chassis assembly. For instance, tube socket prongs should not be covered or obstructed by other components or mechanical pieces. Also, tubes and transistors should be easily removable and all other components should be accessible for testing and for replacement. Terminal and resistor-capacitor board assemblies should be accessible for test and repair.

Heating of the parts by their own internal power dissipation or by proximity to adjacent parts often dictates positioning of certain tubes and components to allow efficient radiation, conduction, or convection of the heat away from the critical item. This is particularly important in most government equipment which must be subjected before acceptance to extremes of temperature, humidity, and vibration.

Equipment designed to withstand extreme vibration or shock tests has layout requirements which may or may not be immediately obvious or in accord with some of the other requirements; such layouts are usually the result of considerable design experience. When extreme vibration is encountered, as in airborne or missile equipment, we must seriously consider the weight of a chassis and its components plus weight distribution among the components. Clamps, braces, ribs, or other strengthening and holding pieces are an important part of good mechanical design and assembly. Likewise, the total weight of an assembly as well as location of its center of gravity must be carefully proportioned.

COMPONENT PART BOARD ASSEMBLIES

These are miniature chassis (of either bakelite or ceramic) upon which are wired a number of similar and related components making up a portion of the main circuit (see Fig. 5(a)-(d)). These are often called subchassis, and they must of course have terminals or means to interconnect them to the remainder of the equipment.

Component boards are used in more permanent, higher-quality construction. In equipment wired to government specifications they are strictly part of the wiring layout because much of the circuit wiring is done on the board itself. Their construction and location are aimed at simplification of wiring, of assembly, and of test procedures, and

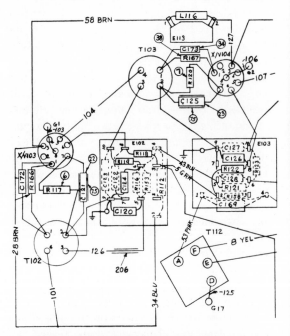

(a) *Wiring of typical board*

(b) *Wiring of removable board*

FIG. 6-4 Details and interboard wiring of two typical component boards

the physical considerations listed in chassis assembly also apply to these boards. Figure 6–4 shows the details and interboard wiring of a typical component board. Layout, wiring, and assembly follow the methods used on a main metal-base chassis.

There are many shapes and sizes of component boards which may be fitted into almost any free space where wiring simplification results. Many times such small boards are positioned on brackets to be perpendicular to the plane at the chassis and thus save space. They are sometimes mounted on chassis side walls on flanges and may even be hinged so that they may be swung aside for access to other parts. Modern hardware uses many built-in varieties—particularly of boards easily removable by plug-in jack-and-socket arrangements. (See Fig. 6–4(b).)

PRINTED CIRCUIT BOARDS

Printed circuit boards may be divided into two categories: (1) those which use "printed on" or "etched on" metal films in place of wires for connections between various circuit elements, and (2) those which *include* etched or printed components along with the printed metallic interconnections.

The techniques of printing conductors on an insulating board is really an etching process. It is accomplished first by silk-screening, or photographically depositing a film of acid-resistant material over the thin layer of copper which has been bonded to the main insulating board and then dipping the board into an acid bath. The unprotected copper is etched away, leaving the pattern of conductors bonded to the insulating plate.

Standard circuit components, subminiature tubes, transistors, and other circuit accessories are then soldered to appropriate terminals (even including tube sockets) which have also been etched onto the board.

The assembly and fabrication of printed boards requires special techniques of wiring and handling, determined by the type of board being used. In most cases the soldering must be very carefully done to avoid destroying the thin copper conductor film or burning the insulating board; as a consequence of such damage the copper coating may become detached and shake loose from the board under vibration. Heat sinks, protective clamps, special solders and fluxes, and very fine-pointed soldering irons are among the necessary precautions.

Figure 6–5(a)-(c) illustrates by diagram and photographs a number of printed boards in which some of the precautions that must be observed are self-evident. It should be noted that in many cases conductor failure or replacement of components can result in destruction of the entire board. In some cases printed boards and their associated piece parts are totally embedded or encapsulated in plastic or resin, so that failure of a piece part means the entire unit must be discarded.

With further refinement it is possible by various lithographic processes to print entire circuits, including resistors, coils, and capacitors, upon printed circuit boards together with their interconnecting conductors. This type of construction, of course, eliminates assembly and wiring and in most cases even precludes part replacement. It is, moreover, the forerunner of microelectronic assembly where both passive and active components are chemically and electronically constructed, in microscopic dimensions, upon silicon blocks (substrates).

WIRING DEVICES AND ACCESSORIES

Under this heading are devices that facilitate any of the processes of assembly and wiring; they may be partly mechanical or partly electrical as the following descriptions indicate. These accessories are included in complete wire lists and are indicated on wiring diagrams. They must be provided for at the wiring technician's discretion when he is wiring directly from the schematic.

STANDOFF AND MOLDED TERMINALS, AND TERMINAL LUGS AND BOARDS, consist of multi-unit terminals attached to or inserted

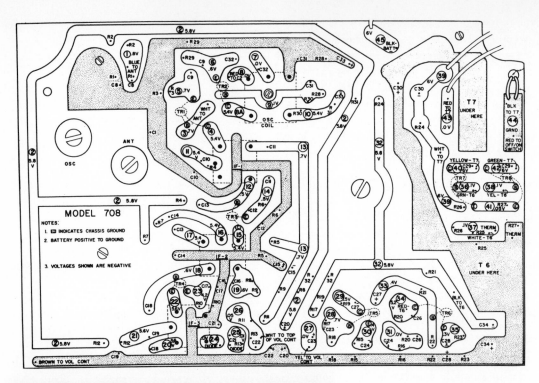

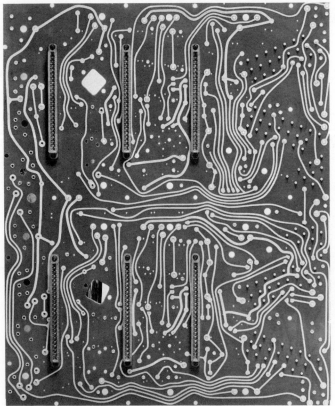

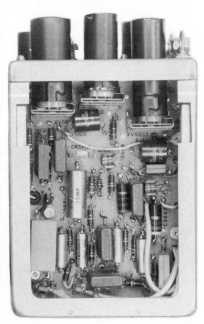

FIG. 6-5 Diagrammatic and photographic examples of printed-circuit boards

in some insulator which in turn may be mounted so that components or component leads may be soldered or attached to it. Single or stand-off terminals are riveted or screwed directly to a chassis base. Multi-unit terminals are fastened to the chassis base by mounting brackets; besides providing a junction with interconnecting points, they may be used as miniature component boards to hold a resistor or capacitor. Figure 6–6 (a) and (b) shows a four-position and ten-position flat ceramic type, Fig. 6–6(c) shows a barrier type assembly, and Fig. 6–6(d), stand-off terminal lugs.

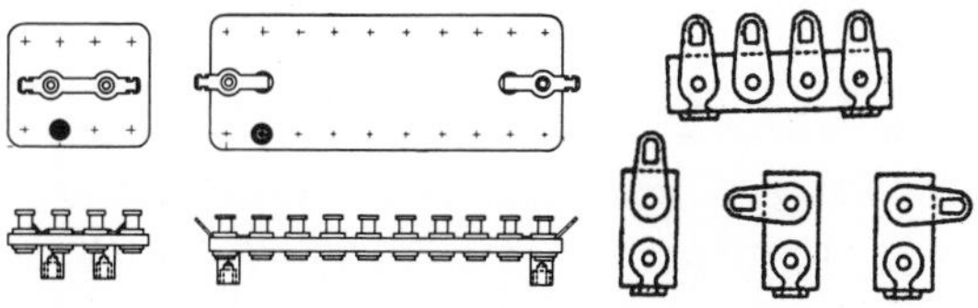

(*a*) *Four-position* (*b*) *Ten-position* (*c*) *Stand-off lugs*

(*d*) *Typical barrier-type assembly*

FIG. 6-6 Standoff and molded terminals, terminal lugs, and boards

FIG. 6-7 Grounding, soldering, terminal lugs, and clips

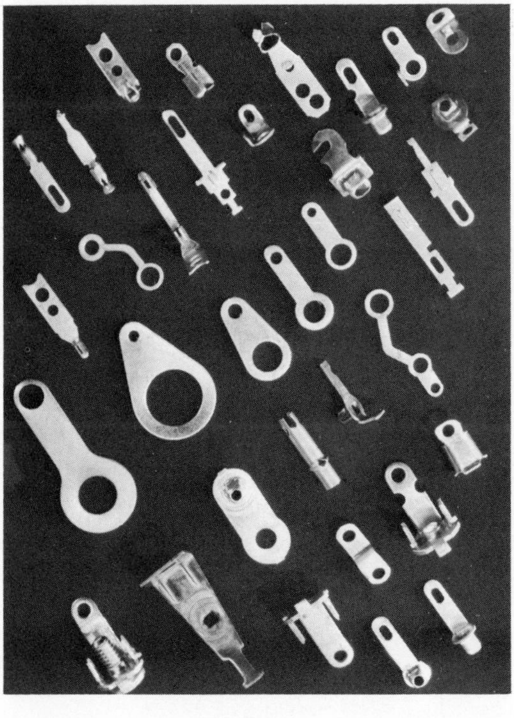

GROUNDING, SOLDERING, TERMINAL LUGS, AND CLIPS, (Fig. 6–7) are used to connect circuit wires directly to chassis-base or other terminals, or to provide a metallic ground to or between the outer shielding of a cable. Grounding lugs afford protective short circuits against any potentials developed in cable shielding by lighting discharge or by power-current return paths. Some types may accommodate several wires at once and rely on fastening between nuts and washers on mounting studs or screws.

CABLE CLAMPS may be made of metal or plastic as defined on the wiring diagram. Figure 6–8 shows the many varieties which hold a range of items from single wires to multiconductor cables.

MISCELLANEOUS HARDWARE—mounting nuts and washers, plug buttons, angle brackets, etc. These provide special support for some components, isolation for others, and serve other special functions as indicated in the wiring directions. (See Fig. 6–8.) Angle brackets provide mounting variations or extensions for awkwardly placed components and may be useful for many other improvisations in wiring.

INSULATING TUBING (sometimes called spaghetti) serves to place a protective cover over exposed wires, shielding or sometimes even

FIG. 6-8 Miscellaneous hardware

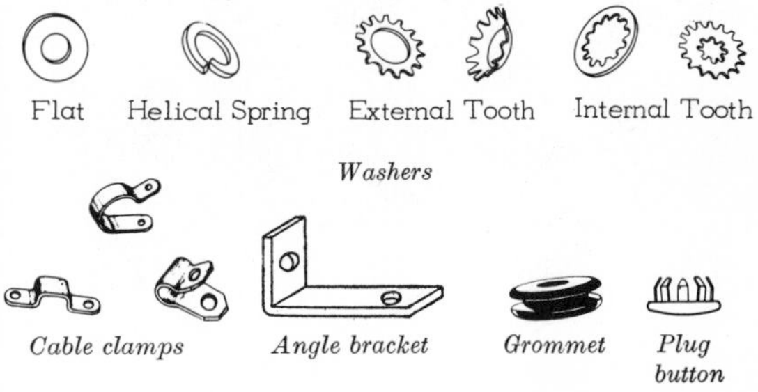

covering small components. It is available in a wide variety of diameters and colors.

TAPE. Insulating tape is used to mechanically protect or to bind wires or exposed shielding or as a substitute when tubing cannot be used. It should never be used for insulation of the body of the wire itself since it may not have the necessary adhering or insulating qualities. Pressure-type plastic insulating tape or fiberglass adhesive tape is acceptable in most commercial and military installations.

LACING CORD is commonly used to tie cables in wiring harnesses and for other protective functions as spelled out on the wiring diagram.

GROMMETS (Fig. 6–8) serve to protect from chafing or to insulate a wire passing through a hole in a chassis base. They may be made of rubber or of plastic and generally are held in their mounting hole by force fit.

TUBE SHIELDS are shown in Fig. 6–9 in a wide variety of types which mate with their counterpart tube socket bases shown in Chapter 3 (Fig. 3–2).

FIG. 6-9 Tube shields

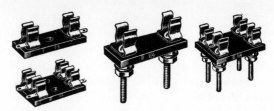

FIG. 6-10 Fuse mountings

FUSE MOUNTINGS. The types shown in Fig. 6–10 are designed to hold the tubular 3AG most conveniently fitted during chassis wiring.

WIRE

In wiring a chassis many types of conductors may be required, each one of which is spelled out on the wire list (Fig. 6–1). This list gives: (1) conductor size and type, (2) type of insulation and voltage rating, (3) the color coding, (4) the length of each piece. Other qualifications (except conductor length), such as shielding, wrapping, and special characteristics, are described in specification drawings or are listed by the wire manufacturer. These are all marked on the spools bearing the wire.

CONDUCTOR TYPE AND SIZE. Interconnecting and hookup wires almost universally use stranded conductors. The conductors are always tinned to facilitate soldering and vary in size according to their current-carrying capacity. Appendix C-3 lists copper wires against gauge numbers, conductor diameters, and a measure of cross-sectional area called the circular mil. Chapter 7 gives examples of use of the circular mil. Briefly, one circular mil is the area of a wire which is 1/1000 inch in diameter. Standard American, British, steel, and metric wire gauges appear in the Appendix.

The most commonly used general wire specification is MIL-W-76A. It is specified for signal and current-carrying conductors (except filament circuits); in electronic equipment it ranges between the #14 and #22 gauges. These wire sizes are equivalent to stranded conductors of 7 strands of #30, 12 strands of #28, 9 strands of #32, etc. Figure 6–11 gives

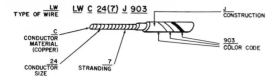

LW   1000 volt plastic insulation (polyvinyl chloride)
C   tinned copper
24   # 24 guage
7   seven strands
J   outer jacketed
9   white insulation
0   black - wide band
3   orange - narrow tracer

FIG. 6-11 Example of color coding for MIL-W-76A

an example of color coding for the above.

Table 6–1 is a summary of applicable military specification of common types of wire.

TRANSMISSION WIRES AND COAXIAL SHIELDED CABLES are special types applicable to micro-wave frequencies. They are listed in Appendix D-3 and utilize specification MIL-17-B. Their use arises in high-frequency electrical circuits where conditions require a shielded single conductor cable in which one path of current flow is along the center conductor and the return path is along the shield. Sizes range from center conductors as small as #28 wire up to heavy power-carrying cables with an inside conductor of #00 wire.

Fine wires of this sort require special connections to the inner conductor and to the external (and usually grounded) shield, and use special connectors. (See connector types in Chapter 5.) Although we cannot list here all the types and sizes of transmission-line fittings and assembly techniques, we have

Table 6–1 Summary of government wire specifications

MIL-W-76A   General specification.

MIL-W-583A   Electrical magnet wire.

MIL-W-3861   Solid, bunch-stranded, concentric-lay-stranded, and rope-lay-stranded round electrical wire.

MIL-W-5086A   600 volt single-conductor insulated copper wire for aircraft electrical use.

MIL-W-5274A   Aircraft wire—600 volts.

MIL-W-6370B   Insulated wire for use in external aircraft antennas.

MIL-W-7072A(ASG)   Aluminum wire, 600-volt, insulated, single-conductor, for aircraft electrical power distribution systems.

MIL-W-7139A   600-volt, single-conductor, insulated, copper wire for 400°F, and to operate for a short time in the event of a fire. For airframe wiring.

MIL-W-8777A(ASG)   Aircraft wire resistant to flame, fuels, abrasions, fungus, and solvents, with an operating temperature range from −55°C to +150°C at 600 volts.

MIL-W-16878C(Navy)   For the internal wiring of meters, panels, and electrical and electronic equipment with minimum size and weight consistent with service requirements. The temperature rating of wire ranges from 80°C to 200°C with potential ratings from 75 to 3,000 volts rms.

MIL-W-19583(Navy)   High-temperature magnet wire, three temperature ranges—130°C, 180°C and 200°C. AWG sizes from 4 to 46.

MIL-C-17B   Flexible shielded cables, employing solid and semisolid dielectrics. For use as radio-frequency transmission lines—covers coaxial, twin conductor, and twin lead.

MIL-C-3432A   Light-, intermediate-, and heavy-duty, flexible and extra-flexible, single-conductor and multiconductor cable, shielded and unshielded, for use in circuits of 300 and 600 volts rms. Also covers heavy-duty, multiconductor, unshielded cable containing ground wires.

MIL-C-3883   Single-wire and multiwire electrical cord, in which wires are all of the same wire size for use in audio-frequency applications. This is a braided armored cable; its applications include shipboard use.

MIL-C-5756B(ASG)   600-volt heavy-duty, single-conductor wire and multiconductor electric cable for severe flexing service.

MIL-C-7078A   This specification covers the application of shields to types listed under MIL-W-5086A.

MIL-C-25038(USAF)   Specification covers high-temperature and fire-resistant electric cable for aircraft. Cable is nickel-clad copper with insulations that will operate in an ambient temperature of 650°F. It is for use in aircraft electrical circuits which may be subject to flames.

NAS-702   Specification by National Aircraft Standards Committee covers wire which operates at 105°C. It is presently finding use as a general-purpose and hookup wire in aircraft for voltages to 2,500 volts.

NAS-703   National Aircraft Standard covers high-temperature insulated, copper hookup wire. Voltage ranges are 600 and 1,000 volts. Temperature range is to 200°C from AWG 32–8.

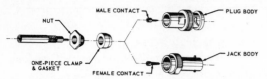

BNC connector assembly

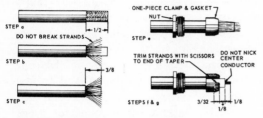

Assembly procedure and soldering detail

FIG. 6-12 Assembly and soldering techniques for the most common BNC type coaxial cable

shown in Fig. 6–12 the assembly and soldering techniques for the most commonly known BNC type. A brief rundown of do's and don'ts for the handling of coaxial cables is given in Fig. 6–13.

SPECIAL WIRES. Many circuits require bare stranded or solid tinned wire (buss wire). A listing of common AWG sizes is given in Table 6–2.

RESISTANCE WIRE—with and without insulation—is sometimes required in special circuits. This wire may be used to wind special resistors or to make heating elements.

Table 6–2   Common AWG special wire sizes

| AWG | Bare Wire Diameter, in. | |
	Solid (buss)	Stranded
2	0.2576	0.346
4	0.2043	0.275
6	0.1620	0.210
8	0.1258	0.167
10	0.1019	0.120
12	0.0808	0.096
14	0.0641	0.077
16	0.0508	0.060
18	0.0403	0.046
20	0.0320	0.038
22	0.0253	0.031
24	0.0201	0.024

CUTTING THE CABLE JACKET: *Do* cut perpendicular to center conductor. *Do not* make jagged incisions.

CUTTING THE DIELECTRIC: *Do* make clear, squarely through the insulation. *Do not* nick center conductor.

FOLDING BACK THE BRAID: *Do* comb out evenly over the clamp. *Do not* bunch any braid wires.

TINNING AND SOLDERING: *Do* apply even heat to well-cleaned conductor. *Do not* overheat, or melt dielectric.

POSITIONING THE CONTACT: *Do* make butt soldered joint with contact flush with dielectric. *Do not* leave space between contact and dielectric; leave solder build-up, extra flux, or foreign matter in contact.

CHECKING FINAL ASSEMBLY: *Do* make dielectric extension beyond the braid conform to instructions. *Do not* leave too little dielectric extending, or allow contact to become eccentric with the connector body.

FIG. 6-13 Do's and don'ts for the handling of coaxial cables

Table 6–3   MIL-STD-122 color code for chassis wiring

Color	Circuits
Black	Grounds, grounded elements, and returns
Brown	Heaters, or filaments, off-ground
Red	Power supply, B+
Orange	Screen grids
Yellow	Cathodes
Blue	Plates
Violet	Power supply, B−
Gray	A-C power lines
White	Miscellaneous, above-ground returns, AVC, etc.

EIA color code for power transformers

Primary leads—Black
   If tapped:
   Common—Black
     Tap—Black and yellow stripe
     Finish—Black and red stripe
High-voltage plate winding—Red
   Center-tap—Red and yellow stripe
Rectifier filament winding—Yellow
   Center-tap—Yellow and blue stripe
Filament winding 1—Green
   Center-tap—Green and yellow stripe
Filament winding 2—Brown
   Center-tap—Brown and yellow stripe
Filament winding 3—Slate
   Center-tap—Slate and yellow stripe

COLOR CODING. The EIA color code for chassis wiring covers all circuits and is in a general way approximated by the government standard MIL-STD-122, which is given in Table 6–3. The braid or insulation over a wire usually carries the identifying color, or the wire may have a white covering with a tracer stripe of the identifying color. Double tracers may be used to further identify leads beyond the single-color coding system. The stripe system applies especially to multiwire cables and follows a schedule whose complexity is beyond the scope of this book.

INSULATION. The insulation for ordinary hookup wire must provide protection of between 300 and 500 volts, a range which covers most circuits on conventional electronic gear. The type of insulation is marked on the spool upon which the wire is supplied and for government work is labeled in the categories listed in Table 6–4. Special wire is usually specified for higher voltages.

Special types of insulation may be necessary for particular operating conditions. For in-

Table 6–4   Specification MIL-W-76A for insulated, stranded, hook-up wire.

MW	C	22	(7)	J	903
Type	Conductor material	AWG	Minimum strands	Outer covering	Color code

Type

Designation	Maximum voltage, rms (80°C)	A.W.G. range	Commonly used primary insulation
LW	300	30–20	Polyvinyl chloride
MW	1,000	24–12	Polyvinyl chloride
HW	2,500	22–16	Polyvinyl chloride
HW	600	14– 6	Polyvinyl chloride
FX	500	30–00	Polyvinyl chloride
HF	1,000	24–16	Polyethylene

Conductor Material

Letter	Description
C	Tinned copper
S	Tinned copper-clad steel

AWG and Minimum strands

AWG nominal	Number of strands (min.)	AWG nominal	Number of strands (min.)
30	3	10	37
28	7	8	127
26	7	7	127
24	7	6	127
22	7	4	127
20	7	2	161
18	16	1	259
16	19	0	259
14	19	00	259
12	19		

Outer Covering

Letter	Description
U	None
J	Jacket
B	Braid
S	Shield
JS	Jacket and shield
BS	Braid and shield
SJ	Shield and jacket
JSJ	Jacket, shield, and outer jacket
BSJ	Braid, shield, and outer jacket

Color Coding

Number	Description
0–9	Solid colored insulation
90–98	One broad colored tracer on white insulation
900–988	One broad colored tracer and one narrow colored tracer on white insulation
9000–9888	One broad colored tracer and two narrow colored tracers on white insulation

0	Black	5	Green
1	Brown	6	Blue
2	Red	7	violet (purple)
3	Orange	8	Gray (slate)
4	Yellow	9	White

First number signifies body color.
Second number is first stripe (larger than second stripe).
Third number is second stripe.
Example: 903—White/Black/Orange.

stance, Teflon insulation may be needed for high-temperature applications. Some wires require tough braided covering for situations where abrasion or rubbing may be encountered; waterproof insulation is necessary for damp places or where the equipment is operating under high humidity; oil-resistive covering may be required for others, and so on.

WIRE LISTS

Using the typical wiring list shown in Figure 6–1, which gives all wire lengths, sizes, colors, etc., the technician-wireman can prepare all of his material in advance in order to concentrate his attention entirely on soldering and wire layout. Note that wiring accessories such as lacing cord, shielding cable clamps, etc., are included in the list. In production wiring where systematically prepared lists are used, each wire may even be machine

stripped and tinned for a short distance back from each end, thus saving the technician further time and labor.

In the absence of a wire list giving sizes, types, insulation rating, etc., the technician must make his own wire selections guided by the general rules given above. To help him, the electrical circuit of such cables is sometimes covered on a schematic which is referenced to the wire list and to the wiring layout. In complicated, interconnected multi-chassis equipment involving a number of complicated cables, an interconnection block diagram is required to show the overall cable relationships and interconnecting plug wiring. (See Fig. 6–14.)

Separate subchassis units containing complete circuits of such complexity that they cannot be wired on terminal boards usually have individual drawings in which each is treated as a complete chassis. If a terminal board is indicated but no drawing provided, the technician must improvise his own completely wired board.

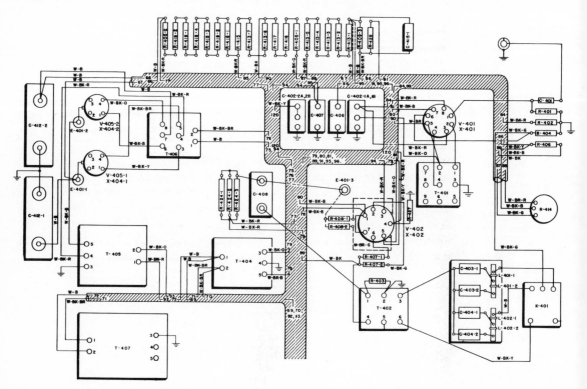

FIG. 6-14 Interconnection block diagram

In wiring a chassis from a wiring diagram and assembly drawing the technician will find the schematic and the electrical parts list (EPL) very useful added information; it should be kept alongside his wiring diagram and working sheets. As we noted earlier, a skilled technician with a good background of shop practices can, if necessary, assemble and wire a chassis from these two drawings alone and in some cases may use only the schematic.

To review the importance of the schematic, we see that this drawing gives the basic electrical relationship between the chassis assembly and the wiring diagram. It does not show physical sizes or relationships between components; it only indicates them functionally. Its chief aim is to serve as a map for signal paths, voltages, and waveform points throughout a complete chassis. In doing this it symbolically represents all components, and it indicates interconnecting wiring by lines which link the parts in order to explain electronic performance. To turn the schematic into physical apparatus the technician must visualize the size of parts called for on the EPL and their relative placement to each other on the chassis base.

Another advantage derived from the schematic is its indication of mechanical motion or interrelated linkages. For instance, the moving arm connection of a variable resistor or potentiometer may be shown with an adjoining arrow pointed so as to indicate the direction of mechanical motion for increasing values. The symbol for a relay shows armature movement by picturing it as a hinged element. The movable feature of an iron slug within a variable inductor is often shown by an arrow drawn slantwise across the symbol of the coil winding. Also, some manufacturers, in endeavoring to place all possible information upon the schematic, show not only the tube prong numbers of a socket but also the physical position of the pins, using a bottom view of the base of the tube. Figure 5–24 shows such detail, which

has the advantage of relating numbering, physical placement, and functional identification all in one package. Although it has some application in quick servicing procedure, is not universal on most manufacturer's schematics, since it may serve to complicate an already complex diagram.

Indirectly, the schematic and EPL give general information about an electronic gear not apparent on the wiring diagram. For instance, we can estimate its total power consumption from the number and types of the various vacuum tubes; from experience with circuit configurations we can estimate electronic performance—say, the gain of the amplifiers; by the number and description of the component piece parts we can estimate a chassis's size, its weight, its cost to manufacture, and the electronic methods employed to attain its particular performance. Many times the EPL gives us the only information we have, upon which to base purchase orders for material and components.

CHASSIS WIRING PROCEDURE

The basic manual operations used in wiring a chassis after it has been mechanically assembled can be listed in a few simple sequences: (1) Cut all connecting wires to desired length. (2) Skin off sufficient end insulation. (3) Position each wire between the indicated component terminals. (4) Attach to terminals by bending or crimping. (5) Solder the attached ends securely to the terminal.

Approach to this operation depends upon whether it is done directly from a schematic or from a wiring diagram. Also, systematic approach depends upon the completeness of the drafted information and upon the type of construction.

In production shops constructing precise military electronic equipment, the directions for selecting each piece of wire and processing it under steps 1 and 2 above exist in the form of drafted information shown on the wire cutting list. (See Fig. 6–1.) In most cases this information is meticulously complete, for the details of the processing call for many sizes, lengths, and colors of wire as well as many specialized techniques in handling it. Included may be: (1) a completely pre-fabricated wiring harness (see Fig. 6–2), (2) specification of size, location, length, and color coding for each individual wire, and (3) terminal and printed circuit board drawings where the majority of all components are mounted and interconnected on separate subchassis.

When the harness is available and when the remaining wires are already cut and collected, and if the component boards have been made in advance, a technician-wireman has a relatively simple task. If, on the other hand, he has only the schematic and the electrical parts list, he must do his own wire handling. This includes requisitioning, cutting, skinning, and tinning plus planning the wire routing. If necessary, he may have to design, plan, and lay out a wiring harness after planning and preparing all wires. He may even be forced to design particular component boards.

POINT-TO-POINT WIRING

A different type of construction is used in commercial radio and TV chassis work and is also used occasionally on government equipment. This method connects wires directly between component terminals or between stand-off terminals located throughout the chassis base and allows for mounting of parts both above and below the base. It usually eliminates the need for a wiring harness while promoting and enlarging the use of individual component boards into small chassis; it really is, in effect, the forerunner of printed circuitry. To demonstrate this evolution, note the similarity between point-to-point wiring in Fig 6–4, and typical component and printed circuit board assemblies in Fig. 6.

In order to transform a collection of components into a working electronic circuit according to its schematic wiring diagram,

a technician must have mastered the techniques of handling, cutting, and soldering wire, must be familiar with wire types and sizes, and must be experienced in wiring accessories and component parts to their terminals.

DETAILED WIRING PROCEDURE

The steps that a technician must follow are:

1. Obtain the key drawings; this includes the wiring diagrams and the wire lists accompanying it, harness drawings and wire lists (if any), and schematic wiring diagrams and the electrical parts list. If component and terminal boards are specified, drawings for these must be obtained.

2. Obtain or requisition the wiring material, the various wires themselves, and the wiring accessories as enumerated below.

3. Set up his tools, jigs, and holders to make parts and wires easily accessible, and pin up or arrange the diagrams for easy reading.

4. Process or build the component boards, special wiring mounts, or other accessories.

5. Place, mount, or attach boards or other accessories, not allied to the final wiring, within or on the chassis.

6. Process or construct the wiring harness if called for.

7. Process the individual wires by laying out, measuring, cutting, skinning, and tinning. In point to point wiring this may be done as each wire is soldered in.

8. Solder and wire in individual wires.

9. Clamp, tie, protect, or insulate any floppy cables or loose wires according to the standards of workmanship prescribed in the technician's particular shop.

10. Finally, before being delivered for inspection, the chassis should be thoroughly shaken in an inverted position to remove loose solder, dust, or other material. Corners and nested wires should then be cleaned with a small stiff brush to dislodge adhering foreign material and the chassis shaken again. It should be blown out with an air stream as a final clean-up.

Wiring a chassis according to the steps enumerated above crystallizes still further into a few basic operations. Simple as these may seem, the following discussion may clarify some of the techniques and tool operations employed.

CUTTING. Hookup wire is easily cut by diagonal hand cutters. The cut should be perpendicular to the axis of the wire and all ends of stranded wire should be of equal length. If heavy wire is deformed by cutting, it should be reformed. Heavy-gauge copper and aluminum wire or cables are best cut by a hack saw.

MARKING. In chassis wiring, marking of individual wires is not necessary because the color coding is sufficient identification.

In aircraft and ship cabling it is necessary to use a wire identification code that is stamped directly on the cables with a hot tool-marking machine, or that which is given by marked lengths of insulating sleeves slipped over the wire at suitable intervals. The identification code, covering radio, radar, and electronic circuits, is spelled out in MIL-W-5088. It uses the following identifications, as exemplified in Fig. 6–15(a): (a) *unit number* prefix to distinguish between identical wires of similar units, (b) *circuit function letter*, such as "A" for amplifier, "M" for modulator, etc., (c) *wire number* to distinguish between wires with in the same circuit and having the same function letter, (d) *wire segment letter* to distinguish between conductor segments in a particular circuit, (e) *wire size number* used to designate AN or AL gauge size of the wire, (f) *ground, phase, or thermocouple wire* used to designate wire to ground, phase, or material of a thermocouple pair and (g) *suffix* indicating construction.

Examples of usage, of sleeve marking on braided cables, of multiconductor identification, and of coaxial cable marking are shown in Fig. 6–15(b)-(e).

STRIPPING. Copper hookup wire may be stripped by a knife, diagonal hand cutters,

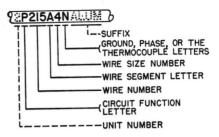

(a) *As applied to all circuit functions except R, S, T, and Y*

(b) *Spacing of identification stamping on wire and cable*

(c) *Location of identification sleeves*

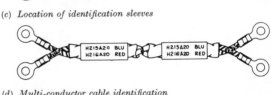

(d) *Multi-conductor cable identification*

(e) *Coaxial cable identification*

FIG. 6-15 Examples of cable marking

or by bench strippers—all processes aiming to pass the cutting edge only *through* the insulation, stopping the blade *at the surface* of the conductor. The basic operation aims at removing insulation from the end of a wire back a suitable length for wrapping or soldering. The operation must not nick or cut any of the strands. Resultant longitudinal scratches are allowed in most work.

Bench strippers of two common types are in use as shown in Fig. 6–16(a). Example of usage is shown in Fig. 6–16(b). These general precautions should be followed: (1) All stripping blades should be sharp, free from nicks, dents, etc. (2) Wire should be held perpendicular to cutting blades. (3) Adjust automatic tools carefully for size of wire according to manufacturers's directions. Make trial cut if possible to establish correct setting. (4) Make sure insulation is clean cut with no

(a) *Two typical types of strippers*

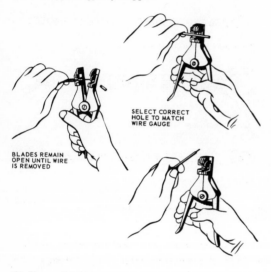

SELECT CORRECT
HOLE TO MATCH
WIRE GAUGE

BLADES REMAIN
OPEN UNTIL WIRE
IS REMOVED

(b) *Usage of strippers*

FIG. 6-16 Bench wire strippers

frayed or ragged edges. Trim with scissors if necessary. (5) Retwist copper strands to restore natural lay and tightness of strands. (6) Check final stripping for complete removal of insulation, since some types have a glassine transparent layer between the conductor and the primary insulation.

TINNING. Bare copper wires may be tinned by dipping in melted solder or by using a conventional soldering iron. Conventional solder for hookup wire is a mixture of 60 percent tin and 40 percent lead and is supplied in reels in the form of tubular wire with a rosin

core. Table 6–5 is a list of the commonly used diameters of this solder. Table 6–6 lists the hardening and softening temperatures plus application of a number of soft-core solders.

With wires smaller than #10, tinning is done by holding a soldering-iron tip and rosin-cored solder together on the wire until solder begins to flow. The tip of the iron should be well cleaned (see Chapter 4) and have enough heat reserve to make the solder melt promptly. Iron sizes for various gauge wires are:

Wire size	Soldering-iron size (watts)
#20–#16	65
#14–#12	100
#10–#8	200

WRAPPING AND CRIMPING. In attaching a wire to a terminal before final soldering, the mechanical joint must be firm, without being

Table 6–5   Standard wire and flux core solders.

% Sn	Wire diam. ±.004	Flux percentage
SN60	.030	1.2—1.6 2.3—2.6 3.3—3.6
	.040	1.2—1.6 2.3—2.6 3.3—3.6
	.062	1.2—1.6 2.3—2.6 3.3—3.6
	.093	1.2—1.6 2.3—2.6 3.3—3.6
SN40	.062	1.2—1.6 2.3—2.6 3.3—3.6
	.093	1.2—1.6 2.3—2.6 3.3—3.6
SN30	.062	1.2—1.6 2.3—2.6 3.3—3.6
	.093	1.2—1.6 2.3—2.6 3.3—3.6

made too bulky by useless and unnecessary wraps. In terminals having a punched hole the wire should be inserted through the terminal material far enough to bend back and make one complete turn around the main wire. Around a stud terminal the joint should be formed by wrapping the wire tightly against it. Excess lead, after wrapping, should not exceed twice the diameter of the wire.

When soldering conductors to terminal posts where wrap-around is necessary, the turns must encircle the post without overlapping each other and must be of adequate diameter to withstand bending. Each wire should have a minimum of 270° wraparound.

SOLDERING TECHNIQUES. In an acceptable soldered connection the contacts must be clean and free of corrosion, oxidation, or foreign matter. The lead wire must be neatly wrapped around its mating lug connector, and only enough solder should be applied to form a thin layer over the wire and terminal, leaving the wire contour visible. The surface of the solder should be bright, smooth, and free of sharp points. Feathering out of the solder to a thin edge is a good indication of proper flowing and wetting action. The joint must be clean and free of excess rosin and of insulation or foreign matter. The wire insulation must not be burned or scorched. Soldering shall be in accordance with specification MIL-S-6872 and shall be performed in such a manner as to insure a positive electrical and strong mechanical connection. See Chapter 3 for details of how to solder properly.

Table 6–6   Properties and uses of soft solders

Composition by wt.			Liquidus temp., °F	Solidus temp., °F	Typical applications
Sn	Pb	Sb			
3	96	..	596	573	Low-grade solder; coating, joining.
15	85	..	553	457	High-temperature uses; filler metal,
20	80	..	533	382	radiators, cans
25	75	..	514	362	
30	70	..	496	362	Wiping solder; coils; radiators, cans
35	65	..	478	362	
40	60	..	460	362	General purpose, sheet metal parts,
45	55	..	440	362	radio and TV, gas meters
50	50	..	418	362	
60	40	..	374	362	Radio, electronics; printed circuits,
62	38	..	362	362	lithographed cans; High-tempera-
95	..	5	467	458	ture uses; Cu joints in refrigerators, coffee percolators
..	95	5	554	486	Body solder; coatings metal
3	92	5	536	462	Cans; coatings
15	84	1	527	428	Radiators
29	70	1	475	366	
38	60	2	442	370	Wiping solder
†	97.5	..	579	579	High-temperature applications; pres-
†	95	..	707	579	sure radiators, percolators
3†	95	..	572	570	
20†	77.25	1.5	503	354	Substitute solders; general purpose
21†	76.5	1.75	503	358	

† Balance silver.

LACING AND TYING. In military equipment, wire groups and bundles are laced or tied with cord to provide ease of installation and guard against loosening under severe vibration. Lacing may be with single or double cords using a starting knot, intermediate half-hitches, and a final knot as shown in Fig. 6–17.

The following general rules are to be followed in lacing:

1. Cables must be laced tightly and the lacing securely fastened at both the start and finish. Twine shall conform to JAN-T-713.

2. The spacing between lacing stitches shall be approximately equal to twice the cable diameter but not less than 1/2 inch with an approved lock stitch being used. Wires should not be intertwined in the cable but should maintain the same relative parallel positions throughout the cable.

3. Cables shall be supported at intervals not exceeding five times the cable diameter or 3 inches, whichever is the greater. Support shall be by means of cable clamps or suitable hold-down devices.

4. Each wire should be broken out of its cable nearest the terminal to which it is to be connected. Lacing stitches shall be uniformly spaced on either side of the breakout and as close to the breakout as possible.

The wiring layouts shown in Fig. 6–18 illustrate a number of typical cabling, lacing, and tying situations.

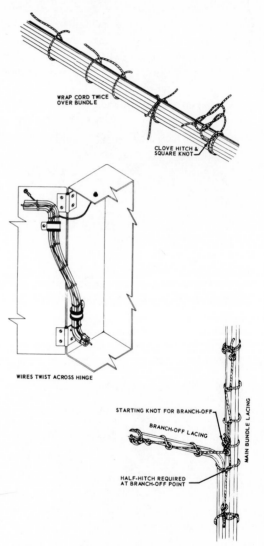

FIG. 6-18 Typical cabling, lacing, and tying situations

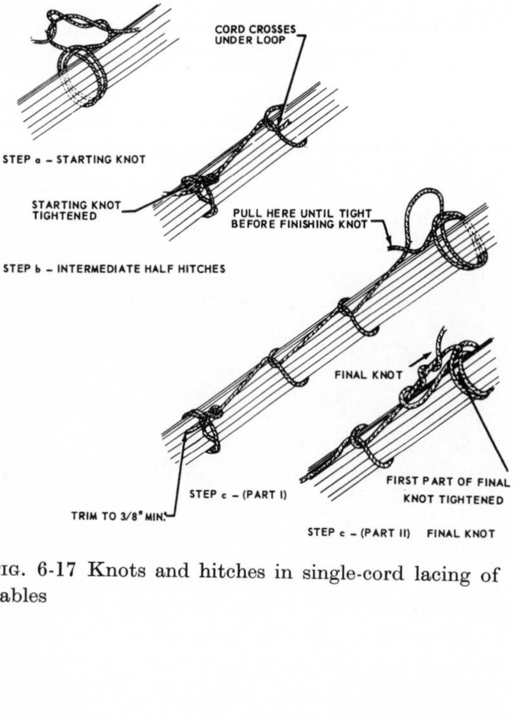

FIG. 6-17 Knots and hitches in single-cord lacing of cables

Mathematics for Electronic Applications 7

INTRODUCTION

The treatment of mathematics in this chapter is kept at a practical minimum and does not include calculus or analytical geometry. It is slanted toward specialized techniques directly useful to the working engineer and technician.

This material assumes that the average technician has a minimum grounding in arithmetic, basic algebra, simple plane geometry, and trigonometry, plus a bare familiarity with logarithms and the slide rule. For the engineer the material may serve as refresher notes.

THE MATHEMATICAL APPROACH

Mathematics is merely a sign language which expresses and predicts electrical quantities or electronic behavior in equipment circuits being studied or measured.

The application of mathematical sign language—numbers, letters and symbols—to the solution of a problem usually resolves itself into three stages: (1) Writing down the physical or electrical conditions in mathematical form using conventional letters, numbers, and symbols. (2) Manipulating the mathematical statements or equations according to prescribed form and processes to obtain a solution. (3) Interpreting, evaluating, or applying the results of the above operations.

SIGNS AND SYMBOLS

Besides numbers and letters, we use, in mathematics, a number of standard symbols which include the Greek alphabet as a supplement to the English alphabet. There are also a number of abbreviations applying specifically to electricity, magnetism, and electronics, plus a number of multiplying factors designated by Greek or Latin prefixes (see Table 7–3); these latter are usually accompanied by their corresponding mathematical factors. Lists of symbols and abbreviations are given in Appendixes F-7 and F-8.

BASIC MATHEMATICAL PROCESSES

For clarity we define basic mathematical processes in the approximate order of their importance as follows:

ARITHMETIC, the science of numbers, is founded on the four basic processes of addition, subtraction, multiplication, and division. Arithmetic also includes the mechanism of dealing with powers and roots by means of what is called the *scientific notation*, which in turn leads to, and includes, the use of logarithms and the slide rule.

ALGEBRA is the process of using letters and symbols instead of numbers to perform the arithmetical operations listed above. Algebraic letters and symbolic expressions which lead to the final solution of a problem are always ultimately converted into numbers; the algebraic manipulations leading to the final expression are merely a convenience or a tool in handling the real figures.

GEOMETRY AND TRIGONOMETRY are concerned with the angular relationship of plane and solid figures when they are resolved into numerical quantities.

EXPONENTS AND POWERS OF TEN

The technique of using powers or exponents of ten can greatly simplify mathematical calculations as shown in the scientific notation method described below.

MULTIPLYING POWERS OF TEN is accomplished by adding or subtracting exponents. Since every exponent has a plus or minus sign, to multiply powers of ten we merely obtain a net sum of the combined *exponents*. For example:

$$x = 10^{+4} \times 10^{-6} \times 10^{-3} \times 10^{+7}$$
$$= 10^{(+4-6-3+7)}$$
$$= 10^{+2} \quad Answer$$

DIVIDING POWERS OF TEN uses algebraic combination of the exponents *but only after first reversing the sign of all exponents or powers in the denominator* and transposing them to the numerator. Thus, if we want to divide

$$10^{+6} \times 10^{+2} \times 10^{-3} \times 10^{-8}$$

by

$$10^{+7} \times 10^{-1} \times 10^{+4}$$

or if

$$X = \frac{10^{+6} \times 10^{+2} \times 10^{-3} \times 10^{-8}}{10^{+7} \times 10^{-1} \times 10^{+4}}$$

then, reversing and transposing,

$$X = (10^{+6} \times 10^{+2} \times 10^{-3} \times 10^{-8})$$
$$\times (10^{-7} \times 10^{+1} \times 10^{-4})$$
$$= (10^{+8} \times 10^{-11}) \times (10^{+1} \times 10^{-11})$$

and, summing the exponents,

$$X = 10^{+9} \times 10^{-22}$$
$$= 10^{-13} \quad Answer$$

Before transposing, the process can be simplified by cancellation of like exponents or equivalent sums of several exponents appearing in both numerator and denominator. For example:

$$X = \frac{10^{+6} \times 10^{-4} \times 10^{-3} \times 10^{+11}}{10^{+6} \times 10^{+3} \times 10^{-3}}$$
$$= \frac{10^{+7}}{10^{+3}}$$
$$= 10^{+4}$$

In actual practice, the plus sign is always omitted in writing a positive exponent.

THE STANDARD SCIENTIFIC NOTATION

The *scientific notation* technique is a form of shorthand which simplifies the multiplication and division of very large and very small numbers. Basically, it substitutes powers or exponents of ten for placement of the decimal point as a means of eliminating the zeros in such numbers. It thus breaks the number into two parts: (1) its combination of digits in decimal form, and (2) a general multiplier or largeness index (determined by powers of ten).

We first write down the digital part in decimal form, or, in other words, as a number between one and ten, with the decimal point following the first digit. For instance, to convert 9,287 we must first move the decimal point three places to the left and jot down the result, 9.287.

We follow this by a multiplication sign ($\times$) accompanied by the appropriate multiplier consisting of 10 to some power or exponent. The "10" multiplier *exponent* tells how many places we moved the decimal point from its original position in order to convert the original number into its standard form. This is then the number's "largeness index," while the specific decimal digits give its size in more detail. The exponential power of 10 is called the *index* of the number. Table 7–1 shows the powers of 10 and their exponents corresponding to a number of large and small numbers.

Table 7–1   Powers of ten

Large numbers	Small numbers
$10^1 = 10$	$10^{-1} = .1$
$10^2 = 100$	$10^{-2} = .01$
$10^3 = 1,000$	$10^{-3} = .001$
$10^4 = 10,000$	$10^{-4} = .0001$
$10^5 = 100,000$	$10^{-5} = .00001$
$10^6 = 1,000,000$	$10^{-6} = .000001$

In converting 9,287, since we have moved the decimal three places to the left, the index number is 3. Three thus becomes the exponent of our 10-power multiplier so that the complete scientific form of the number is

$$9,287 = 9.287 \times 10^{+3}$$

If the number were .0009287 it would be written scientifically as

$$9.287 \times 10^{-4}$$

where we have moved the decimal point four places to the *right* and must consequently use a multiplier with a negative exponent. Thus, a negative 10-power exponent is in effect a divider rather than a multiplier.

The rule for this transposition of the decimal point and the corresponding insertion of the 10-power figures may be summarized in four steps:

1. For very large numbers, move the decimal point to the left and position it just to the right of the first digit. As we have seen, the result is an integral number. Example: 987,623 becomes 9.87623.

2. After the decimal number, place a multiplier consisting of 10 with an exponent equal to the number of places the decimal point has been moved. Example: $9.87623 \times 10^{+5}$— the decimal point has been moved five places.

3. For very small or decimal numbers move the decimal point to the *right* and locate it after the first full digit, again arriving at a decimal between one and ten. Example .00067325 = 6.7325.

4. Following this number place a 10 to the *minus* power corresponding to the number of places the decimal point has been moved. Example:

$$.00067325 = 6.7325 \times 10^{-4}$$

In texts it is often convenient to express

the multipliers in words or by Greek or Roman prefixes as shown in Table 7–2.

Table 7–2   Common multiplier prefixes

mega	= 10^{+6}	= 1 million
kilo	= 10^{+3}	= 1 thousand
centi	= 10^{-2}	= 1 one-hundredth
milli	= 10^{-3}	= 1 one-thousandth
micro	= 10^{-6}	= 1 one-millionth
nano	= 10^{-9}	= 1 thousandth of one millionth
pico	= micromicro	= 10^{-12}
		= 1 millionth of one millionth

EXAMPLES USING THE STANDARD SCIENTIFIC NOTATION

ADDITION AND SUBTRACTION OF NUMBERS IN SCIENTIFIC NOTATION. Numbers expressed in scientific notation can be added or subtracted only if the powers of 10 are the same. For example, 3×10^5 can be added to 2×10^5 to get 5×10^5; however, 3×10^6 can not be added to 2×10^5 because the powers of 10 are not the same. The number 3×10^6 can be changed to 30×10^5, however, and it can then be added to 2×10^5 to obtain 32×10^5.

EXAMPLE 1
Add 450,000 and 763,000.

$$450,000 + 763,000 = 45 \times 10^4 + 76.3 \times 10^4$$
$$= 121.3 \times 10^4$$
$$= 1,213,000$$

EXAMPLE 2
Add .000,068,25 and .000,007,54.

.000,068,25 + .000,007,54
$$= 6,825 \times 10^{-8} + 754 \times 10^{-8}$$
$$= 7,579 \times 10^{-8}$$
$$= .000,075,79$$

EXAMPLE 3
Subtract .000,004,33 from .000,05.

.000,05 − .000,004,33
$$= 5,000 \times 10^{-8} - 433 \times 10^{-8}$$
$$= 4,567 \times 10^{-8}$$
$$= .000,045,67$$

MULTIPLICATION OF NUMBERS IN SCIENTIFIC NOTATION

EXAMPLE 1
Multiply 100,000 by 1,000.

$$100,000 \times 1,000 = 10^5 \times 10^3 = 10^{5+3}$$
$$= 10^8 = 100,000,000$$

EXAMPLE 2
Multiply 25,000 by 5,000.

$$25,000 \times 5,000 = 2.5 \times 10^4 \times 5 \times 10^3$$
$$= 2.5 \times 5 \times 10^{4+3}$$
$$= 12.5 \times 10^7$$
$$= 125,000,000$$

EXAMPLE 3
Multiply 1,800, .000,015, 300, and .0048.

$$1,800 \times .000,015 \times 300 \times .0048$$
$$= 1.8 \times 10^3 \times 1.5 \times 10^{-5} \times 3 \times 10^2 \times 4.8$$
$$\times 10^{-3}$$
$$= 1.8 \times 1.5 \times 3 \times 4.8 \times 10^{3-5+2-3}$$
$$= 38.88 \times 10^{-3}$$
$$= .03888$$

DIVISION OF NUMBERS IN SCIENTIFIC NOTATION

EXAMPLE 1
Divide 75,000 by .0005.

$$\frac{75,000}{.0005} = \frac{75 \times 10^3}{5 \times 10^{-4}} = \frac{75}{5} \times 10^{3+4}$$
$$= 15 \times 10^7 = 150,000,000$$

EXAMPLE 2
Divide 14,400,000 by 1,200,000.

$$\frac{14,400,000}{1,200,000} = \frac{144 \times 10^5}{12 \times 10^5} = \frac{144}{12} = 12$$

EXAMPLE 3
Divide 98,100 by the product of .0025,180, and 1,090,000.

$$\frac{98,100}{.0025 \times 180 \times 1,090,000}$$
$$= \frac{9.81 \times 10^4}{2.5 \times 10^{-3} \times 1.8 \times 10^2 \times 1.09 \times 10^6}$$

$$= \frac{9.81 \times 10^4}{2.5 \times 1.8 \times 1.09 \times 10^{-3+2+6}}$$
$$= \frac{9.81 \times 10^4}{4.905 \times 10^5}$$
$$= 2 \times 10^{-1}$$
$$= .2$$

FINDING THE POWER OR ROOT OF A NUMBER IN SCIENTIFIC NOTATION

EXAMPLE 1
Find the square root of 144,000,000.

$$\sqrt[2]{144,000,000} = \sqrt[2]{144 \times 10^6}$$
$$= 12 \times 10^3$$
$$= 12,000$$

EXAMPLE 2
Find the cube root of .000,008.

$$\sqrt[3]{.000,008} = \sqrt[3]{8 \times 10^{-6}}$$
$$= 2 \times 10^{-2}$$
$$= .02$$

EXAMPLE 3
Square 15,000.

$$(15,000)^2 = (15 \times 10^3)^2$$
$$= 225 \times 10^6$$
$$= 225,000,000$$

EXAMPLE 4
Find the square root of $(160,000)^3$.

$$\sqrt{160,000^3} = (160,000)^{3/2}$$
$$= (16 \times 10^4)^{3/2}$$
$$= 64 \times 10^6$$
$$= 64,000,000$$

EXAMPLE 5
Find the square root of $\frac{86,900}{3,560,000}$.

$$\sqrt{\frac{86,900}{3,560,000}} = \sqrt{\frac{8.69 \times 10^4}{3.56 \times 10^6}}$$
$$= \sqrt{2.44 \times 10^{-2}}$$
$$= 1.56 \times 10^{-1}$$
$$= .156$$

The root of a number is *one* of its two or more equal factors. We can express this as a *power* of the number by using a *fractional* exponent. It is then referred to as having its *root* taken. For example, we say $3 \times 3 = 3^2 = 9$, so that the fractional exponent or root of 9, $9^{1/2} = 3$. Or, writing it in symbolic form:

$$9^{1/2} = \sqrt[2]{9} = \sqrt{9} = 3$$

(When no number appears in the notch of the root sign the root is assumed to be the second or square root.) Now, likewise, if the root is 3, or 6, or 12, we express it as follows:

the cube root of 9 $= \sqrt[3]{9} = 9^{1/3}$

the sixth root of 9 $= \sqrt[6]{9} = 9^{1/6}$

the twelfth root of 9 $= \sqrt[12]{9} = 9^{1/12}$

Now if the root is an improper fraction or if its denominator is more than one, say 3/2, we write the expression in the usual form:

$$\sqrt[3/2]{9}$$

But since the improper fraction denoting the entire expression is an exponent, the part of it in the denominator is a *root* while the part in the denominator is a *power*. It can thus *directly* be placed within the root bracket. The steps in writing this are:

$$\sqrt[3/2]{9} = \sqrt[3 \times (1/2)]{9} = \sqrt[1/2]{9^3}$$
$$= \sqrt{729} = 27, \quad \textit{Answer}$$

For most calculations these figures give a close enough approximation. When higher or lower roots and powers are desired or when fractional roots and powers must be calculated, longhand calculation is not simple, and logarithms are used.

Longhand calculation of square roots is described in many texts; however, it is none too simple. Common practice is to perform extraction using the number function table in Appendix F-2.

LOGARITHMS

Logarithmic calculation is a process of handling numbers whereby they are mani-

pulated in *terms of their own exponents*. Logarithms are used where extreme accuracy is desired or where it is impossible to solve a problem by simple mathematical processes. The case of obtaining fractional roots, for instance, is one where logarithms are almost an absolute necessity.

Every number can be expressed exponentially in logarithmic form. As a logarithm it has two parts representing the power *to which another number* (called the base) must be raised to equal the original number.

A typical logarithm is 3.3010. Here, the figure 3 to the left of the decimal point is called the *index* or *characteristic*, while the figure .3010 to the right of the decimal point is called the mantissa.

The *index* of a logarithm greater than unity is the *number of digits* the decimal point must be moved to the left in the original number in order to convert it to a standard scientific number. In this sense it is an exponential 10 multiplier; in the case above, it is 10^{-3} or 1,000. Other examples:

Original	Standard notation	Index
97,640.	$9.764 \times 10^{+4}$	$+4$
9,764.	$9.764 \times 10^{+3}$	$+3$

If the original number is less than unity the same rule holds and the index is negative.

.9764	9.764×10^{-1}	-1
.00976	9.764×10^{-3}	-3

The *mantissa* of a number's logarithm is found in the body of a log table—that is, in the area to the right and under the heavy lines framing the tabulated values. Mantissa values are picked off in a particular row to the *right* of the left-hand column (where the first two digits of the original number are selected). The particular final value in this row is the one coming directly under a top-row digit corresponding to the *last* figure of the *original number*. For instance, to find

$$\log_{10} 97,640$$

the index is

$$+4$$

the mantiissa is

$$.9894 + .0002 = .9896$$

thus, $\log_{10} 97,640 = 4.9896$. Similarly,

$$\log_{10} .9764 = \bar{1}.9896.$$

(Note that we place a *bar* over *negative* mantissas.)

ANTILOGARITHMS

When a logarithm is given, to obtain the original number (or antilog) antilog tables may be used. More commonly, we use log tables in reverse.

For example, let us find the number whose logarithm is 2.5712. The mantissa is .5712, and the nearest lower logarithm on the table is 5705, the difference being 7 (in the fourth figure). The number whose log = 5705 is 3720, and to this must be added the figure 6, which corresponds to the difference of 7 in the fourth column; the number is therefore 3720 + 6 = 3726. The decimal must be fixed three places to the right, giving 372.6, as determined by the original index. Table 7–3 lists a

Table 7–3A   Complete logarithms

log 1200	= 3.0793	log .067	= $\bar{2}$.8261
log .230	= $\bar{1}$.3617	log 78.	= 1.8921
log 360.	= 2.5563	log .000089	= $\bar{5}$.9494
log .00045	= $\bar{4}$.6532	log 9.5000	= 4.9777
log 56,000	= 4.7482		

Table 7–3B   Example of interpolation

log 1 = .000	
	log 1.23 = .0899
log 2 = .3010	
	log 2.34 = .3692
log 3 = .4771	
	log 3.65 = .5623
log 4 = .6021	
	log 4.56 = .6590
log 5 = .6960	
	log 5.67 = .7536
log 6 = .7782	
	log 6.79 = .8312
log 7 = .8451	
	log 7.89 = .8971
log 8 = .9631	
	log 8.91 = .9499
log 9 = .9542	
	log 9.52 = .9786

number of complete numbers and their logarithms plus examples of interpolation.

To multiply numbers logarithmically, as in multiplying the powers of ten, we merely add their logarithms (both indexes and mantissas) and find the number corresponding to the sum (the antilog), which gives simultaneously a complete figure of another index and another mantissa.

To divide numbers logarithmically we subtract their logarithms and find the antilog of the result. To find the powers or roots of numbers we multiply the logarithm by the power or root number and find the corresponding antilog.

EXAMPLE 1

To multiply 371.6×58.24 we convert them to logs from our table.

log 371.6	= 2.5701
log 58.24	= 1.7652
log of product	= 4.3353

Next, referring to the log table, we look up the number (the antilog) corresponding to the mantissa 3353. This yields 2.164. We now move the decimal point *four* places to the right as directed by the index giving a final product of

$$371.6 \times 58.25 = 21,640$$

When multiplying numbers whose indexes are negative (denoted by the overbar) we add indices algebraically as follows.

Suppose we are to multiply .785 by .0039.

log. .785	= $\bar{1}$.8949
log .0039	= $+\bar{3}$.5911
log product	= $\bar{3}$.4860
its antilog	= .003062

Note that in adding the mantissas, a +1 is carried over into the index column. This +1 is combined with the two negative indexes:

$$(+1 - 1 - 3) = \bar{3}$$

EXAMPLE 2

Division of these two numbers follows a

similar procedure except that we subtract the log of the denominator from that of the numerator.

$$\frac{371.6}{58.24} = \frac{\log 371.7}{\log 58.24} = \frac{2.5701}{1.7652}$$

$$\text{log of quotient} = .8049$$

Looking up the antilog of .8049, we find it to be 6.37. Since there is no index the quotient remains 6.37.

When dividing numbers (by subtracting logs) whose indexes are negative we algebraically summate all index quantities as in the example of multiplication.

Divide .01193 by 2.3.

$$\log .01193 = \overline{2}.0766$$

$$\log 2.3 = 0.3617$$

$$\text{log quotient} = \overline{3}.7149$$

$$\text{its antilog} = .005187$$

Note in the last digital operation that in subtracting the lower mantissa we must *borrow* or subtract a $+1$ from the top *index*. This changes $\overline{2}$ to $\overline{3}$, from which the lower index (0) is subtracted, leaving a final index of $\overline{3}$.

Taking the cube (or any power) of a number involves multiplying its logarithm by the degree of the power, as shown in the next example.

EXAMPLE 3

$$(3.762)^3 = 3 \times \log (3.762)$$
$$= 3 \times .5754$$
$$= 1.7262$$

So, looking up the antilog of 1.7262, we find

$$(3.762)^3 = 53.23$$

HOW TO USE LOGARITHMS—DETAILS

The brief examples given above are intended to be purely introductory. For details and simplified methods of handling all operations over wide ranges of numbers and with particular attention to interpolation and negative mantissas standard texts should be used.

THE SLIDE RULE

To further simplify the standard notation and to eliminate the use of log tables, the technician may use a slide rule, a mechanical method of applying the principles of logarithmic manipulation just covered. Although the technician need not understand logarithms to use the slide rule, he can operate it more efficiently if he does; conversely, a knowledge of the mechanism of the slide rule will improve his understanding of logarithms. The standard-notation method will help him fix the decimal point in solutions involving complicated operations with very large and very small numbers, since the *slide rule deals only with mantissa quantities.*

BASIC OPERATION OF THE SLIDE RULE

The slide rule is a mechanical means of adding or subtracting the logarithms of numbers by combining logarithmically proportionate measurements scribed in its body and associated slide. Thus, we can perform multiplication and division directly by measurement without tedious calculations and without even looking up logarithmic mantissas in printed tables.

CONSTRUCTION The slide rule is constructed of three parts: (1) the body, which has a main grooved and recessed portion; (2) the slide, which moves within the groove in the body; and (3) the runner, which is a movable piece of glass or celluloid marked with a vertical hairline so that it may be positioned perpendicularly at any point across both the slider and the body of the rule. (See Fig. 7–1(a).)

The slider has three sets of logarithmic gradations: (1) the B scale along its top edge, (2) the C scale along its bottom edge, and (3) the C-1 scale inscribed along its center line. It will be seen that C-1 is merely a horizontal inversion of the C scale—that is, its gradations are marked left to right in the same way that C is marked right to left.

The body of the rule has two scales marked

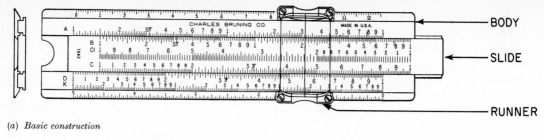

(a) *Basic construction*

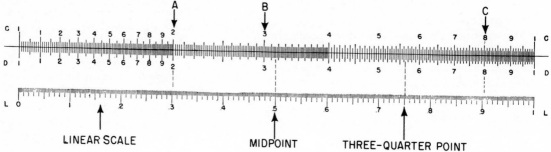

(b) *Operation*

FIG. 7-1 The slide rule

so that all lines terminate at the edges of its center groove. This enables each individual scale line to adjoin and be aligned with its counterpart or with any other lines of the slider B and C markings. These scales are: (1) the A scale at the top which adjoins the B scale and is identical to the B scale in the slider, and (2) the D scale which is along the bottom edge of its groove adjoining the slider C scale and is likewise identical to it. When aligned in the center position the markings of the A and B scales, as well as of the C and "D" scales, abut one another so that all markings coincide.

Slide rules are made in many styles, some of which are very complicated. Some have extra scales on the front and back of both the slider and the body. Rotating slide-rule mechanisms have been devised, using the basic principles but condensing the scales to reduce the overall dimensions of the mechanism. Our explanation will confine itself to basic operation of the "C" and "D" scales.

OPERATION. The operation of the slide rule involves mechanically adding or subtracting the distances engraved on its scales by sliding one scale alongside another and adding the combined distances by help of the runner. Since these distances are *scaled*

to be *proportional* to *their logarithms* but are *marked according to their antilog*, the combining of distances therefore results in the final logarithm distance but delivers, in marking, the antilog solution which is read directly.

For instance, on the identical C and D scales all numbers and parts of numbers from one to ten have assigned to them a certain *logarithmically proportionate* length of the whole scale. (See Fig. 7–1(b).) In position B, the number 3 has a length proportionate to .4771; in position C, 8 is proportional to .9031, and so on. All numbers and their lengths are proportional to the *marked* number's logarithm. Decimal and fractional parts of a number can be just as easily located on the logarithmic scale; the number 3.162, for instance, is at the halfway point of the whole scale (antilog 5.0 = 3.162), and the number 5.624 is at the three-quarters point (log 5.624 = 7.5).

To illustrate the basic operation, say, in multiplying 2 by 3, we merely superimpose these corresponding distances by setting the end, or 1, of scale C over the 2 of scale D and then adjusting the runner to the right until it is over 3 of scale C. Directly under the slider hairline we find the product 6 on scale D, which represents the sum of the log-proportionate distances of the numbers 2 and 3. (See Fig. 7–2(a).)

Now, taking an example such as 6 × 3, we find that the product runs off the scale on the right-hand end. In this case we invert our procedure (see Fig. 7–2(b).) by placing the 1 (or 10) of the right-hand end of scale C on 6 of scale D and running the slider down to the left and placing it over 3 (of scale C). The answer under the hairline on scale D is 18.

Division by slide rule is performed in reverse fashion to multiplication. To divide, say, 8 by 2, we start with 8 on scale D and place 2 of scale C directly above it. Running the slider to 1 on C we find our quotient of 4 directly below on scale D. (See Fig. 7–2(c).)

The decimal point in slide-rule operation is fixed by methods outlined under scientific notation. The slide-rule operation itself uses only the actual sequence of digits. After the

operation has been performed, the movement of the decimal point from the standard-notation position is determined by the sum of the indicated powers of ten resulting from its original translation to the standard-number form.

Powers and roots of numbers are obtained through use of scales A and D (or, if desired, scales B and C). Every number on scale A is the square of its corresponding number on scale D—that is, 4 is directly on the hairline above 2, 9 above 3, 16 above 4, etc. See Fig. 7–2(d), for an example showing the square of 12.5 (156). Note here that if we assume that scale A runs from 1 to 100, D runs from 1 to 10 then, so that the engraved numeral 1 of midscale

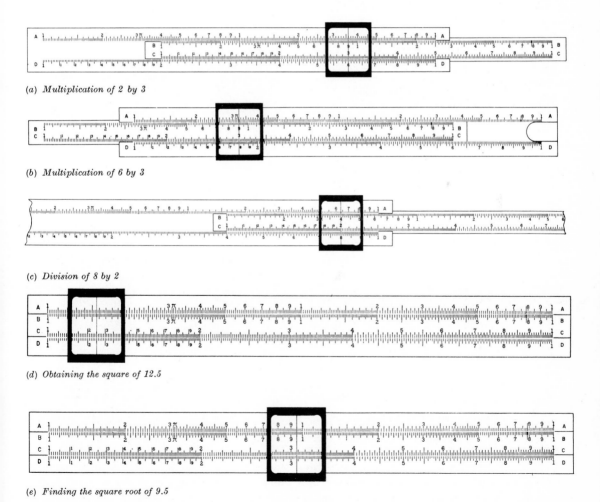

(a) *Multiplication of 2 by 3*

(b) *Multiplication of 6 by 3*

(c) *Division of 8 by 2*

(d) *Obtaining the square of 12.5*

(e) *Finding the square root of 9.5*

FIG. 7-2 Use of the slide rule

on A stands for 10, while the right-hand end 1 stands for 100. Decimal points on square or root operations should be established by the previously described standard-notation method. Figure 7–2(e) demonstrates how to find the square root of 9.5.

ALGEBRA

Algebra is a convenient way of handling arithmetical expressions by using letters and symbols instead of numbers. The symbols selected are usually as brief as possible and their meaning must be agreed upon by those who use them. In electronics we make symbolic use of descriptive letters, such as the first letter of a word, using R for resistance, C for capacitance, V for voltage, and so on. Other symbols generally indicate numbers: x, y, z or a, b, c, for instance, often stand for constant quantities.

The following phrases and expressions are commonly used in algebra:

AN ALGEBRAIC EXPRESSION consists of combinations of numbers, symbols, or letters used for numbers, linked together by the signs of arithmetical operation but written and arranged according to the rules of algebra. $(6a + 3c)$ is an expression which calls for the product of 6 times a to be added to the product of 3 times c.

ALGEBRAIC TERMS are the building blocks of algebraic expressions. They are composed of combinations of letters, numbers, and symbols. $11d$, $24y$, and $\dfrac{16dt}{4}$ are all terms. *Similar terms* are those with the same letter or letters. $6x$, $20x$, $\dfrac{4x}{5}$ are *similar*, as are $24ab$, $98ab$, $\dfrac{6ab}{5}$.

THE FACTORS OF A TERM PRODUCT are the separate numbers and letters which exist among the terms of an expression resulting from an indicated multiplication. In algebraic terms the multiplication sign is implied as existing between the numbers and symbols written adjacent to each other. xyz, for example, is a term made up of the factors x times y times z.

THE NUMERICAL COEFFICIENT is the *number factor* in a term. It is the 10 in the term $10x$ or the 42 in the term $42abc$. Similar terms may be combined in an expression by adding the numerical coefficients, remembering that subtraction results in an additive process when a particular term has had its sign reversed.

ALGEBRAIC RULES

1. In the addition process, although terms may be written down in any order, it is usually conventional to group similar terms together within a parenthesis. For instance,

$$84l + 22m + 6l - 18a + 24l$$

may be grouped:

$$(84 + 6 + 24)l + 22m - 18a$$
$$= 114l + 22m - 18a$$

2. Multiplication and division may be carried out only with similar terms. For instance,

$$6n(2a + 3b) = 12an + 18bn$$

$\dfrac{24x}{4y}$ can not be simplified beyond $\dfrac{6x}{y}$, while $\dfrac{24x}{4x}$ can be simplified to the simple number 6, since the x's are similar and can be cancelled.

3. The rule of signs. In multiplying or dividing terms of *like* signs the result is *positive* (having a plus sign). Multiplying or dividing terms with unlike signs yield *negative* results (minus sign).

$$+x \times +y = +xy, \qquad \frac{+x}{+y} = +\frac{x}{y}$$

$$-x \times -y = +xy, \qquad \frac{-x}{-y} = +\frac{x}{y}$$

$$-x \times +y = -xy, \qquad \frac{-x}{+y} = -\frac{x}{y}$$

$$+x \times -y = -xy, \qquad \frac{+x}{-y} = -\frac{x}{y}$$

4. Removal of parenthesis. When a parenthesis preceded by a + sign is removed, the terms within remain unchanged, maintaining their original signs. When a parenthesis preceded by a minus sign is removed, the

signs of all terms within are reversed. This follows logically from the rule of signs for multiplication of a number of associated terms, since the coefficient preceding a bracket or parenthesis is multiplied by each of the inner terms when the parenthesis is removed. Table 7–4 is a list of typical bracket- and parenthesis-removal procedures such as may be encountered in typical algebraic manipulations.

Table 7–4   Typical bracket and parenthesis removal procedures.

$$a(a + b) = a \times a + a \times b = a^2 + ab$$
$$x(a + b - c) = xa + xb - xc$$
$$-x(a + b) = -xa - xb$$
$$-x(a - b) = -xa + xb = x(b - a)$$
$$-[(a - b) - (c + d)] = -(a - b) + (c + d)$$
$$= -a + b + c + d$$
$$= (b + c + d) - a$$
$$\frac{ax + bx}{cx + dx} = \frac{(a + b)x}{(c + d)x} = \frac{a + b}{c + d} \times \frac{x}{x} = \frac{a + b}{c + d}$$
$$(a + b)^2 = (a + b)(a + b) = a(a + b) + b(a + b)$$
$$= a^2 + 2ab + b^2$$
$$(a - b)^2 = (a - b)(a - b) = a(a - b) - b(a - b)$$
$$= a^2 - 2ab + b^2$$
$$(a + b)(a - b) = a(a - b) + b(a - b) = a^2 - b^2$$
$$(a + b)(x + y) = ax + ay + bx + by$$
$$(a + b + c)^2 = a^2 + b^2 + c^2 + 2ab + 2bc + 2ca$$
$$\frac{a}{-b} = -\frac{a}{b}; \quad \frac{-12ac}{4a} = -3c; \quad \frac{a^5}{a^2} = a^3$$
$$+\frac{a}{b} = \frac{-a}{-b} = -\frac{-a}{b} = -\frac{a}{-b}$$

5. Factoring. When expressions or parts of expressions have common symbols or numbers we may remove or factor out the common term and place it before a parenthesis containing the factorial results. Thus, in the expression

$$6a^4 - 18a^3 - 12a^2$$

we can factor out $6a^2$, leaving the expression

$$6a^2(a^2 - 3a + 2)$$

As another example,

$$6xy + 3xz = 3x(2y + z)$$

Again, in the expression

$$a^2 + ab + ac + bc$$

we can take a out of the first two terms and c out of the last two:

$$a(a + b) + c(a + b)$$

and if, in turn, we take $(a + b)$ out of this last

expression we have

$$(a + b) \times (a + c)$$

Using the same approach,

$$6x^2 + 4xy - 6zx - 4zy$$
$$= 2x(3x + 2y) - 2z(3x + 2y)$$
$$= (3x + 2y) \times 2(x - z)$$

Sometimes it is necessary to use trial-and-error methods—for example,

$$2a^2 + 7ab + 3b^2$$

equals by trial

$$(2a + b) \times (a + 3b)$$

Squared expressions are quite often obvious if one looks for square roots of the first and last terms. Thus

$$9x^2 - 12xy + 4y^2$$

is the square of $(3x - 2y)$, so the original expression may be written

$$(3x - 2y)^2$$

ALGEBRAIC EQUATIONS

Equations express equality between two expressions containing one or more symbols representing unknown quantities. Thus,

$$a + c = b + c \quad \text{and} \quad a - c = b - c$$

are both equations resolving to the solution $a = b$. Other examples are

$$y = x + w + z \quad \text{and} \quad x = y - 3ab$$

The process of determining values of the unknowns that will satisfy the equation is called *solving* the *equation*. Several types of equations may be identified by the nature of their terms, function, or means of solution:

A LINEAR EQUATION (or first-order equation) is one which in its final simplified form (after clearing of fractions) has only one independent variable. For example,

$$y = 14x + 10.$$

(x is the first-order linear term).

A QUADRATIC EQUATION is one in which the variable is of the second order, consisting of squared terms. Example:

$$y = 6x^2 + 3x + 5$$

A CUBIC EQUATION is one in which the variable is of the third order, consisting of cubed terms. Example:

$$y = 4a^3 + 2a^2 + 3a + 2$$

SIMULTANEOUS EQUATIONS with two unknowns must have two sets of conditions from which to solve the unknowns.

$$an + by = 6, \qquad dx + cy = 17$$

SOLVING EQUATIONS

Several methods and approaches may be used in solving equations. Only by experience will one become expert in the techniques, although a few simple rules may be followed:

1. In any manipulation both sides of an equation must be operated upon equally. Multiplication or division of, and addition to or subtraction from, any equation must be alike for both sides.

EXAMPLE 3. $x + 6 = 9$.

$x + 6 - 6 = 9 - 6$ so that $x = 3$

EXAMPLE 2. $x - 3 = y + 6$.

We may solve this equation by dividing both sides by 3. Thus,

$$\frac{x - 3}{3} = \frac{x + 6}{3}$$

so that

$$\frac{x}{3} - 1 = \frac{y}{3} + 2$$

Then

$$\frac{x}{3} = \frac{y}{3} + 3$$

and multiplying both sides by 3

$$x = y + 9 \quad \textit{Answer}$$

2. A term can be moved from one side to another provided that its sign is changed:

$$x - y = 3,$$
$$x - y - 3 = 0$$

3. All signs in an equation may be changed together.

$$a + b - c = x + y - z$$
$$c - a - b = z - x - y$$

4. The reciprocal of one side equals the reciprocal of the other. Examples:

$$a + n = b \mp m, \qquad \frac{1}{a + n} = \frac{1}{b + m}$$

$$x = yz, \qquad \frac{1}{x} = \frac{1}{yz}$$

5. Terms can be replaced by other equal terms. Example:

$$a + c = b + z$$

Now, if $a = x$, $z = 2c$, replacement gives

$$x + c = b + 2c$$
$$x = b + c$$

6. Both sides of an equation can be raised to the same power or can have the same root extracted. Examples:

(a)
$$y = b$$
$$y^2 = b^2$$

(b)
$$(a + 2x) = 3n + 1$$
$$(a + 2x)^2 = (3n \mp 1)^2$$

(c)
$$x = 24$$
$$x^2 = (24)^2 = 576$$

TRIGONOMETRY

Trigonometry is a branch of mathematics dealing with the properties of triangles. It is both algebraic and geometric in nature and applies only to three-sided, plane surfaces bounded by straight lines as compared to poly-sided figures of straight, curved, or irregularly shaped boundaries.

The basic trigonometric figure is the *right triangle*, because it forms a component part of all other triangular shapes. Since one of its angles is 90°, the sum of its remaining two angles must be 90°, a fact upon which we base the fundamental trigonometric definitions.

If we picture the basic right triangle in Fig. 7–3 as having angles A, B, and C, with corresponding opposite sides a, b, c, we arrive at the *basic trigonometric definitions* and angular relationships. These definitions hold for

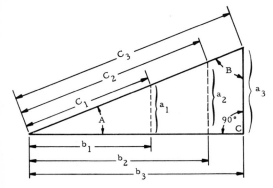

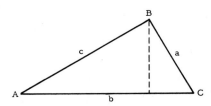

(a) *Typical right triangle with sides of unequal length*

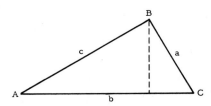

(b) *Typical oblique triangle composed of two right triangles*

FIG. 7-3 The basic right triangle

all right triangles, no matter what their size, because all right triangles having one common angle are similar. Figure 7–3(a) pictures a typical triangle with three sides of different lengths in order to show that the ratios of the sides of the three different-sized triangles are all equal. In other words, the following ratios hold:

$$\frac{b_1 : c_1}{a_1 : c_1} = \frac{b_2 : c_2}{a_2 : c_2} = \frac{b_3 : c_3}{a_3 : c_3}$$

For any other acute angle or other right triangles the same ratios hold so that our trigonometric relationships apply to all acute angles from 0 to 90°. Figure 7–3(b) shows a typical oblique triangle made up of two right triangles formed by dropping a perpendicular line from B to side b.

BASIC TRIGONOMETRIC EXPRESSIONS

Since A and B are acute angles in any right triangle, we may define the basic trigonometric ratios as follows:

$$\text{sine of } A = \frac{\text{length of side opposite } A}{\text{length of hypotenuse}}$$

$$= \sin A = \frac{a}{c}$$

$$\text{cosine of } A = \frac{\text{length of side adjacent } A}{\text{length of hypotenuse}}$$

$$= \cos A = \frac{b}{c}$$

$$\text{tangent of } A = \frac{\text{length of side opposite } A}{\text{length of side adjacent } A}$$

$$= \tan A = \frac{a}{b}$$

Likewise for angle B

$$\sin B = \frac{b}{c}, \quad \cos B = \frac{a}{c}, \quad \tan B = \frac{b}{a}$$

Also,

$$\sin A = \cos B, \quad \cos A = \sin B$$

since $A + B = 90°$. Then

$$\sin A = \cos (90° - A),$$
$$\cos A = \sin (90° - A)$$

Now, if we use the inverse ratios of the sides of our basic triangle we define them as follows:

$$\text{cosecant of } A = \frac{\text{length of side opposite } C}{\text{length of side opposite } A}$$

$$= \cos A = \frac{c}{a}$$

$$\text{secant of } A = \frac{\text{length of side opposite } C}{\text{length of side opposite } B}$$

$$= \sec A = \frac{c}{b}$$

$$\text{cotangent of } A = \frac{\text{length of side opposite } B}{\text{length of side opposite } A}$$

$$= \cot A = \frac{b}{a}$$

Likewise, as in the case of sines and cosines:

$$\tan A = \cot B,$$
$$\sec A = \csc B$$

$$\cot A = \tan B,$$
$$\csc A = \sec B$$

$$\tan A = \cot (90° - A),$$
$$\sec A = \csc (90° - A)$$

$$\cot A = \tan (90° - A),$$
$$\csc A = \sec (90° - A)$$

Table 7-5-(a) is a summary of the more obvious trigonometric solutions using simple functions.

Table 7-5(b) lists formulas for a number of the more complicated relationships used in calculating trigonometric quantities. Table 7-5(c) lists all possible solutions for elements of an oblique triangle.

Table 7-5A

$$\sin (A \pm B) = \sin A \cos B \pm \cos A \sin A$$
$$\cos (A \pm B) = \cos A \cos B \pm \sin A \sin A$$
$$\sin A + \sin B = 2 \sin \tfrac{1}{2} (A + B) \cos \tfrac{1}{2} (A - B)$$
$$\cos A + \cos B = 2 \cos \tfrac{1}{2} (A + B) \cos \tfrac{1}{2} (A - B)$$
$$\sin A \sin B = \tfrac{1}{2} [\cos (A - B) - \cos (A + B)]$$
$$\cos A \cos B = \tfrac{1}{2} [\cos (A + B) + \cos (A - B)]$$
$$\sin A \cos B = \tfrac{1}{2} [\sin (A + B) + \sin (A - B)]$$
$$\sin^2 A + \cos^2 A = 1$$
$$\sin^2 A = \tfrac{1}{2} (1 - \cos 2A)$$
$$\cos^2 A = \tfrac{1}{2} (1 + \cos 2A)$$
$$\sin 2A = 2 \sin A \cos A$$
$$\cos 2A = \cos^2 A - \sin^2 A$$

TRIGONOMETRIC TABLES

If all physical angles from 0 to 90° are evaluated, we may compile a table of trigonometric functions as given in Appendix F-3.

Since the inverse functions are easily derived from the equations above, only sines, cosines, and tangents are given in tabular form.

Examples:
$$\sin 26° = \cos 64° = \tan 23.5°$$
$$\sin 87° = \cos \ 3° = \tan 15°$$

It is sometimes convenient to memorize a few of the more common angular relationships centering around 0°, 30°, 45°, 60°, and 90°. They are listed in the following table.

Function	Angle				
	0°	30°	45°	60°	90°
Sine	0	.5	.707	.866	1
Cosine	1	.866	.707	.5	0
Tangent	0	.5774	1	1.732	Infinity

The graphic solution of trionometric problems involving oblique triangles is usually done by dropping perpendicular lines from proper vertexes so as to break the unknown surface down into right triangles. With one angle and one side of a right triangle known, it is a simple process to solve trigonometrically for the other side. In oblique triangles, any combination of three items among the three sides and angles can yield complete solution

Table 7-5B   Solution of right-angle triangles

Given	Sought	Formulas		
a, c	A, B, b	$\sin A = \dfrac{a}{c}$	$\cos B = \dfrac{a}{c}$	$b = \sqrt{c^2 - a^2}$
	area	$\text{area} = \dfrac{a}{2} \sqrt{c^2 - a^2}$		
a, b	A, B, c	$\tan A = \dfrac{a}{b}$	$\tan B = \dfrac{b}{a}$	$c = \sqrt{a^2 + b^2}$
	area	$\text{area} = \dfrac{ab}{2}$		
A, a	B, b, c	$B = 90° - A$	$b = a \cot A$	$c = \dfrac{a}{\sin A}$
	area	$\text{area} = \dfrac{a^2}{2} \cot A$		
A, b	B, a, c	$B = 90° - A$	$a = b \tan A$	$c = \dfrac{b}{\cos A}$
	area	$\text{area} = \dfrac{b^2}{2} \tan A$		
A, c	B, a, b	$B = 90° - A$	$a = c \sin A$	$b = c \cos A$
	area	$\text{area} = \dfrac{c^2}{2} \sin A \cos A \quad$ or $\quad \dfrac{c^2}{4} \sin 2A$		

Table 7–5C   Solution of oblique-angle triangles

Given	Sought	Formulas		
a, b, c	A	$\sin \dfrac{A}{2} = \sqrt{\dfrac{(s-b)(s-c)}{bc}},$	$\cos \dfrac{A}{2} = \sqrt{\dfrac{s(s-a)}{bc}},$	$\tan \dfrac{A}{2} = \sqrt{\dfrac{(s-b)(s-c)}{s(s-a)}}$
	B	$\sin \dfrac{B}{2} = \sqrt{\dfrac{(s-a)(s-c)}{ac}},$	$\cos \dfrac{B}{2} = \sqrt{\dfrac{s(s-b)}{ac}},$	$\tan \dfrac{B}{2} = \sqrt{\dfrac{(s-a)(s-c)}{s(s-b)}}$
	C	$\sin \dfrac{C}{2} = \sqrt{\dfrac{(s-a)(s-b)}{ab}},$	$\cos \dfrac{C}{2} = \sqrt{\dfrac{s(s-c)}{ab}},$	$\tan \dfrac{C}{2} = \sqrt{\dfrac{(s-a)(s-b)}{s(s-c)}}$
	area	$\text{area} = \sqrt{s(s-a)(s-b)(s-c)}$		
a, A, B	b, C, c	$b = a\dfrac{\sin B}{\sin A},$	$C = 180° - A - B,$	$c = a\dfrac{\sin C}{\sin A} = a\dfrac{\sin(A+B)}{\sin A}$
	area	$\text{area} = \dfrac{ab}{2}\sin C = \dfrac{a^2}{2} \times \dfrac{\sin B \sin C}{\sin A}$		
a, b, A	B, C, c	$\sin B = \dfrac{b}{a}\sin A,$	$C = 180° - A - B,$	$c = a\dfrac{\sin C}{\sin A} = b\dfrac{\sin C}{\sin B}$
	area	$\text{area} = \dfrac{ab}{2}\sin C$		$= \sqrt{a^2 + b^2 - 2ab \cos C}$
a, b, C	A, B	$\tan A = \dfrac{a \sin C}{b - a \cos C},$	$\tan \dfrac{A-B}{2} = \dfrac{a-b}{a+b}\cot \dfrac{1}{2}C$	
	c	$c = \sqrt{a^2 + b^2 - 2ab \cos C} = a\dfrac{\sin C}{\sin A}$		
	area	$\text{area} = \dfrac{ab}{2}\sin C$		

$$a^2 = b^2 + c^2 - 2bc \cos A, \qquad b^2 = a^2 + c^2 - 2ac \cos B, \qquad c^2 = a^2 + b^2 - 2ab \cos C$$

of all parts. Use the formulas of Table 7–6(c) and the typical triangle of Fig. 7–4.

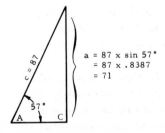

a = 87 x sin 57°
= 87 x .8387
= 71

FIG. 7-4 Typical right triangle

EXAMPLE

Solve for side a in the right triangle of Fig. 7–4 when angle A equals 57° and $c = 87$.

$$\sin A = \frac{a}{c} = \frac{a}{87}, \qquad a = 87 \sin A$$

but

$$\sin A = \sin 57° = .8387$$

$$a = 87 \times .8387 = 71$$

Other applications of trigonometry deal directly with alternating-current electricity and with the accompanying vector notation discussed in the following sections.

TRIGONOMETRY AND VECTORS IN A-C ELECTRICITY

Trigonometry has valuable applications to alternating-current electricity, because some electrical quantities are best expressed as "vectors," or lines forming angular relationships with each other. Angular vector positions, lengths of vector sides, and other problems can thus be dealt with using trigonometry. This usage may be briefly explained as follows.

THE VECTOR CONCEPT

Any a-c current, voltage, or impedance (such as offered by a coil, a capacitor, or a resistor) can be represented by a *vector quantity*, more commonly called a *vector*. We indicate vector quantities by straight arrow-tipped lines (see *OM*, *ON*, *OP*, *OQ*, in Fig. 7–5(a), whose length is proportional to the size of the quantity and whose force or action is applied *for the instant*, in the direction of,

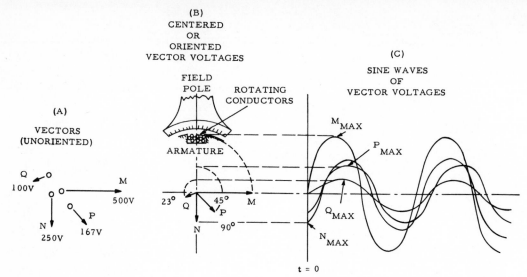

FIG. 7-5 The vector concept

or at the angle in which the vector arrow is pointing.

Thus, we may have voltage outputs of a number of a-c generators (Fig. 7–5(b)) whose instantaneous outputs at a specific time are a 500-volt vector OM, which is double the length of the 250-volt output ON of a smaller machine, three times that of OP, five times that of the third voltage source OQ. Electrically, we deal with these quantities in amplitude as well as in direction. Thus, the first vector OM, at a certain instant, may be effectively putting out its electromotive force in a horizontal direction while the second machine is delivering its impulses in a purely vertical direction and the third is generating at a downward direction 45° from the horizontal, and the fourth at a 23° angle to the left. These directions are called the *phase* of the vector, there being in this case a 90° phase difference between the first two voltages.

Now, the net, or effective, emf of a vector is its component in the vertical direction. In the case of OP, it is partly downward since it is pointing "southeast," so to speak, and that of vector ON is entirely vertical. This downward or upward vertical component of instantaneous electromotive force is easily calculated trigonometrically from a vector's length and angular direction. We thus see that vector OM has no vertical component,

while OQ has a downward vertical component somewhat less than that of ON—an amount which, as we shall see, can be calculated trigonometrically.

If all these vectors are coordinated into a single system to represent varying alternating emfs or voltages generated by conductors that are rotating in a magnetic field (note field pole in Fig. 7–5(b)), they go through a whole cycle of amplitude change from zero to maximum and back to zero again and become oriented so that we draw them from a common center point. (See Fig. 7–5(c).) Dynamically, they can then be considered and drawn, as shown, to be continuously going through these alternating-up-and-down, or sine-wave, variations at the same rate but *constantly lagging or leading* each other by different angular amounts or phases. Under these conditions, the instantaneous variation in amplitude and phase of each vector and its components is readily solved trigonometrically, thus making this mathematical tool indispensable to certain techniques in electronic engineering.

COMBINING AND RESOLVING VECTORS

Figure 7–6 illustrates the various geometrical and trigonometric processes involved in adding, subtracting, multiplying, or dividing vectors.

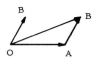

Tandem addition   *Parallelogram addition*
of vectors   *of vectors*

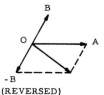

-B
(REVERSED)

Subtracting vectors

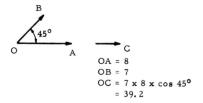

OA = 8
OB = 7
OC = 7 x 8 x cos 45°
   = 39.2

Multiplying vectors

OA = 8
OB = 3
$\frac{OA}{OB} = \frac{8}{3}$ x cosθ
   = 2.7 x cosθ = 18.9

Dividing vectors

FIG. 7-6 Combining and resolving vectors

Horizontal component
= OA × sin 20°

Horizontal component
= OA × cos 40°

Vertical component
= OA × sin 30°

Vertical component
= OA × sin 45°

FIG. 7-7 Resolving vector components

Resolving vectors from their instantaneous values into their effective (vertical) or horizontal components is accomplished by simple trigonometry, using sines and cosines. (See examples in Fig. 7–7.)

POLAR COORDINATES

Many times it is convenient to express a vector only in terms of its angle and amplitude. In Figure 7–8(a) we merely say $OA = 600$ volts at an angle of 20° in the fourth quadrant shown by the position of the angle sign bracketing the angle number. In Fig. 7–8(b), OA is 80 volts at 40° in the first quadrant.

(A)   (B)

OA = 600 $\underline{20°}$ OA = 80 $\underline{40°}$

FIG. 7-8 Polar coordinates

BINARY NUMBERS

The binary numbering system, like the decimal system, is a *positional method* of *writing numbers* by listing and adding the count of powers of some base number. It uses the number 2 as a base or radix instead of 10, which is used in our decimal numbering system, and, moreover, it uses only either of *two* radix counts or multipliers—hence the word binary. These are either 0 or 1 for each position of the main number rather than the ten individual digital multiplier or count numbers (0–9) used in the decimal system. Thus, in decimals with 10 as the base, 6,248 is constructed:

$$6 \qquad 2 \qquad 4 \qquad 8$$
$$(6 \cdot 10^{+3}) + (2 \cdot 10^{+2}) + (4 \cdot 10^{+1}) + (8 \cdot 10^{0})$$
$$(6000) + (200) + (40) + (8) = 6248$$

In the binary system the decimal number 15 is constructed as 1111:

$$1 \qquad 1 \qquad 1 \qquad 1$$
$$(1 \cdot 2^{+3}) + (1 \cdot 2^{+2}) + (1 \cdot 2^{+1}) + (1 \cdot 2^{0})$$
$$(8) + (4) + (2) + (1) = 15$$

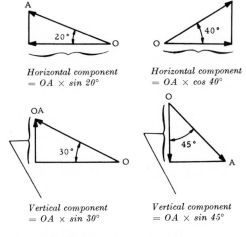

The decimal number 10 is represented in binary as 1010:

$$1 \qquad 0 \qquad 1 \qquad 0$$
$$(1 \cdot 2^{+3}) + (0 \cdot 2^{+2}) + (1 \cdot 2^{+1}) + (0 \cdot 2^{0})$$
$$(8) \quad + \quad (0) \quad + \quad (2) \quad + \quad (0) = 10$$

Again, since only one of the two multipliers can be used at one time, the system is binary in nature and fits well into computer circuitry where all electronic circuits are bi-stable, able to be only completely "on" or completely "off."

CONVERTING TO BINARY NUMBERS

Without using tables, to *convert* from *decimal* to *binary*, the process calls for repeatedly dividing each decimal dividend by 2 until division is no longer possible. When there is a remainder, mark 1 to the right (as shown below), and when there is no remainder, mark 0.

EXAMPLE

Convert 77 into its binary equivalent.

The binary numerals arranged from *bottom* to *top* give us the final conversion: $77 = 1001101$.

Successive dividers	Original no. and dividends	Remainder
2	77	1
2	38	0
2	19	1
2	9	1
2	4	0
2	2	0
2	1	1

To convert *binary* 1001101 to *decimal* 77 we proceed as shown below:

Binary number	1	0	0	1	1	0	1
Powers of base 2	2^6	2^5	2^4	2^3	2^2	2^1	2^0
Products	64	+ 0	+ 0	+ 8	+ 4	+ 0	+ 1
Add horizontally	64			+ 8 + 4			+ 1 = 77

Thus, 1001101 becomes decimally 77

GENERAL RULES

(1) $0 + 0 = 0$.

(2) $0 + 1 = 1$.

(3) $1 + 0 = 1$.

(4) $1 + 1 = 10$.

(5) $1 + 1 + 1 = 11$ with 1 carried to the next place on the left.

Table 7–6   Tabular conversion of decimal numbers to binary numbers

Decimal numbers	Binary numbers					
	2^5	2^4	2^3	2^2	2^1	2^0
	32	16	8	4	2	1
0	0	0	0	0	0	0
1	0	0	0	0	0	1
2	0	0	0	0	1	0
3	0	0	0	0	1	1
4	0	0	0	1	0	0
5	0	0	0	1	0	1
6	0	0	0	1	1	0
7	0	0	0	1	1	1
8	0	0	1	0	0	0
9	0	0	1	0	0	1
10	0	0	1	0	1	0
20	0	1	0	1	0	0
30	0	1	1	1	1	0
40	1	0	1	0	0	0
45	1	0	1	1	0	1
50	1	1	0	0	1	0
57	1	1	1	0	0	1

EXAMPLE 1 Add $13 + 15$

Decimal	Binary
13	1101
+15	+1111
28	11100

BINARY NUMBER SUBTRACTION

GENERAL RULES

(1) $0 - 0 = 0$.

(2) $1 - 1 = 0$.

(3) $1 - 0 = 1$.

(4) $0 - 1 = 1$, and then reverse all minuend (top row) numbers to the left until a reversal of 1 to 0 is reached; then go no further on that reversal.

EXAMPLE 1 Subtract $11 - 5$:

Decimal	Binary
11	1011
-5	-0101
6	0110

EXAMPLE 2 Subtract $3338 - 1837$:

Decimal	Binary
3338	1101 0000 1010
-1837	$-111\ 0010\ 1101$
1501	101 1101 1101

BINARY NUMBER MULTIPLICATION

GENERAL RULES
(1) $0 \times 0 = 0$.
(2) $0 \times 1 = 0$.
(3) $1 \times 1 = 1$.

Note that to do multiplication, addition is necessary; note also the *shift* of successive products.

EXAMPLE 1 Multiply 11×2:

Decimal	Binary
11	1011
$\times 2$	$\times 10$
22	0000
	1011
	10110

EXAMPLE 2 Multiply 59×5:

Decimal	Binary
59	111011
$\times 5$	$\times 101$
295	111011
	000000
	111011
	100100111

BINARY NUMBER DIVISION

GENERAL RULES
(1) $-0 \div 0 = 0$.
(2) $0 \div 1 = 0$.
(3) $1 \div 1 = 1$.

Note the importance of subtraction and, again, the number shift step:

EXAMPLE 1 Divide 14 by 2:

Decimal	Binary
7	111
$2\,)\,\overline{14}$	$10\,)\,\overline{1110}$
14	10
	11
	10
	10
	10

EXAMPLE 2 Divide 58 by 6:

Decimal	Binary
4	100
$9\,\overline{6}$	$1001\ \overline{110}$
$6\,)\,\overline{58}$	$110\,)\,\overline{111010}$
54	110
4	1010
	110
	100

BINARY FRACTIONS

To express fractions by binary numbers we proceed initially as in decimals. For instance,

$$\frac{3}{5} \text{ decimally} = \frac{11}{101} \text{ binary}$$

Now this means that the radix employs *negative* powers or exponents. Thus, for example, binary .011 ($= .375$ decimal) represents

$$(0 \times 2^{-1}) + 1 \times 2^{-2} + 1 \times 2^{-3}$$

$$0 \qquad + \quad \frac{1}{4} \quad + \quad \frac{1}{8} \quad = .375$$

Table 7–7 converts a number of common decimal fraction to binary equivalents.

Table 7–7 Fractions, decimals and binary equivalents

Decimal equivalents		Power of 2	Binary equivalent
1/2	or .5	2^{-1}	.1
1/4	.25	2^{-2}	.01
1/8	.125	2^{-3}	.001
1/16	.065	2^{-4}	.0001
1/32	.03125	2^{-5}	.00001
1/64	.015625	2^{-6}	.000001
1/128	.0078125	2^{-7}	.0000001
1/256	.00390625	2^{-8}	.00000001
1/512	.001953125	2^{-9}	.000000001

8 Organization of the Laboratory

Modern engineering and technological advances require the laboratory technician to orient himself to standard military practices, procedures, and techniques—particularly in the handling of component parts and in hardware fabrication. In the finished-equipment phase, he will find that government practices in measurement and instrumentation likewise require special attention; in some cases they have undergone radical changes from commercial practices.

Most particularly, military equipment (beyond piece-part applications) has become so complete that it requires a system approach. Although the "black box" or drawer must still be tested, it now has a close relationship to a number of other drawers and black boxes because they are all part of a system. Support devices and procedures such as spare-parts provisioning, modularizing the contents of black boxes, and automatic monitoring and testing are increasingly important, and the technician is increasingly called for help and guidance. In short, the modern technician must "think big." He must take a broad view of all that he does and, above all, he must use careful planning in his everyday work.

To make clear the breadth of the system approach and of the support function, Table 8-1 lists the levels and factors contributing to the instrumentation for testing a large electronic system.

The material that follows states general guidelines for the technician in carrying out test and measurement tasks, the details of which constitute the remainder of this book.

PLANNING THE WORK

The system approach to a measurement and testing program logically involves good planning. The technician must study the basic principles of operation and acquire a thorough physical and electronic familiarity with operational features of the hardware itself.

Next, the work plan calls for collection and study of all printed information upon the equipment being measured. This includes: (1) the basic specifications, (2) block functional diagrams, (3) major schematics, (4) test procedures and related specifications, (5) listing and location of test points, (6) instruction book on overall operation and maintenance.

Following the printed information from sources (1), (2), and (6), the measurement work sequence usually becomes obvious. The general course of action calls for:

1. Placing the equipment in normal operational condition.
2. Measuring static and supply voltages in order to verify normal operation.
3. Selecting and measuring individual sections within the systems.
4. Measuring key performance quantities such as noise factors, standing wave ratios,

Table 8–1   Functional measurement levels

level	Nature	Quantities	Units	Using	Method
I	Electrical quantities	E I F P	Volts Amperes Cycles/sec Watts	Voltmeters Ammeters Frequency meters Wattmeters Counters	Direct measurement
II	Components	R C L V Q	Ohms Farads Henrys Transconductance Beta	Ohmmeters Bridges Test sets Q-meters R_x checker	Direct measurement
		Forming	Performing	Characteristics	Procedures
III	Circuit and stage characteristics	Stages Networks Filters	Amplification Oscillation Detection Switching Comparing	Gain Output Conversion Leakage Selectivity, Q	Indirect—2- to 3-step methods by instrument-meters
IV		Boxes Drawers Racks Consoles Systems	Communication Navigation Tracking Radar Sonar	Power output Sensitivity Selectivity Noise Image ratio Response-bandwidth % Modulation Cross modulation	Indirect—3- to 8-step methods by instrument-meters

etc. These measurements generally indicate the harmonization or electronic dovetailing of overall sectional performance; they will be considered in detail later.

ORGANIZING THE FACILITIES AND INSTRUMENTATION

Although the measurement procedures may be obvious, as noted above, preparing for them often takes longer than the measurements themselves.

Facilities should be procured as follows (in the order of their importance):

1. Bench room or equipment space plus room for recording, record keeping, etc.

2. Power facilities (perhaps special ones, such as 400-cycle, 230-volt) with proper fusing provisions etc.

3. High-voltage safety precautions. In transmitters these are vital and include such things as cages with interlocked doors, grounding plates, short-circuiting bars, etc.

4. Illumination for operation and for supporting electrical operations; heat and controllable humidity for personnel comfort and particularly for operating the gear under specified environmental conditions.

5. Provision for proper repair and spare-part back-up. Rapid repairs and replacements sometimes prove vital in important measurement runs.

The general approach outlined above will usually reveal the instrumentation necessary for a system test. Specifications and test procedures also indicate the nature, style, type, accuracy, and other characteristics of the meters and equipment needed. The technician's familiarity with the equipment and his general knowledge and electronic experience also dictate many of the steps he will take in planning.

THE LABORATORY NOTEBOOK

Before taking readings the technician must obtain a standard laboratory notebook in which to record the data. To use the notebook intelligently he must: (1) use adequate titles and subtitles, (2) set down the date that information is being recorded, (3) obtain circuit diagrams of each part of the test and insure that all components are labeled, (4) observe data, (5) calculate results for check upon procedures, (6) make sample calculations, (7) draw curves, (8) make sketches of waveforms expected and those actually obtained, (9) record notes and explanations as necessary.

One can not emphasize too highly the importance of recording *accurate and systematic data* on any complicated operation, both for reference and as a guide to future effort.

REPORTING AND RECORDING

Engineering data are recorded in a similar way in most laboratories as a matter of logical necessity. Figure 8-1 shows sections from a typical laboratory notebook. The upper right-

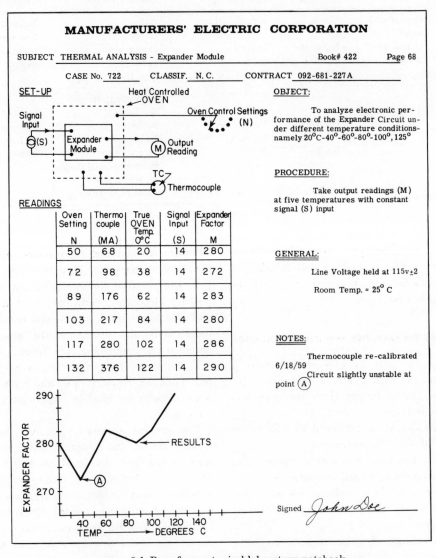

FIG. 8-1 Page from a typical laboratory notebook

hand corner of each page usually contains information about the basic operation. At the upper left the data are recorded in logical sequence. Further down on the page to the right, room should be left for rough plotting of calculations concerning the data. When these curves must be amplified or extended they are usually drawn on separate sheets, which should be pasted in the notebook along with the recorded data.

Many notebooks include pages with ruled-off squares; these are useful in the sketching of parts, the making of schematics, and the ruling of columns when tabulated readings must be listed.

NOTES ON MEASUREMENT

THE TECHNICIAN'S ELECTRONIC BACKGROUND

After breadboarding, planning, fabricating, assembling, and wiring a piece of hardware the modern technician approaches the final stages of completing a project: the delivery of the hardware in operating condition. At this point he must make a series of widely varying electrical and electronic measurements. He will be concerned chiefly with the equipment's overall performance, but sometimes with components and individual circuits.

In the remainder of this book it is assumed that the technician has mastered fundamental magnetic, electronic, and electrical principles and is familiar with active components such as vacuum tubes, transistors, and diodes as well as with the fundamental characteristics of batteries, resistors, capacitors, and inductors. He must also have a good grasp of networks and circuitry. Of equal importance is his knowledge of physics and functional electronics —the operation and measurement of vacuum

Table 8-2   Functions and applications of vacuum tubes and solid-state devices

Functions	Applications		
	Measurement and control	Communication	Industrial
Amplification	Transducing	Radio (FM-AM)	Electronic heating, drying, tempering
Oscillation	Counting and timing	Telephone	Power rectification transformation or inversion
Light to electron flow	Tracking	Television	
Rectification	Indicating	Facsimile	
Switching	Comparing and sorting	Telemetry	Power control
Electron flow to light		Radar	Motors
		Sonar	Welding
		Motion pictures	Protection
		Anti submarine warfare	Illumination
			Fluorescence

Table 8-3

Basic measurement instrument types

Voltmeters	Ohmmeters	Impedance meters	Frequency meters	Oscilloscope	Special
Vacuum tube a-c, d-c	V-A type: series, shunt	Capacity meter	Counters	Waveform	VSWR
Analog		Inductance	Wavemeters	Modulation	Wave analyzer
Digital	Vacuum tube type	R-X checker		Frequency	Phase meter
		Q-meter		Distortion	Spectrum analyzer
		Ratiometers			
		Bridges: resistance, capacitance, inductance			

tubes, transistors, and their associated circuits.

In brief, the technician's activities are widespread and must encompass the electronic and physical principles and applications listed in the following six categories (see also Table 8-2): (1) amplification, (2) oscillation, (3) detection, (4) switching, (5) conversion of electricity to light (display and cathode-ray tube techniques) (6) conversion of light to electricity (photoelectricity)—which may in itself be complicated.

Assuming that the reader has a reasonable electronic background this volume attempts to define, describe, and summarize rather than to explain basic electronic phenomena and measurements.

METERS AND MEASUREMENT

Table 8-3 gives a bird's-eye view of the basic types of instruments encountered in circuit measurement. These are functional down to the circuit and electronic level; they are, of course, expanded when applied to more complex equipment such as radars, transmitter-receiver sets, digital computers, and the like.

The Approach to Measurement: Components 9

Electronic measurements are vital in design, evaluation, or field operation of any piece of electronic equipment. They guide the design process and they help one to ascertain normal operation and to isolate or analyze failure.

Measurements must be approached at the correct equipment *level* for maximum effectiveness. Measurement levels progress from piece-part, to circuit, to equipment, to system as discussed below. Table 9-1 summarizes these levels, their functional and electronic composition, and finally the characteristics, equipment, and techniques necessary at each level.

At the *piece-part component level*, for instance, we definitely tailor our measurement techniques to the characteristics of resistors, capacitors, coils, tubes, or transistors.

At the stage or *circuit level*, on the other hand, we want to know about one or all of the basic and fundamental electronic functions performed by piece-parts when combined operationally in electrical and electronic circuits. These basic electronic functions, as noted earlier, are: (1) amplification, (2) oscillation, (3) detection (providing modulation or demodulation), (4) Switching—providing controlled OFF or ON states of conduction in a tube or transistor, (5) conversion of electricity to light (the display function), (6) conversion of light to electricity (the photoelectric effect), (7) reproduction of elec-

trical signals as sound signals (loudspeaker effect).

Going one degree higher—or at the *equipment level*—we must measure combinations of the basic functions. For instance, in a television receiver we use RF, IF, video, and audio *amplifiers*, first and second *detectors*, *oscillator* performance for heterodyning the signal, and *conversion* of electricity to *sound* in the loudspeaker and to visible *light* in the picture tube.

At the *system level* we have (for example) radars which are a combination of the transmitting and receiving functions. Analysis here involves a series of composite equipment and basic circuit measurements plus special indication of such things as antenna radiation, reflection (echo) phenomena, and power transfer.

Returning to measurement at the circuit level we consider amplifier gain first, since it is the most important of the basic functions. Taking a receiver with all its different amplifiers we might, in effect, consider it as a single high-gain amplifier even though it also utilizes detection and oscillation.

AMPLIFICATION

The primary measurement in any type of amplifier is power gain, although voltage gain seems to be paramount in vacuum-tube amplifiers where grid-to-grid measurements

141

Table 9–1 Equipment measurement levels

Level	Mechanical makeup	Electronic composition	Functional makeup	Characteristics measured	Equipment and techniques employed
System	Geographically dispersed	Complex equipment groups	Radar Navigation Sonar Communication Data-processing centers	Availability Flow of information	4th level action Complex instrumentation
Subsystem	Located in one area or vehicle	Racks Cabinets	Transmitters Displays Arrays Control units	Power output Signal strength Noise Light output % modulation	4th level action Complex instrumentation

Equipment	Complete drawers
	Parts of racks
		Power supplies
		Functional units or sections
			Complete:
			Freq. sources
			Multipliers
			  Receivers
			  Modulators
			Control units
			Servo units
				Sensitivity
				Selectivity
				Stability
				Distortion
				% modulation
					3rd level action
					Characteristic instrument analysis

Composite function	Assemblies Sections of drawers	Functional units Circuit combinations	*Sections of:* Amplifiers Modulators Switches Generators Control units	Sensitivity Selectivity Stability Distortion	3rd level action Composite instrument approach
Integral function	Modules Subassemblies	Combined stages Units	Amplification Oscillation Detection Switching Display	Db Gain Bandwidth Watts output Cycles/sec drift Conversion output Speed of switching Foot lambert Light output	2nd level action Functional instrument approach
Circuits	Printed boards Insulated assembly boards Mounting items	Stages Units	Filters Networks Resonant and dissipative circuits	Attenuation Losses Output Selectivity	2nd level action Instrument techniques
Piece parts Passive {	Resistors Capacitors Inductors	Composition or wire Plates-dielectric Coiled wire	Dissipate or conduct Storage Attract or induce	Ohms Farads Henries or gauss	1st level Direct reading: Meters
Active {	Vacuum Tubes Transistors } Diodes }	Hot cathode in vacuum Solid-state junction	Valve action or emission Current Control	Transconductance Beta	Bridges Instruments

are common. In one sense both viewpoints are correct, for in a microphone audio amplifier we concern ourselves only with voltage amplification until the last stage, where we drive the output tubes into high-level sound-power output (with little voltage amplification) while the voice signals have been amplified by high-mu, low-power, voltage-amplifier tubes. Actually the output voltage across the loudspeaker coil in such an amplifier is far less than the voltage on the primary of the output transformer, so we may say, strictly speaking, that voltage amplification has been lost. The power, however, has been greatly amplified throughout.

We can also reconcile this seeming anomaly in receiver gain measurements by noting that grid impedances across which the voltage amplification is commonly measured are completely ignored. We do this because *power gain* is irrelevant in such an amplifier; each plate circuit and the grid circuit succeeding it needs only *voltage* output. In most cases a grid, no matter what impedance drives it, will accept voltages in any phase whatsoever in order to give the most voltage output. Since we have neither reason nor method to determine the phase and exact value of the load impedance, we are not interested in the power gain anyway.

Amplifier voltage gains therefore are expressed in two ways: (1) as ratios of output to input voltages, or (2) in decibels of power gain calculated on the basis of equal interstage impedances.

THE DECIBEL IN AMPLIFIER GAIN MEASUREMENTS

In commercial audio amplifiers we use the decibel voltage gain plus a rating of the power output capabilities. In pure voltage amplifiers (where power output is of no interest) we express gain in terms of input-to-output voltage ratio or in terms of decibels—where the input is essentially a voltage figure just above the thermal noise input signal. The following brief discussion of decibels is amplified in Appendix E-1, which includes tables and detailed examples of calculation.

Briefly, the decibel is a power ratio; it may be calculated from the following formula:

$$db = 10 \log_{10} \frac{P_2}{P_1}$$

where $P_2 =$ output power, $P_1 =$ input power, so that for a power gain of 10:1

$$db = 10 \log_{10} 10 = 10 \times 1 = 10$$

If the above amplifier had a known *voltage* gain we would calculate the decibels from the formula:

$$db = 20 \log_{10} \frac{V_2}{V_1}$$

where $V_2 =$ output voltage, $V_1 =$ input voltage.

TYPES OF VACUUM TUBE AMPLIFIERS

Vacuum tube amplifiers may be categorized in several different ways. Generalizing, they are most frequently listed according to: (1) the type of coupling used between stages, (2) details of their bias voltage and its application, (3) frequency range, (4) the type of circuitry inputs, output, etc., being used, and (5) the special function or application associated with the use.

Amplifier types according to coupling is the most widely referred to classification. It has five categories: (a) Resistance-capacity coupling. (b) Transformer coupling. (c) Impedance coupling. (d) Tuned circuit. (e) Direct coupling. Figure 9–1 summarizes typical circuit configurations applying to this listing; this diagram includes condensed notes describing various characteristics with additional comments and applications.

RESISTANCE-CAPACITANCE COUPLED AMPLIFIERS are, in general, the simplest and most economical type to construct. Used extensively in audio amplifiers, high-gain tubes using this circuit easily attain gains of 100 × per stage. Control of input is necessary in these amplifiers to eliminate overload distortion; design problems usually concern nonlinearity and its attendant distortion, or frequency response which is dependent upon disposition of impedances in the coupling networks. See Fig. 9–1(a).

TRANSFORMER-COUPLED AMPLIFIERS (Fig. 9–1(b)) depend for their performance upon impedance matching and proportionment.

The most striking example of this is in the output stage of an audio power amplifier where the output-tube plate impedance must undergo transformation to the voice-coil impedance of the loudspeaker with a minimum of distortion and power loss.

Interstage coupling in audio and in IF amplifiers rely on the transformer coupling for voltage step-up.

Push-pull transformer coupling (shown

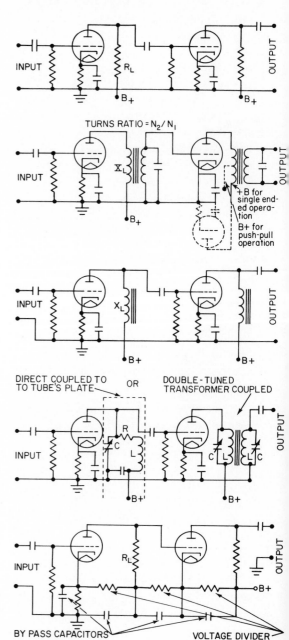

(a) RESISTANCE-CAPACITANCE COUPLED has simple, economical construction, and wide frequency range.

$$\frac{\text{Stage}}{\text{Gain}} = \frac{V_{\text{out}}}{V_{\text{in}}} = \mu \times \frac{R_L}{R_L + P_P}$$

(b) TRANSFORMER COUPLED has no coupling capacitor, uses full +B voltage on plates; receives step-up from transformer, restricts frequency range.

$$\frac{\text{Stage}}{\text{Gain}} = \frac{V_{\text{out}}}{V_{\text{in}}} = \frac{N_2}{N_1} \times \frac{X_2}{X_L + R_P}$$

(c) IMPEDANCE COUPLED has single winding plus coupling capacitor. Restricts frequency range; full +B voltage on plates.

$$\frac{\text{Stage}}{\text{Gain}} = \frac{V_{\text{out}}}{V_{\text{in}}} = \mu \times \frac{X_L}{X_L + R_P}$$

(d) TUNED CIRCUIT COUPLED has high gain, good selectivity, tunes out grid and plate capacities.

$$\frac{\text{Stage}}{\text{Gain}} = \frac{V_{\text{out}}}{V_{\text{in}}} = G_M \times \frac{L}{CR}$$

(e) DIRECT COUPLED has no coupling capacitor nor grid and cathode resistors, uses large, expensive voltage divider, bypassing capacitors. State gain same as resistance coupled stage, with wide frequency range.

FIG. 9-1 Typical circuit configurations for vacuum tube amplifiers

dotted) permits the use of two output tubes in order to transfer double power to a voice coil. This circuit has advantages in low distortion, low hum, and good overload characteristics that would not exist if the two tubes were each used in parallel and the outputs combined. The necessary tapped transformer primary is shown for application of the supply (+B) voltage in the push-pull case.

IMPEDANCE-COUPLED AMPLIFIERS utilize an inductive plate load in order to permit greater supply voltage to reach the tube. Variations of this circuit utilize tapping and self-resonance of the plate coil, as we shall see further on. In some cases, this type of construction offers performance and cost advantages possessed by neither the d-c nor the transformer-coupled amplifier. See Fig. 9–1(c).

TUNED-CIRCUIT AMPLIFIERS utilize a resonant circuit for the amplifier tube's plate load. High impedance, developed only at the resonant frequency, results in high stage gain. The response of this type of circuit is restricted to a frequency region adjacent to the resonant point. Thus the property of *selectivity* enters the design of tuned-circuit amplifiers. In radio, television, or radar receivers we must provide correct alignment in order to get the maximum performance out of cascaded tuned circuits. See Fig. 9–1(d).

DIRECT-COUPLED AMPLIFIERS are resistance coupled, eliminating the coupling capacitor and its attendant restrictions on frequency response. Such amplifiers directly connect the top side of the plate load resistor to the grid of the following tube. To obtain correct operating voltages, the various plates, grids, and cathodes are placed at successively descending points on a main voltage divider or bleeder resistor. See Fig. 9–1(e).

AMPLIFIER TYPES ACCORDING TO BIAS VOLTAGE

This categorization is summarized in Figure 9–2. The following notes give further descriptive information:

CLASS A AMPLIFIERS operate directly on the middle portion of the mutual characteristic with just enough signal input grid voltage applied to never exceed the normal bias. These amplifiers are probably the most widely used; they deliver the lowest in distortion, but for high-power use they are low in efficiency.

CLASS AB$_1$ AND AB$_2$ operate beyond the middle, linear range, AB$_1$ operating with a grid swing never into grid current, and AB$_2$ running with grid swings somewhat past zero bias and drawing grid current. These amplifiers are slightly more efficient than Class A, but they must be operated in push-pull arrangement so that some of the distortion due to nonlinear operation is cancelled.

CLASS B AMPLIFIERS always operate in push-pull, since they are biased to cut-off; if they operated single-ended the distortion would be excessive. Because cancellation of even harmonics occurs in push-pull operation, these tubes give fair performance and are quite efficient since the plate current of but one tube is flowing at a time. In high-power audio circuits—particularly in modulators for transmitters—the high plate-circuit efficiency of this arrangement makes its use almost imperative.

CLASS C AMPLIFIERS are used chiefly as RF amplifiers because of their high efficiency. With bias at about twice cut-off value, the grid excitation is just enough to start the resonant circuit in the plate circuit of the tube on a single oscillation. While the grid is on its negative swing, the "flywheel" effect of the resonant circuit completes the other half of the RF cycle until the next grid pulse arrives to start the process over again. The efficiency of these amplifiers runs as high as 80 per cent.

TRANSISTOR AMPLIFIERS

Transistor amplifiers are classified, with one exception, according to coupling in the same general groups applied to vacuum tube amplifiers. The exception is the classification by bias grouping.

Figure 9–3 illustrates the commonly used transistor amplifier circuits listed according to coupling. The discussion of each type parallels that given with vacuum tube amplifiers.

RESISTANCE-CAPACITY COUPLED AMPLIFIERS are well suited to low-level audio amplification where transformer coupling, which incurs the danger of hum pickup, is more expensive and occupies more space. In addition electrolytic

CLASS A has bias voltage in linear region—generally midway between cutoff and zero grid voltage. This gives low distortion but has poor power output efficiency.

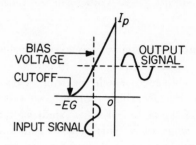

CLASS AB$_1$ has bias voltage beyond the midpoint but has grid swing allowing no grid current. This arrangement is used in push-pull circuits to cancel distortion. Efficiency is better than Class A.

CLASS AB$_2$ has bias voltage still farther towards cutoff, but grid current is allowed to flow. Tubes must be used in push-pull circuits. Efficiency is slightly better than Class AB$_1$.

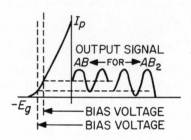

CLASS B has bias voltage at cutoff. Tubes are always used in push-pull circuits, with only one tube working at a time. Efficiency is 53%.

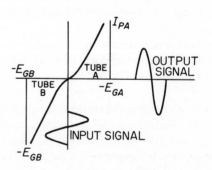

CLASS C has bias voltage at twice cutoff and is used chiefly in R.F. transmitters. Efficiency is as high as 80%. The lower part of the output voltage (dashed curve) is supplied by the "flywheel effect" of the tuned circuit into the plate of the output tube.

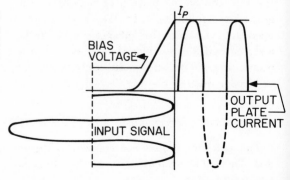

FIG. 9-2 Vacuum tube amplifiers grouped according to their bias voltage

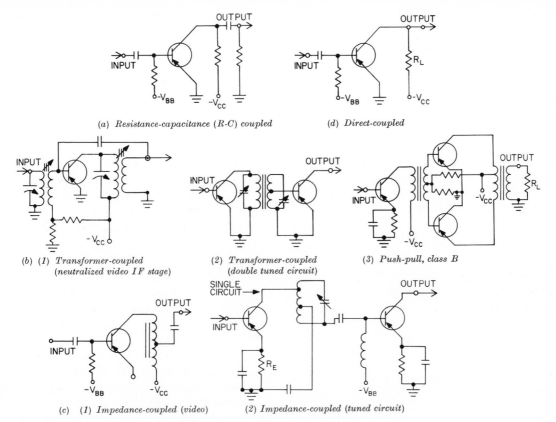

(a) *Resistance-capacitance (R-C) coupled*

(d) *Direct-coupled*

(b) (1) *Transformer-coupled*
(neutralized video IF stage)

(2) *Transformer-coupled*
(double tuned circuit)

(3) *Push-pull, class B*

(c)   (1) *Impedance-coupled (video)*

(2) *Impedance-coupled (tuned circuit)*

FIG. 9-3 Commonly used transistor amplifier circuits listed according to coupling

coupling capacitors may be used since leakage currents are not as critical as they are in electron tube amplifiers. See Fig. 9–3(a).

TRANSFORMER COUPLING. The single-stage grounded-emitter amplifier (Fig. 9–3(b)) uses step-down transformers for best impedance match and maximum power gain into base-emitter circuits. The combination of fixed and self-bias is provided with an emitter resistor for stabilization. Push-pull and tuned circuits are also shown.

IMPEDANCE COUPLING. This circuit employs coils in place of the collector load resistors in an *RC*-coupled circuit (Fig. 9–3(c)). In the video amplifier circuit illustrated both shunt and series peaking coils are employed. Impedance may also be developed by a tuned circuit.

DIRECT-COUPLED circuits (Fig. 9–3(d)) employ a common collector load and emitter bias resistor, thus saving a coupling capacitor.

Functionally this circuit has use where restoration of the d-c component of the signal is desired.

TRANSISTOR AMPLIFIER TYPES GROUPED BY BIAS VOLTAGE. This type of amplifier grouping is basically the same in both transistor and vacuum tube circuits. Discussion of Class A and B amplifiers (Fig. 9–2) parallels that on page 145; collector current flows continuously in the Class A type (analogous to plate current in the vacuum tube) and flows only half the time in the Class B type, which in both groupings always uses a push-pull circuit.

Class AB and Class C amplifiers find little usage in transistor circuits.

OSCILLATION

The fundamental circuit function of oscillation may be distributed throughout many areas in almost all general types of equipment;

147

for instance, every superheterodyne receiver has a local oscillator for heterodyning the signal, and the heart beat of any transmitter is the primary crystal oscillator. A radar has in addition to its primary crystal oscillator numerous sweep oscillators connected with its display function.

Testing and measurement of oscillator performance within an equipment, therefore, boils down to the measurement of: (1) absolute frequency, (2) frequency stability, (3) power output sufficient to drive associated equipment, (4) waveform contour suitable to function as required.

Assuming the technician has fundamental knowledge of oscillator action, the chief phases of oscillation—namely, frequency, waveform, and power output—are covered in Chapters 5, 6, and 11, respectively.

TYPES OF VACUUM TUBE OSCILLATORS

Oscillator circuits fall in two broad categories—sine wave oscillators and relaxation oscillators. Sine wave oscillators in turn are distinguished by the type of feedback coupling utilized to produce oscillation. Figure 9–4 shows a number of typical circuits accompanied by notes concerning the feedback mechanism. Additional notes concerning each circuit are given below.

SINE WAVE OSCILLATORS

(A) HARTLEY OSCILLATOR. Part of the voltage developed across the inductance L_1 of the main resonant circuit is fed back directly to the grid through the coupling condenser C_1 (serving also as a charge storage condenser).

(B) COLPITTS OSCILLATOR. Feedback is accomplished by using as grid feedback the C_1 portion of the total voltage developed across C_1 and C_2, which form the capacitive element of the resonant circuit.

(C) TUNED-GRID, TUNED-PLATE OSCILLATOR.

The two resonant circuits L_1C_1 and L_2C_2 respectively (in the grid and plate of the tube) are coupled by the feedback through the grid-to-plate capacity of the tube, C_p. In pentodes, since this capacitance is very small, an external capacitor is sometimes added to provide feedback voltage for oscillations.

(D) CRYSTAL OSCILLATOR. This oscillator is a modification of the tuned-grid, tuned-plate type using a resonant circuit in its plate circuit. A piezoelectric quartz crystal is used in place of a tuned circuit in the grid circuit, since it has the property of simultaneously combining mechanical and electrical vibrations, and acts as a high-Q resonant circuit. For resonance and correct feedback, the device must have very accurate mechanical dimensions; it then acts as a precise resonant circuit and mechanically vibrates at the radio frequency for which it is ground and polished.

Crystal oscillators are widely used in high-frequency radio equipment because of their high degree of frequency stability. Relatively insensitive to supply-voltage changes, temperature, humidity, or mechanical circuit differences, the crystal closely maintains its natural resonant frequency.

(E) TICKLER COIL OSCILLATOR. A version of the Hartley circuit is embodied in this oscillator. Feedback from the resonant circuit is led back through the small winding L of the main coil, to couple the plate energy to the grid circuit. The coupling between the coil sections is made variable by winding the tickler section on a movable rotating form so that, by means of a knob, the operator can control the degree of coupling with the grid part of the coil. This feature, used in early receivers with grid leak detectors, was arranged so that the detector tube could be adjusted to the verge of oscillation, thus producing a very sensitive performance.

(F) ELECTRON-COUPLED OSCILLATOR. In this form of the Hartley oscillator the cathode is connected through a tap on the tuned-circuit coil, and the plate is grounded to radio

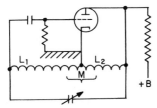

(A) HARTLEY OSCILLATOR has inductive feedback due to coupling between L_1 and L_2.

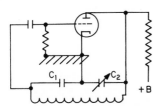

(B) COLPITTS OSCILLATOR has capacitive feedback due to voltage across C_1.

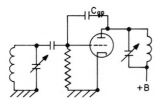

(C) TUNED GRID-TUNED PLATE OSCILLATOR derives feedback to grid from plate through grid-plate capacity C.

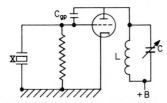

(D) CRYSTAL OSCILLATOR utilizes resonant properties of crystal X, derives feedback from resonant circuit LC through C.

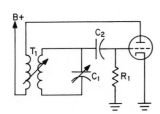

(E) TICKLER COIL OSCILLATOR has feedback via transformer coupling through adjustable "tickler" coil primary.

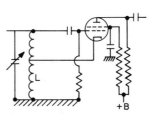

(F) ELECTRON COUPLED OSCILLATOR has feedback effected by coupling plate currents with resonant circuit in L. Oscillator output is "electron coupled" to plate, thus freeing tank circuit from load variations.

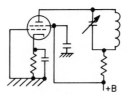

(G) DYNATRON OSCILLATOR has electron coupling of plate to screen (at higher voltage) and gives *negative* resistance which sustains oscillations.

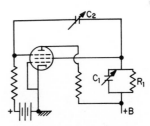

(H) R-C OSCILLATOR has feedback from $C_1 R_1$ network; through C_2 utilizes negative resistance developed in screen circuit to maintain oscillation; must operate at low voltages; has better frequency range than L-C oscillators.

FIG. 9-4 Sine-wave vacuum-tube oscillators

frequencies by means of a capacitor. The circuit then effectively becomes the same as if the plate were connected to the grounded side of the tuned circuit. Electron coupling occurs because the plate-circuit output voltages are coupled to the oscillating circuits through the electron stream rather than by any electrical element such as a capacitor. This isolates the output circuit so that changes due to load conditions are in no way reflected back into the frequency-determining circuits.

(G) DYNATRON OSCILLATOR. The dynatron oscillator may be called a two-terminal oscillator since a resonant circuit placed between its plate and cathode will oscillate continuously without feedback when the plate becomes a negative resistance. This condition occurs when the screen voltage is lowered below the plate voltage. The negative resistance thus produced balances the positive resistance existing in the way of losses in the resonant circuit itself, and allows natural oscillation to continue since the tube *supplies* power to the resonant circuit. A number of types of negative-resistance oscillators exist but the dynatron is the most common one. Owing to the variable nature of screen-current characteristics in the average receiver tube it has proved none too reliable in commercial use.

(H) RESISTANCE-CAPACITY OR PHASE-SHIFT OSCILLATORS. A resistance-coupled amplifier operating at low voltages with carefully proportioned feedback will develop sine waves quite satisfactorily at audio frequencies. If the phase and amplitude of feedback are accurately controlled by means of *RC* networks these oscillators will operate over a wider frequency range than the conventional tuned-circuit oscillator using an inductance and a variable capacity.

VACUUM TUBE RELAXATION OSCILLATORS

These oscillators are so named because they depend on the charge and discharge of a condenser when it is related to the voltage feedback, causing the grid in a vacuum tube to become blocked. *Blocking* is another expression for driving the grid of a vacuum tube beyond cut-off potential and holding it there for a significant time. The generated wave in relaxation oscillators is not a sine wave; usually it is rectangular, sawtooth, or some other irregular shape. Multivibrators or flip-flop oscillators are the most common types and illustrate their waveforms by dependence upon the rapid transition of plate current from beyond cut-off to the conducting condition. During condenser charge, we encounter the relaxation period alternately interspersed with the conduction period,

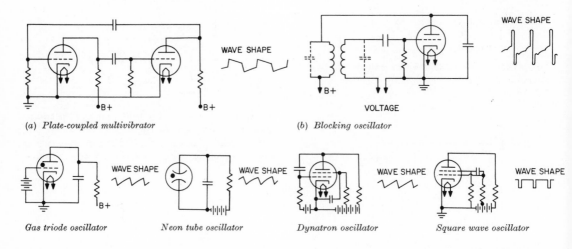

(a) *Plate-coupled multivibrator*   (b) *Blocking oscillator*

Gas triode oscillator   *Neon tube oscillator*   *Dynatron oscillator*   *Square wave oscillator*

FIG. 9-5 Summary of vacuum tube relaxation oscillator types and their respective wave shapes

representing condenser discharge. These two periods alternate to form a periodic cycle, starting generally at the beginning of each discharge cycle where triggering usually occurs. A summary of relaxation oscillator types and their respective wave shapes is given in Fig. 9–5, to which the following notes refer.

(A) MULTIVIBRATOR. This oscillator generates square or rectangular waves of alternating current which may or may not be symmetrical about the horizontal axis. (Fig. 9–5-(a)). In circuit detail, this is called the plate-coupled type, consisting of a two-stage resistance-coupled oscillator with feedback from the plate of the output tube V_2 through capacitor C_2 to the grid of the input tube V_1. Description of all types of multivibrators is beyond the scope of this book.

This oscillator is usually free-running and, in operation, is started by a sudden positive pulse of voltage (such as closing the power switch) which initiates a plate-current surge on, for example, V_2, which is transferred to the grid of V_1 where this grid is driven positive. In its positive condition, grid current flows and eventually develops enough voltage to cut off the plate current in V_1 and also to negatively charge the condenser C_1. After having been rapidly charged negatively to its maximum value for the duration of the applied pulse of voltage to the plate and causing the grid of V_2 to be removed far beyond its cut-off grid voltage, the condenser discharges through the resistor R_1 for an interval that is proportional in length to the values of the combination of R_1 and C_1. While the charge on the condenser is leaking off, the grid of V_1 slowly moves in a less negative direction to somewhere near zero bias; when it reaches that point, the plate current in V_1 suddenly jumps to full positive value. In doing this, it in turn drives the grid of V_2 positive in the same manner that grid 1 was driven positive, and the cycle is repeated. Plate-current excursions thus cause alternate pulses to be coupled to the following grids and cause blocking and unblocking on every other half-cycle. Output consists of rectangular pulses or square waves of voltage generated across either plate resistor R_3 or R_4. The size of the grid resistor and condenser combinations determines the frequency and width of the pulses. If both combinations are alike, the waves are symmetrical and of equal width; if the waves are unlike, the widths of the respective square pulses of plate voltage are alternately unlike.

(B) THE BLOCKING OSCILLATOR is a sine wave inductively coupled oscillator, in which grid blocking or relaxation is produced as in the multivibrator. The primary and secondary windings of T_1 (respectively in the grid and plate circuits of the oscillator tube) form, by themselves, an oscillating circuit, whose frequency is determined by the inductance of the respective coils and their own distributed capacity. If the R and C elements were short-circuited, the tube could be made to oscillate independently at some high audio frequency.

At the start of oscillation on the first positive plate-voltage swing, the grid is pushed into conduction so that it draws grid current, which instantaneously moves the grid negative and charges the condenser C so that the tube is blocked at cut-off. Only when the condenser C is again discharged through the resistor R can the grid assume normal amplifying voltage. So, until this happens, nothing is transferred through the transformer circuit.

At normal operating bias, the tube jumps into conduction, the generated pulse passes through the transformer again, a quarter-cycle of oscillation occurs, and the cycle is repeated.

This specialized type of oscillator has particular use where sharp pulse voltages are needed for triggering or for driving deflection circuits.

(C) SAWTOOTH OSCILLATORS. A neon tube placed across a condenser in a resistance-capacitor circuit will generate a sawtooth voltage waveform. The action again depends upon the charge and discharge of a condenser through a resistor. At the start, when battery voltage is applied, the neon lamp is not conducting so that voltage across the condenser C will start from zero and rise as current flows to fill it. At a certain voltage (about 62 volts for low-voltage neon lamps) the neon lamp suddenly conducts and acts as a short circuit, rapidly discharging the condenser. This action reduces the voltage across the neon lamp, which immediately becomes nonconducting, and the battery again starts to charge the condenser through the resistor R. This cycle repeats itself periodically, its frequency depending upon how large the resistor-condenser combination happens to be.

A neon lamp of another type has a grid located between the anode and cathode. Potential upon it regulates breakdown voltage and thus gives another control of the frequency. This oscillator was common in simple sweep circuits used by early oscilloscopes.

A sawtooth can be generated using the dynatron connection shown where slow charging of the grid condenser is followed by rapid discharge as the grid becomes sufficiently positive, giving the accompanying waveshape.

The square wave generated in the pentode oscillator (commonly used in sawtooth circuits) is attained in a manner similar to that used in triode multivibrators. Screen and control grids alternately block the plate current being controlled by condenser charge and discharge; common coupling is obtained electronically through the common plate current.

SPECIAL VACUUM TUBE OSCILLATORS (Figure 9–6).

(A) THE KLYSTRON OSCILLATOR capitalizes on the speed of flight of an electron as it travels from an emitter to the anode of an electron vacuum tube. At high frequencies this distance is often important, since the time required for an electron to traverse it is sometimes equal to the frequency of the oscillation. The klystron has an elongated electron path— sometimes feet in length—and utilizes this phenomenon physically by placing side by side in the path of the beam, two resonant

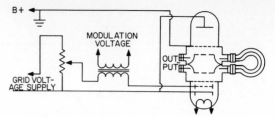

(A) KLYSTRON OSCILLATOR is used at ultra high frequencies. Frequency is adjustable over a small range.

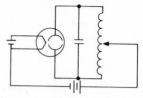

(B) MAGNETRON OSCILLATOR is used for centimeter waves and has a relatively large power output.

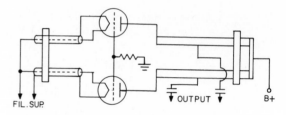

(C) HIGH FREQUENCY PUSH-PULL OSCILLATOR uses balanced circuits for minimizing tube capacity.

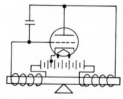

(D) MAGNETOSTRICTION OSCILLATOR is used for stability in audio circuits.

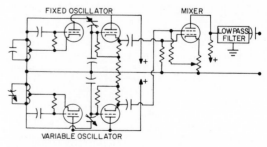

(E) BEAT FREQUENCY OSCILLATOR is used as audio generator and gives a wide audio range.

FIG. 9-6 Special vacuum tube oscillators

circuits plus a control grid structure. These circuits or resonator cavities are in the form of heavy, doughnut-shaped copper cylinders which are excited by the passage of electrons through the gridlike portion of the first doughnut structure located at a position on the tube's axis corresponding to the hole of the doughnut. This first circuit, by virtue of the circulating resonant currents (through its frame and grid structure), alternately speeds up and slows down sections of the electron stream as they go through the structure and between the grids. In passing through the resonator circuits magnetic and electrostatic forces act to "bunch" the electron stream periodically into groups; thus the circuit simulated by the cavity resonator is called the "buncher."

As these bunches of electron energy pass through the grid structure of the second resonator, called the "catcher," this circuit is also induced to resonant oscillation and generates relatively high power. Now, since the buncher and catcher resonator chambers are mechanically and electrically coupled, some feedback current returns from the catcher to the buncher and keeps it energized, dissipating only a small part of the total energy developed by the catcher. The whole operation is similar to the action of a normal oscillator acting like a self-energized Class C amplifier. The pulses of bunched electrons thus act like the pulses of oscillator grid current when they start the resonant circuit in the tuned-plate circuit on its first cycle of each new oscillation.

(B) THE MAGNETRON is an electron-tube structure utilizing magnets to deflect an electron beam. It capitalizes on the fact that an electron on its travel (even in the case of a cathode-ray tube) follows a spiral trajectory. In addition the electrons are acted upon by a strong magnet, so that they may be sufficiently spiralled and delayed and caused to circle around for several oscillations within the magnetic field before they reach the plate. After one such round trip, an electron has, in effect, completed a single oscillation and

has thus generated an alternating impulse. This is the basic principle on which the magnetron operates.

The frequency of the oscillations is governed by the strength of the magnetic field, the anode potential, the physical dimensions of the tube, and many variations including multiple or split anodes, plate accelerating anodes, and tilted magnetic fields. Peak power of several million watts may be obtained from magnetron oscillators at upper microwave frequencies. Their stability, simplicity of structure, and ease of modulation have led to their wide use in radar transmitter designs.

(c) THE PUSH-PULL OSCILLATOR takes two forms: (1) the two inductive sections of plate and grid circuits are mutually coupled magnetically to give the correct feedback to their respective grid circuits, or, (2) the opposite grid circuit and plate circuit are cross-connected to obtain the correct phase of feedback. The second circuit is called a two-terminal oscillator, since any single resonant circuit may be placed across the points A and B to produce oscillation regardless of the type of feedback.

Push-pull oscillators have some of the characteristics of push-pull amplifiers, the chief of which is that when the circuits are balanced the mid tap of the plate winding, by inherent symmetry, is electrically at ground potential. This feature is useful in high-frequency circuits where by-passing of such frequencies is difficult because of the inductance of the lead lengths of the by-pass capacitors. At these frequencies another advantage arises in that the tube capacities themselves are then in series with each other, permitting operation of the resonant circuit at higher frequencies than when the tubes are being operated in a parallel, single-ended mode. In Fig. 9–5(b) is shown a high-frequency push-pull oscillator employing a resonant circuit in both the plate and cathode circuits. This arrangement is equivalent to a tuned-grid, tuned-plate circuit, since cathode (or filament) excitation resulting from plate-current flow, gives the necessary feedback to sustain oscillation.

(D) THE MAGNETOSTRICTION OSCILLATOR makes use of the fact that a magnetized material changes both its electrical and physical dimensions. The effect, called magnetostriction, is utilized by placing the respective ends of a magnetic bar inside the plate and grid coils of a Hartley oscillator circuit, which are otherwise not magnetically coupled. If the grid and plate coils are part of an electrically resonant circuit of the same frequency *at which the magnetic bar is mechanically resonant*, feedback voltages are induced by the physical movement of the bar itself and sustained oscillations are produced. Such oscillators usually operate at audio frequencies and have the property of good frequency stability, being independent of tube and circuit variations and depending almost wholly on the realtively stable mechanical constants of the vibrating bar.

(E) THE BEAT-FREQUENCY OSCILLATOR is an electronic generator used extensively as a laboratory instrument and also in radio communication receivers. It consists of two radio-frequency oscillators, one of fixed frequency and the other variable, both feeding a detector and amplifier. The oscillator frequency ranges are so proportioned that variation in the variable unit produces a heterodyne beat note covering the audio-frequency spectrum.

TRANSISTOR OSCILLATOR CIRCUITS

Categorically, except for special oscillators, transistor oscillator circuits parallel those for vacuum tubes. Figure 9–7 illustrates the basic types; the operation of individual circuits follows that of their electron-tube counterparts.

RECTIFICATION AND DETECTION

All equipment measurements encounter at one time or another several forms of rectifi-

cation. Rectification is a general term and infers detection (or demodulation) when applied to the low-level signals encountered in receivers. It also refers to relatively high-power circuits in power supplies, and in transmitters it is allied to the function of modulation.

In power rectification of transmitter and receiver power supplies, the process is one of conversion—of converting a-c to d-c. In doing so rectification really extracts or *separates* the power-line frequencies from products of unidirectional conversion and delivers demodulated or resultant d-c, for operating potentials throughout an equipment's circuitry. The technician is concerned with testing and measuring the separated components.

POWER-RECTIFIER CIRCUITS. Equipment for converting alternating current into undirectional or direct current uses three basic circuit categories: (1) half-wave rectification, (2) full-wave rectification, (3) bridge circuits. Variations of these include voltage doubler circuits, transformerless arrangements, and a number of systems of constant voltage and constant current regulation. Details of these are given together with testing and measurement techniques in Chapter 21.

Basically, the power-rectification process utilizes (1) the unidirectional conduction feature of a power diode (whether it be a vacuum tube or a solid-state device), (2) the further demodulating of the applied power-line frequencies by means of filters, and finally (3) delivery or the processing of the resultant d-c by means of regulators or diodes to appropriately usable output terminals.

DIODE DETECTION CIRCUITS employ the same basic components and principles at a lower power level. Here we must have a unidirectional diode (a nonlinear triode plate characteristic can, however, be used), a suitable load circuit where *maximum transfer* of signal power is necessary, and a filter network which eliminates the undesired products of detection. In signal detection, however, there are usually *two* desired products of rectification:

(1) the modulation or informational a-c voltages riding on top of the applied and rectified carrier plus (2) the rectified d-c developed from direct rectification. This potential in high-gain, regulated signal amplifiers is used for automatic gain control by feeding it back to the main amplifier string so that the gain of its tubes or transistors may be altered to meet changing input-signal levels.

MODULATION

AMPLITUDE MODULATION (AM) in a radio or TV carrier wave utilizes nonlinear rectifier

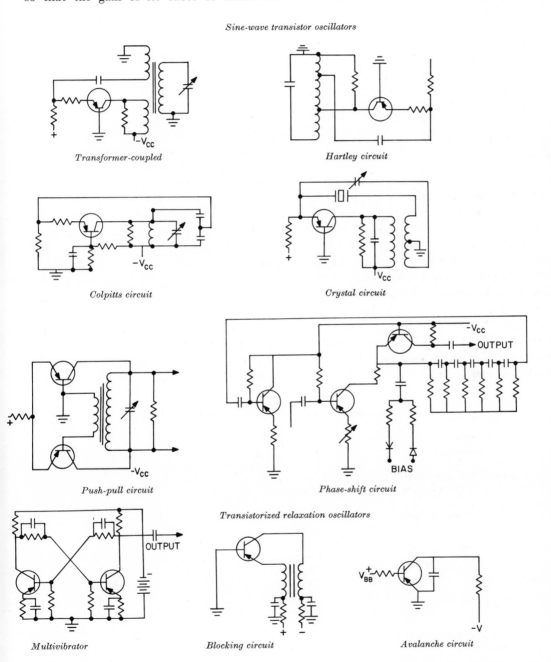

Sine-wave transistor oscillators

Transformer-coupled

Hartley circuit

Colpitts circuit

Crystal circuit

Push-pull circuit

Phase-shift circuit

Transistorized relaxation oscillators

Multivibrator

Blocking circuit

Avalanche circuit

FIG. 9-7 Transistor oscillator circuits

or detector characteristics to accomplish frequency conversion. It is a process which *converts through mixing* a pure RF carrier wave to one containing AF combined with RF components. The conversion consists of *generating* new sum- and difference-frequency currents derived from the addition and subtraction of AF currents to and from the carrier-frequency currents. The same frequency-conversion effects appear in a receiver when we mix the received carrier frequencies with those of a local oscillator and synthesize sum and difference frequencies, specifically using the latter in an IF amplifier chain to obtain more efficient low-frequency amplification.

FREQUENCY MODULATION (FM) applies intelligence to a carrier by nondetector techniques utilizing a reactance-tube modulator which shifts the mean carrier frequency in distance and frequency according to the varying amplitude and frequency of the modulating AF intelligence. Modulation, both in transmitters and receivers, is thus of prime importance. Details of measuring techniques concerning the AF products, distortion, efficiency, and other factors are covered in Chapters 17 and 18.

The Federal Communications Commission requires that all transmitters having significant power be licensed and classified in order to simplify labeling and specification of the various types. This classification briefly covers three types of modulation: amplitude modulation, frequency modulation, and pulse modulation. Under amplitude modulation we can include (1) speech and facsimilie, (2) television, and (3) telegraphy. Each of these has its special characteristics concerning the carrier, sidebands, amplitudes, frequency spacing, and so on.

For reference, or when measuring and testing, Table 9–2 lists the main types of modulation. Rectification or other conversion characteristics peculiar to each of these types of modulation will be discussed in Chapters 17 and 18. Based on this classification, the Federal Communications Commission has established a coding system for conveniently labeling transmitter modulation characteristics. (See Table 18–3.)

SYSTEM AND EQUIPMENT MEASUREMENT CONCEPT

Returning to the discussion of measurement levels, we take note that any measurement requires planning and preparation. The steps in planning and making a simple meter

Table 9–2   Transmitter modulation classifications

Type of modulation	Type of information	Supplementary characteristics
Amplitude modulation (AM)		Carrier
Continuous wave (CW)	No keying	Full
		Reduced
Conventional envelope	Telephony	Side band
	Facsimile	Single
		Independent
Pulse	Telegraphy	Pulse
	Simplex	Amplitude (PAM)
	Multiplex	Width (PWM)
	Frequency shift	Position (PPM)
	Television	
	Radar	
Frequency modulation (FM)		
Frequency		
Phase		

measurement are obvious; in a complex system we may have a whole set of conditions and requirements, all of which require planning, organization, specific procedures, and a great deal of instrumentation and operational support.

THE MEASUREMENT AND TESTING CYCLE

Basically, all measurements are concerned with (1) the kind of meter or device, (2) the means or circuit for using it, (3) some kind of eyeball indication (whether direct or indirect), and (4) finally, a step involving adjustments or manipulation of electrical quantities or component parts, plus the conclusion or interpretation of the observed results. Table 9–3

and inductance—are at the second level (see Table 9–1) and depend generally upon the combinations of first-level indications of voltage and current. The elementary approach is thus based on the application of Ohm's law and from calculations using the results of simple current and voltage readings under individual conditions of d-c or a-c signals and circuitry. Extending this method, we may use substitution methods in the basic circuit manipulations or we may measure our component by bridge methods. Figure 9–8 summarizes the d-c and a-c circuit approach to component measurement and the Ohm's-law calculation. Appendix A-10 describes variations

Table 9–3   The measurement cycle

ITEMS OF MEASUREMENT

CURRENT	VOLTAGE	FREQUENCY	IMPEDANCE	WAVEFORM	POWER	SELECT
Ammeter	Voltmeter	Counter Bridge Wavemeter	Volt-ammeter Volt-ohmmeter Bridge	Oscilloscope Distortion Meter	Wattmeter Absorption	Kind of meter
Series	Parallel	Parallel Coupled	Parallel Substitution	Parallel	Series-parallel Coupled	The circuit
Direct	Direct	Indirect	Indirect	Direct	Indirect	
		Balance Adjust	Balance Adjust	Synchronize Adjust		
Read	Read	Read	Read	Read	Read	Kind of reading adjustments

R E C O R D

shows these steps in diagrammatic form.

Following this diagram through at the second measurement level we see that the basic functional procedures concern current, voltage, frequency (or phase), impedance, waveform, or power, listed in the right-hand column.

MEASUREMENT OF PASSIVE COMPONENTS

OHM'S LAW. Passive component measurements—that is, of resistance, capacitance,

in these measurements for simple circuits by using a universal Ohm's-law calculator.

It should be noted that bridge circuits are used extensively in all measurements requiring extremely accurate results. Such instruments usually are within themselves complete measuring set-ups in which the input signal and the output indicator are self-contained. The procedure and the calculations necessary to make bridge measurements will be described further in Chapter 11, since this circuit is automatically categorized as an instrument.

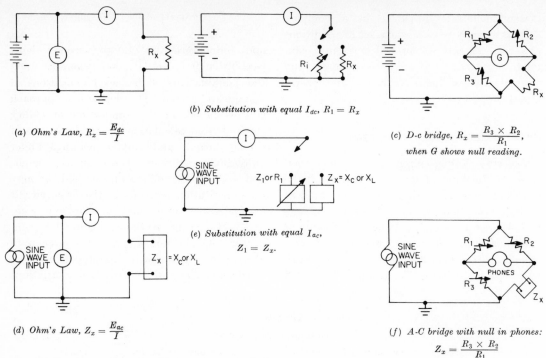

(a) Ohm's Law, $R_x = \dfrac{E_{dc}}{I}$

(b) Substitution with equal I_{dc}, $R_1 = R_x$

(c) D-c bridge, $R_x = \dfrac{R_3 \times R_2}{R_1}$, when G shows null reading.

(e) Substitution with equal I_{ac}, $Z_1 = Z_x$.

(d) Ohm's Law, $Z_x = \dfrac{E_{ac}}{I}$

(f) A-C bridge with null in phones: $Z_x = \dfrac{R_3 \times R_2}{R_1}$

FIG. 9-8 Summary of component measurement techniques

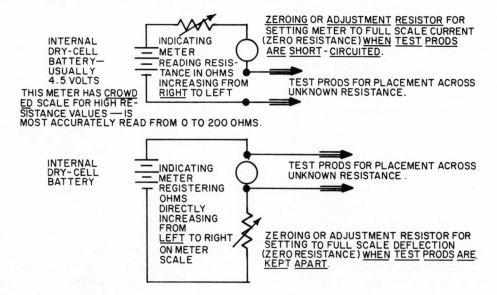

FIG. 9-9 Volt-ohmmeter set-up

RESISTANCE MEASUREMENTS are relatively simple, exemplifying the Ohm's-law procedure in the volt-ohmmeter set-up described in Fig. 9–9. (Details are given below.)

CAPACITANCE MEASUREMENTS are most commonly made by one of three basic methods.

1. Large capacitors from .01 to 10 MF use a commercial condenser checker. This device is based on Ohm's-law; the 110-volt, 60-cycle a-c power is the signal source and an a-c ammeter is the indicating device.

2. Capacitors from 1 MF down to a few micromicrofarads use the a-c bridge or for

158

FIG. 9-10 Commercial condenser checker

Typical Q-meter

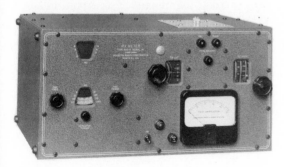

RX meter

FIG. 9-11 Instruments for measuring capacitance by the substitution method

extreme accuracy use a calibrated, self-contained RF source in conjunction with an indicating VTVM shown in Fig. 9–10.

3. For small values of capacitance the substitution method may be used on a Q-meter or on an RX checker. These instruments use an RF source and measure the resonance indication on a VTVM before and after the substitution measurement. Figure 9–11 shows a typical Q-meter and an RX checker.

INDUCTANCE MEASUREMENTS usually concern either (1) iron-cored chokes and transformers, which operate at audio frequencies, or (2) radio-frequency inductances.

Most audio-frequency measurements are made on conventional bridge equipments.

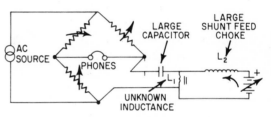

FIG. 9-12 Audio bridge inductance measurement

A departure from conventional procedure is sometimes necessary in measuring circuits where the coil, under some conditions, must carry direct current while the measurement is being made. Some power-supply filter chokes operate in this way. Figure 9–12 shows such a measurement set-up using an audio bridge. Choke L_2 usually has a value over 20 times that of the unknown L_1 so that its influence is negligible on the final measurement of L_1.

High-frequency inductors are best measured at their operating frequency. On the Q-meter or the RX checker the procedure is to resonate the coil under test by a self-contained variable capacitor and to then read resonance on the output meter. From the known value of the applied frequency and the value of the capacitor at the resonant setting the value of the inductor can be calculated. The use of the reactance chart described in Appendix A-7 is recommended for this procedure. If necessary, by calculation we solve:

$$L = \frac{1}{4 \times \pi^2 \times f^2 \times C}$$

where L is in henries, F is in cycles/sec, C is in farads.

EXAMPLE

If an unknown inductor resonates at 1 megacycle with a capacitor of 200 MMF, what is its value?

$$L = \frac{1}{4 \times (3.1416)^2 \times (10^6)^2 \times 200 \times 10^{-12}}$$
$$= 125 \, \mu h$$

Inductance measurements on the Q-meter or the RX checker have other implications because the measurement is not one of pure inductance. Besides inductance these meters measure the combined resistance losses associated with a coil due to the coil winding as well as all other induced losses due to high frequencies. This gives a figure of merit known as Q, which will be discussed in a later chapter.

NOTES ON BRIDGE CIRCUITS

In the course of all types of component measurement many variations in bridge circuitry have been evolved. Some versions use inductors, capacitors, or a combination of the two for various purposes and are referred to as resonance bridges, Maxwell bridges, Hay bridges, Wien bridges, or Shering bridges. These are covered in the next chapter.

Applying Ohm's law according to Fig. 9–8 is usually referred to as the *voltmeter-ammeter* method. This most direct method of measuring the value of a resistance connects it across a known voltage while measuring the current through the resistor. (See Fig. 9–8(a).) The readings obtained are inserted in the Ohm's-law equation and the resistance is thus calculated. Practically, we may find that the unknown resistance is so low that an excessive current flows. In this case a current-limiter resistor must be inserted in the circuitry as shown.

In other cases, an appreciable error may be encountered in using the voltmeter-ammeter method because of the current taken by the voltmeter or by the voltage drop across the ammeter. Two general cases of error may be particularly noted:

1. If, for example, a relatively low-resistance voltmeter is connected directly across the resistor the current reading will not be true, since the ammeter will read the voltmeter current as well as the resistor current.

2. If the voltmeter is connected outside the ammeter, the ammeter will read the actual current through the resistor, but the voltmeter will read the voltage drop across the resistor plus the ammeter in series.

Frequently these errors are *not* negligible. They may be made negligible by connecting the voltmeter in the proper place. Thus, if the voltmeter current is appreciable compared with the load current, the voltmeter should be connected ahead of the ammeter. If the drop across the ammeter is appreciable, a voltmeter should be connected across the load. In some cases the error will be appreciable for either connection, and correction must be made.

Indicating Meters and Measurement Procedures

10

DIRECT INDICATING METERS

Any measurement requires, first, some physical stimulus to the human brain. The brain may respond to the visual stimulus of light reflected from a meter pointer or emitted by a lamp. Or the response may be auditory—to bells, a loudspeaker, or buzzers emitting musical tones. In auditory sensing, of course, loudness or output can not be accurately measured.

Table 11–1 lists under meters the general categories and the special types of direct indicating meters to be discussed below.

D-C METERS

Fundamentally, all meters (except the electrostatic type) measure current and in this sense are ammeters. When they have low internal resistance so as to produce no effect on a circuit's performance and are actuated through direct connection in series with the main current path, they are truly ammeters. When they have high resistance so that they may be placed in shunt or directly across a voltage source (without affecting it) they are called *voltmeters* and of course under these conditions draw a minimum of current. Their indication of voltage is based on the product of a known, internal calibrated resistance in series with the meter movement, and the current flowing through that resistance.

Most meters are constructed to use the attractive and repulsive force characteristics of magnetic structures to produce deflection of a pointer. In the most common, permanent-magnet type mutual force is exerted upon a movable, pivoted coil which itself becomes a magnet (upon which the pointer is mounted) when it passes d-c current being measured. To elaborate: when a movable magnet is mounted in the field of a fixed permanent magnet and when it is passing current of the correct polarity, a force is exerted upon the movable magnet. In the resultant alignment of the fields, definite and proportional movement is produced against the restraining force of a spring connected to the pivoted coil. Deflection is arranged to be proportional to the amount of current through the coil, so that when the meter scale over which the pointer moves is calibrated, a true indication of current is obtained.

Figure 10–1 shows the basic d-c meter movement using the pivoted coil and a permanent magnet (PM). This basic construction is sometimes called the Weston meter movement. The electrodynamometer type of instrument, which is less common than the PM type, employs the same basic moving-coil mechanism but uses a fixed electromagnetic field actuated by current which is related to or proportional to that in the moving coil. Figure 10–2 shows a typical movement of this type.

When the current through a circuit is sent through the fixed-magnet coil and the voltage across it applied to the movable coil, this

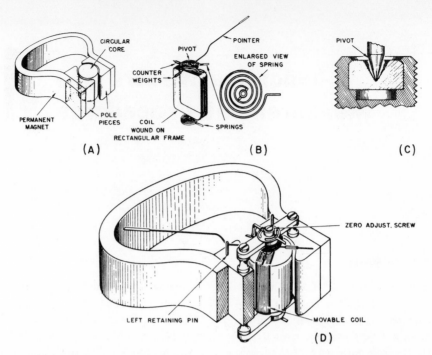

FIG. 10-1 Basic d-c meter movement using pivoted coil and permanent magnet

instrument becomes a wattmeter, since deflection is then proportional to the product of voltage and current.

Dynamometers are less flexible than the PM type meters, less sensitive, and generally more expensive. Their basic arrangement, however, allows them to be used on either a-c or d-c when appropriate scale, multiplier,

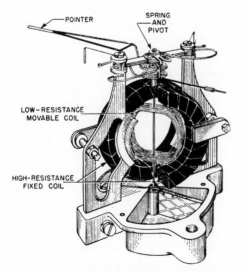

FIG. 10-2 D-c meter movement using electrodynamometer type of instrument

and shunt arrangements are included in their internal circuitry.

THE MOVING IRON-VANE TYPE is the most common a-c meter. In it, induced eddy currents are used to produce magnetic force on a structure bearing a pivoted pointer and a thin iron element called a vane. The vane has no coil. The stationary magnetic field (also eddy-current actuated) is produced by a single current-carrying coil surrounding both the fixed metal element and the pointer movement. This coil is so arranged that its *own* field induces a field in the moving vane and in addition generates attractive or repulsive magnetic forces with respect to its own self-produced magnetic field. Deflection is basically proportional to the current through the main coil.

Figure 10–3(a)-(b) shows two arrangements of the vanes: (1) a radial type, aimed to give a logarithmic deflection, and (2) a concentric type, intended for linear deflection.

Moving iron-vane meters usually have relatively low impedances (without multi-

162

pliers) and are simple and inexpensive. They measure either voltage or current, but their use must be restricted to the frequency for which they are designed.

RECTIFIER TYPE METERS utilize permanent-magnet d-c movements actuated by current

developed from rectifying the applied a-c being measured. Rectifier elements mounted within the meter case may be copper oxide, selenium, germanium, or silicon. The developed d-c is proportional to the applied a-c, while the rectifiers and associated circuitry are designed for operation over as wide a band of frequency as possible. Figure 10–4 shows electrical arrangement of the rectifier units.

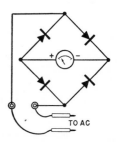

FIG. 10-4 Electrical arrangement of rectifier meters

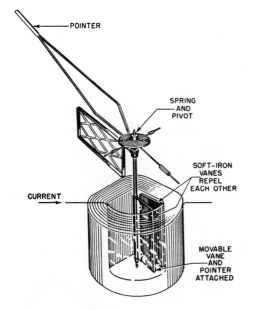

(a) Radial arrangement

SPECIAL METERS

THE HOT-WIRE AMMETER has a pointer actuated by heat-induced expansion or lengthening of a wire caused by current passing through it. The arrangement of the pointer, and the mechanical movement caused by the heated wire, are shown in Fig. 10–5.

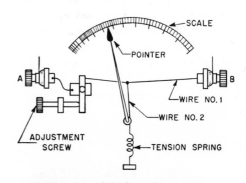

FIG. 10-5 Operation of the hot-wire ammeter

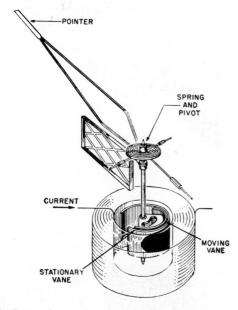

(b) Concentric arrangement

FIG. 10-3 Two arrangements of the moving iron-vane a-c meter

THERMOCOUPLE meters convert applied current (a-c or d-c) by thermoelectric effects into deflection currents which register on a PM moving-coil meter. The conversion is through a thermocouple actuated by heat generated at the junction formed by two strips of dissimilar metal. One strip carries the heat-generating input currents; the other carries

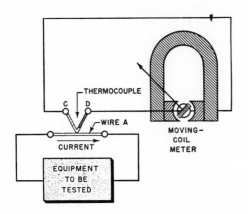

FIG. 10-6 Arrangement of thermocouple meters

heat-produced d-c currents to the meter movement. (See Fig. 10–6.)

Thermocouple meters are used to measure a wide range of either a-c or d-c currents and give an accurate picture of the *effective*, or heat-producing, value of a current no matter what its nature. The meters are relatively expensive, and the thermal delay in converting input electricity to heat makes them sluggish.

ELECTROSTATIC VOLTMETERS are designed specifically for high-voltage measurements— 5,000 to 100,000 volts—and they are relatively large owing to the spacing between the stationary and moving element that is necessary to avoid breakdown. They operate through the electrostatic repulsion produced by input voltage-charged condenser plates. Figure 10–7 shows a typical design.

CLIP-ON METERS are a-c ammeters that measure current through a lead by clipping around it a coupling loop connection from the meter circuitry. (See Fig. 10–8.) The device operates through transformer action; the current-bearing lead acts as a one-turn primary which induces a-c voltage in the multiturn clip-around circuit. The transformation produces a-c through the meter, which is correctly calibrated so as to correct for the transformation ratio and effectively read out the current through the lead being tested.

THE DIGITAL VOLTMETER is a completely automatic, direct read-out instrument which displays its measurements of d-c voltage as a row of illuminated numerals in the decimal number system. (See Fig. 10–9.)

Such meters automatically measure voltage by the comparison method; that is, for any single measurement they automatically generate or provide an internal voltage equal to the unknown input by successively adding

FIG. 10-8 Clip-on meter

FIG. 10-7 Electrostatic voltmeter

FIG. 10-9 Reed relay battery operated digital voltmeter

(or subtracting) known measured voltages to (or from) the initial internal voltage (after it has been compared to the unknown) until equality or balance has been attained. The internal mechanism, in other words, by means of an error detector senses initial unbalance between the input and the internal voltage and initiates action by stepping switches or by electronic switches to bring the two voltages to equality, where the final generated voltage is read out or displayed.

DVM's, as they are called, are accurate, convenient, and fully automatic. No adjustments of knobs, scales, polarity, or anything else are necessary. They possess high impedance and are extremely rugged.

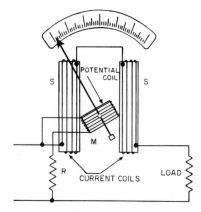

(a) *Operation of the wattmeter*

(b) *A typical wattmeter*

FIG. 10-10 The wattmeter

THE WATTMETER, conventionally a 60-cycle power meter, is not frequently used in the modern electronic laboratory. This is because phase differences are difficult to handle, and because power consumption and losses at communication frequencies have a different significance and are usually not measured by direct-reading meters. In the case of transmitters, where considerable power exists, dissipative methods are used.

Briefly, in 60-cycle measurements the wattmeter has a dynamometer movement; load current is sent through one coil and load-proportional voltage produces a current which is sent through the other. Phase differences between the two inputs reflect themselves in the repulsive or attractive forces between the coils, and a true reading of power is given by the final deflection. (See Fig. 10–10.)

A wattmeter has two sets of terminals— heavy, current-carrying terminals and smaller load-voltage terminals. Correct connection of these for power measurement is analogous to the volt-ammeter procedure discussed later in this chapter.

METER CHARACTERISTICS

Meters may vary widely in type, size, and in current or voltage characteristics. Table 10–1 summarizes the models used in the commercial meter field. Sizes, shapes, mount-

Table 10-1   Direct indicating meters

General Categories:

Voltmeters	a-c or d-c
Ammeters	
Wattmeter	a-c or d-c
Frequency	Reed type

Types:

Moving coil	d-c
Electrodynamometer	wattmeter
Iron vane	a-c
Thermal	a-c and d-c
Rectifier	a-c current or voltage
Clip-on	a-c only
Electrostatic	d-c (high voltage)

FIG. 10-11 Varieties of meters

ings, and other general physical characteristics are shown in the photographs of Fig. 10–11.

Laboratory meters are usually mounted in a case or holder having easily accessible terminals. Many types are heavily shielded from stray magnetic fields or from electrostatic interference.

Diameters may range from less than an inch up to a foot or more, the latter for powerhouse control panels where visibility and accuracy are the prime considerations.

Sensitivity of a meter depends, in general, upon the size and weight of its movement and the efficiency of its magnetic circuitry. The index of sensitivity is given in the amount of current required to produce full-scale deflection and is directly linked to the meter's internal resistance, which in ohms per volt is really a current index.

Ammeter current ranges are extended by using a meter shunt, a calibrated precision resistor which is connected in parallel across the meter terminals to by-pass most of the main current being measured. The ammeter and shunt together constitute a current divider, since the meter deflects only a given *proportion* of the total current through the main circuit or that amount which passes through it in going around the shunt.

Voltage dividers, in a similar way, deliver to the meter for final indication only a small portion of the total voltage appearing across it.

MEASUREMENT PROCEDURES

The techniques involving direct indicating meters are presented below in the form of step-by-step procedures for the various types

of measurement. These steps are, in general, functionally common to all measurements.

MEASUREMENT OF DIRECT CURRENT

Direct-current measurements in electronic equipment circuitry are chiefly concerned with electron-tube or transistor circuits and

FIG. 10-12 Basic current and measurement set-up

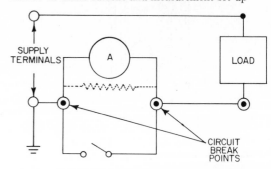

(a)

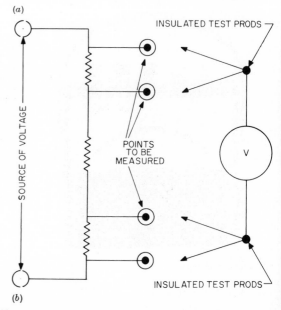

(b)

166

deal with values in milliamperes, seldom ranging over one ampere except in power installations and in total power supply sections.

OBJECT: To ascertain the current passing between two points in the series path of significant electron flow in a circuit. (See basic schematic, Fig. 10–12.)

SELECT:

1. Appropriate meter having correct scales, shunts, etc.
2. Set meter scale to correct anticipated value.

CONNECT:

1. With all power off, open the circuit to be measured and provide terminals for the insertion of meter so that current flow must be *through* the meter.
2. Before measurements are made, arrange for a short-circuiting meter switch across the meter terminals in order to pass current *around* the meter between measurements.

This short-circuiting or shunting switch is a convenience and not to be associated with calibrated *meter shunts* used in conjunction with meter readings. It should always be closed except when taking measurements.

NOTES: Always arrange the meter and short-circuiting switch on the lowest possible potential point in the circuit being measured.

Check meter ranges before removing the short circuit; if the range is variable, start with a range higher than anticipated for the measurement.

Be sure meter resistance is negligible with respect to the rest of the circuit being measured.

MEASUREMENT OF D-C VOLTAGE

OBJECT: To obtain (1) the total potential from a point in an operating circuit *to ground* or (2) the potential *drop* between two points in an operating circuit.

SELECT:

1. Appropriate meter having correct resistance.

2. Set correct scale or start with higher than needed.

CONNECT:

1. In point-to-ground measurements attach the meter ground terminal firmly to chassis frame or other ground. (D-c voltage measurements in probably 95 percent of all cases are measured from the point in question to ground. This is the value listed in most instruction books and on commercial schematics. Often these same points are used for resistance measurements to ground.)
2. Touch or lightly attach meter test prod to terminal for trial measurement and finally attach firmly by spring clamp or "alligator" type lead.

READ: Average value of scale selected (if reading is fluctuating) in order to smooth out transient inputs that produce "wobble" beyond that taken care of by the inertia of the meter movement.

NOTES: Arrange to take high-voltage meter readings using insulated, long shaft prods to remove the possibility of personal injury from accidentally touching adjacent equipment.

The actual high-voltage prod should always be *attached last* and *removed first;* and *never without ground terminal connected.*

In "drop" voltage measurements, since both test prods may be connected above ground, the operator must be extremely careful to have no physical contact with *the metallic part of either* test prod. It is preferable to grasp the insulating handles of both prods at once and *simultaneously* touch on the two points in question.

Remember that if one or another of the prods is not at ground the *whole* meter may have voltage on it and prove hazardous.

MEASUREMENT OF ALTERNATING CURRENT

Most electronic equipments (with the exception of power transmitters) deal with low-power, 60-cycle or 400-cycle alternating current ranging from 1 to generally not more than 20 amperes. General procedure is the same as that applying to direct-current measurements.

OBJECTIVE: To measure the current through a circuit by introducing a meter between two separate terminals which interrupt (are in series with) the path of energy flow.

SELECT:
1. Proper range meter capable of passing the required amperage.
2. Adjust meter range switch to correct or to next larger meter current range.

CONNECT:
1. Open the circuit and provide terminals for insertion of meter so that a-c will flow *through* it.
2. Arrange for short-circuiting meter switch across the measurement terminals in order to pass current *around* the meter between measurements.

This short-circuiting switch should always be closed *except* when taking measurements; it is a convenience not to be associated with *meter shunts* used in conjunction with meter readings.

NOTES: Always arrange the meter and short-circuiting switch on the lowest possible potential point in the circuit being measured. Check meter ranges before removing the short circuit—if the meter range is variable start with a range higher than anticipated for the measurement.

Be sure meter resistance is negligible with respect to the rest of the circuit being measured.

Insure that *no d-c can pass* through the a-c meter movement. If d-c is present across the main terminals use a large capacitor (of sufficient voltage rating) between one or both of the terminals and the a-c current meter.

MEASUREMENT OF A-C VOLTAGE

Two types of a-c are usually present in most equipment:
1. The a-c concerned with power devices such as filaments or synchros.
2. A-c signal voltages passing through an equipment's circuits.

Signal impulses are usually in one of the communications bands and are not subject to the use of direct-reading meters unless they are of relatively low frequency.

OBJECT: To obtain the a-c potential difference between two points in an operating circuit.

SELECT:
1. Appropriate meter with regard to impedance, voltage capability, and frequency range.
2. Set or switch meter scales for correct correspondence to measured signal.

CONNECT:
1. Connect meter ground lead firmly to chassis frame or other ground if a point-to-ground measurement is being made. If a "drop" or series voltage measurement is being made, plan to connect the test prods *across* the two points whose difference is to be measured.
2. Touch test leads lightly across the measurement points before firmly attaching for final measurement.

READ: Scale indications, accounting for variations. Check meter for zero-set conditions.

NOTE: High-voltage a-c measurements require the same practices noted in high d-c voltage readings. Use insulated leads and always remove the ground connection last.

Electronic Instruments: 11
Voltmeters, Ohmmeters, Bridges

Many *instruments* are erroneously called meters; commercially we use vacuum tube volt*meters*, ohm*meters*, *Q-meters*, and so on, each one giving ultimate indication on a *meter movement* but at the same time requiring a considerable amount of auxiliary circuitry and many supporting components.

For this reason it is necessary to distinguish *direct indicating meters* (described in Chapter 10), which essentially consist of meter movements, from *electronic instruments*, which are functionally more complicated and sophisticated but which also deliver their final indication by way of a meter movement. (See Table 11–1.)

This terminology would classify a vacuum tube voltmeter as an instrument; a common wattmeter would be an indicating meter. Likewise a simple volt-ohmmeter would be classified as an instrument, although it is not much more complicated than a multirange direct indicating voltmeter. Most frequency meters involve relatively complicated circuits and accordingly are classed as instruments; there are, however, a number of special, direct-reading, reed-type frequency indicating meters (having a limited range), which are truly meters according to this classification.

Instruments, as we shall see, in adding complexity to a basic functional measurement usually contribute valuable characteristics over and above those possessed by the indicating meter using simple magnetics and electricity. The vacuum tube voltmeter (VTVM), for instance, in measuring pure voltage across a low-impedance source, often does no better than a conventional voltmeter. It does, however, have the added attribute of placing a negligible shunt load (say, of the order of 10 to 100 megohms) across the voltage source being measured, thus adding to the accuracy and other qualities of the measurement when the voltage source increases in impedance. In many cases, even a high-accuracy conventional voltmeter (having, say, 100,000 ohms impedance) would never suffice since its own current drain would pull down the true voltage. A striking example is the necessity of using an electronic high-impedance meter when taking a measurement across the output of a phototube whose internal impedance may be of the order of several megohms.

In defense of low-impedance simple indicating meters, their use is recommended in the measurement of current. Instrument meters can only indirectly indicate current by measuring voltage across a current-carrying resistor. This, in some cases, is not as simple as merely inserting a meter movement coil itself directly in a current path, although the latter procedure in heavy-current circuits usually requires use of a very low shunt resistor anyway.

Two of the more popular VTVM's are shown in Fig. 11–1.

Table 11-1 Summary of electronic instruments

Electrical and component measurement meters	Meters	Radio frequency and microwave meters	Special purpose meters
Electrical Quantities	*Time and Frequency*	*Power*	*Magnetic*
Watts	Direct frequency meter*	Field strength meter	Flux meter
Kilowatts	Output meter	Deviation meter	Gaussmeter
Volts	Phase angle meter*	Thermal meter	Magnetometer
Kilovolts	Decibel meter	Bolometer	Tachometer
Microvolts	Counters	Noise meter	
Power-factor	Elapsed-time meter		*Electro-mechanical and other*
Amperes	Vibrating reed meter*	*Impedance*	Goniometer
Microamperes	Oscilloscope	Standing wave meter	Speedometer (tachometer)
Charge (electrometer)	Grid-dipmeter*	Wavemeters: absorption,	Mach-meter
Resistance		reaction, heterodyne	Dosimeter
Conductance	*Waveform*	Q-meter	Accelerometer
	Noise meter	R-X checker	Light meter
Components	Distortion meter	Slotted line	Infrared meter
Ohmmeter	Modulation and		Pyrometer
Megohmmeter	intermodulation meter		Spectral analyzer
Capacity meter	WOW meter		Vibration meter
Impedance meter	Flutter meter		Radiation meter
	Ratiometer		X-ray intensity meter
	Rate meter		Straingauge
	Rise-time meter		Micromanometers
	Oscilloscope		Ultraviolet meters
			pH meter
			Hygrometer
			Audiometer
			Pressure gauge
			Fuel gauge

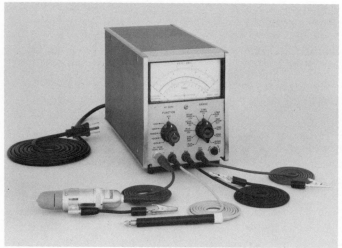

FIG. 11-1 Typical electronic VTVM's

Electronic instruments are used to measure six basic characteristics (besides current) found in electronic circuits. Referring to Table 9–3, these basic functions and their variations are:

Voltage
Impedance
Waveform
Ohms (Pure Resistive)
Frequency
Phase

Electronic and functional description covering instruments categorized as above will constitute the remainder of this chapter plus some of the material in Chapter 13, covering the oscilloscope.

ELECTRONIC VOLTMETERS

Instrument voltmeters, universally vacuum tube voltmeters, may be sub-categorized into three main groups:

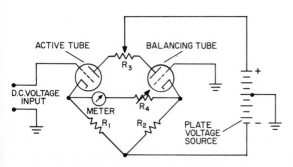

(a) *Functional arrangement*

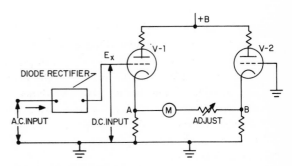

(b) *Practical arrangement*

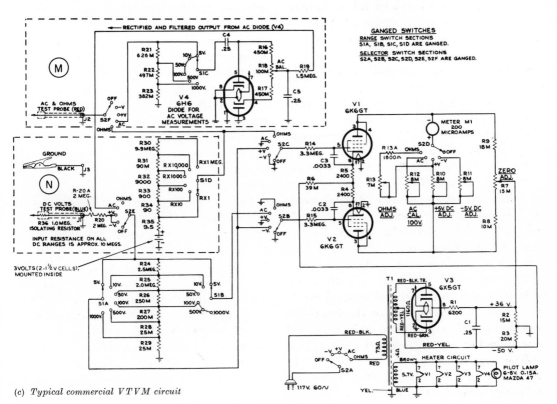

(c) *Typical commercial VTVM circuit*

FIG. 11-2 Typical balanced bridge vacuum tube voltmeter circuit

1. *Balanced bridge type* (using triode amplifiers). This is the most commonly used of laboratory or commercial service meters. It includes ohmmeter and a-c measurement provisions.

2. *Diode peak reading or rectifying type* (using d-c amplifiers).

3. *Triode rectifying and amplifying type.*

THE BALANCED BRIDGE VOLTMETER

This is the basic laboratory and service type vacuum tube voltmeter. It obtains sensitivity by using the difference produced by d-c input voltages on two d-c amplifier tubes whose plate circuits represent the arms of a modified bridge circuit. The unbalance of the plate currents caused by this difference voltage reflects itself in amplified cathode currents (and voltages) which in turn cause meter deflection.

Figure 11–2(a) shows the functional arrangements of a typical balanced bridge vacuum tube voltmeter circuit. Figure 11–2(b) is a practical arrangement. It operates as follows: If the input voltage on V_1 is zero, the two tubes are operating at the same grid voltage; hence, the potential difference across A-B is zero and the meter reading is zero. If E_x is made positive, the plate current of V_1 will increase, and the potential of point A will decrease. Hence, point B is positive with respect to a point A, and the milliammeter will read upscale. If E_x were made negative, the potential of point A would rise because of the decrease of plate current in V_1, and the meter would read down-scale. Thus, this circuit may be used for measuring d-c voltages of either polarity with respect to ground.

This circuit is extremely sensitive, has a high input impedance, and is invulnerable to excess input voltage since the imbalance caused by such a condition rapidly cuts off one or another of the tubes without too much voltage appearing across the meter. The function of measuring a-c input voltages can be easily added to the basic circuit by converting the input a-c to d-c through rectification. This provision, as used in a typical commercial model, is shown in part M of the sectionalized schematic, Fig. 11–2(c).

In order to convert this VTVM to an ohmmeter, we merely switch in a small d-c battery with voltage so interconnected at the measuring terminals that the d-c voltage is resultant to the ohm-current-voltage relationship appearing across the grid of the input vacuum tube. The circuitry providing this feature parallels the common volt-ohmmeter procedure outlined further on in this chapter. This function is shown in section N of the schematic, Fig. 11–2(c).

DIODE PEAK READING TYPE

The diode peak reading meter is most commonly used for measurement of a-c and most particularly RF sine waves. Figure 11–3(a) shows a typical shunt circuit where the diode acts as a half-wave rectifier when its associated capacitor holds the charge between positive sine-wave peaks. The net load current (shown in M) and the resultant voltage developed across R represent a d-c quantity proportional to the applied voltage. Most meters of this type use a d-c amplifier to obtain a suitable output meter indication.

The diode part of such meters is usually encased in a measuring probe at the end of a cable; the d-c amplifier and the output meter are within the accompanying meter case. The output is linear with respect to the input voltage.

Figure 11–3(b) shows a series diode peak reading meter. Here the input pulses or half sine waves appear in rectified form across the cathode resistor and its shunting capacitor. Rectified charging voltage is thus applied to a d-c amplifier and its accompanying indicating output meter. To extend the range of such a meter, an amplifier stage is sometimes inserted before the diode circuitry (see Fig. 11–3(c).) This arrangement aims, by inserting a cathode follower and an amplifier ahead of the diode, to lower the instrument's parallel input capacity and associated loading effects

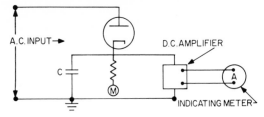

(a) *Shunt type*

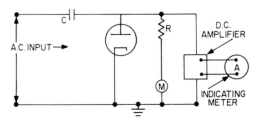

(b) *Series type*

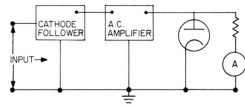

(c) *Amplifier-rectifier type*

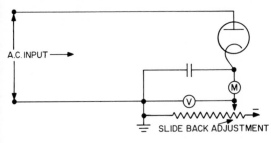

(d) *Slide-back type*

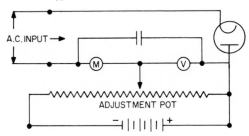

(e) *Trough type*

FIG. 11-3 Diode peak reading voltmeters

across the measuring point. Rectification, amplification, and indication are by the series or shunt methods described above. The limitation of this type of instrument depends upon

how much its high-frequency range is limited by the bandwidth of the preamplifier.

THE SLIDEBACK DIODE PEAK READING METER has the circuitry shown in Fig. 11–3(d). The bucking voltage developed across V is adjusted to make the signal current meter, M, read zero when input is applied. The adjusted reading then equals the peak of the applied-signal sine or pulse waveforms.

A TROUGH TYPE slideback meter (Fig. 11–3 (e)) is used to measure the minimum positive voltage of an a-c wave superimposed on a larger d-c voltage. By reversal of the cathode and plate terminals and the battery polarity, the voltage indicated at V is a minimum positive excursion of the a-c cathode voltage with respect to the plate voltage.

TRIODE AMPLIFIER VOLTMETERS

The following triode vacuum tube voltmeter circuits employ the basic principles of diode circuits. Figure 11–4(a) differs from diode circuits in that the triode input utilizes half-

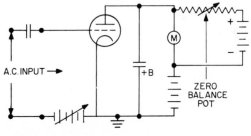

(a) *Plate rectifier type*

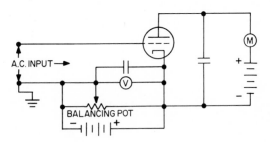

(b) *Slide-back type*

FIG. 11-4 Triode amplifier voltmeters

wave rectification in its grid, the effects of which are amplified and appear as plate current. Changes in plate current are proportional to input voltage after grid bias voltage adjustment and after bucking out the zero signal plate current. The circuit in Fig. 11–4(b) uses the slideback input potentiometer principle described in Fig. 11–3(d).

THE OHMMETER

This meter is in effect a complete resistance-measuring circuit within itself since it consists of a battery, adjustable-range resistances, a switch, and a sensitive meter movement. The measuring action is based on Ohm's law: any unknown external resistance placed between the ohmmeter test-prod terminals will deliver a known current when the source voltage and the additional, switched-in series resistance are known. The current (and meter deflection) is therefore inversely proportional to the resistance. If the meter scale is appropriately marked in ohms, we have a direct-reading measuring instrument.

The ohmmeter is a basic test *instrument* along with the direct-reading voltmeters and ammeters. For laboratory and commercial applications the single meter movement in an ohmmeter can be switched free of its ohmmeter function for direct measurement of voltage and current. Rectifying elements within the meter can be switched into its circuitry so that the instrument can measure a-c as well. In these combined roles, the instrument is called a *multimeter* or a *volt-ohmmeter*, as distinguished from an electronic VTVM, which as noted above has volt-ohmmeter provisions.

The multimeter is almost universal in its application. Besides all the basic functions it can be combined with a simple detector probe and other auxiliary devices for RF voltage, circuit continuity, and many other handy measurements. The present discussion is concerned only with the non vacuum tube type.

There are two types of ohmmeter: *series* and *shunt*. The difference concerns whether the resistance to be measured is connected in series or in parallel with the meter.

SERIES OHMMETER

In the basic ohmmeter circuit of Fig. 11–5(a), a variable resistor, R_1, and a fixed resistor, R_2, are connected in series with a milliammeter. The two leads P_1 and P_2 represent test prods which are connected across the resistance to be measured, R. The placing of the prods across an unknown resistor connects it in series with the ohmmeter circuit so that the current is reduced. For an inserted zero resistance the meter pointer would read full-

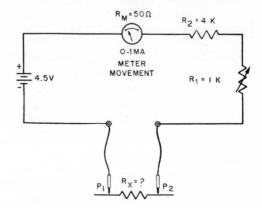

(a) *Simple basic circuit*

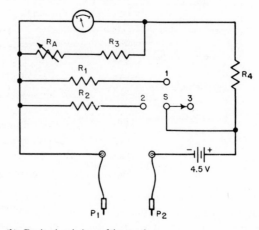

(b) *Basic circuit in multirange form*

FIG. 11-5 Series ohmmeter circuits

scale, and for greater resistances would read proportionately less. This circuit has range limitations, for if the value of R_x is equal to the combined resistance of the meter, the total circuit resistance is then limited to twice R_x and the meter pointer is deflected only half-scale.

Such meters usually have a 0- to 1-ma movement, requiring 1 ma of current for full-scale deflection; the internal resistance thus is 50 ohms. The fixed resistor R_2 limits the flow of current; it prevents damage in case the variable resistor is adjusted to some value low enough to exceed the meter's reading. The variable resistor R_1 adjusts the series resistance in the circuit so that 1 ma flows and full deflection exists when the test prods are shorted together. This full-scale deflection position of the needle corresponds to the condition when we wish to measure zero resistance; consequently, low values of resistance are read at this end of the meter scale. The opposite end of the scale accordingly represents highest resistance readings.

To maintain correct scale calibration, we use this same full-scale deflection condition, for when the battery ages (and its available voltage decreases), the variable resistor R must be adjusted to the zero, full-scale position. Location of zero resistance and other points on the ohmmeter scale can be calibrated conveniently from the formula:

$$R_x = R_c \times \frac{I_1 - I_2}{I_2}$$

where R_x = unknown resistance,
$\quad R_c$ = total circuit resistance with prods shorted together,
$\quad I_1$ = ohmmeter current with prods shorted,
$\quad I_2$ = ohmmeter current with R_x connected across prods.

The series-ohmmeter circuit can not be used to accurately measure the low resistances of coils, chokes, and transformer windings, which are often 5 ohms or less. These low values of resistance produce crowding on the right-hand side of the meter scale so that distinction between them is impossible. For example, if a resistance of 500 ohms causes the ohmmeter

pointer to deflect over nine-tenths of the scale, any value less than 500 ohms must be read within the crowded limits of the final one-tenth scale division.

Figure 11–5(b) shows the basic circuit in *multirange* form.

SHUNT OHMMETER

Low values of resistance can be measured accurately by means of a shunt ohmmeter (Fig. 11–6). The unknown resistor, R_x, is shunted across the meter and some of the current in the circuit takes the path through R_x. If R_x is reduced, the current through the meter is also reduced and the amount of deflection drops proportionately. The current flowing through the meter thus depends on the ratio of the shunt resistance, R_x, to the internal resistance R_m. When the meter

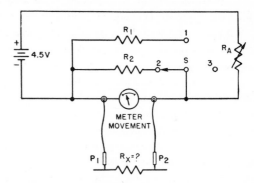

(a) *Basic*

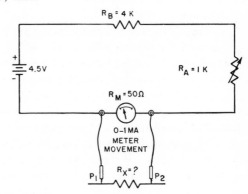

(b) *Multirange*

FIG. 11-6 Shunt ohmmeter circuits

resistance is known, the value of R_x can be determined from the following formula:

$$R_x = R_m \times \frac{I_1}{I_1 - I_2}$$

R_x = unknown resistance,
R_m = meter resistance,
I_1 = ohmmeter current—R_x not in circuit,
I_2 = ohmmeter current—R_x in circuit.

The entire meter scale can be calibrated by means of the formula given above. The indicated resistance value increases progressively from left to right, reading maximum resistance value on the meter full-scale deflection. This is the reverse of the scale used with the series circuit of Fig. 11–5.

As shown in Fig. 11–6(a), with test prods P_1 and P_2 open, R_a is adjusted to provide full-scale deflection on the meter, and so that a current of 1 ma flows through the circuit.

When the test prods are connected across the unknown resistor, R_x, placing it in shunt with the meter, the current flowing in the ohmmeter circuit divides at the junction of the meter and R_x, part of it flowing through R_x and the rest flowing through the meter. The current through the meter is directly proportional to the resistance of R_x and causes a reduced deflection of the meter pointer. For example, when the value of R_x is the same as the 50-ohm internal resistance of the meter, the current in the circuit divides equally, one-half flowing through the meter and one-half through R_x, so that the pointer deflects only half-scale.

Shunting the meter resistance with resistor R_x, has negligible effect on the total resistance of the ohmmeter circuit, since the combined resistance is less than 50 ohms for any value of R_x. Variations of less than 50 ohms in a series circuit having a total of 4,500 ohms represent a small fraction of the total resistance. The increase in current caused by the shunting effect of R_x is thus only a few micro-amperes. This small increase in the ohmmeter current has little effect on the ohmmeter readings and for all practical purposes can be disregarded.

A shunt ohmmeter providing three ranges for lower resistance measurement is shown in Fig. 11–6(b). With the selector switch in neutral position 3, the unknown resistor, R_x, is connected directly across the meter. This provides a meter range extending to about 400 ohms.

BRIDGES

A bridge is a sensitive device used to measure resistance, capacitance, or inductance when great accuracy of measurement is desired. Bridges are commonly used for measuring the reactance of components and for accurately determining audio frequencies. Bridge circuits for component measurement include a source of a-c or d-c voltage; an indicating device, usually a sensitive galvanometer or headphones; an adjustable standard, usually a resistor or capacitor; the component whose value is to be measured; and a method of determining how much the unknown value differs for the standard.

WHEATSTONE BRIDGE

The bridge most commonly used is the Wheatstone bridge. The bridge circuit shown in Fig. 11–7(a) is known as the diamond arrangement, because the four resistors are shown schematically in the form of a diamond. Resistor R_x is the unknown resistor; R_a and R_b are fixed resistors which provide a specific ratio of R_a/R_b. Maximum accuracy and sensitivity result when this ratio is 1/1. With R_x, inserted in the bridge, rheostat R_s is adjusted until the galvanometer reads zero; when this occurs, the voltage drops across R_a and R_b are equal, the voltage drops across R_s and R_x are equal, and zero meter reading results.

The basic ratio and unknown-arm balancing function in a bridge may apply to a-c as well as d-c voltage sources. We may, for instance, in Fig. 11–7(a) place an a-c wave source in place of the battery and use headphones or an a-c meter in place of the galvanometer. We thus transform the bridge into an imped-

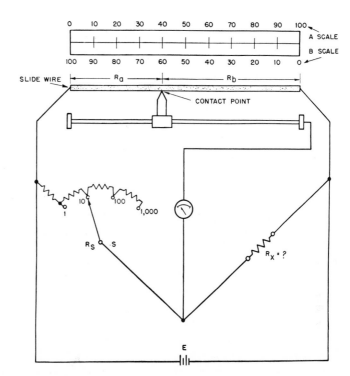

(a) *Basic circuit*   (b) *Slide-wire bridge circuit*

FIG. 11-7 The Wheatstone bridge

ance-measuring device, to be described further on in this chapter.

Likewise, if an unknown frequency is applied across the supply corners of the diamond, we can adjust inductive, capacitive, and/or resistive elements in the arm to balance the circuit (across the earphones); at this point, by observing correctly calibrated ratios of the adjustable arm elements, the supply frequency can be determined.

Another Wheatstone bridge circuit, known as a slide-wire bridge, is shown in Fig. 11–7(b). A slide-wire, made of a material such as manganin and consisting of single wire divided into 100 equal parts, forms the ratio arm of the bridge. A contact point is provided that can be moved manually along the wire; the resistance to the left of the contact point represents R_a and that to the right, R_b. Moving the point along the slide-wire varies the R_a/R_b ratio. The standard resistor, R_s, in the

third arm has four steps corresponding to 1, 10, 100, or 1,000 ohms, making it possible for the bridge to measure different ranges of resistance.

A-C BRIDGE CAPACITANCE MEASUREMENT

CONVENTIONAL TYPE. This circuit uses an a-c voltage source to measure unknown capacitances. Balance of the unknown reactance against a standard by means of resistance ratio arms gives calibrated readings directly in capacitive reactance.

In the series-resistance conventional capacitive bridge of Fig. 11–8(a), the a-c generator replaces the battery used in resistance measurements. Headphones instead of a galvanometer are used as null indicators. The ratio arms consist of R_a and R_b with R_a adjustable so that the R_a/R_b ratio can be varied. In the standard arm, a calibrated variable capacitor,

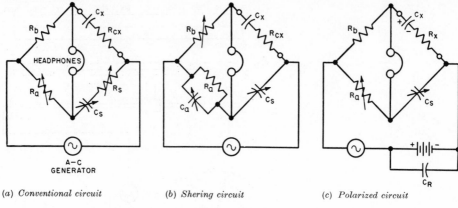

(a) *Conventional circuit*   (b) *Shering circuit*   (c) *Polarized circuit*

FIG. 11-8 Capacitance bridges

C_s, is in series with an adjustable resistor R_s. Capacitor C_x is the unknown capacitance and R_{cx} represents the leakage resistance of the capacitor. When the bridge is balanced, the voltage drops across R_a, C_s, and R_s equal those across R_b, C_x, and R_{cx}.

The steps in adjustment are:

1. R_a is adjusted to give a specific R_a/R_b ratio.

2. R_s is adjusted to give a specific R_a/R_b ratio.

3. R_s is adjusted to compensate for the effects of R_{cx}.

4. C_s is adjusted to equal C_x.

5. R_s and C_s are varied alternately until a null is obtained in the headphones. The dial setting of C_x represents the unknown capacitance. The unknown capacitance can be computed mathematically by the relationship:

$$C_x = C_s \times \frac{R_a}{R_b}$$

SHERING BRIDGE. Another method of determining the unknown capacitance is illustrated in Fig. 11–8(b). This is known as the Schering capacitance bridge; its distinguishing feature is that the leakage resistance, R_{cx}, of the unknown capacitor is compensated for by the adjustable capacitor, C_a, which is in parallel with R_a. The fixed ratio arm, R_a, and the adjustable ratio arm, R_b, are connected across the headphones. C_a and the standard

calibrated capacitor, C_s, are tuned until a null is obtained in the headphones.

The capacitance of electrolytic capacitors, also, can be determined by using a capacitance bridge. However, a polarizing voltage must be supplied by a battery to the electrolytic capacitor, as shown in Fig. 11–8(c). Capacitor C_r must be large enough so that its reactance at the frequency of the a-c generator is at a minimum, and also so that the a-c voltage will be bypassed around the battery. Otherwise the operation of this type of bridge arrangement is conventional.

SUBSTITUTION MEASUREMENT. When an unknown capacitance is small and great accuracy of measurement is desired, the substitution method is commonly used. The resistors comprising the two ratio arms are made equal in value, and a known capacitor is connected across the terminals that are used to measure the unknown capacitor. The bridge is then balanced by adjusting the standard capacitor, and the reading of the dial setting is noted. The unknown capacitor is connected in parallel with the known capacitor. The new reading of the dial setting is noted. The difference in the two readings is then equal to the unknown capacitance.

DISSIPATION FACTOR. The dissipation factor, the ratio of a capacitor's resistance to its reactance, is a direct check of the capacitor's quality. It is equal to:

$$D = \frac{R_{cx}}{X_{cx}} \quad \text{or} \quad R_{cs} \times 2 \times f_{cx}$$

where D is the dissipation factor and R_{cx} is the capacitive reactance of the capacitor. The greater the leakage resistance, the greater the dissipation factor; many capacitance bridges have calibrated dials on which this factor is directly indicated. D is the inverse of the Q factor described below.

INDUCTANCE MEASUREMENT

In making measurements with the various types of inductance bridges, the limitations, ranges, accuracy, frequency, and other characteristics of each should be known and accounted for. For instance, the accuracy of a measurement may be affected by the D or the Q of the coil being measured at a specific frequency. In measuring very small inductances,

lead lengths must be accounted for; and the overall grounding and shielding of a particular bridge set-up may be important at high frequencies.

An unknown inductance can be determined by using the Maxwell bridge shown in Fig. 11-9(a). In this circuit, R_a and R_b are the ratio arms, and both are adjustable to obtain various R_a/R_b ratios. L_x represents the unknown inductance and R_x the resistance of the inductor. The standard resistance, R_s, is adjusted for null in the headphones to cancel the standard and unknown inductor resistances. The inductance of L_s as read on a calibrated dial equals the unknown inductance.

The unknown inductance also can be computed by the relationship:

$$L_x = \frac{L_s \times R_b}{R_s}$$

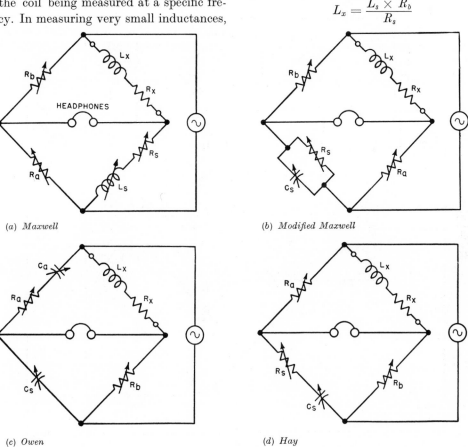

(a) Maxwell

(b) Modified Maxwell

(c) Owen

(d) Hay

FIG. 11-9 Inductance bridge circuits

Since it is difficult to accurately calibrate a standard inductor, variable capacitors are often used instead of fixed inductors.

One type of bridge using a capacitor as its standard is a variation of the Maxwell bridge (Fig. 11–9(b)). The standard capacitor, C_s, is adjusted to obtain the proper voltage drops around the circuit, and R_s is adjusted to cancel the effects of R_x. The ratio arms, R_a and R_b, are used to help balance the bridge and are connected to opposite sides of L_x. Dials on the equipment are read to determine directly the inductive value of L_x in henrys, millihenrys, or microhenrys. Inductance also can be directly computed from the relationship.

$$L_x = C_s \times R_a \times R_b$$

OWEN BRIDGE. In the Owen bridge (Fig. 11–9(c)), as in the Maxwell bridge, L_x is located opposite the standard capacitor, C_s, so that a comparison can be made between C_s and L_x. A fixed capacitor or a series of capacitors which are switched into the arm, one at a time, can be used to replace C_s. The variable capacitor, C_a, is used to balance out R_x, and R_a and R_b balance the bridge. The mathematical relationship used for determining the unknown inductance in the Owen bridge is identical to that for the Maxwell bridge.

HAY BRIDGE. The Hay bridge is similar to the Owen bridge (see Fig. 11–9(d)). Here the standard capacitor, C_s, located opposite the unknown inductance, L_x, is in series with R_s. R_x is balanced by R_s, L_x is balanced by C_s, and the variable resistors, R_a and R_b, complete

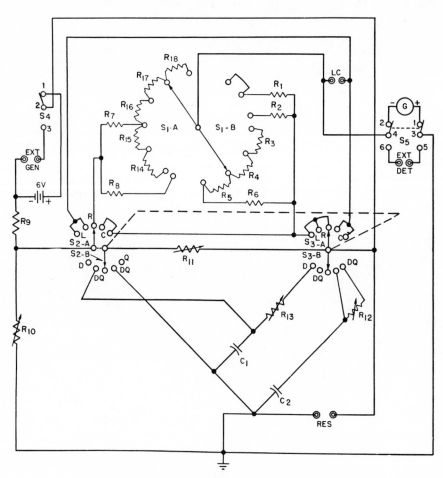

FIG. 11-10 Typical practical impedance bridge

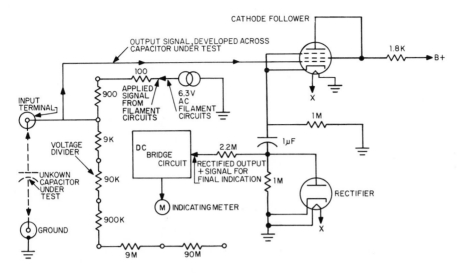

FIG. 11-11 Capacity meter (60-cycle actuated)

the balance of the bridge. This type is generally used for measuring inductances having a $Q (X_L/R_L)$ greater than 10.

Q FACTOR. Just as the dissipation factor is used to measure the quality of a capacitor, the "Q" or storage factor is used to measure the quality of an inductor. "Q" is defined as the reciprocal of the dissipation factor and is equal to:

$$Q = \frac{X_L}{R_L}$$

where X_L is the inductive reactance of the coil and R_L its effective resistance. As noted above, in making a measurement, a high Q is a desirable quality for an inductance to have just as a low dissipation factor is desirable in the case of a capacitor.

A practical impedance bridge employing many of the features of the above circuits is shown in Fig. 11–10.

CAPACITY METERS

Capacity meters are not usually categorized as bridge circuits. They are really impedance-measuring devices using a-c volt-ohmmeter methods. The simplest type, sometimes known as the reactance type, uses a portion of the 60-cycle 110-volt power supply (usually 6.3 volts from the filament supply) to send a-c through the unknown capacitor. A calibrated a-c ammeter placed in series with the supply voltage and the adjustable-range resistors and other switches reads current, which is inversely proportional to the size of the capacitor. Figure 11–11 illustrates the circuit of a simple instrument of this type. In this electronic volt-ohm-capacitance-milliammeter 6.3 volts a-c, taken from the filament supply, is applied to a network of resistors, some or all of which —depending upon the capacitance range selected by a seven-position switch—are used as dropping resistors in series with the capacitor under test. The voltage developed across the capacitor is fed to the cathode follower circuit used as an impedance-matching device and then rectified by means of the 6X5 tube. The rectified voltage is applied to the bridge circuit, which causes proper meter deflection for any selected range.

Analyzers of this type have an appreciable internal wiring capacitance, negligible on the higher capacitance ranges but affecting the accuracy considerably on the two lower ranges. For measurements taken on these two ranges,

181

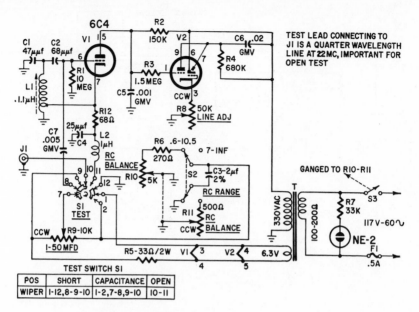

FIG. 11-12 R. F. oscillator type of capacitor meter

the initial meter reading should be subtracted from the final reading to produce the true value of the capacitor under test. The test equipment should be zero-adjusted on one of the higher ranges that is not affected by this internal capacitance.

Still another capacitor measuring instrument uses its own local source of a-c to produce current flow in the indicating meter. Here, in Fig. 11–12(a), the a-c generating source is an RF oscillator operating in the range of 20 to 30 MC.

If a generating source of this frequency is chosen, the meter is able to measure small capacitances which otherwise (when a 60-cycle source is used) give too small a deflection. This we can appreciate when we observe that the impedance of a 100-μf capacitor, which at 60 cycles is 4–5 megohms, at 200 KC is 1,350 ohms.

Often the use of such a frequency allows us to check a capacitor by placing the test prods directly across the unit in its circuit without unsoldering its leads. This is possible where

capacitors which are electrically isolated by series resistors (say in an AGC line) develop low enough impedance to become the deciding factor in the measurement.

OTHER INSTRUMENTS CALLED METERS

As noted above, a great number of instruments are called meters. Each of these performs some far more complicated function than pure voltage, current, frequency or impedance measurement. The function and operation of many of them is made self-explanatory by their naming and categorization. Many will be described in the material on equipment testing.

To summarize, it should be emphasized that the more complicated types of so-called meters are merely sophisticated devices that accept some physical or electrical stimulus and turn it into a calibrated or measured electrical voltage (or current) so that a visible or audible response results.

Frequency Meters and Measurement 12

Frequency measurement techniques vary according to the range covered by the electronic equipment being measured. The common communication and radar ranges are summarized in Fig. 18–1 and this breakdown of ranges is paralleled by the applicable types of frequency meters. (See Table 11–1.) The ranges may be summarized as:

1. Low or audio frequencies,
2. Supersonic,
3. Radio or HF communications frequencies,
4. UHF and microwave frequencies.

Each of these "instruments" is a piece of electronic equipment, and the items marked with an asterisk use a meter movement for final indication. In the lowest ranges the test engineer usually uses direct measurement by means of a counter or an oscilloscope; when measuring high-frequency ranges, he uses the wavemeter or heterodyne meter.

All methods of measurement require a sampling of a small amount of energy from the frequency-generating device; this energy must have its variations per second directly counted or compared with some local standard or stable source. In broad terms the various methods can be grouped into two categories:

1. *Direct counting methods*, using the direct meter, the electronic counter, the bridge, or the oscilloscope.

2. *Comparison methods*, using wavemeters and heterodyne meters.

FIG. 12-1 Frequency discriminator circuit

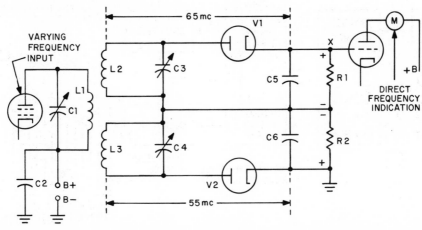

DIRECT COUNTING METHODS

DIRECT-READING FREQUENCY INSTRUMENTS

This type of instrument delivers direct cycle-per-second readings on a calibrated meter scale (with several ranges). The reading is derived by converting frequency-varying input signals to frequency-proportional d-c output voltages, using a *discriminator* circuit which in effect is a frequency-sensitive detector.

Figure 12–1 illustrates a typical frequency discriminator circuit covering the range around 60 MC. Being a voltage-proportional system, it delivers a variable, direct meter reading over the selected range.

FREQUENCY COUNTERS

These are additively operating devices which trip successive electronic flip-flop or switching elements in "ring" counter circuits. In contrast to discriminator circuits, they deliver by means of a numerically marked neon-lamp display an indication of the total count or number of individually tripped switching operations over an interval (usually 1 second).

Counters thus have the advantage of displaying instantaneous and discrete numbers of cycles per interval in directly readable,

illuminated figures on an instrument panel.

The neon-lamp displays are activated by high-speed counting circuits which are referred or compared to some self-contained standard frequency. The principle of operation centers around a comparison-counter system, whereby the unknown frequency actuates a "scaler" or a counter circuit which operates only over a definite predetermined interval of time set up by the frequency standard. The number of cycles of counted input voltage which are passed through the counter and displayed at its output, say in one second of standard interval, may be read directly as the frequency.

The basic frequency-counter mechanism is shown in Fig. 12–2. Both the known and unknown frequencies are passed through pulse-forming circuits N_1 and N_2, through gates G_1 and G_2, and to scaler counters C_1 and C_2. If both gates are opened by the start-time switch S and remain so, the circuits function simultaneously and C_1 and C_2 deliver counted output pulses. If, at some predetermined count, say at exactly one second, or at 100,000 pulses of the initiating standard oscillator, C_1 sends out a stop signal which closes F_1 and F_2, the measurement appearing at the indicator output on the meter panel will be an exact count of the unknown pulses or, in other words, a direct frequency measurement.

Extremely stable frequency counters of this

FIG. 12-2 Basic frequency counter mechanism

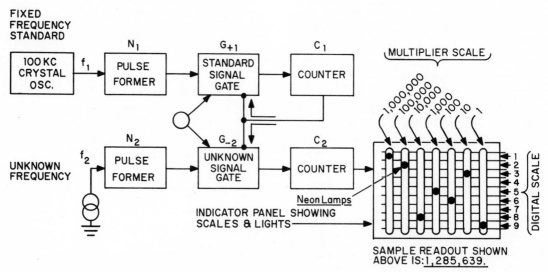

type are now available up to 100 MC. Their main advantage is the convenience of their displaying a direct, readable measurement in cycles at selected intervals, with no personal attention, manual procedure, or adjustment.

BRIDGE METHODS FOR FREQUENCY MEASUREMENT

The most common bridge method of reading frequency is employed in the Wien bridge circuit of Fig. 12–3, where an unknown fre-

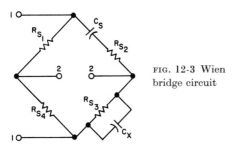

FIG. 12-3 Wien bridge circuit

quency can be determined by properly applying it so that output balance depends upon frequency. With application of an unknown signal frequency followed by proper settings of the adjustable components for electrical balance, the value of the applied frequency can be calculated. In the bridge shown, balance is obtained over a wide frequency range by merely varying two adjustable resistance elements. In this circuit, R_3 and R_4 are identical slide-wire resistors mounted on a common shaft, together with the frequency dial which is directly calibrated. Multiplying factors depend upon the ratios of C_3 and C_4 while the potentiometer X is used to obtain sharp balance. The bridge is simple; and since it contains no large inductances which would normally be used to adjust a bridge for low audio frequencies, it is particularly free from stray energy pickup which might obscure balance.

THE OSCILLOSCOPE AS A FREQUENCY METER

Lissajous oscilloscope patterns are a common visual method used to equate two frequency waveforms or to establish phase and harmonic relationships between them. Frequency ratios of up to 10:1 may be conveniently measured and with care values of 200:1 have been used. The device thus becomes a simple and powerful way of instantaneously and continuously monitoring the frequency relationships of two sine-wave voltages. The procedure calls for applying waveform inputs of both known and unknown sine waves of equal amplitudes directly to the separate plates of an oscilloscope and observing patterns similar to those shown in Fig. 12–4(a). When inputs of equal amplitude and equal frequency are applied to both plates the result is a circle, an ellipse, or a straight line, depending upon the relative phase of the input voltages.

At very high ratios of unknown to known input frequencies, methods other than the Lissajous patterns are desirable.

One alternative is to create a circular pattern in Lissajous manner on a cathode-ray tube by applying the same frequency across each pair

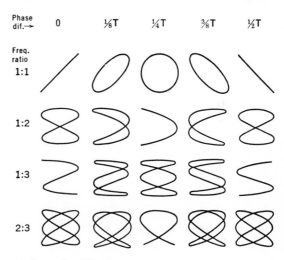

(a) *Conventional lissajous patterns*

(b) *Gear tooth display*

FIG. 12-4 Lissajous frequency determining patterns

of plates but with the applied voltages displaced from each other by 90°. Then if we modulate the electron beam by some higher frequency—say by a factor of six—we should have the circular pattern on the face of the CRT modulated into six sectors, giving a display analogous to "gear teeth." By observing an unknown modulating frequency and counting the number of gear teeth, we can thus determine the input frequency ratio with respect to the standard or comparison deflecting frequency. If we had applied an even higher unknown frequency to the deflecting plates (Say 10:1), we would have obtained more teeth in the pattern, as in Fig. 12–4(b).

Modulating one of the applied inputs at a known variable frequency produces a spot-wheel display from which measurements may be made.

FREQUENCY COMPARISON METHODS

ACTIVE DEVICES—FREQUENCY STANDARDS

All frequency measurements made by comparison methods must basically refer to some standard. In most laboratories these are called secondary standards, although they represent highly accurate sources, having been derived from some even more accurate source called a *primary frequency standard* which is ultimately derived from the period of rotation of the earth. Primary frequency standards are international in character and are periodically broadcast through world-wide radiation originating at the National Bureau of Standards. These signals from stations WWV and WWVH are broadcast on a number of wavelengths and at scheduled intervals throughout the day and night. They cover most of the world and are used by all broadcast stations in setting up local secondary standards in order to maintain their assigned frequency.

In practical usage, a secondary frequency standard (which is usually a stabilized crystal oscillator) delivers frequencies which are derived from the main oscillator (keyed in on WWV broadcasts) by means of subharmonic count-down circuits (frequency dividers) or by

harmonic generators synchronized with the basic oscillator. Thus, in the chain of frequency dividers pictured in Fig. 12–5, we may generate, and thus measure, any frequency from a few cycles up to gigacycles and be assured that it is reasonably stable.

The technique for very low frequencies in the audio range is to generate a local signal from an adjustable interpolation oscillator, which in turn is periodically checked against the frequencies of the final count-down stage in the subfrequency multivibrators. This oscillator has very fine frequency controls so that it can be adjusted to an accuracy of fractions of a cycle after its basic frequency range has been adjusted to that of the selected count-down standard output.

The ultimate comparison of the standard

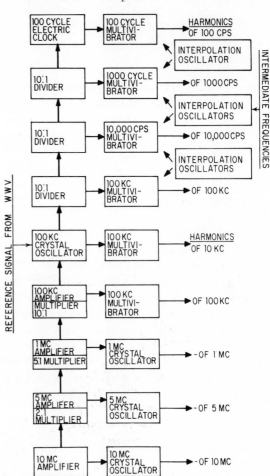

FIG. 12-5 Frequency standard and generating system by chain of frequency dividers

frequency and the unknown frequency, after the various stages of frequency subdivision, is accomplished by exactly *heterodyning* or forming an audio "beat" note between the two voltages. Some subfrequency of the standard frequency is adjusted until it gives a resulting audio beat note of zero frequency when mixed with the unknown frequency, or until its output is observed at zero frequency difference on an oscilloscope display. At zero beat, we know that the measured and standard frequency are alike.

The technician assigned to obtaining frequency measurements from a full-scale laboratory secondary standard will find that the equipment is relatively complicated, consisting of several rack- mounted and auxiliary units. The measurements are, accordingly, highly scientific and must be made with care and precision. A functional block diagram of the equipment is shown in Fig. 12–6.

The block diagram shows that the procedure requires the following auxiliary equipment: (1) a high-frequency receiver to obtain and adjust the secondary standard to the primary frequency of WWV's broadcast signals, (2) an oscilloscope as a visual means of indicating comparison, and (3) a flexible, stable, interpolation oscillator. For less precise measurements, smaller, compact secondary-standard oscillators described below are used with good success.

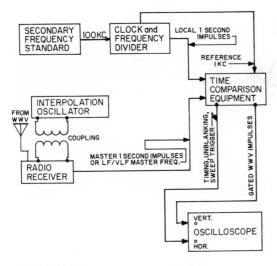

FIG. 12-6 Frequency measurement setup

PORTABLE SECONDARY FREQUENCY STANDARD

A commonly used portable secondary standard derives its output frequency from a self-contained crystal oscillator, which in turn may be used to calibrate the variable oscillator contained within less accurate equipments. The crystal oscillator in this secondary frequency standard, when referenced to WWV, can be used to check the accuracy of any equipment oscillator within its frequency range and does not require a separate piece of equipment for calibration purposes.

Its operation is described in the block diagram shown in Fig. 12–7. When the INTERVAL switch is in the 1,000-kc position, the 1,000-kc crystal oscillator and buffer amplifier feed the harmonic amplifier. The harmonic amplifier is used to amplify the harmonics fed from the 1,000-kc oscillator and the 100-, 25-, and 10-kc multivibrators. The output of the harmonic amplifier then beats against the external signal input in the mixer amplifier. If the difference frequency is in the audio range, it is heard in the headphones. If the frequency of the external signal input equals the fundamental frequency, or a harmonic of the 1,000-kc crystal oscillator, no sound is heard in the headphones.

For example, if the external frequency is 2,000 kc, the second harmonic of the oscillator will beat with it, and because the difference frequency is zero, no output will appear in the headphones. However, if the signal is 2,010 kc, or 1,090 kc, there is a 10-kc difference between the two frequencies and a high-pitched 10,000-cycle beat note will sound in the headphones.

When the signal is 2,020 kc or 1,080 kc, the difference frequency is 20,000 cycles; this signal can not be heard in the headphones because it is above the audible range. Thus as the difference frequency approaches the audible range, a high-frequency beat note is heard that gradually decreases in pitch until the zero-beat frequency is reached. If the signal is tuned past the zero-beat frequency a low-frequency note appears that gradually

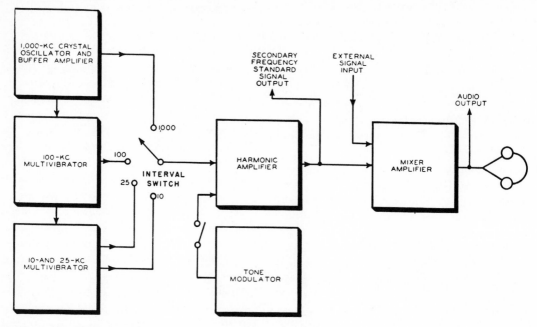

FIG. 12-7 Block diagram of typical secondary frequency standard

increases in pitch until the audio range of frequencies is past and the signal is no longer heard.

When the INTERVAL switch is in the 100-kc position, a 100-kc multivibrator feeds the harmonic amplifier, and in the 25- and 10-kc positions, a 10- and 25-kc multivibrator feeds the harmonic amplifier. These multivibrators produce signals at 100-, 10-, and 25-kc intervals to extend the range of the secondary frequency standard, and are synchronized by the 1,000-kc crystal oscillator. The tone modulator shown is an audio-frequency oscillator that can be connected to the harmonic amplifier by a switch when a modulated signal is required at the output.

THE HETERODYNE FREQUENCY METER

A good example of practical workable equipment using the heterodyne principle is in the small, high-stability heterodyne frequency meter schematically shown in Fig. 12-8. In this device a detector, an audio amplifier, and headphones follow the highly stable, calibrated, adjustable oscillator whose output heterodynes the unknown signal. The range of this meter may be extended when harmonics of its basic frequency are used; its stability is enhanced in some designs by including within the circuitry a temperature-stable crystal oscillator, which is used as check with reference points on the main frequency calibration.

Operation of the heterodyne meter is shown in block form in Fig. 12-9. It consists basically of a frequency-calibrated oscillator which beats, or heterodynes, as described above, against the frequency to be measured. To operate, the pickup antenna is coupled loosely to the device under test and the calibrated oscillator is then tuned so that the difference in frequency between the oscillator and the unknown frequency is in the AF range. This difference or beat frequency is detected and amplified and can be heard in the headphones. If the dial setting of the calibrated oscillator is tuned to the frequency of the device under test, the difference frequency is zero, or zero-beat frequency, and no sound is audible in the

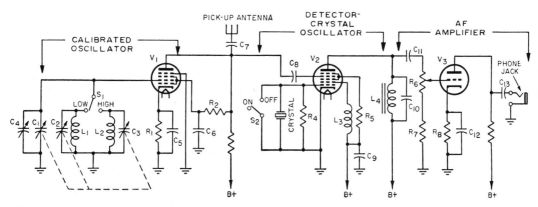

FIG. 12-8 Heterodyne frequency meter

headphones; the position of the pointer on the dial setting now represents the unknown frequency.

Figure 12–10 shows how the developed beat frequencies vary when plotted against the audible range of frequencies. When the difference frequency between the two signals is above the audible range, no sound is heard; the shaded area on the graph indicates these frequencies. As the two frequencies are brought closer to each other (*A* on the curve), a high-pitched note is heard in the headphones. This tone gradually decreases in frequency to a point, *B*, where it is replaced by a series of rapid clicks; the difference frequency is then only a few cycles per second. At *C*, the clicks have stopped completely, the two original fre-

quencies are equal to one another, and this is the exact point of zero-beat. Clicks are heard at rather infrequent intervals at point *C*, since it is difficult to maintain a condition of absolute silence in the headphones over a prolonged interval of time because of a certain amount of circuit instability. As the standard oscillator frequency is varied beyond the zero-beat point, the number of clicks increases to point *D*. A low-pitched tone again is heard at this point. Varying the frequency in the same

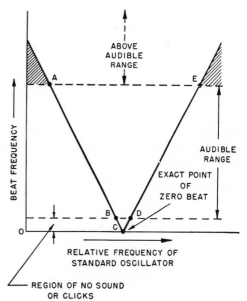

FIG. 12-10 Beat frequency chart

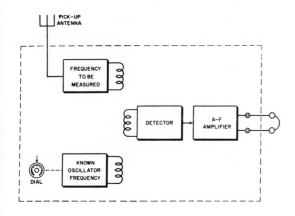

FIG. 12-9 Functional description of the heterodyne meter

direction will cause a gradual increase in frequency until point E is reached, where the beat note is again inaudible.

CALIBRATION. Most heterodyne frequency meters contain a stable crystal oscillator which is used for calibrating the frequency of the variable oscillator. The crystal oscillator produces a number of harmonics permitting calibration of the meter at various frequencies. These points of calibration are called crystal check points, and the frequencies at which they occur are given in a calibration book which is used to determine the frequency of the dial setting.

Figure 12–11 shows in block-diagram form a typical arrangement for calibrating a variable-frequency oscillator. Assuming that the calibration book shows a crystal check point at a frequency of 3,000 kc, the dial setting of the variable-frequency oscillator is adjusted to represent a frequency of 3,000 kc. If the second harmonic of the 1,500-kc crystal oscillator (3,000 kc) zero-beats against the 3,000-kc output of the variable-frequency oscillator, the output frequency is zero. There is then no sound in the headphones; the variable-frequency oscillator, being already calibrated, requires no compensating adjustment. However, if the output of the variable-frequency oscillator is some frequency other than 3,000 kc when the dial is set to 3,000 kc, the variable-frequency oscillator must be calibrated. If it is set at 3,000-kc and the actual frequency is 2,999.7 kc, the output of the detector then will produce a beat frequency

of .3 kc, or 300 cycles, that can be heard in the headphones. The corrector control, usually a small variable capacitor, is then adjusted until the frequency of the variable-frequency oscillator changes to 3,000 kc. When this is done, no tone is heard in the headphones and the variable-frequency oscillator has been calibrated. This procedure can be used for all crystal check points listed in the calibration book. Before making a correction in the calibration, the frequency meter should be turned on and allowed to warm up for 15 to 20 minutes to permit the operating temperature within the meter to become stable.

BASIC PRACTICAL CIRCUIT. A basic circuit of the heterodyne frequency meter is shown in Fig. 12–8; it operates as follows: The circuit uses tube V_1 as the variable-frequency oscillator whose output beats against the unknown frequency entering by way of the pickup antenna. The circuit containing V_2 is the mixer stage designed to combine these signals, and serves also as a pentagrid converter when the variable oscillator is being calibrated. During calibration, the crystal oscillator is in the control-grid circuit of V_2 and the output of V_2 is fed to an AF amplifier, V_3, which drives the headphones.

PASSIVE FREQUENCY COMPARISON DEVICES—WAVEMETERS

The accuracy of the heterodyne schemes of frequency measurement involving self- or locally generated frequencies is a maximum; but because of their complexity and the time consumed in operating them, their convenience rating is low. For this reason and often because we wish to examine single-frequency determining circuitry, various types of tuned resonant circuits are employed; these frequency-measuring devices are called *wavemeters*.

Wavemeters are always adjustable to a calibrated scale so that when coupled to an active circuit bearing an unknown frequency they act to absorb some of the generated power, causing a deflection either on their self-contained indicator or on the indicator of power passing through the circuit being measured.

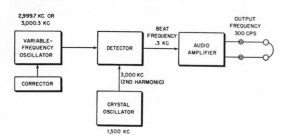

FIG. 12-11 Typical arrangement for calibrating a frequency oscillator

They are inherently high-frequency devices, since at lower frequencies the physical size of resonant circuits would be too great to be practicable. Consequently, wavemeters seldom are used on frequencies below 1,000 kc.

The resonant circuits used in wavemeters vary with the frequency at which they are being used. For lower frequencies the circuit constants are lumped; that is, they consist of complete, identifiable coil-and-capacitor assemblies. For intermediate frequencies so-called "butterfly" tuning circuits or coaxial, two-wire lines are used; for high frequencies and microwaves, adjustable resonant cavities make up most conventional wavemeters.

Figure 12–12 shows a lumped-constant wavemeter. The procedure is to move the wave-

meter into proximity for suitable coupling with one of the frequency-sensitive circuits and adjust the variable capacitor until a dip is noted on the wavemeter indicating meter. At this setting, the wavemeter's circuits are in resonance with the circuit to which it is coupled; its corresponding frequency setting may be read from the calibrated capacitor dial. With the "butterfly" type of meter the procedure is the same.

Resonant cavities, extensively used as wavemeters at microwave frequencies, have the advantages of accuracy and simplicity. Several types are shown in Fig. 12–13. More accurate models have a plunger or piston tuning element with a micrometer adjustment for accurate reading of the setting of the movable cylindrical element and, consequently, of the frequency. Their operation is one of power absorption, so some means of observing a dip in the transmitted power either at its source or further along in the circuit must be provided. The accuracy of frequency measurement by resonant cavities is excellent, and they may often be used as secondary standards. Precision of one part in 100,000 can be achieved by careful mechanical design and good temperature and moisture compensation.

FUNCTIONAL WAVEMETER TYPES

Functionally there are two basic types of wavemeter: (1) the reaction wavemeter, (2) the absorption wavemeter. Both absorb part of the output power of the device whose frequency is to be measured. Either type

FIG. 12-12 Lumped-constant wavemeters

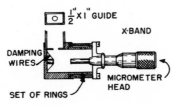
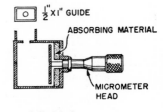

(a) *Coaxial*   (b) *Transition coaxial to cylindrical*   (c) *Cylindrical*

FIG. 12-13 Resonant cavity wavemeters

may have resonant circuits in the categories described above.

The reaction wavemeter absorbs very little power, and an RF ammeter (in effect) located in the circuit of the device whose frequency is to be measured usually serves as an indicator. Since the power it absorbs does not appreciably load the equipment being measured, the reaction wavemeter can be used to measure the frequency of low-power equipment.

The absorption wavemeter is more accurate than the reaction wavemeter and absorbs slightly more power from the equipment whose frequency is being measured, tending to load it; for the latter reason it is generally used only on high-power equipment. An ammeter, a lamp, or an earphone is used to indicate the unknown frequency.

REACTION WAVEMETER. The basic circuit of a reaction wavemeter containing a coil, L, and a variable capacitor, C, is shown in Fig. 12–14(a). The external coil, L, is loosely coupled to the output coil of the device whose frequency is to be measured. The capacitor, C, then is tuned until the resonant frequency

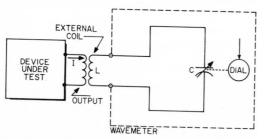

(a) *Reaction wavemeter*

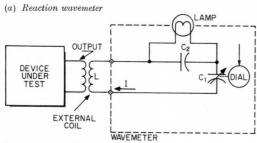

(b) *Absorption wavemeter*

FIG. 12-14 Basic circuits

of the wavemeter is equal to the frequency of the device under test. At this point the ammeter indicates resonance by deflecting to either a maximum or a minimum reading, depending on where the ammeter is located in the device under test. The capacitor is operated by an accurately calibrated vernier dial, with the graduations marked in terms of some arbitrary unit. The frequency or wavelength is found by means of a calibration curve or chart which relates the dial setting to either frequency or wavelength.

When the wavemeter is moved into the RF field of the device under test, the coupling produces a change in the current, and increases the load. At resonance, this load becomes maximum and the indicating ammeter reads a minimum or a maximum, depending on its location. To prevent loading, the wavemeter is moved away until the least possible variation of the tuning capacitor causes a detectable deflection on the meter.

A plot of output current versus wavemeter frequency for various degrees of coupling is shown in Fig. 12–15(a). When the wavemeter is resonant, the load on the device is a maximum and the current is a minimum. The dips in the curves indicate a dip in the reading of the ammeter. Curve A indicates loose coupling (the wavemeter has been moved away). As the coupling is increased, the dip in primary current becomes greater. Curve B represents tight coupling, curve C critical coupling, and curve D overcoupling. For accurate frequency measurements, the coupling is decreased until there is a very small dip in the current meter. Loose coupling is thus ideal for accurate measurements, since the dip at resonance is very sharp.

ABSORPTION WAVEMETER. Although the absorption wavemeter is similar to the reaction wavemeter, it also contains a resonant-frequency indicating device. Figure 12–14(b) shows an absorption wavemeter circuit using a lamp to indicate resonance. The functions of tuning capacitor C_1 and external coil L are the same as those explained in the discussion of the reaction wavemeter. The lamp is at maximum brilliance when the wavemeter is at the resonant frequency of the device under test. The amount of brilliance that results depends on the voltage appearing across fixed capacitor C_2. The capacitive value of C_2 is much larger than that of C_1 and, since its reactance is negligible at the resonant frequency, C_1 and L determine the resonant frequency of the wavemeter.

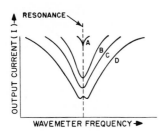

(a) *Output current in reaction wavemeter*

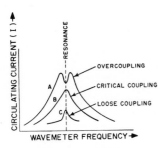

(b) *Circulatory current in absorption wavemeter*

FIG. 12-15 Wavemeter currents *versus* frequency

When the wavemeter circuit is tuned to the same frequency as the unknown frequency, a maximum circulatory current flows in the wavemeter circuit. Since this circulatory current occurs at resonance and current is maximum at resonance, voltage drops appear across L, C_1, and C_2 and the voltage drop across C_2 causes the lamp to glow. As C_1 is tuned to either side of resonance, the circulatory current becomes less and the lamp grows dimmer.

In Fig. 12–15(b), the circulatory current is plotted against the wavemeter frequency for various degrees of coupling. For frequency measurements, the external coil of the wavemeter is loosely coupled to the device under test. The accuracy of this coupling is indicated by the sharpness of curve C at resonance.

Although overcoupling, as shown in curve A, produces a greater circulatory current and lamp brilliance, it results in inaccurate frequency measurements, as shown in the double-humped curve, where a maximum circulatory current is obtained on either side of resonance.

FREQUENCY MEASURING TECHNIQUES

THE REACTION WAVEMETER. The unknown frequency is measured in the following manner: The external coil of the wavemeter is moved into the RF field of the device whose frequency is to be measured. The knob on the dial setting then is slowly rotated through its frequency range until some reaction is noted on the indicating meter in the device under test. The wavemeter is moved slowly away from the oscillator until the deflection on the indicating meter is barely perceptible. The dial setting knob now is adjusted for a maximum deflection on the meter and then converted to a frequency reading from a calibration chart.

THE ABSORPTION WAVEMETER. An unknown frequency is measured as described below: With a lamp used as an indicator, the wavemeter is brought near the device under test. The dial setting knob is turned slowly through its range until the indicator lamp just begins to glow. (The knob is not turned for maximum brilliance, which might cause the lamp to burn out.) The wavemeter is then moved slowly away from the oscillator until the lamp glows more dimly or goes out. It then is tuned for maximum lamp brilliance. For accuracy, the wavemeter should be located as far as practical from the device to still maintain a faint glow but close enough to discern maximum brilliance.

Wavemeters usually contain several external coils of the plug-in variety. Each coil represents a specific frequency range, and if the approximate frequency to be measured is known, the selection of the proper coil is simplified. Where the approximate frequency is unknown, each coil must be tried separately for indications of resonance. The tuning capacitor is of the air type and the frequency range it covers determines the number of plug-in coils needed.

Many wavemeters use a micrometer-type tuning dial (Fig. 12–16). The micrometer consists of a thimble with a vernier scale which is rotated about a barrel with a coarse scale. To read a typical micrometer dial, we first note that the barrel has major divisions marked on it which represents tenths of an inch or any desired unit that may be represented by tenths of an inch. Each of the four minor divisions between the major divisions thus represents .025 inch. The rotatable thimble is divided into 25 parts around its circumference so that one full rotation moves the thimble one minor division on the barrel or .025 inch. Since the thimble is divided into 25 parts, one division is equal to .025/25 or .001 inch. Consequently, to interpret the reading of the micrometer setting in Fig. 12–16(a), we must observe the dial reading, .1, and add to it .075 (.025 times 3) plus

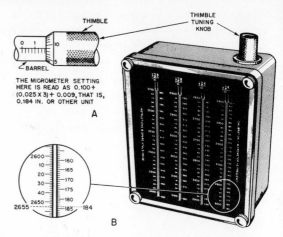

FIG. 12-16 Micrometer reading with typical calibration chart

.009 (the thimble reading), yielding a total of .184 inch. The frequency which represents a reading of .184 inch then is obtained from a calibration chart (Fig. 12–16(b)), and is found to be 2,655 mc. The calibration chart, which in this case represents a frequency range from 2,400 to 3,400 mc, for micrometer readings from .0557 to .46, is usually etched on a metal plate attached to the wavemeter case.

Oscilloscopes and Waveform Measurements 13

Waveform analysis generally implies measurement of transient or a-c voltage with the aid of an oscilloscope. By virtue of the inherent nature of the cathode-ray tube and its associated circuitry, most oscilloscope voltage waveform displays are periodic. Such regular recurring voltages are compatible with the oscilloscope electronic mechanism since it also is adjusted for periodic operation; its electron beam or "writing" point of light sweeps crosswise over its display tube's viewing face in *synchronism* with periodic input waveforms as they are applied to the deflecting system operating the up-and-down movement of the writing beam. Thus a waveform is a pictorial representation, with relation to time, of an amplitude-varying potential. In another sense, waveforms are really irregularly contoured a-c voltages since they periodically vary about a horizontal axis. When they are synchronized with the periodic sweep feature of an oscilloscope (using a *linear time base* or the regular repetition of the uniform sweep of its electron beam across the face of the cathode-ray display tube) an unknown waveform becomes automatically displayed, plotted, or traced as if it were standing still on the face of the CRT.

This is because successive traces of the waveform appear superimposed on one another. With rectangular markings on the tube's face the waveform contours can be analyzed by using the common x, y system of coordinates. Figure 13–1 describes the major elements of the basic oscilloscope.

Such stationary displays allow analysis of all the details of a voltage waveform, yielding information concerning the signal or operating characteristics of many electronic (and some mechanical) devices. For instance, the progress of a signal with known input amplitude and waveshape may be traced by means of the variations in its waveshape as it passes through the stages of an amplifier. The gain and distortion characteristics of the amplifier itself may then be quickly and easily determined by comparing waveforms at successive points. Such display analysis becomes a great aid in circuit design and in trouble-shooting electronic equipment; it is extensively used in TV receiver trouble-shooting.

Waveform analysis gives other information. For instance, the waveform of a signal may indicate the presence of harmonics or parasitic oscillations, or it may indicate how closely a device is following a desired cycle of operation. Also, of primary importance is the fact that an oscilloscope can provide a pictorial presentation of a waveform at the instant of its occurrence in a circuit. Delays, phases, and other time-significant quantities can thus be measured.

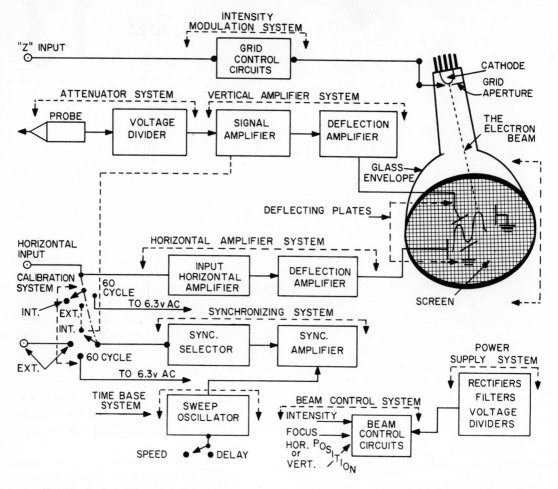

FIG. 13-1 The basic oscilloscope

SINE-WAVE AND PULSE VOLTAGES—PULSE TECHNIQUES

Inspection of a number of typical waveforms in Fig. 13-2 shows that the label "transient" given above does not always apply to all types of waveforms, for we are omitting pure a-c sine waves which are not transient variations although they possess many of the characteristics of typical pulse waveforms.

Sine waves are distinguished from transients on an oscilloscope in that their excursions above and below the center reference axis are uniformly "smooth" while transient voltages have sharp discontinuities. Sine waves

are thus true alternating-current voltages symmetrically displayed equally above and below their center axis, and their electronic processing is not, strictly speaking, among the pulse techniques.

However, the distinction of sine waves from nonsine waves is not sharp, for we may encounter symmetrical waveforms which do not have very sharp discontinuity points such as the modified sine-wave and triangular waveforms shown in Fig. 13-2(c).

Non-sine waves that have sharp steep edges are usually classified as *pulse* voltages since in effect they are caused by abrupt switching action in pulse-generating circuits. Here transients are more obvious and may become important. (See Fig. 13–2(b).) A number of the irregular pulse voltages encountered in electronic circuitry are shown in Fig. 13–2 (c)(d).

A pulse therefore may be defined as a brief or transient surge or excursion of voltage or current. As a transient it may or may not be periodically recurrent, although an oscilloscope inherently displays irregularly shaped

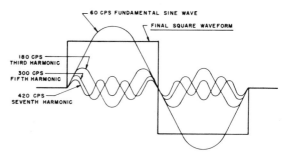

FIG. 13-3 Harmonics in rectangular square waveforms

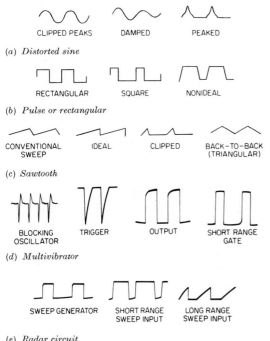

(a) Distorted sine

(b) Pulse or rectangular

(c) Sawtooth

(d) Multivibrator

(e) Radar circuit

(f) Miscellaneous

FIG. 13-2 Types of waveforms

waveforms as if they were occurring at regular intervals.

Pulse measurement, interpretation, and analysis depend almost wholly upon display by means of an oscilloscope. Logically enough, the mathematical breakdown of pulse waveforms in based on waveform synthesis using sine-wave components; these form the basic building blocks of current and voltage making up a pulse or any other waveform. A simple

example of the contribution of harmonic sine waves to form the sharp edges of a composite pulse waveform synthesized from a pure sine-wave fundamental is shown in Fig. 13–3.

PULSES AND WAVEFORM CHARACTERISTICS

As we have noted, the envelope or contour characteristics that distinguish pulse waveforms from other general waveforms are matters of degree. We might, for instance, square off the top of a sine wave and call it a periodic pulse waveform, or we might lopsidedly sharpen the top and bottom halves of a sine wave and thus convert it to a sawtooth waveform (Fig. 13–2(a).)

TERMINOLOGY

In general, however, most pulse waveforms are described with reference to a square or rectangular shape, which we can define in terms of certain conventional characteristics. Figure 13–4(a) shows an ideal rectangular pulse and labels its basic characteristics. Figure 13–4(b) give complete details of a pulse that has undergone deterioration.

PULSE REPETITION RATE is the frequency at which the pulse is repeated—100 times per second, 1,000 times per second, etc. This frequency is usually expressed as the pulse period—the time between pulses. The pulse period in microseconds (μsec) is the inverse of the frequency. Thus pulses of 100-cycle repetition rate are 10,000 μsec apart, 1,000-

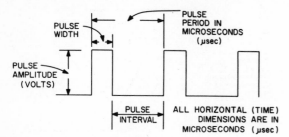

(a) *An ideal rectangular pulse*

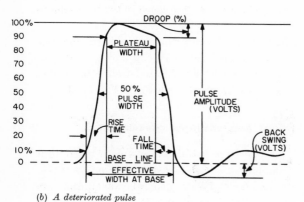

(b) *A deteriorated pulse*

FIG. 13-4 Rectangular and deteriorated pulse dimensions

cycle repetition rate 1,000 μsec apart, and so on.

PULSE AMPLITUDE is a voltage (or current) value measuring the *height* of the pulse from its horizontal bottom level or base to the effective top level of the main pulse body. In essentially flat-topped pulses the height does not include any overshoot. In a triangular pulse, however, it does mean the distance from base to highest point. In nonrectangular pulses, where the front and back edges have a pronounced slope, the height is usually measured between the 10% and 90% amplitude points.

PULSE WIDTH OR DURATION is the time-width dimension (expressed in microseconds) beyond the front edge or starting point and terminating at the rear edge. In nonrectangular pulses where the front and back edges have a pronounced slope the width is usually

measured across the 50-percent amplitude point.

RISE TIME is the time required for the pulse to increase from 10 to 90 percent of normal amplitude.

FALL TIME is the time required for the trailing edge of a pulse waveform to fall from 90 to 10 percent of normal amplitude.

WIDTH OF PULSE AT TOP (PLATEAU) is the time consumed in a nonrectangular pulse between the front and rear 90-percent amplitude points. In a pure rectangular pulse it is the time-width of the entire flat top area or between the end of the front edge and the beginning of the trailing edge.

WIDTH AT THE BASE OF THE PULSE is the time between the 10-percent points on the front and rear edges of the pulse. In the perfectly rectangular pulse with zero rise and fall time the base and the top of the pulse have the same time-width.

PULSE INTERVAL is the time between the back edge of a pulse and the beginning or front edge of the next pulse.

PULSE PERIOD is the average time between similar points on successive pulses; generally it is measured between the start of each front edge of two repetitive pulses. It is also (in seconds) the inverse of the repetition rate; thus with a repetition rate of 1,000 times per second the pulse period is $\frac{1}{1000}$ sec or 1,000 μsec.

WAVETRAIN is a series of pulses either alike or unlike in width, configuration, and frequency which make up a periodic recurrent group. The horizontal, equalizing, broad vertical, serrated, and vertical pulses which make up the standard television signal waveforms can be called a wavetrain. Note that the wavetrain may be composed of a number of nonidentical pulses but that the *group of pulses* by themselves must be regularly repetitive to be displayed on an oscilloscope.

DUTY CYCLE of a train of pulses applies only to total peak-to-peak amplitude pulses when the negative peak is considered as being the zero level or baseline. It generally applies to transmitter power output. It is the percent of the total time between pulses that the pulse is "on." Figure 13–5(a) shows 10-percent and 50-percent duty-cycle waveforms, the latter, of course, being a symmetrical waveform when the main axis is considered to be at the 50-percent level.

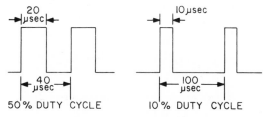

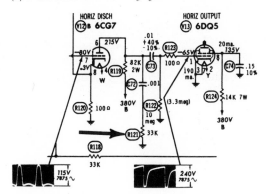

(a) *Pulse dimensions and duty cycle*

(b) *Waveform labelling on schematic*

FIG. 13-5 Pulse duty cycle and waveform labelling

PEAK VALUE (OR PEAK-TO-PEAK VALUE).

When the bottom peaks of a wavetrain are used as the zero level, the maximum amplitude of the pulses when measured from this point is the peak value. When the axis is symmetrically located, the voltage or current amplitude between peaks is called the peak-to-peak value.

MEASURING WAVEFORMS

Oscilloscope measurement of waveforms involves placing the oscilloscope terminals across the circuit point under analysis, adjusting the synchronizing, width, and amplitude control for suitable display, and interpreting the amplitude and waveform shape.

The actual width, amplitude, slope, and other quantities involved in measurements at any point within a circuit are usually specified directly on the circuit schematics or given in instruction handbooks. The technician's function is to match these quantities with his measurement or interpret his measured results in terms of the specified information. Figure 13–5(b) shows conventional methods of labeling most waveform characteristics.

Of course, the technician must understand his scope's capabilities, and any measurement must not disturb the circuit being tested, by loading or by introducing unwanted feedback or any other abnormal condition; in other words it must be the equivalent of a voltage measurement taken by a high-impedance meter.

In most cases, it is assumed also that the pulses being studied are periodic in nature and can be synchronized with the sweep mechanism of the oscilloscope circuits— although triggered, nonrecurrent voltages can be displayed with the proper type of oscilloscope. Also, using the conventional oscilloscope terminals at the end of a probe, care should be taken to see that the static high voltage at the measurement point is not sufficient to break down the oscillator probe input capacitor or burn out the terminating resistor at a probe cable's input, if one is used. Amplitude-range switching components in the oscilloscope input attenuator circuits should also be properly proportioned in order that correct peak-to-peak voltages are being measured

RULES AND PROCEDURES FOR OSCILLOSCOPE USAGE

THE CATHODE-RAY OSCILLOSCOPE

The formal name *cathode-ray oscilloscope* is usually abbreviated in common terminology to *oscilloscope*. In laboratory jargon it is called a "scope." An *oscillograph* is the pictorial representation of an oscilloscopic trace. Some older texts, however, use the word oscillograph to denote the whole equipment.

The following discussion of basic oscilloscope operation uses typical sectional schematics to simplify operational explanations. It should be noted that much of the basic operation is explained on the basis of free-running synchronization, although most modern scope designs utilize triggered sweep synchronization (described further on under the synchroscope). In addition, especially in pulse-voltage analysis, the scope utilizes vertical amplifiers, with a bandpass that is very broad so as to faithfully reproduce narrow, steep-sided waveforms.

FUNCTIONAL ORGANIZATION. In providing a visual representation of waveforms the oscilloscope depends upon the cathode-ray tube; this in turn depends upon the formation and control of a beam of electrons which produces a visible trace on a fluorescent screen. Since

the electron beam has negligible inertia, the cathode-ray tube responds to much higher frequencies than any other electrical indicating device.

Operationally an oscilloscope consists of a number of interleaved electronic systems, described in Fig. 13–1 and listed below. This functional breakdown ties in with the basic *beam control* breakdown given in Fig. 13–6.

The respective systems are:

1. Display.
2. Beam-control.
3. Vertical amplifier.
4. Horizontal amplifier.
5. Time-base.
6. Synchronizing.
7. Intensity-modulation.
8. Power-supply.
9. Calibration.

THE DISPLAY SYSTEM: THE CATHODE-RAY TUBE

The heart of an oscilloscope is the cathode-ray tube—a special type of electron tube in which a stream of electrons emitted by a heated cathode are focused and accelerated to form a narrow beam having high velocity. This beam, controlled in direction, is allowed

FIG. 13-6 Functional oscilloscope layout and controls

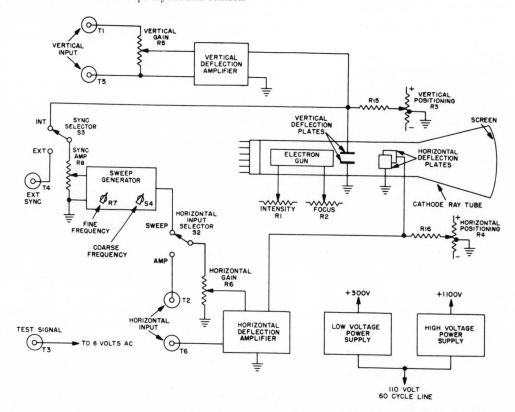

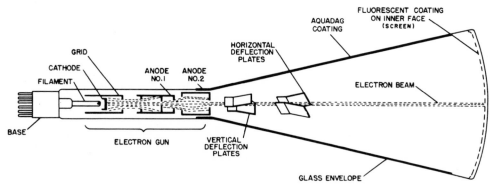

FIG. 13-7 The electron optics of the CRT electron beam

to strike a fluorescent screen (on the inside face of the tube) whereupon light is emitted at the point of impact, producing a visual indication of its position.

The electronic process of forming, focusing, accelerating, controlling, and deflecting the electron beam is accomplished by the following principal elements making up the cathode-ray tube (see Fig. 13–7):

1. The electron emitter—a heated cathode and beam-forming aperture.

2. A grid for controlling beam intensity.

3. A focusing anode for concentrating the electron stream.

4. An accelerating anode for intensifying the electron beam.

5. A deflection system, for controlling the direction of the beam emanating from the electron gun.

6. A fluorescent screen, for visually indicating the movement imparted to the electron beam.

7. An evacuated glass bulb, which encloses and supports all the above elements of the cathode-ray tube. Partially covering the inside of the glass bulb and located back some distance from the fluorescent screen is an aquadag (graphite) coating which provides a return path for electrons and at the same time serves to electrostatically shield the electron beam.

THE ELECTRON GUN

The electron gun, shown functionally in Fig. 13–7, provides a concentrated beam of high-velocity electrons. These are emitted from the cathode, which is an oxide-coated metal cylinder properly heated and oriented within the tube structure. They are attracted toward the accelerating and focusing anodes because of their high positive potential in relation to the cathode.

In order to reach these anodes, however, the electrons are forced to pass through a control grid (a cylindrical piece of metal, closed at one end except for a tiny circular opening), which concentrates the electrons and starts the formation of a beam. Electrons leaving the grid aperture are strongly attracted by the positive charge on the focusing (No., 1) and accelerating (No. 2) anodes, which are cylindrical and have small openings to permit passage of the beam. Between these two anodes an electrostatic field exists in the direction shown by the dotted lines in Fig. 13–7.

Here the electrons move in a direction that is the resultant of their initial forward motion and of the electrostatic forces exerted by the anodes which cause them to converge into a more concentrated beam. Since the electrons are now moving faster because of their attraction to the high positive potential of anode 2, the tendency to continue as a beam is greater than the tendency to diverge and follow the electrostatic lines of force.

Thus, the electrostatic field existing between the first and second anodes serves as an electron lens, which focuses the electrons in somewhat the same manner as a double convex lens focuses a beam of light.

However, the electron lens differs from the optical lens in that its focal length can be changed by simply changing the ratio of potentials between the first and second anodes. This ratio is changed by varying the potential on anode 1 by means of the FOCUS CONTROL, R_2 (Fig. 13–6), which is a potentiometer located on the front panel of the oscilloscope. The potential on the second, or accelerating, anode remains constant.

The intensity of the beam (number of electrons comprising the beam) is varied by potentiometer R_1 (INTENSITY CONTROL) which changes the grid potential with respect to the cathode, thus permitting more or fewer electrons to flow. Because the potentials applied to the grid and both anodes are taken from a common voltage-divider network, any change made in the setting of the intensity control will require a compensating change in the setting of the focus control, and vice versa.

ELECTROSTATIC DEFLECTION SYSTEM—BEAM POSITIONING

After the emitted electrons have been accelerated and focused to form a high-velocity beam, they continue their travel toward the viewing screen until they strike it, causing it to fluoresce or give off light within the region bombarded; thus a spot of light is formed at or near the center of the tube when no deflecting voltage has been applied. Other areas of the tube screen may be similarly activated by deflecting the beam from its normal path. The beam, when guided on any curved and varying path, in effect "writes out" information delivered to the deflecting system.

The electrostatic deflecting system is predominantly used in oscilloscopes; magnetic deflection is more often used in TV picture tubes and in radar displays.

Electrostatic beam deflection is accomplished through the use of two pairs of parallel plates that straddle the path of the beam. The second pair is perpendicular to the first; thus, the electrons must pass between two sets of deflection plates (see Fig. 13–7).

If no electric field exists between the plates

of either pair, the beam will follow its normal straight-line path, and the resulting spot will be at or near the center of the viewing screen. A voltage potential applied to one set of plates will cause the beam to bend toward the plate that has the positive potential and away from the plate that has the negative potential. Deflection of the beam is virtually instantaneous, since it possesses an infinitesimal mass. The second pair of plates deflects the beam in the same way but in a plane perpendicular to the first.

The plates located nearest the gun structure are generally designated as the y-axis deflection since they bend the beam upward when the cathode-ray tube is properly mounted. Those nearest the screen are the x-axis plates, deflecting the beam sideways. Voltages *simultaneously applied* to both plates will move the beam to intermediate positions on the screen, depending upon the relative values of the deflecting voltages.

A single voltage that is variable and recurrent with time, when applied to either set of plates, will cause the spot to move back and forth across or up and down the screen along a straight line, which will appear as a solid trace when its cyclic rate exceeds the persistence of human vision or the persistence of the phosphor material forming the screen.

RESULTANT MOTION OF ELECTRON BEAM

Nearly all applications of electrostatic-type cathode-ray tubes require that each pair of deflection plates act upon the beam independently and simultaneously to produce a motion of the spot *along the resultant* of *those electric forces* exerted by each set of deflection plates. In this case the electron beam is continually acted upon by two forces which are at right angles to each other.

Figure 13–8 illustrates the resultant motion produced by independent deflection voltages that are applied simultaneously to the horizontal and vertical plates (the x and y axes).

When the sliders of potentiometers R_1 and R_2 are at ground potential, all four deflection plates are at ground potential and the spot appears at O on the screen.

If the slider on R_1 is moved in a nega-

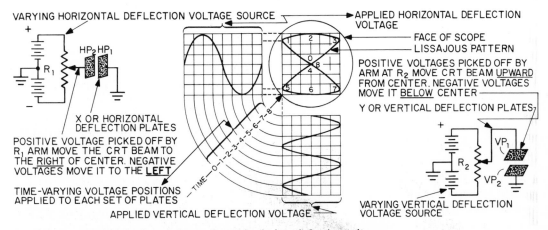

FIG. 13-8 Beam positioning by resultant of combined plate deflection voltages

tive direction, horizontal-deflection plate HP_2 becomes negative with respect to HP_1, and the electron beam is repelled by the negative voltage on HP_2. Under the action of this repulsion, the spot moves to the extreme left on the screen.

If the slider on R_2 is moved in the positive direction, the vertical-deflection plate VP_1 becomes positive with respect to VP_2, causing the beam to be moved to the bottom of the screen.

Now, if the above adjustments of R_1 and R_2 are made simultaneously but with R_2 changing at twice R_1's frequency, the resultant of the electrostatic forces exerted along the x and y axes will cause the spot to form a figure 8 as shown.

Thus it is demonstrated that when two voltages, whether they be steady state or of a variable nature, are applied simultaneously, one to each pair of deflection plates, the position of the spot at any instant is proportional to the resultant of the simultaneous electrostatic forces exerted upon the beam at that instant.

POSITIONING (CENTERING) CONTROLS

Many times, slight structural imperfections in the manufacture of cathode-ray tubes may cause the beam to strike at some point other than the exact center of the screen when no signals are applied. For those defects and for certain measurements it is necessary to provide some means of positioning the beam.

Such centering provisions are accomplished by applying small independent internal d-c potentials to the deflection plates and controlling them by means of potentiometers similar to those in the circuit described above (Fig. 13–6). In most modern scopes d-c voltages, externally applied, can produce the same effect. Centering, or positioning, controls are also useful during enlargement of a waveform for examination of minute characteristics. Here the portion of interest may move off the cathode-ray tube screen so that centering controls are necessary to bring it back on again.

DEFLECTION SENSITIVITY

The distance that the spot may be moved on a scope's viewing screen, in either the horizontal or the vertical direction, by a potential of one volt applied to the deflection plates defines the *deflection sensitivity* for the axis under consideration. This figure in millimeters per volt (d-c) is usually listed by the manufacturer as one of the cathode-ray tube's basic characteristics. Deflection sensitivity is determined by applying a known d-c potential directly to the deflection plates and then measuring the distance that the spot moves. This distance, in millimeters, divided by the voltage applied is the deflection sensitivity for that pair of deflection plates.

Another way of expressing the ability of an applied voltage to cause beam deflection is by use of a deflection factor, which is defined as the voltage required on a pair of deflection plates to produce unit deflection of the spot; it is usually expressed as d-c (or rms) volts per inch.

If the cathode-ray tube has a deflection factor of 60 volts (d-c) per inch, it should be understood that for every 60 volts applied to the deflection plates the electron spot moves a total distance on the screen of one inch; 60 peak-to-peak a-c volts or 120 volts would displace the spot 2 inches.

A-c voltage applied to one pair of the deflection plates produces a movement of the spot on the screen of the scope which is at all times proportional to the applied voltage. Under these conditions the electron beam scans the screen to produce a straight luminous line, the length of which is determined by the peak-to-peak value of the voltage. It can be seen in Fig. 13–7 that, when an a-c voltage is applied to the vertical-deflection plates, the electron beam is deflected upward and downward from its rest position by equal amounts. Assuming that the vertical-deflection system shown in Fig. 13–7 has a deflection factor of 40 volts (d-c) per inch and that the sine-wave voltage applied to the plates has a peak-to-peak value of 40 volts, the upward and the downward deflection at the frequency of the applied signal will each be $\frac{1}{2}$ inch, producing a vertical line one inch long.

The X and Y deflection sensitivities for cathode-ray tubes employing electrostatic systems are not equal—the vertical, or "Y," plates generally have the greater sensitivity owing to their greater distance from the viewing screen. Deflection sensitivity depends upon: (1) the length of the tube, (2) the second-anode potential, (3) the effective lateral spacing of the deflection plates.

Other performing factors requiring design trade-off decisions concern spot size, brilliance, plate shape and bending, etc.

FLUORESCENT SCREEN

The area on the inside of the front of the tube is coated with a phosphor chemical which, when bombarded by electrons, has the property of emitting light. This process converts the energy of the electron beam into visible light and is known as fluorescence. The intensity of the fluorescent spot on the screen depends upon three factors—the speed of the electrons in the beam, the number of electrons that strike the screen at a given point per unit of time, and the efficiency of the phosphor coating. In practical usage, since the accelerating voltages are fixed, the intensity is controlled by varying current emitted by the cathode.

PERSISTENCE. All fluorescent materials have some afterglow, which varies with the screen material and with the amount of energy expended to cause the emission of light. This afterglow property of a coating is defined as *persistence;* it is the length of time required for the light output to diminish by a given amount after excitation has ceased. Screen materials may have long, medium, or short persistence. White and blue-white phosphors having relatively short persistence are used for photographic work, while for general service work, where visual observation is most important, a green phosphor having medium persistence is used. In viewing a line or pattern that is traced by a moving spot of light, the persistence of human vision, as well as that of the screen material, plays an important part. When the pattern is retraced at a rate of 16 times or more a second, the persistence of the eye retains the image from the previous sweep, and therefore the spot in its movement is no longer distinguishable as a spot and the path travelled appears as a continuous illuminated line. In cases of long-persistence phosphor materials, the persistence of the screen rather than that of the eye will govern, and the scanning rate, to

AQUADAG COATING. In bombardment of the fluorescent screen a return path for the electrons must be provided; if the impinging electrons were allowed to accumulate upon the screen it would soon acquire a negative charge that would effectively repel and disperse the electron beam, thus blocking the tube from performing its primary function. This is prevented by applying a positive potential to the aquadag coating which (together with the other positively charged elements) attracts dislodged electrons resulting from bombardment of the screen by the electron beam.

This dislodgment of electrons is known as secondary emission. The dislodged electrons follow a return path to the power supply by way of the coating of graphite deposited upon the inner bulb surfaces. This coating also serves as an electrostatic shield against external electric fields and in addition acts as an accelerating anode.

THE BEAM-CONTROL SYSTEM

This system and its associated controls utilize power-supply voltages enabling an operator to manipulate the focus, the brightness, and the position of the beam. The controls, appropriately labeled, are usually located on the front panel in or around the face of the display tube. Focus and brightness of the beam are controlled by variable potentials applied to the cathode-ray tube elements, while positioning results from application of d-c voltage variations to the network of resistors supplying the deflection plates.

THE ATTENUATOR AND VERTICAL AMPLIFIER SYSTEMS

In order that an oscilloscope may have a wide range of use, both the attenuator and the vertical amplifier circuit must be able to accept and process signals of small amplitude and must accurately reproduce the shape of the applied voltage waveform. To meet

these requirements they must have uniform gain for all frequencies over a wide band, uniform phase shift for the same wide frequency band, and freedom from nonlinear distortion caused by the curvature of the amplifier tubes' transfer characteristic. In addition, the vertical amplifier must be so operated that the restricted input signal causes variation of plate current only over the linear range. In short, the vertical amplifier, then, is a video amplifier.

The wide band requirements of video amplifiers stem from the fact that pulse waveforms are compositely formed of many sine waves covering a wide band of frequencies. As noted earlier a square wave or a sawtooth wave is composed of component voltages whose frequencies are harmonics of the fundamental. Thus if a waveform passing through an amplifier is to retain its shape, all of these several harmonic voltages must be present in the output at the same amplitude and phase that they had in the input, relative to the fundamental with which they are associated.

If the high frequencies are not amplified sufficiently, the corners of a square wave will round off as in the "output" waveform example of Fig. 13–2(d). If the low frequencies are not amplified sufficiently, the top of the square wave will be dished, since the corners are overemphasized. If the phase shift of all the harmonics is not proportional, the square-wave output will be lopsided. Since most waveforms are affected by a combination of these factors, a wide variety of waveshapes may be obtained from deficiencies in a scope's vertical amplifier.

ATTENUATOR SYSTEM

The wide band requirements noted above, when applied to an input probe and an attenuator, call for a compensated voltage divider. Forgetting the probe for the present, let us consider Fig. 13–9 picturing this type of attenuator. This unit is so designed that

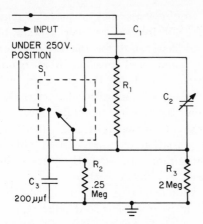

FIG. 13-9 Voltage attenuator network

when adjusted with switch S_1 thrown to the UNDER 250V RMS position, the stray instrument capacitances plus the series capacitors C_2 and C_3 form a divider which cuts down the signal by the same ratio that the resistance divider does. The resistance voltage divider consists of R_1 in series with R_2 and R_3 in parallel. It is so proportioned that the total resistance to the first stage is approximately 2 megohms in either position of S_1, and high enough so that negligible loading effects are produced on the circuit under test.

In order to accept and deliver signals of large amplitude beyond the range of the amplifier output an additional gain control is usually provided within the amplifier itself in order to vary the amplitude of the signal applied to the deflection plates.

PROBE ATTENUATORS

All oscilloscopes use a probe attenuator located at the end of a shielded coaxial cable to enable placement of the probe's tip at remote or inaccessible points within the equipment being tested.

The probe, used as an attenuator, must likewise be frequency compensated and meet the general attenuation requirements described above. It must have low inherent parallel capacity so that it does not load down the

circuit which is being tested; in addition, it must use input capacitors with high enough voltage ratings to be placed at relatively high d-c voltage points.

The probe output cable must also be electrically matched on both ends—that is, to the output of its self-contained voltage-divider network and to the input stage of the vertical amplifier. The cathode-follower circuit described in Fig. 13–10 does this; it has low input capacity and low impedance output for matching the cable leading to the main instrument terminals.

A number of probes with different attenuations are usually provided with a given oscilloscope design to accommodate various measurement conditions. Some designs provide variable frequency compensation by an adjustable capacitor located on the body of the probe itself, or they may contain a crystal

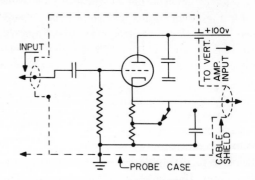

FIG. 13-10 Cathode follower probe circuit

diode detector which rectifies RF input, attenuates it, and passes the resulting waveform to the vertical amplifier terminals.

VERTICAL AMPLIFIER SYSTEM

A typical first vertical amplifier stage uses a cathode follower. (See Fig. 13–11.) Such an input stage has very high input impedance and reduces the danger of distortion caused by its grid's drawing current. Since the gain of the cathode follower is less than 1, the applied signal appears across R_4 with less amplitude than at the input, but with the same undistorted waveshape. However, since the cathode follower is normally conducting,

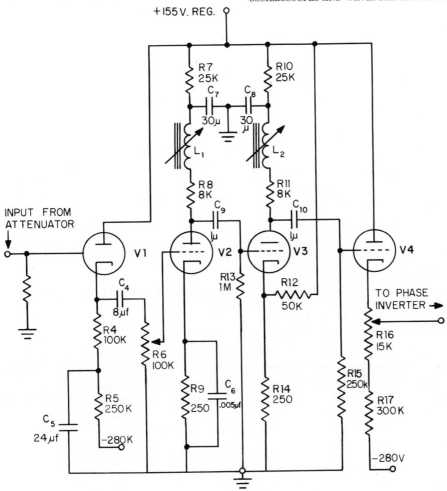

FIG. 13-11 Vertical deflection amplifier

there is a direct voltage at the cathode, although simultaneously the impressed signal causes this voltage to vary. The following stage accepts this varying voltage through capacitor C_4, which is large ($8\,\mu f$) since it must pass very-low-frequency components of the signal.

After the signal passes through C_4, it is impressed on potentiometer R_6 which can select any desired fraction of the signal voltage, thus in effect serving as a gain control, although strictly speaking it does not at all alter the gain of the amplifier. It is really an electronic input attenuator enabling the amplifier to be operated at some fixed point, preferably on the most linear part of its characteristic.

The second and third stages of the vertical-deflection amplifier are compensated video amplifiers using resistance-capacity coupling modified by series and shunt networks to increase the high-frequency bandpass characteristics. Uniform gain over a wide band is attained by using 8,000-ohm plate-load resistors (R_8 and R_{11}) which are much lower than normally would be used in a narrow-band RC-coupled circuit. Inductors L_1 and L_2 thus compensate for the effect of stray capacitances at high frequencies, and since the reactance of an inductor increases as the frequency increases, the effective plate load likewise tends to increase at the high frequencies. To compensate for too much of this tendency with increasing frequency we use the shunting effect of stray capacitances, which tends to reduce the useful gain as frequency is increased. All the while, constant plate-load impedance is maintained by properly adjusting L_1 and L_2, so that the high-frequency gain of the two stages can be made nearly constant up to several megacycles.

Now at very low frequencies, the gain of the amplifiers is normally reduced by the voltage drop occurring across the grid coupling capacitors. This effect is compensated for by the resistance-capacity network R_7 and R_{10}, which has no effect on high frequencies but which is by-passed by the particularly selected reactances of capacitors C_7 and C_8 and which effectively increases the net load reactance at low frequencies. The overall plate-load resistors can now be effectively much larger than they would be in a conventional RC amplifier since the low-frequency voltages developed across R_7 and R_{10} are not completely by-passed by the capacitors C_7 and C_8. The gain of the two stages is accordingly increased, with a larger effective plate load at both high and low frequencies. Low-frequency response in typical amplifiers can be extended down to nearly 2 cycles per second.

THE HORIZONTAL AMPLIFIER SYSTEM

The fast-sweep-time horizontal amplifier pictured in Fig. 13–12 utilizes many of the same techniques appearing in the vertical amplifier system. Briefly, by means of a cathode-follower circuit it converts the single-ended sawtooth output of the time-base generator into a push-pull signal suitable for driving the horizontal plates of the cathode-ray tube. Also provided is a magnifier amplifier gain control for expanded sweep, plus positioning and linearity adjustments. In the circuit shown, heavy feedback is relied upon to provide linearity in conjunction with a special push-pull system of cathode-follower output tubes.

THE HORIZONTAL TIME-BASE OR SWEEP OSCILLATOR SYSTEM

The sweep or time-base oscillator is the heart of the timing system providing sweep voltages to a display tube's horizontal deflection plates. This type of oscillator generates a linear sawtooth voltage for ultimate application to the deflection plates. Its repetition rate is adjustable over a range of frequencies and may be either triggered by sync input pulses or switched to a free-running mode

FIG. 13-12 Horizontal amplifier system

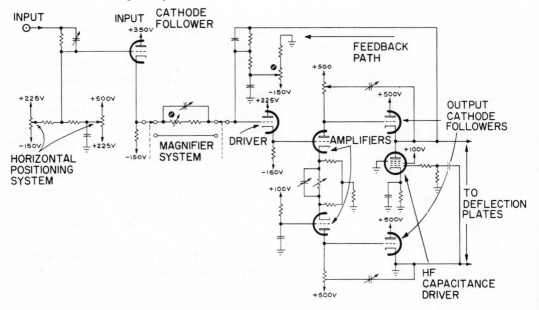

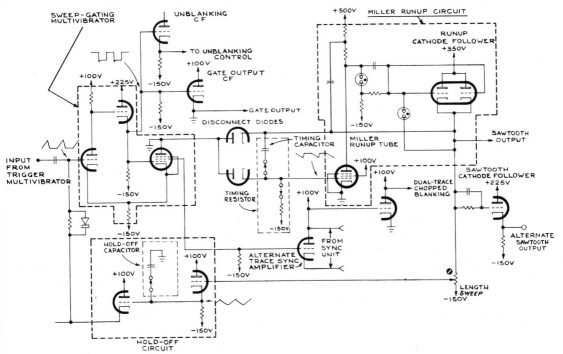

FIG. 13-13 Modern time base generator

FIG. 13-13 Modern time base generator

of operation which is independent of sync triggering.

Early types merely employed simple neon-lamp or thyratron sawtooth generators plus refinements to improve linearity and range. Modern instruments are far more complex and might use the circuit pictured in Fig. 13–13, where a sweep-gating multivibrator, a Miller run-up circuit, and a hold-off circuit are necessary to meet all requirements. Explanation of these specialized circuits is beyond the scope of this volume.

Control dials indicating the frequency of the time-base oscillator are most conveniently calibrated in time per centimeter (sec/cm) of spot travel across the centimeter-spaced markings on the face of the display tube. Modern instruments can be as fast as a few nanoseconds or as slow as 13 seconds per centimeter.

THE SYNCHRONIZATION SYSTEM

In forming an oscilloscope display from repetitive excursions of the CRT spot across

its screen it is necessary that the start of the sweep bear a constant time relationship to the appearance of the input waveform. This timing or triggering the start of the sweep constitutes the main process in the synchronizing function.

Most commonly the sweep oscillator is triggered by the waveform being displayed; however, two other alternatives are provided on most instruments—(1) linear 60-cycle triggering or (2) external triggering—both systems using starting voltages other than those derived from the displayed waveform. These modes of triggering (usually controlled by a selector switch) are useful when special or precise waveform conditions must be studied. For instance, if external triggering is taken from successive circuit input points through which a signal is passing, the time relationships and phase differences of the waveforms of each point can be compared to those of the initial input point. Also, using external triggering we may observe jitter in the waveform which otherwise would be unobservable.

Modern oscilloscopes derive actual starting

voltages during the various modes by extracting them from either the rising or falling edge of the triggering waveform. This provision allows flexibility of inspection of different parts of the waveform being studied and many times insures stability of the synchronizing process.

Other synchronizing controls concern (1) the triggering level, which may be adjusted to the conditions of measurement, (2) the stability control, which is an adjunct to the triggering-level control, (3) the d-c triggering mode, which allows automatic triggering for all waveforms from d-c to around five megacycles, (4) the a-c triggering control, which allows triggering from 15 cycles to 8 mc, and (5) special high-frequency triggering modes providing synchronization on waveforms above 5 mc.

For measurements in which it is desirable to reverse the triggering process—that is, to adjust the sweep oscillator to the input waveform frequency—oscilloscopes must provide an adjustable or free-running time-base mode. Old-style oscilloscopes usually provided this mode only.

Following synchroscope practices (see Chapter 19) it is often necessary to delay the start of the sweep excursion from 1 to 10 microseconds beyond the start of triggering. Control of this function is usually provided by one of the settings on the triggering-mode selector switch. Some triggering systems may have provisions for delaying the triggering pulse in order to allow observation under special conditions.

In some designs where repetitive sweep is unsatisfactory or delivers a jumbled display, provision is sometimes made to eliminate all sweeps past the first one, thus giving a single-sweep display.

In all oscilloscopes except old-style models or the most simple designs, special synchronization circuitry is used to process the triggering impulse for correct application to the time-base generator. The synchronization circuits in Fig. 13–14 show a triggering amplifier and multivibrator combination which accepts triggering signals from several sources, including voltage samples from the signal present in the vertical amplifier. This circuit is a polarity-inverting cathode-coupled amplifier which feeds a multivibrator, which in turn is applied to the time-base generator

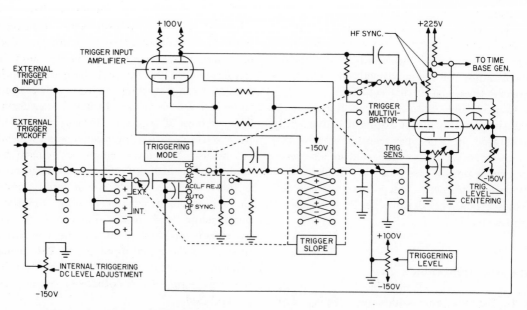

FIG. 13-14 Time base synchronization circuit

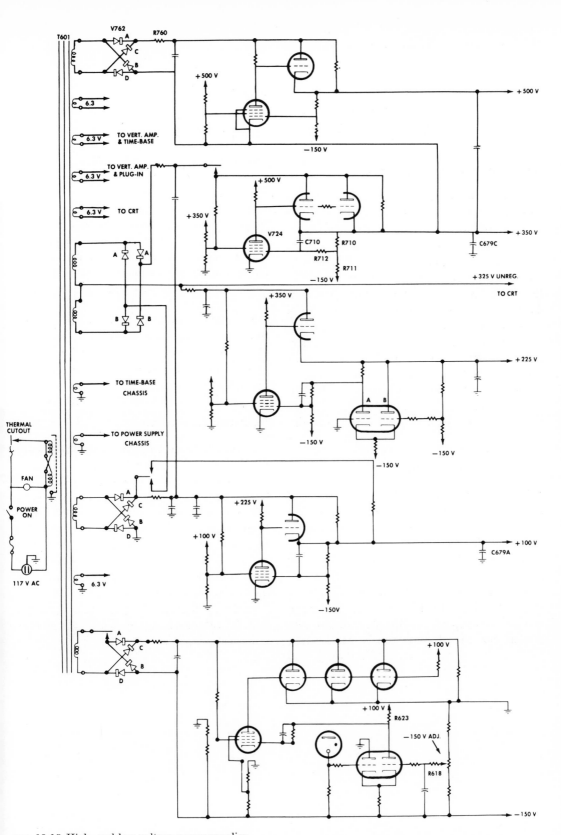

FIG. 13-15 High- and low-voltage power supplies

circuit. This multivibrator allows all the delay, slope, level, and mode variations in the synchronization functions to be used without affecting sweep or triggering.

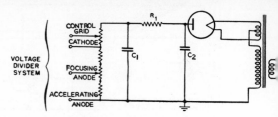

FIG. 13-16 High- voltage power supply

THE INTENSITY-MODULATION SYSTEM

Intensity modulation, sometimes known as z-axis modulation, is accomplished by inserting a signal between ground and the cathode of the display tube. When such a periodic voltage is large enough, it can cut off the tube on selected parts of its excursion. It is also known as retrace blanking since it extinguishes the steep (or retrace) portion of a sawtooth waveform in order to isolate the linear, sloping section for visual examination.

Periodically applying positive pulse voltages to the beam brightens throughout its trace to give a third or z dimension. Periodically brightened spots also become markers for time calibrations of the main waveform.

THE POWER-SUPPLY SYSTEM

Modern oscilloscopes utilize two ranges of supply voltage: (1) high voltages suitable for the display tube, (2) low voltages suitable for operating the receiver-type tubes or for the transistors used in the deflection and control system.

A typical high-voltage power supply is shown in Fig. 13–16 where a half-wave rectifier is adequate for the limited currents needed for the display tube's accelerating

potentials. In some cases the RC filter consisting of R_1, C_1, and C_2 may be more than enough, since the current supplied may be as low as 50 microamperes. For economy a single capacitor C_1 sometimes provides sufficient filtering.

Standard, regulated, low-voltage supplies feed the remaining oscilloscope circuitry. Figure 13–15 includes a typical low-voltage system providing four regulated and one unregulated voltage outputs.

THE CALIBRATION SYSTEM

Internally generated and stabilized waveforms of known amplitude form the measurement reference source for most oscilloscopes. Such square waveforms generated in a multivibrator are usually made accessible on a front panel jack, where vertical circuits may be measured by comparison with the precise generated waveforms. Adjustments for reference calibration range from a few millivolts up to 100 volts peak-to-peak.

Early oscilloscope designs often utilized a built-in calibrator actuated by the 60-cycle power-supply line.

The Testing and Measurement of Vacuum Tubes **14**

Besides the normal amount of technical proficiency, the checking and measurement of vacuum-tube characteristics requires that the technician or engineer be thoroughly familiar with all types of vacuum tubes. This familiarity requires considerable background beyond the techniques of simple measurement, since one must deal with all physical and electrical characteristics of over 3,000 types of receiving tubes, some 700 types of transmitting tubes, over 500 types of display tubes, and several thousand special tubes. Foreign tubes sometimes enter American design considerations, so for expediency this volume can list only a skeleton breakdown of the three main functional categories: receiving, transmitting, and picture-display tubes. A generalized breakdown of the basic circuitry in which vacuum tubes are used was given in Chapter 9; functional details of tubes themselves are discussed in the present chapter.

Table 14–1 gives functional subdivisions within each of the main categories listed below. It should be remembered that Appendix B-2 lists all receiving-tube characteristics suitable for the generalized testing procedures described in this chapter, plus coded base-pin layouts, socket dimensions, and bulb size charts, etc., necessary for the chassis constructional details of Chapter 6.

Table 14–1 Categories of vacuum tubes

Receiving tubes:

Power-supply rectifiers	Voltage amplifiers
High-voltage rectifiers	Power amplifiers
Damper tubes	Converters
Detector diodes	Mixers and mixer
TV deflection tubes	oscillators
Complex-wave	HF and UHF oscillators
generators	Regulators
Relay-control tubes	FM detectors
Electron-ray tubes	Gated amplifiers

Picture-display tubes:

Black and white TV	Special Purpose
tubes	Kinescopes
Rectangular—round	Monitor—projection—
glass—metal	viewfinder
Color TV tubes	Storage tubes
Round-metal-glass	Flying-spot tubes

Transmitting tubes:

Class A amplifiers—AF	Class B amplifiers—
Class C amplifiers	AF-RF telephony—
RF telephony—TV	TV service
service	Rectifiers
RF telegraphy	

Special industrial tubes:

Low microphonic	Computer types
Switching diodes	Frequency dividers
High-altitude types	Gating amplifiers
Special regulator types	

GENERAL APPROACH TO TUBE TESTING

After becoming familiar with tube classifications, sizes, shapes, etc., the engineer-

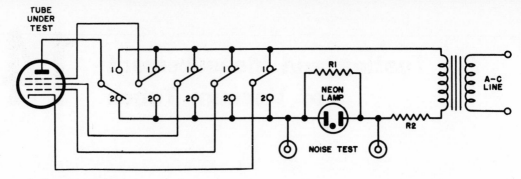

(a) *The test for short circuits*

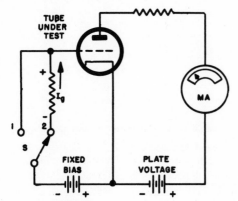

(b) *The test for excessive gas*

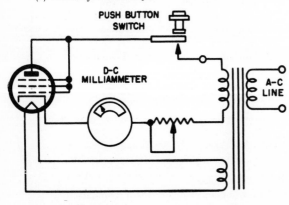

(c) *The emission test*

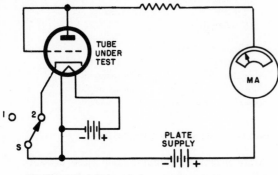

(d) *The cathode-leakage test*

FIG. 14-1 Basic operational tests for vacuum tubes

technician will find that the basic characteristics in which he is interested are: (1) *emission*, and (2) *mutual conductance* commonly represented by G_m. This quantity represents the ability of a tube to convert grid-voltage changes into plate-current changes; in other words, it provides an index of amplifier voltage gain.

First, however, the technician must find out whether the tube has any short circuits between elements or whether it is gassy. It is a routine function of tube testers described below to perform these two preliminary checks before making the basic measurement of G_m. Although the measurement of G_m is more or less a routine functional test, it paves the way to the determination of other precise quantities and associated factors necessary to design and operation.

PRELIMINARY OPERATIONAL TESTING

Tube testers thus accomplish five basic tests: (1) short circuits, (2) excessive gas, (3) emission, (4) cathode leakage, (5) mutual conductance. As noted the first four are routinely operational and the fifth concerns the fundamental characteristic of amplification. All tests are briefly described as follows; for detailed explanation see p. 219.

THE TEST FOR SHORT CIRCUITS between electrodes in a tube is made by connecting one electrode to one side of a power-supply voltage through a neon bulb, and all or some of the remaining electrodes to the other side of

214

the power supply. If two electrodes are touching, or connected within the tubes, the neon bulb glows because there is a complete circuit through the electrodes. (See Fig. 14–1(a).)

THE TEST FOR EXCESSIVE GAS is made by applying normal operating voltages to the various electrodes of the tube, and recording the plate current. A biasing resistor is then placed in the control-grid circuit; if gas is present, the introduction of this resistor causes the grid to go more positive, in turn causing an appreciable grid current and an increase in plate current. (See Fig. 14–1(b).)

THE EMISSION TEST measures the tube cathode's ability to emit electrons under standard conditions, showing particularly whether the cathode coating has deteriorated. If the cathode heater is open, there is of course no emission. (See Fig. 14–1(c).)

THE CATHODE-LEAKAGE TEST involves measurement of any conductive path between a tube's heater and cathode. (See Fig. 14–1(d).)

THE MEASUREMENT OF MUTUAL CONDUCTANCE (the G_m of an electron tube) requires that typical operating voltages be applied to its electrodes. The mutual-conductance value is compared with the published ratings of the manufacturer for that tube, thus indicating its electrical condition. Many mutual-conductance tube testers do not give specific values but are calibrated to read the G_m of the tube in terms of good, bad, or weak ranges printed on the meter scale. Details of the two basic mutual-conductance measurement methods will be given after a discussion of preliminary checking methods.

PRELIMINARY TUBE CHECK BY SUBSTITUTION

Before conducting a detailed tube measurement, a simple test for suspected tube failure is the replacement of the suspected tube with a tube known to be good. For example, if a weak tube is suspected in a receiver-amplifier as judged from the loudspeaker or earphone sound output level, substitution of a good tube may produce increased output. Sometimes the apparently weak tube thus identified can be used in another circuit where its amplifying characteristics are not so important.

When a radio receiver using avc (*automatic volume control*) has low sensitivity, the avc rectifier tube should be checked first. Since this condition also can be caused by an open resistor in the rectifier circuit, tube substitution quickly reveals whether the tube or some other component in the circuit is faulty. Substitution testing, however, can not always be used to advantage to locate more than one faulty tube in a single circuit. For instance, if both an IF amplifier tube and an RF amplifier tube are defective in a single receiver, replacing either one does not necessarily make the receiver operative. Also, when all of the tubes are replaced, and the receiver operates, there is no way of knowing which tubes were defective. Use of a tube tester under these conditions is recommended.

TESTING MUTUAL CONDUCTANCE

The preliminary emission testing as shown in Fig. 14–1(c) prepares for mutual-conductance measurement. It tells whether the cathode-to-plate emission is low by measuring one of the primary factors, plate current. The procedure uses the tube as a half-wave rectifier connecting the plate and all of the grids of the tube to one side of a 110-volt a-c line transformer's secondary and with milliammeter and resistor, R, placed in series with the tube. All of the grids and the plate are at the same potential with respect to the cathode, and the tube acts as a diode, half-wave rectifier, conducting current only during that half-cycle input when the grids and plate are positive. The amount of current flowing in the circuit during this half-cycle is an indication of the cathode emission. Detector and rectifier diodes require a current-limiting resistor tube inserted during test.

The mutual-conductance test supplies additional information about the quality of a multigrid electron tube beyond that given by the emission test.

Mutual conductance, sometimes called grid-plate transconductance, is the ratio of the change in plate current to the change in control-grid voltage assuming that all other tube-element voltages are kept constant.

True transconductance is measured in mhos, the unit of conductance; however, this quantity in a vacuum tube is so small that it is expressed in micromhos. The equation representing this is:

$$G_m = \frac{\Delta I_p}{\Delta E_g} \qquad (1)$$

where G_m is the mutual conductance in micromhos (E_b = constant), ΔI_p is the change in plate current in microamperes, and ΔE_g is the change in control-grid voltage in volts. When the grid voltage is changed 1 volt, positive or negative, the *amount* of *plate-current change* in *microamperes* is numerically equal to the value of mutual conductance in micromhos.

For example, if a tube in an amplifier circuit has a mutual conductance of 1,500 micromhos, changing its grid bias 1 volt positive or negative causes an increase or a decrease in plate current of 1,500 microamperes.

The mutual conductance of a triode varies with the particular plate voltage, plate current, and grid bias being used although it is not greatly sensitive to plate-voltage changes. In a pentode, however, it does vary considerably with screen voltage, plate current, and grid bias. In practice we thus compare the mutual conductance as measured by a tester with the mutual-conductance values specified by the manufacturer under standard, plate, screen, and grid-bias voltages (see Appendix B-2).

Two tests—the *static* and the *dynamic*—may be applied to an electron tube to find its mutual conductance. In the static test, sometimes called the "grid-shift" method, the d-c bias on the grid of the tube is changed a small amount and the resultant change in the steady plate current is measured as in Fig. 14–2(a). With switch S in position 1, some selected negative bias voltage with respect to the cathode is applied to the grid of the tube, and plate current is allowed to flow. Then if the switch is thrown to position 2, where the grid bias is made less negative, the plate current accordingly increases. The ratio of these changes by formula (1) is the mutual conductance.

In practical circuits provisions are made for adjustable plate and grid voltages so that specific operating voltage can be applied. Since the mutual conductance of a tube is effectively the slope of the mutual characteristic curve (grid voltage versus plate current) it may vary with the particular d-c grid bias being used. Therefore, in measurement a small shift in bias must be taken to typify the mutual conductance under the chosen conditions.

The *dynamic* method for finding mutual conductance (see Fig. 14–2(b)) uses a circuit which applies an a-c signal to the control grid from a third transformer winding and superimposes it on the operating d-c grid bias. In this test, since the tube under test has a-c voltage on it, the plate circuit also serves as the load for the full-wave rectifier circuit. The milliammeter measuring plate-current change is connected across R_m, a center-tapped resistor, and also across the primary of the transformer connected to the a-c line.

When E_g, the bias on the grid of the tube under test, is placed at some fixed value, the entire circuit operates as a simple full-wave rectifier having a diode load provided by the tube under test. When plate P_2 is on the positive half of the a-c cycle there is an electron flow through the upper half of resistor R_m, and the d-c meter needle tends to deflect in one direction—say for a value of $G_m = 2,000$ micromhos. When the a-c voltage across the secondary reverses and plate P_1 is positive,

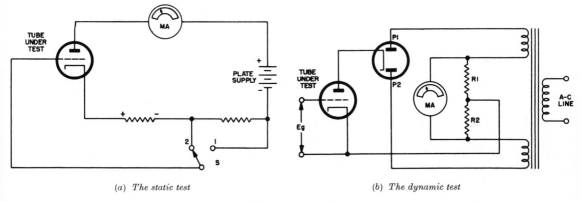

(a) *The static test*   (b) *The dynamic test*

FIG. 14-2 Grid shift and dynamic mutual conductance measurement

the electron flow is through the lower half of R_m, and the needle tends to deflect in the opposite direction. Since the forces on it are periodically equal and opposite in direction, the meter needle cannot follow these 60-cycle variations and it consequently stays in the selected 2,000-micromho position.

When an alternating voltage is applied to the grid of the tube in addition to the fixed d-c bias it causes "in-phase" voltage swings producing positive cycles on P_2 so that the plate current of the tube increases an additional amount over that produced when no a-c is applied to the grid. Because P_2 is positive and conducting, current flows through the upper half of R_m and increases the deflecting force on the meter needle. On the other half-cycle (when P_1 is positive) the a-c voltage applied to the grid swings negative, reducing plate current, and the net rectified current through the lower half of R_m *decreases* so that the resulting deflecting force on the needle is decreased.

We thus have unbalanced currents in successive alternations causing a definite meter reading which is proportional to the difference in currents created by the a-c voltage applied to the grid. The meter, therefore, indicates true G_m showing a change in plate current produced by a change in grid voltage under the particular conditions of applied d-c potentials.

Converter tubes are tested by the dynamic mutual-conductance method, and the oscillator and mixer sections are tested separately.

In checking the oscillator section, the alternating grid voltage is fed to the oscillator grid and the current is measured in the oscillator plate circuit. The mixer section is tested by feeding an alternating grid voltage to the signal grid of the tube and measuring the current in the plate circuit.

In an oscillator section (of a receiving converter tube) a much more important factor than mutual conductance is the *conversion transconductance*. This is the ratio of the change in IF output current in microamperes to the corresponding change in alternating voltage on the RF signal grid in volts. The mutual-conductance reading for the oscillator section of the converter when measured separately is from 2 to 10 times the normal conversion transconductance of the tube in micromhos.

Figure 14–3 is the schematic diagram for a practical commercial tube tester. Note the provisions for accepting all types of tube base-pin arrangements and for applying specific electrode voltages. The basic operational tests described above are also included.

DETAILS OF PRELIMINARY OPERATIONAL TESTS

SHORT-CIRCUIT TEST

Short circuits between the electrodes of a tube can cause excessive current flow in the plate circuit, tube noise, or intermittent operation of the tube.

A circuit for detecting short circuits in a tube is shown in Fig. 14–1(a). With the switch

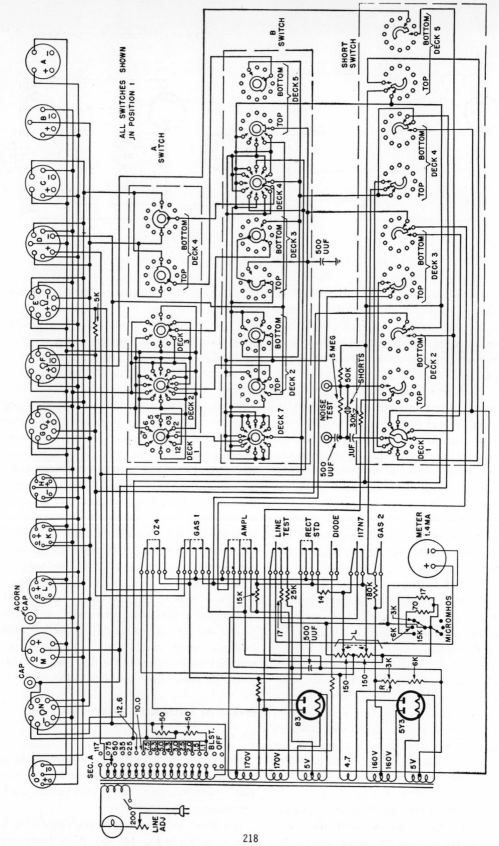

FIG. 14-3 Commercial tube tester

218

in the first position, the plate is connected to the neon-bulb side of the transformer secondary; then each of the other electrodes of the tube under test is successively connected through switches to the opposite side of the secondary. If the plate is touching any of the other electrodes a complete secondary circuit exists in the transformer secondary, and both plates of the neon bulb glow. If the plate is not shorting out, only one plate of the neon tube glows, and then only during that half of the input a-c cycle when it is positive with respect to the cathode. Each of the other electrodes is tested for shorting in a similar manner. The element to be tested is connected to one side of the secondary, and all other electrodes are connected to the opposite side. Resistor R_1 limits the current through the neon bulb to a safe value and resistor R_2 by-passes any small alternating currents in the circuit caused by the stray capacitance of the wiring between other parts of the tester. This prevents stray currents from causing the neon tube to glow.

Sometimes two electrodes in the tube do not touch at ordinary temperatures, but expand enough when heated to cause a short circuit. Therefore, the tube under test should be allowed to warm up to its normal operating temperature before making the test for shorts. Also, if the tube must operate under conditions of vibration it should be tapped gently during the test.

This circuit can be used also to test tubes for noise by connecting a pair of headphones or a loudspeaker in series with a .1-μf capacitor across the neon bulb. An intermittent short circuit, occurring too quickly to cause the neon bulb to glow, will cause an intermittent hum or crackle in the headset or speaker.

GAS TEST

When gas is present in a vacuum-type electron tube, the electrons emitted by the cathode collide with the molecules of the unwanted gas, knocking electrons out of these gas molecules and causing an excess of positive gas ions; the gas is then said to be ionized. These positive gas ions move to the negatively biased grid of the tube and draw electrons from the grid circuit. The circuit used to check for the presence of gas is shown in Fig. 14–1(b).

With switch S in position 1, plate current flows through the d-c meter. When the switch is thrown to position 2, if gas is present the current in the grid circuit will cause a voltage drop to appear across resistor R, resulting in an increase of plate current. Small current increases are normal; large plate-current increases indicate excessive gas.

LEAKAGE TEST

A leakage path between the cathode and the heater in an electron tube can be detected with the circuit shown in Fig. 14–1(d). With switch S in position 1 leakage currents will appear because d-c flows through the meter and R. Normal plate current flows with S in position 2.

EXACT MEASUREMENT OF G_m, R_p, AND MU

The precise determination of G_m in most tube testers is partially automatic because preselected, and standardized grid, plate, screen, and filament potentials are switched into the test circuit at the beginning of a particular measurement. These may also be varied under specific conditions by means of dial-calibrated controls on the operating panel; these also switch in the correct meter scale. Usually the G_m meter on commercial testers has a dial with limit marks or has colored ranges to show a "good" or "bad" characteristic rather than the actual G_m measurement figure. Engineering and operating conditions, however, require that exact G_m must be obtained rather than the degree of goodness or badness. In these cases the technician or engineer must go to the advertised and printed engineering data concerning exact characteristics and compare recommended values with those measured. When the tube is operated under special voltage or signal conditions that deviate from the standards prescribed by the manufacturer, individual, special measurements are necessary. Engineering tube manuals usually list G_m under several operating conditions so that values under special conditions can be extrapolated.

There are, however, two other basic tube characteristics which require some special technical background and usually more precise measurement techniques. These are the plate resistance, R_p, and the amplification factor, mu(μ). Two general methods apply to the measurement of these two characteristics and to the mutual conductance of electron tube amplifiers.

The *incremental method* uses a plate-circuit bucking battery, and small changes in the electrode voltages are compared directly on meters without regard to the total voltage or current upon which the increments are superimposed. It is equivalent to the grid-shift procedure described above and amounts to plotting a tube's characteristics and scaling off the increments which make up the final calculation, arriving at a particular coefficient. As a refinement of the grid-shift method it produces more precise readings.

Hence, in Fig. 14–4 for a small change in

$$G_m = \frac{\Delta I_{plate}}{\Delta E_{grid}}.$$

Note that all of the meters are so arranged *with a bucking battery* that after adjusting for

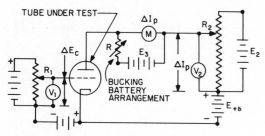

TUBE UNDER TEST

FIG. 14-4 Incremental tube testing circuit

zero reading under static conditions they read only the incremental voltage. Likewise plate resistance

$$R_p = \frac{\Delta E_{plate}}{\Delta I_{plate}}$$

and thus the amplification factor

$$\mu = \frac{G_m}{R_p}$$

can be calculated.

The second method of tube measurement uses *a-c bridge measurement circuits* and null balance indications to measure the incremental quantities. For instance, in Fig. 14–5(a) we may measure the plate resistance of a tube by making it the unknown arm of an a-c bridge. If a-c is applied as an increment to the d-c plate voltage we can make an adjustment for null on R_3 and C_3 while simultaneously adjusting the ratio arms R_1 and R_2. Dial readings will then yield usable quantities so that we can readily calculate

$$R_p = \frac{R_1 \times R_3}{R_2}.$$

Such a bridge must be shielded and operated at selected plate-supply (E_b) potentials. For perfect balance a variable capacitance C_3 must be adjusted to compensate for the plate-to-cathode capacitance of the tube.

The measurement of the amplification factor by the bridge method is shown in Fig. 14–5(b) where an oscillator voltage is applied to resistances R_2 and R_1 in series. This causes a-c increments E_2 and E_1 to be applied to the two electrodes so when the ratio of R_2 to R_1 is equal to the amplification factor, a null will appear across the phones connected between the junction point of the resistors and the cathode of the tube. As we see by the tube capacitances (shown dotted) the circuit is also a bridge type and it becomes necessary to add a variable capacitor C_1 to attain a sharp null for final balance of all the reactive currents in the various parts of the circuit.

The bridge circuits of Fig. 14–5(c) provide current from the oscillator to induce a drop across R_1 which is hence applied to the control grid; this input produces plate-current variations across R_3. Now when the bridge is properly balanced the voltage across the phones will be a null when the plate-current voltage produces an equal and opposite value to that produced by oscillator current flowing through

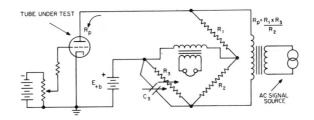

(a) *Measurement of the plate resistance of tube*

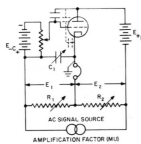

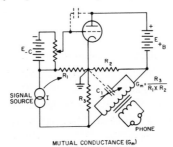

(b) *Measurement of the amplification factor by the bridge method*

(c) *Bridge circuits with oscillator-induced resistor drops*

FIG. 14-5 Bridge measurement circuits

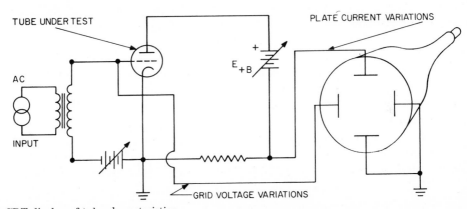

FIG. 14-6 CRT display of tube characteristics

R_3. Thus:

$$G_m = \frac{R_3}{R_1 \times R_2}.$$

Differences due to circuit and tube capacitances are balanced out by adjusting C_1. Many other types of bridge and null-indication measurement circuits have been used; the foregoing examples illustrate the general techniques.

Tube characteristics can be visibly and conveniently displayed on a cathode-ray tube. This method is a powerful one since the characteristics appear on the screen only periodically so that when abnormal voltages and currents occur they can be displayed without overloading or burning out the elements. Figure 14–6 shows the basic method of displaying a grid voltage-plate current characteristic.

15 Testing and Measurement of Transistors, Diodes, and Special Semiconductors

Solid-state scientific developments have produced radical changes in electronic equipment technology. This development stems from the physical chemistry existing at the junction between two specially treated pieces of semiconductor material. The treatment consists of impurity doping of germanium or silicon crystals with chemically similar semiconductor materials (arsenic, indium, gallium, etc.). When electric potentials are applied properly across the junction, rectification occurs, and when two semiconductor junctions (or diodes) are arranged back-to-back, so to speak, they form a transistor. Invention of the transistor was a major scientific breakthrough because it provided simple, efficient electronic amplification without many of the disadvantages common to vacuum tubes.

Transistors and semiconductor diodes have thus become the backbone of modern electronic equipment design where power-handling capacity and commercial or economic factors are not primary considerations.

Many types of transistors and diodes have been developed, varying according to the constructional and functional factors connected with their design, manufacture, or usage. Most particularly, commercial transistors can be functionally divided into the categories listed in Chapter 5 and in Appendix B-3. These types are based on performance in electronic circuitry in operational equipment.

Transistors may be listed chemically and physically according to current construction and processing. Table 15–1 categorizes these types according to five basic manufacturing methods.

THE FUNCTIONAL TRANSISTOR

Transistors in general can and do perform most of the six fundamental functions handled

Table 15–1 Transistor types

Diffused	Alloy	Epitaxial	Grown	Electrochemical
Alloy-diffused	Alloy junction	Epitaxial mesa	Grown diffused	Electrochemical diffused collector
Double-diffused	Fused alloy	Epitaxial	Grown junction	Surface barrier
Grown-diffused	Fused junction	Planar epitaxial	Rate grown	
Diffused junction	Micro-alloy diffused base		Meltback	
Diffused mesa	Precision surface			
Double-diffused mesa				
Diffused planar				
Drift				
Mesa				
Planar				
Triple-diffused planar				

by electron tubes in electronic equipment. They amplify, oscillate, detect or demodulate, and perform switching functions. They can also, to a limited extent, transform light to electricity (phototransistor) and in recent developments show promise of being able to transform electricity to light. Five basic techniques—alloy, diffusion, epitaxial, grown, and electrochemical—determine the basic groupings.

Transistors have introduced new concepts of current flow. Solid-state physicists have found that vacant energy states exist in and around abutting semiconductor surfaces and that, owing to displacement of electrons, molecules in these areas are virtually electron-deficient and become holes, so to speak, subject to applied electric fields in an opposite manner (since the holes are positively charged) to that existing on electrons themselves when they are acting as negative charge carriers. Thus, in a semiconductor junction between different materials subject to applied voltage the current is a mixture of charge movements, mainly because of the *charge carriers* (electrons or holes) that are in the *majority* under the particular condition of voltage and orientation of the two semiconductor materials.

TRANSISTORS AND ELECTRON TUBES

In practical design and operational usage the basic differences and similarities between electron tubes and transistors are as follows:

(a) The main current flow in an electron tube is from cathode to plate; in a junction transistor the main current flow is from emitter to collector.

(b) The current in the electron tube passes through the grid. In the transistor, the current passes through the base.

(c) The cathode, the grid, and the plate of the electron tube, are comparable respectively to the emitter, the base, and the collector of the transistor.

(d) Electron-tube plate current is determined mainly by grid-cathode voltage while transistor-collector current is determined mainly by emitter-base voltage and most particularly by the emitter-base *current* flow

resultant to this voltage. In this respect the collector current-collector voltage characteristic of a transistor with fixed emitter-base voltage (Fig. 15–1(a)) is analogous to the plate current-plate voltage characteristic of the pentode tube with fixed grid-cathode voltage (Fig. 15–1(b)).

In the transistor, the steady rise of current from 0 to X with a rise of collector voltage indicates that a sufficient supply of carriers is flowing from the emitter-base barrier through

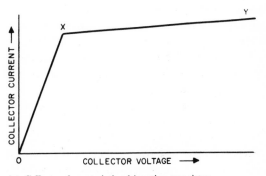

(a) *Collector characteristic of junction transistor*

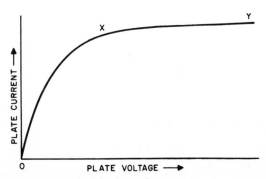

(b) *Plate characteristic of pentode*

FIG. 15-1 Tube versus transistor—plate and collector characteristics

the base-collector barrier to satisfy the applied collector voltage. This section of the characteristic represents low collector resistance.

From X to Y, the collector current remains relatively constant in spite of the rising collector voltage, because the supply of carriers through the emitter-base barrier does not increase. This section of the characteristic represents high collector resistance.

In the pentode electron tube, the leveling off of plate current from X to Y is due to the shielding of the plate from the grid by the screen and the suppressor grids.

(e) The electron tube requires heater current to boil electrons from the cathode. The transistor has no heater.

(f) For current flow in an electron tube, the plate is always positive with respect to the cathode. For current flow in a transistor, the collector may be positive or negative with respect to the emitter, depending on whether electrons or holes respectively are the emitter-to-collector carriers. These conditions respectively apply to the NPN and the PNP transistors. In the PNP type the collector voltage is always negative; the reverse is true in the NPN type.

(g) For most electron-tube applications, grid-cathode current does *not* flow. For most transistor applications, current *does* flow between emitter and base. Thus, in these cases, the input resistance of an electron tube is much higher than its output resistance and similarly the input resistance of a transistor is much lower than its output resistance. Control of collector current is thus by means of base-to-emitter *current*, while *grid voltage* controls plate current in a vacuum tube.

TRANSISTOR AMPLIFIERS

LABELING—POLARITIES—BIASING

The following generalizations are extremely helpful in analyzing the qualitative (non-mathematical) behavior of transistor circuitry. These generalizations apply to a transistor circuit that is operated as a Class A amplifier.

(a) The first and second letters of the type of transistor indicate the relative polarities of the *emitter* voltage with respect to either its base or to its collector.

Following this rule Fig. 15–2(a)–(c) shows the biasing battery polarities necessary to operate PNP or NPN transistors in the three basic circuit configurations, namely the common base, common emitter, or common collector.

(b) The d-c electron-current direction is always against the direction of the arrow on the emitter.

(c) If the electrons flow into or out from the emitter, the electrons flow respectively out from or into the collector.

(d) The base-emitter junction is always forward biased.

(e) The collector-base junction is always reverse biased.

(f) A base input voltage that aids (increases) the forward bias increases the emitter and collector currents.

(g) A base input voltage that opposes (decreases) the forward bias decreases the emitter and collector currents.

BIAS CIRCUIT DESIGN CONSIDERATIONS

One of the basic problems in the design of transistor amplifiers is that of establishing and maintaining within the circuit the proper d-c collector-to-emitter voltage and emitter current. These biasing conditions must be maintained despite variations in ambient temperature and under variations of gain and leakage current between transistors of the same type. The factors that must be taken into account in the design of bias circuits include:

1. The specified maximum and minimum values of current gain at the operating point for the type of transistor used.

2. The variation of gain with temperature, or the determining of maximum and minimum values over specified temperature ranges of operation.

3. The variation of collector leakage current (I_{co}) with temperature. For most transistors, I_{co} increases at approximately 6.5–8 percent per degree centigrade and doubles with a temperature change of 9–11°C.

4. The variation of base-to-emitter voltage drop (V_{BE}) with temperature. Under normal bias conditions, V_{BE} is about .2 volts for germanium transistors and .7 volts for silicon transistors and has a temperature coefficient of about -2.5 millivolts per degree centigrade.

5. The tolerance of the resistors used in the bias networks and the tolerance of the supply voltages.

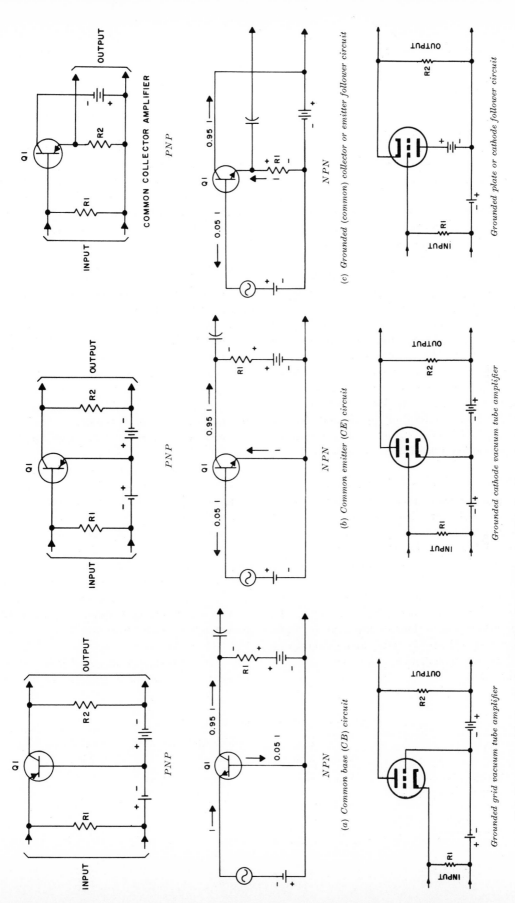

FIG. 15-2 Summary of basic transistor and analogous vacuum tube circuits

TRANSISTOR AMPLIFIER CIRCUITS

Three basic input-output circuit arrangements are commonly used:

COMMON- OR GROUNDED-BASE (CB) AMPLIFIER. Referring to Fig. 15–2(a), input signal is applied between the emitter and the base, and extracted from between the collector and base. The grounded base element of the transistor is common to both the input and the output circuit.

A similar circuit arrangement employing a triode as a grounded-grid amplifier is shown at the bottom of Fig. 15–2(a). This circuit is analogous in that comparable elements of the transistor and the electron vacuum-tube elements assume the same relative input and output positions. Unlike vacuum tubes, transistor emitter input resistances are low and collector or output impedances are relatively high. Typical values of input and output resistance, voltage, current, and power gains for the CB amplifier appear in Table 15–2.

COMMON- OR GROUNDED-EMITTER AMPLIFIER. In the grounded-emitter circuit (Fig. 15–2(b)) input signal is applied to the base-emitter circuit and output extracted from the collector-emitter circuit. The grounded emitter element is common to the input and output circuits.

The analogous electron-tube circuit is the conventional grounded-cathode triode amplifier. For typical values of input and output resistance, voltage, current, and power gains of the common-emitter amplifier, refer to Table 15–2.

COMMON- OR GROUNDED-COLLECTOR AMPLIFIER. In Fig. 15–2(c) input signal is applied to the base-collector circuit and output extracted from the emitter-collector circuit. The collector element of the transistor is common to input and output circuits.

The analogous electron-tube circuit is the grounded-plate amplifier, commonly known as the cathode follower. Note that in Fig. 15–2(c) output is taken from across a series resistor in the emitter circuit, while in (a) and (b) output passes from across the collector load circuit itself.

BIAS ARRANGEMENTS

COMMON-BASE AMPLIFIER. Most circuits operate the common-base amplifier with a single battery so that a voltage-divider network is required. In the circuit of Fig. 15–3(a) the collector-base bias voltage comes directly from the battery in the collector-base circuit. Since the transistor shown is a PNP transistor, reverse bias is achieved by connecting the collector negative with respect to the base, as shown. Since forward bias in the emitter-base circuit requires that the emitter be positive with respect to the base, this condition is achieved by using the voltage-divider network consisting of resistors R_3 and R_4 connected so that the electron current (I) from the battery and through the voltage divider is in the direction shown. This current flow causes the correct polarity through the voltage drop across resistor R_3, and thus places the emitter at a positive potential with respect to the base. If an NPN transistor were used, the battery would be reversed.

COMMON-EMITTER AMPLIFIER. Using a single battery in the common-emitter single-stage

Table 15–2   Transistor amplifier characteristics

Characteristic	Amplifier type		
	Common base	Common emitter	Common collector
Input resistance	30–150 ohms	500–1,500 ohms	20–500 kilohms
Output resistance	300–500 kilohms	30–50 kilohms	50–1,000 ohms
Voltage gain	500–1,500	300–1,000	Less than 1
Current gain	Less than 1	25–50	25–50
Power gain	20–30 db	25–40 db	10–20 db

audio amplifier (Fig. 15–3(b)), the required reverse bias voltage in the collector-base circuit and the forward bias between the emitter and the base are automatically produced by using the potential drops through the internal transistor resistances, which cause the two PN junctions themselves to act as a voltage divider. Thus the PN junction between the collector and the base represents a high resistance and develops the larger voltage drop, while the NP junction between emitter and base represents a low resistance. With the appropriate shunting resistors R_1 and R_2 to maintain stability we develop the correct bias for base-emitter operation. Figure 15–3(c) shows a similar circuit using self-bias in an NPN amplifier circuit and omitting one of the stabilizing resistors.

COMMON-COLLECTOR AMPLIFIER. Two methods using separate batteries for biasing the common-collector amplifier are shown in Fig. 15–3(d)(e). In each case the batteries establish the proper forward (base-emitter) and reverse (base-collector) bias. If an NPN transistor were substituted, the polarities of both batteries in each circuit would have to be reversed.

A common-collector amplifier can be biased with a single battery by obtaining reverse bias directly and forward bias from the internal resistance of the base-emitter junction. (See Fig. 15–2(c).)

TRANSISTOR PARAMETERS AND MEASUREMENT TECHNIQUES

The technician must be familiar with the nomenclature of all transistor parameters specified by the manufacturer or in operating instructions.

In testing it should be realized that in most applications a transistor uses the low input impedance of the common-emitter circuit; it should also be noted that this circuit is a current-input, voltage-output device while the analogous grounded-cathode grid-input high-impedance vacuum-tube amplifier is a voltage-input, voltage-output device.

The major difference between tube and

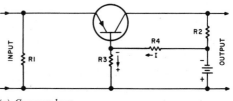

(a) *Common base*

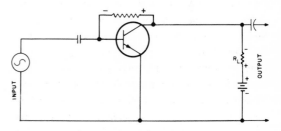

(b) *Common emitter*

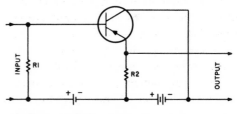

(c) *Common emitter, with self-bias in NPN*

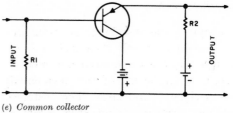

(d) *Common collector*

(e) *Common collector*

FIG. 15-3 Transistor biasing circuits

transistor *parameters*, however, is due to the fact that transistor input and output constants depend upon one another even when the output terminals are open or short-circuited to a-c signals. Transistor input and output circuits are thus interconnected resistance networks. This means also that current and voltages at these points are different under the open- or short-circuit conditions because there is *interaction* between the circuit elements under both conditions, and feedback of energy from output to input occurs when signals are passing through.

This is in general not true in vacuum tubes, where, for instance, the grid (except of very high frequencies) is not affected by plate conditions since it is physically isolated and electronically decoupled from the plate element.

The feedback effect of output on input thus gives us in transistors what are known as *transfer circuit constants* or *parameters* under both open- and short-circuit conditions of the input and output terminals. These parameters are called forward and reverse transfer resistances, forward and reverse conductances, forward and reverse amplification factors, etc. Thus two entire sets of short- and open-circuit voltage, current, and impedance relationships exist (one for input and one for output), both of which are used in design and in circuit calculations. Many times each manufacturer and author has his own set of letters and subscripts in describing the open- and short-circuit parameters as shown in Table 15–3. Most of these parameters, however, are of no particular interest to the laboratory technician.

HYBRID PARAMETERS

To simplify the handling of transistor circuit constants we call them *hybrid parameters* since they are a combination or mixture (or hybrid arrangement) of the open-circuit and short-circuit parameters. For instance, one of the most important (the common-emitter forward current gain) (h_{fe}) shows the relationship between input or base *current* and output collector *current*. This is analogous to the approach used in the grounded-cathode vacuum-tube amplifier where we use the

amplification factor (mu) to show the relationship between signal grid voltage and plate voltage. Appendix B-5(b) lists convenient formulas when converting common emitter parameters to common base and common collector configurations.

Hybrid parameters are used only with the assumption that *small signals* are to be carried by the transistor circuit. Any large variation in signal voltage operates the transistor in

Table 15–3   Generalized and hybrid transistor parameters

With input current, i, and output current, i_2, output voltage, V_2, and input voltage, V_1

Generalized:
  "*Y*" *closed-circuit and* "*Z*" *open-circuit parameters*
  $y_{11} = 1/h_{11}$, short-circuit input admittance
  $\mu_{12} = h_{12}$, reverse open-circuit voltage gain
  $a_{21} = h_{21}$, forward short-circuit current gain
  $Z_{22} = 1/h_{22}$, open-circuit output impedance using the following:
Hybrid parameters
  h_{11} = input resistance
  h_{12} = voltage feedback ratio
  h_{21} = forward current ratio
  h_{22} = output admittance

Common-emitter hybrid parameters	*Hybrid analogy*
h_{ie} = input resistance	h_{11}
h_{re} = voltage feedback ratio	h_{12}
h_{fe} = forward current gain	h_{21}
h_{oe} = output admittance	h_{22}

nonlinear portions of its characteristics, and constants are therefore no longer valid since they change with signal level.

For small signals hybrid parameters are labeled with a lower-case letter h and with subscripts using lower-case letters (h_{fe}); when referring to d-c conditions, capital letters and subscripts are used. (H_{FE}).

VOLTAGES AND CURRENTS

Capital letters likewise apply to operating d-c voltages and currents under which transistors operate. Table 15–4 lists the common d-c notations.

TRANSISTOR TEST INSTRUMENTS

Transistor testing instruments, in general, aim to measure, under d-c conditions, two

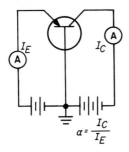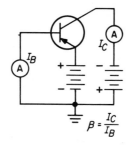

$$\alpha = \frac{I_C}{I_E}$$

$$\beta = \frac{I_C}{I_B}$$

(a) *Alpha and beta measurements*

EMITTER OPEN CIRCUITED

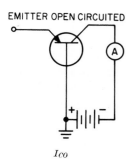

I_{CO}

EMITTER GROUNDED
THROUGH RESISTOR

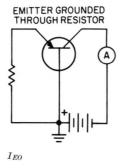

I_{EO}

EMITTER SHORTED

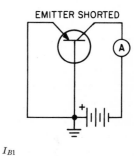

I_{B1}

(b) *Leakage current measurements*

FIG. 15-4 Basic transistor measurement circuits

Table 15-4   D-c operating parameters

V_{EB1}, V_{CB1}, V_{CE}	Terminal voltages— emitter to base, collector to base, collector to emitter	BV_{CBO1}, BV_{EBO}	Respective breakdown voltages from collector and emitter to base at specified current
I_{B1}, I_{E1}, I_C	D-c currents in base, emitter, and collector	$BV_{CEO}, BV_{CER}, BV_{CES},$ BV_{CEX}, V_{RT}	Breakdown voltage from collector to emitter under the following conditions:
$I_{CO} = I_{CBO}$	Collector leakage current (reverse voltage with emitter open)—positive for NPN, negative for PNP types		BV_{CEO} = with base open-circuited BV_{CER} = with base connected to emitter through a resistor
$I_{EO} = I_{EBO}$	Emitter leakage current (reverse voltage with collector open)—positive for NPN, negative for PNP types		BV_{CES} = with base shorted to emitter BV_{CEX} = with base reverse biased
R_{B1}, R_{E1}, R_C	Ohmic resistance internal to transistor in series respectively with base, emitter, and collector	V_{RT}	= "Reach-through" or "punch-through" voltage
α	Normal alpha, small-signal common-base forward-current transfer ratio from emitter to collector with output a-c short-circuited	D-c beta (β)	Collector current gain with emitter grounded
		(H_{FE})	Forward current transfer

229

basic constants: beta (β)—more commonly known as the forward transfer current gain (h_{fe})—and the collector-base leakage current I_{cbo} or I_{co}. Measurement of hybrid and some of the small-signal parameters is provided for in some commercial instruments, but the general trend has restricted instrumentation to simple devices with internal battery and providing proper switching and metering. Figure 15–4 schematically illustrates test circuits for measuring alpha (collector-to-emitter current gain), beta, and leakage currents under three conditions.

In order to measure some of the more detailed characteristics such as high-frequency alpha cut-off, base spreading resistance, and collector-to-base capacitance, more elaborate instrumentation is necessary; discussion of such tests is beyond the scope of this volume. One of the more common measurements is that of breakdown voltage. Figure 15-5 shows the possible variations in this test circuitry.

Figures 15-6 and 15-7 show two commonly used circuits used in transistor testers. The former measures d-c constants as defined in the basic measuring circuits shown in Figures 15-4 and 15-5 while the latter adds the pro-

vision of switching the transistor under test into an audio oscillator circuit. In the latter, if the transistor under test has an acceptable value of beta, it provides the adjustable feedback circuit enough impulse to start oscillation. The amount of feedback control inserted through the adjustable circuit (on a calibrated dial) indicates the relative value of the transistor's beta.

Figure 15-8 illustrates the circuitry of a commercial tester.

CONVERSION TABLES AND NOMOGRAPHS. The measurement and calculation of small-signal open-circuit and short-circuit parameters is usually too complicated for routine test by the laboratory technician. Often they are provided in specifications but must be converted to hybrid units for other circuit configurations. Using appendix B-11, we find the more common formulas for obtaining common-base and common-collector values by using common-emitter expressions:

ALPHA AND BETA CONVERSION. Many times it is necessary to convert measured or specified values of beta to alpha or vice versa. The nomograph in Appendix B-13 provides a convenient tool for making this conversion.

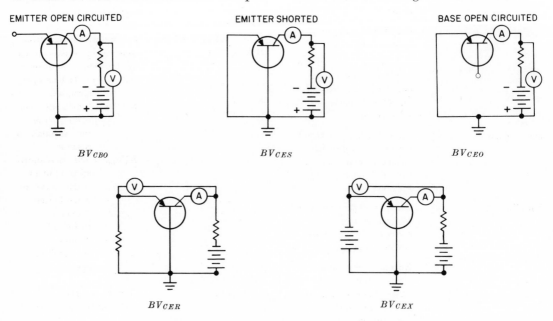

FIG. 15-5 Breakdown voltage measurements

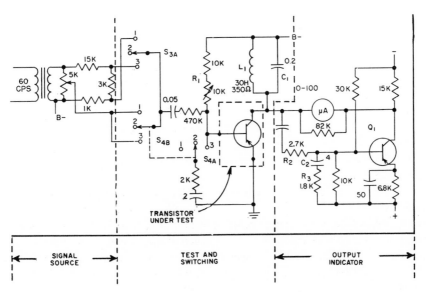

FIG. 15-6 Simplified test circuit

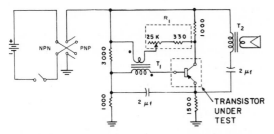

FIG. 15-7 Audio oscillator for a-c beta test circuit

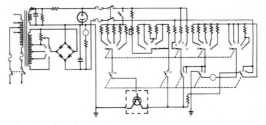

FIG. 15-8 Typical commercial transistor checker

DETAILS ON INSTRUMENTS AND PROCEDURES

The testing of transistors, like that of vacuum tubes, may be divided into two categories:

1. Test and measurement of d-c parameters —directly and easily accomplished with instruments consisting of simple milliammeters and voltmeters, appropriate sockets and switching arrangements, necessary load resistors, meter scales, power supplies, etc.

2. Dynamic testing, using a-c inputs and arriving at the small-signal parameters.

D-C TEST AND MEASUREMENT

In the majority of transistor testers, four quantities are commonly measured: (a) Alpha (α), or collector-to-emitter current gain, I_C/I_E.

(b) Beta (β), or collector-to-base current gain, I_C/I_B, for common-base connection. Also known as the forward current transfer ratio (H_{FE}). (c) Collector leakage current, I_{CB} or I_{CBO}. (d) Collector reverse breakdown voltage, BV_{cbo} or BV_{ceo}.

A number of other, more detailed and scientific measurements are sometimes necessary, most of which are beyond the scope of this book, although a few will be touched upon briefly. These do not include the "h" parameters or the maximum and minimum of collector and emitter voltages and currents. These characteristics may be summarized as follows: (Also see Table 15-4.)

1. Alpha frequency cut-off: an indication of the transistor's ability to deliver high-frequency response.

2. I_{eo} or I_{ebo}: emitter leakage current (reverse emitter voltage applied with collector open)

3. Other breakdown voltages:

(a) BV_{CEO}: collector to emitter; with base open.

(b) BV_{CER}: collector to emitter; base connection emitter through resistor.

(c) BV_{CES}: collector to emitter; base shorted to emitter.

(d) BV_{CEX}: collector to emitter; with base reverse biased.

(e) V_{RT}: collector to emitter; "punch-through" voltage.

Figure 15-9 shows the simplified circuits used to measure each of these voltages.

4. C_{CE} and C_{ob}: output capacitances respectively of common-emitter and common-base configurations.

5. t_p: rise time in microseconds of a switching transistor when an ideal pulse input is applied.

6. t_s: storage time in switching transistors.

7. R_b: base spreading resistance. This requires a highly complicated measurement, plus additional calculations, seldom required in measurement and testing.

8. f_t: gain-bandwidth product. This is the product of a transistor alpha cut-off frequency and the small-signal gain. It is calculated from measured constants.

D-C TESTING CIRCUITS AND PROCEDURES

Measurement techniques applying to the alpha, beta, and collector leakage currents referred to above are shown in skeleton schematic form in Fig. 15-4. Together with the appropriate circuit provisions, testers usually include switching for the checking of interelectrode short circuits, a necessary preliminary operation which usually precedes all measurements.

In the wide variety of d-c transistor testers available (excepting the dynamic a-c beta tester) three fundamental instruments are commonly used:

1. An accurate multirange VTVM capable of accurately measuring very small and very large voltages.

2. Micro- or milliammeters from 10 microamps(μa) to 500 milliamps(ma).

3. A constant-current low-impedance regulated power source or a provision for calibrating other supply sources such as batteries or rectified inputs.

Commercial instrument schematics are shown in Figs. 15-6, 15-7, and 15-8. The last includes switching to accommodate particular circuit arrangements, for the various measurements for the type of transistor (PNP or NPN) to be measured, for the correct levels of voltage and current for low-medium, and high-power transistors. Most instruments have their indicating meters arranged so that they can be read directly as on-scale beta readings applicable to the standardized conditions of operation being used.

MEASURING D-C BETA (H_{FE})

Large-signal, common-emitter current gain is measured by inserting a known fixed current at a transistor's base and measuring the resulting collector current. Beta is the ratio of change in the measured collector current to change in the base current, and since the base current can be preadjusted to the appropriate power level of the transistor under test, the collector current can be directly calibrated in beta.

Practical details of commercial transistors must, however, take account of a number of other factors, such as the following:

1. Collector and emitter load resistances must be correct in power and in value to handle the current in the particular transistor element being measured—that is, for power transistors, collector leakage currents may vary from a few microamperes to a few milliamperes.

2. Meter impedances must not upset circuit current readings. For instance, when measuring beta, the collector is assumed to be short-circuited to ground so that unless the measuring meter is considerably less than the transistor output impedance measured, beta values will not be correct.

3. The collector leakage current must be accounted for in test conditions where it is large enough to affect measured collector currents.

4. When making dynamic measurements, the a-c indicator impedances must not destroy element circuit impedances. This condition can occur when low-frequency (60-cps) signal inputs are applied for the measurement of small-signal beta. Some tester circuits isolate the signal-measuring circuits by means of amplifiers or remove the meter shunting effects by choke feed while still measuring current.

MEASURING COLLECTOR LEAKAGE CURRENT (I_{CO} OR I_{CBO})

This measurement should be made with the emitter open. Correct collector series resistors must, however, be inserted for different transistor power ratings. To avoid meter damage in measurement of low- and medium-power units, use 50,000- to 100,000-ohm collector resistors and 5,000 to 10,000 ohms for high-power units.

MEASURING COLLECTOR REVERSE BREAKDOWN VOLTAGES (BV_{CBO})

Referring to Fig. 15-4(b), we see that this measurement is made with the emitter open-circuited. Using a variable voltage source, some arbitrary value of reverse collector current must be established as the voltage breakdown point, since when collector avalanche occurs here, current becomes independent of voltage, and overheating may occur to destroy the transistor, This current value is between 50 and 100 times the normal collector-base I_{CBO} leakage current.

Some testers, to avoid transistor damage by overheating, use sweep methods with an oscilloscope and sine-wave generator input so that collector voltage versus collector current can be observed and breakdown can be clearly indicated before undue heating occurs.

MEASUREMENT OF A-C BETA

A number of commercial testers combine both d-c and a-c measurements—the latter,

of course, concerning the dynamic small-signal, common-emitter gain figure. Most of these apply an a-c signal (60 cps or 1,000 kc) to the base input and directly measure the gain at collector output. See the commercial circuit in Fig. 15-8.

Another simple method mentioned above is to insert the transistor under test into an audio oscillator circuit and adjust the amount of feedback by means of a calibrated control, until it just oscillates, using loudspeaker output tone as the indicator. Current gain at the oscillator starting point can be read directly from the dial calibration.

The circuit is similar in principle to one used to measure vacuum-tube transconductance where plate signal output is fed back into the grid circuit through proper resistor and transformer coupling to cause oscillation. Similarly, in testing a transistor for beta, output (see Fig. 15-7) is fed back through R_1 and through T_1 primary winding to the base circuit. R_1 has a calibrated dial (using substitution methods) which reads directly in beta to an accuracy of a few percent of full scale.

In using this instrument for low- and medium-power transistors, beta may be accurately measured over a range of 10 to 170. Circuit parameters are so chosen that the transistor under test will adjust to a specified operating point, which in the circuit shown is selected to be at 5 v collector potential and 1 ma collector current. The transformer selected has a broad response, being essentially flat between 1 kc and 12 kc, so that with transistors having a small phase shift the oscillation occurs in this audio-frequency range.

COMMERCIAL INSTRUMENTS

Commercial instruments, exclusive of their a-c beta measuring provisions, differ only in the means of applying test voltages, switching, and applying their d-c power. Some fairly reliable information can be obtained by simple resistance measurements with a volt-ohmmeter, taken in the forward and reverse direction across the various combinations of junctions. A simple adapter using a self-contained battery and switching arrangements, can be attached to the conventional VTVM for measurement of d-c beta and I_{CBO}. Figure 15–9 is a schematic showing typical test terminals, switching, and interconnections.

An interesting refinement is the block diagram for making transistor measurements shown in Fig. 15–10, where all current measurements are made by a multirange VTVM utilizing the voltage drop across precision resistor networks, thus eliminating the use of meter shunts. This method requires but one instrument for current and voltage readings and also provides a direct means to measure breakdown voltages.

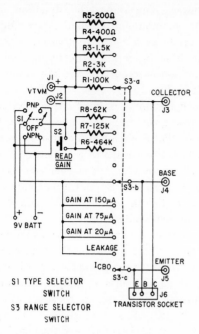

FIG. 15-9 Transistor test adaptor for use with VTVM

TRANSISTOR CHARACTERISTICS AND SPECIFICATIONS

Semiconductors are available in a large variety of different types, each with its own unique characteristics. At present there are over 2,200 different types of diodes and rectifiers and over 750 different types of transistors being manufactured.

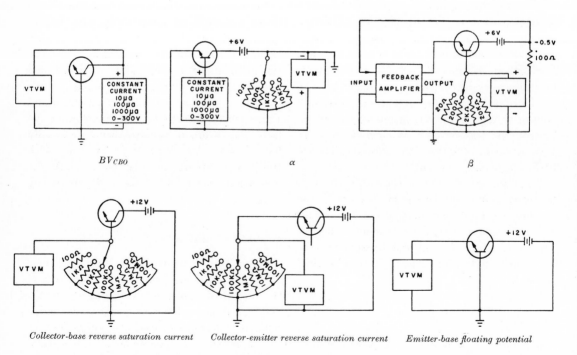

FIG. 15-10 Transistor measurements using precision VTVM

Table 15–5   Typical transistor specification 2N332

ABSOLUTE MAXIMUM RATINGS (25°C.)

Voltages:

Collector to base (emitter open)	V_{CBO}		45 volts
Emitter to base (collector open)	V_{EBO}		1 volt

Collector current I_C 25 ma

Power*

Collector dissipation (25°C.)	P_C		150 mw
Collector dissipation (125°C.)	P_C		50 mw

Temperature range:

Storage	T_{STG}		−65°C. to 200°C.
Operating	T_A		−55°C. to 175°C.

ELECTRICAL CHARACTERISTICS (25°C.)
(Unless otherwise specified, $V_{CB} = 5$ v; $I_E = -1$ ma; $f = 1$ kc)

Small signal characteristics:		min.	nom.	max.	
Current transfer ratio	h_{fe}	9	15	20	
Input impedance	h_{ib}	30	53	80	ohms
Reverse voltage transfer ratio	h_{rb}	.25	1.0	5.0	$\times 10^{-4}$
Output admittance	h_{ob}	0.0	.25	1.2	μmhos
Power gain					
($V_{CE} = 20$ v; $I_E = -2$ ma; $f = 1$ kc;					
$R_G = 1$ K ohms; $R_L = 20$ K ohms)	G_e		35		db
Noise figure	NF		28		db
High frequency characteristics:					
Frequency cutoff					
($V_{CB} = 5$ v; $I_E = -1$ ma)	f_{ab}		15		mc
Collector to base capacity					
($V_{CB} = 5$ v; $I_E = -1$ ma; $f = 1$ mc)	C_{ob}		7		$\mu\mu$f
Power gain (common emitter)					
($V_{CB} = 20$ v; $I_E = -2$ ma; $f = 5$ mc)	G_e		17		db
D-c characteristics:					
Collector breakdown voltage					
($I_{CBO} = 50$ μa; $I_E = 0$; $T_A = 25$°C.)	BV_{CBO}	45			volts
Collector cutoff current					
($V_{CB} = 30$ v; $I_E = 0$; $T_A = 25$°C.)	I_{CBO}		.02	2	μa
($V_{CB} = 5$ v; $I_E = 0$; $T_A = 150$°C.)	I_{CBO}			50	μa
Collector saturation resistance					
($I_B = 1$ ma; $I_C = 5$ ma)	R_{SC}		80	200	ohms
Switching characteristics:					
($I_{B_1} = 0.4$ ma; $I_{B_2} = -0.4$ ma;					
$I_C = 2.8$ ma)					
Delay time	t_d		.75		μsec
Rise time	t_r		.5		μsec
Storage time	t_s		.05		μsec
Fall time	t_f		.15		μsec

*Derate 1mw/°C increase in ambient temperature.

The characteristics of each of these devices are usually presented in specification sheets similar to those in Table 15–5. These specifications contain the more important constants of the transistor when used as a circuit element.

TYPICAL TRANSISTOR SPECIFICATIONS 2N332

The type 2N332 is a silicon NPN triode transistor intended for amplifier applications in the audio-and radio-frequency range and for general-purpose switching. It is a grown junction device with a diffused base. Electrical stability is insured by means of a minimum 150-hour, 200°C cycled aging operation included in the manufacturing process. All units are subjected to a rigorous mechanical drop test to control mechanical reliability. This transistor is hermetically sealed in a welded case. The case dimensions and lead configuration conform to the JETEC TO-5 package and are suitable for insertion in printed boards by automatic assembly equipment.

NOTES ON TYPICAL TRANSISTOR SPECIFICATIONS

1. The lead paragraph (exemplified above) is a general description of the device and usually contains three specific pieces of information: (1) the kind of transistor (in this case a silicon NPN triode), (2) a few major application areas (amplifier and switch), (3) general sales features (electrical stability and a standard-size hermetically sealed package).

2. The *absolute maximum ratings* are those ratings which should not be exceeded under any circumstances. Exceeding them may cause device failures.

3. The *power dissipation* of a transistor is limited by its junction temperature. Therefore, the higher the temperature of the air surrounding the transistor (ambient temperature), the less power the device can dissipate. A factor is usually given telling how much the transistor must be derated in milliwatts (mw)

for each degree of increase in ambient temperature in degrees centigrade. Notice that the characteristic shows the unit can dissipate 150 mw at 25°C. By applying the given derating factor of 1 mw for each degree increase in ambient temperature we find that the power dissipation has dropped to zero milliwatts at 175°C., which is the maximum operating temperature of this device.

4. All of the remaining ratings define what the device is capable of under specified test conditions. These characteristics are needed by the design engineer to design matching networks and to calculate exact circuit performance.

5. *Current transfer ratio* is partially dependent on frequency, so some specifications list h_{fe} or β for more than one frequency.

6. The *noise figure* is a measurement derived to evaluate the amount of electrical noise produced by the transistor in a circuit.

7. The *frequency cut-off* (f_{ab}) of a transistor is defined as that frequency at which the grounded-base current gain drops to .707 of the I_{kc} value. It gives a rough indication of the useful signal-frequency range of the device.

8. The *collector cut-off current* is the leakage current from collector to base when no emitter current is being supplied. This leakage current varies with temperature changes and must be taken into account whenever any semiconductor device is designed into equipment used over a wide range of ambient temperature.

9. The *switching characteristics* given show how the device responds to an input pulse under the specified driving conditions. These response times are closely dependent on the circuit used and are explained by terminology accompanying the curves at the right.

DIODES

In categorizing semiconductor diodes, we may expand the number of types listed in Chapter 5 by dividing all diodes into power-rectifier and nonrectifier types. The power-rectifier types are summarized in Table 15–6, where the characteristics of silicon, germanium,

Table 15-6   Power-rectifier characteristics

	Silicon	Germanium	Selenium	Copper oxide
Size	Very small	Very small	Large	Large
Weight	Very light	Very light	Light	Heavy
Cooling	Natural or forced	Natural or forced	Natural or forced	Natural or forced
Life	Very long	Very long	60,000 to 100,000 hours normal; can vary according to rating and cooling means	Very long
Aging (forward resistance)	None	None	Increases	Stabilizes
Forward loss at same current density	Good	Excellent (lowest)	Fair (highest)	Good
Approx. d-c forward voltage drop per cell	.9 volts	.65 volts	1.0 volts	.5 volts
Leakage (reverse) current	Excellent	Excellent	Good	Fair
Ability to recover from voltage transients	None	None	Excellent	Good
Uniforming (loss of rectifier characteristic)	None	None	Some	None
Series operation of cells	Good	Good	Excellent	Excellent
Parallel operation of cells	Good	Good	Excellent	Excellent
Present cell operating temperature limit	200°C.	105°C.	130°C.	75°C.
Thermal capacity	Poor	Poor	Fair	Best
Efficiency at low voltage	Good	Excellent	Fair	Good
Humidity effects	Hermetically sealed	Hermetically sealed	Negligible	Negligible
Frequency response	Good	Good	Poor	Fair

selenium, and copper-oxide types are listed together with their applicability to power-supply usage.

Special semiconductor diodes and other semiconducting devices include: (1) tunnel diodes, (2) Zener diodes, (3) silicon-controlled rectifiers, (4) thermistors, (5) voltage-sensitive resistors (varistors), (6) varactors or parametric diodes.

TUNNEL DIODES utilize a heavily doped PN junction in such a way that with suitable forward bias they pass current through or "tunnel" it under the potential barrier provided by the applied bias voltage and produce, in effect, a gain in energy. The effect occurs because regions or bands of atomic energy in the junction elements become displaced so

as to be potentially opposite one another, rather than at a potential difference apart, and thus allow electrons to pass instantaneously from one side of a junction to the other.

The net effect is that the junction represents a negative resistance over a certain range of applied bias and can be used advantageously in oscillator and amplifier circuits. Industrially, tunnel diodes can operate at higher temperatures than other semiconductor devices. The instantaneous transit time allows for their use in high-speed switching and high-frequency tuned circuits.

ZENER DIODES are most commonly used in voltage reference circuits, where they act as a variable resistance connected to maintain a constant voltage drop across the unit itself, much as the gaseous voltage-regulator tube does in vacuum-tube circuits. The Zener effect occurs over a limited region of reverse voltage where the normally low reverse currents suddenly "avalanche" or increase with applied voltage. The phenomenon is similar in nature to breakdown, but if controlled by suitable series resistance it can be nondestructive and the constant-drop characteristic can be used for voltage-stability purposes.

The constant-drop feature of Zener diodes can also be applied to power-supply filter units in voltage-decoupling circuits where it is desirable to attenuate a-c ripple. It is also used in limiting and clipping circuits.

These units are available in a much wider range of operating voltages and are smaller, lighter, and much more reliable than voltage-regulator tubes.

SILICON-CONTROLLED RECTIFIERS (SCR) are four-layer, semiconductor power devices which incorporate a gate or switching mechanism within the semiconductor structure in order to obtain complete control of the rectifying action in an applied power cycle. The SCR is, in effect, a semiconductor thyratron where conduction can be started at will with suitable trigger voltages applied to the gate control element. The gate exercises no control in turning the SCR off.

The physical arrangement of the device is a four-layer assembly of P and N elements accomplished by adding another N element to the conventional PNP assembly. Figure 15–11 shows the physical arrangement and the schematic of an analogous arrangement of two transistors. The conventional unit is turned on by current in the gate element shown in (a). The addition of the third PN junction enables the device to be operated as a switch or relay or, in a-c circuits, as a conventional rectifier.

With supply potential applied as pictured, and with the gate "on," forward current flows through the internal end junctions, controlled by the leakage current, then through the

middle junction. As voltage is increased, the middle conductor conducts to avalanche proportions, allowing heavy currents to flow through the entire unit.

In the analogous two-transistor arrangement (Fig. 15–11(b)), the collector current of the NPN unit feeds the base of the PNP junction and its collector current feeds the base of the NPN. Gate voltage is applied to this point. The positive feedback loop, created by the product of the two transistor gains, is controlled by this small forward bias current and conduction is rapidly started from the "off" condition where, at low overall gain, both units are reverse biased.

Silicon-controlled rectifiers have several outstanding advantages over other control devices

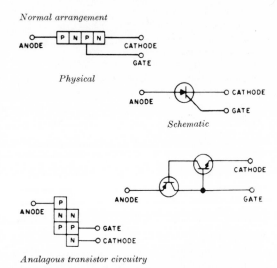

Normal arrangement

Physical

Schematic

Analogous transistor circuitry

FIG. 15-11 Physical and electronic arrangement of silicon controlled rectifier (SCR)

such as relays, switches, or thyratrons. Silicon-controlled rectifiers: (1) Have a very low voltage drop when conducting. (2) Utilize no moving parts or wearout mechanisms. They accordingly have high reliability and long life. (3) Fire and recover very rapidly. Very fast switching is possible. (4) Require no filament power, warm-up delay, stand-by power consumption, etc. (5) Can operate up to 125°C. (6) Are physically small and light. (7) Have extreme ruggedness. (8) Operate above 99 percent efficiency at relatively low voltage.

Thermistors are temperature-sensitive devices whose characteristics stem from the effects of electron and hole movement in the semiconductor materials of which the unit is made. In another light, they are resistors possessing negative temperature characteristics where the ratio of hot resistance to normal ambient resistance decreases with temperature. They are relatively stable and are widely used in temperature compensation, flow measurement, slow speed amplification and switching, measurement of radiant energy, time delay, etc.

VARISTORS (VOLTAGE-SENSITIVE RESISTORS) are units that exhibit a large change in resistance as a function of applied voltage, all the while retaining a nonpolarized attitude and producing no rectified current. A varistor behaves as if it were made of two identical and parallel rectifiers, conjugately polarized so that the combination will permit current flow equally in either direction. Apparently, the powdered ingredients when bound in a solid and heat-treated mass become homogeneously mixed P and N semiconductor regions and produce the effect of an infinite number of minute rectifiers, all in contact, which simultaneously produce symmetrical rectification.

Commercially and practically, a type of these, called thyrite units, are used in load stabilizing and compensating circuits. They can also provide load-sensitive voltage protection and are useful in bridge circuits where constant voltage regulation is desired.

DIODE TESTING

Simple diode checking usually involves nothing more than continuity. Figure 15–12(a) shows one of the simplest testers of this type, which is applicable to power diodes and to switching diodes at medium- and high-power ratings.

A more complete checker is shown in the circuit of Fig. 15–12(b). This tester is also

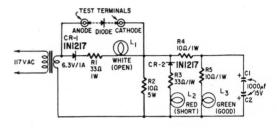

OPERATION:
L1 lights only—diode is good
L2 lights only—diode is good, reversed in polarity
L1 and L2 both light—diode is shorted
L1 and L2 both fail to light—diode is open

(a) *Simple continuity checker*

LEGEND:
L1—white—open
L2—red—short
L3—green—good

All lamps are #49 miniature type

(b) *Direct indicating checker*

FIG. 15-12 Diode testers

intended for power rectifiers and switching diodes rated at 250 ma or more. It directly shows diode condition by one of three indicator lamps. Details of operation are as follows:

With an open diode or no connection across the test terminals, L_1 is lit by current flow through CR_1, R_1, and R_2. Here the voltage drop across R_2, positive at the top end, is too low to light L_3, and L_2 does not light because CR_2 is back-biased by the positive voltage developed by CR_1. If a good diode is connected across the test terminals with polarity as shown, L_1 is shorted out and does not light. Likewise L_2 does not light because CR_2 is now back-biased by voltage developed by the diode under test. C_1 then charges, permitting L_3 to light and indicate that the diode is good.

A shorted diode shorts out L_1 and allows full a-c to appear across R_2. CR_2 then conducts on negative half-cycles and lights L_2. A-c appears across R_4, R_5, L_3, C_1, and C_2. The capacitors appear as a low-reactance shunt across R_5 and L_3 so L_3 does not light. Thus L_2 is the only light to indicate that the diode is shorted.

All lamps light when a good diode is connected to the test terminals with polarity reversed. Here CR_1 conducts on positive half-cycles so L_1 lights. The test diode then conducts on negative half-cycles and develops a d-c voltage across R_2, with the upper end negative. CR_2 then conducts and L_2 lights. C_2 charges and permits L_3 to light.

DETAILED DIODE TESTING

Complete diode characteristics for small-signal and low-power switching types require

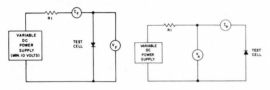

(a) D-c forward voltage drop test circuit

(b) D-c reverse leakage test circuit

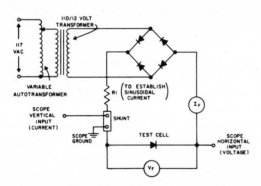

(c) Test circuit for scope display of forward characteristics

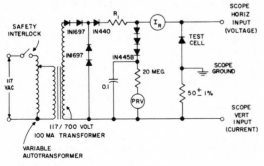

(d) Test circuit for scope display of reverse characteristics

FIG. 15-13 Diode test circuit

at least five specific tests and measurements beyond the simple continuity checks described above. These measurements call for fairly elaborate test equipment and procedures, which are beyond the scope of this volume. However, the nature of the equipment and measurements is indicated in the following rundown of the tests:

1. *Reverse dynamic characteristic*, which is a measure of a diode junction's reverse resistance under applied a-c input. The diode under test is placed in a bridge circuit and balanced against a reference resistor in the standard arm, with application of variable input voltages up to 400 volts.

2. *Reverse current measurement* with a small fixed voltage across the diode and low current (0–10 μa).

3. *Reverse current measurement* with 20 volts across the diode and up to 100-μa current.

4. *Forward voltage drop* with diode passing from 3 to 10 ma.

5. *Forward voltage drop* with diode passing around 100 μa.

In addition to the above, switching diodes have a *rise-time* (or switching-speed) requirement, a *storage factor* related to their inherent internal resistance and shunt capacity, and a *noise factor* which depends on a number of complicated contributory factors. All of these tests extend beyond the scope of this volume, although some of them will be briefly described in the material on tunnel-diode testing. Figure 15–13 illustrates practical circuits used for measuring forward and reverse diode characteristics.

THE TUNNEL DIODE

This component is characterized by operation in a negative-resistance area of its low, forward-bias region. The measurement calls for either a dynamic or a curve trace oscilloscope-type output display.

Figure 15–14(a) shows the conventional tunnel-diode characteristic with its negative-resistance slope, plus peak and valley currents.

Figure 15–14(b) is a simple checker designed to measure tunnel-diode characteristics. Here we see the diode under test being placed across a low impedance which is part of a voltage divider.

By adjusting the supply potentiometer with the diode in circuit and proceeding upward from low applied voltage, the diode current will go through a peak value (I_p) and then drop to a minimum or valley point (I_v), after which the current will again increase.

The values of I_p and I_v should reasonably match the manufacturer's specifications, the former varying from 1 to 10 ma, the latter

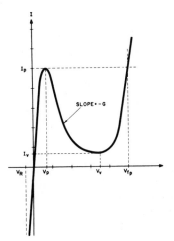

(a) *Typical static diode characteristic curve*

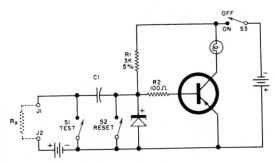

(b) *Typical tunnel diode tester*

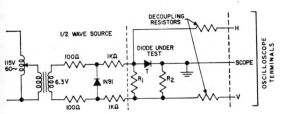

FIG. 15-14 Tunnel diode characteristics and test set-ups

from 100 to 600 μa. The voltages across these points range in hundreds of millivolts and must be measured with a high-impedance VTVM. (See typical characteristics in Fig. 15–14(a).)

In rough approximation negative resistance of the tunnel diode is equal to

$$R_d = \frac{E_v - E_p}{2(I_p - I_v)}$$

or may be derived by measuring the slope of the current-voltage curve between I_p and I_v. This approach is not always precise enough, so use is made of pulse-measuring techniques. Briefly, the measurement centers around observing the *reduction* in pulse deterioration brought about by the tunnel diode's being tested when it is connected in series with a known series resistance. For convenience oscilloscope display may be used, following the hook-up shown in Fig. 15–14(c). Conventional diode characteristic curves appear when the scope sweep is synchronized at 60 cps.

APPLICATIONS. The negative-resistance characteristic of a tunnel diode can be directly applied to several common circuits. In the RF and IF amplifier circuits shown in Fig. 15–15(a)(b) the diode negative resistance is coupled into the main amplifier tuned circuits; the net effect is a greater dynamic impedance and concomitantly a higher stage gain.

In detector circuits the subtractive resistance allows circuit operation at a considerably lower level than when using an ordinary diode, where contact potential must be overcome.

Relaxation and sine-wave oscillators become more efficient and more stable when tunnel diodes are used; this is in bearing with the reduction in loading produced by negative resistance.

The tunnel diode, being a bistable element, can act efficiently as a switch; the action covers the range in the *I-E* curve range (see Fig. 15–14(a)), from operation just before the peak-current condition to action just after the peak current.

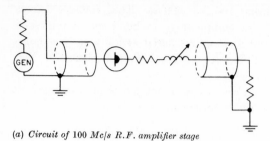

(a) *Circuit of 100 Mc/s R.F. amplifier stage*

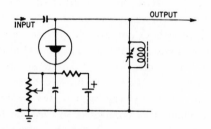

(b) *I.F. amplifier circuit*

FIG. 15-15 Tunnel diode in amplifier circuits

THE ZENER DIODE

This semiconductor possesses conventional diode characteristics but is operated *in the avalanche condition.* (See Fig. 15–16(a).) This means that a diode operating under enough applied reverse bias voltage goes suddenly into heavy conduction at a certain "Zener" or avalanche potential. At this point the junction becomes a variable-resistance, constant-voltage device operating much like the conventional voltage-regulator (VR) vacuum tube.

In this condition the Zener junction presents a stable voltage source, since the product of junction-current and resistance changes remains constant under a specified range of input conditions.

In testing of the Zener diode, we are interested in obtaining the Zener voltage (Fig. 15–16(b)), the forward voltage drop (Fig. 15–16 (c)), and the diode impedance (Fig. 15–16(d)). Zener-diode current in the *reverse*-bias direction is, of course, measured when checking by the point-by-point method.

Figure 15–16(e) shows a simple measurement set-up for displaying characteristics on an oscilloscope.

APPLICATIONS. The Zener diode's particular attribute—its dynamic resistance in the Zener region—finds application in a wide range of electronic circuitry.

(a) As a voltage-reference source, its maintenance of a constant voltage allows use in the regulation of power supplies. Here the technique depends upon sensing the difference

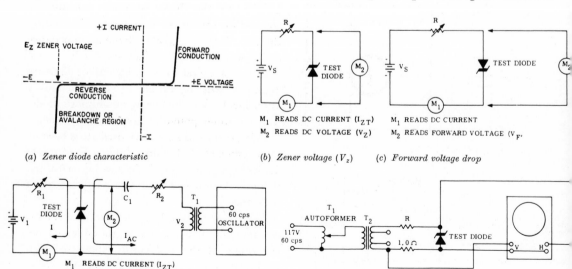

(a) *Zener diode characteristic*

(b) *Zener voltage (V_z)*

(c) *Forward voltage drop*

(d) *Impedance*

(e) *Scope display of diode characteristics*

FIG. 15-16 Zener diode testing

between the reference voltage and the voltage change to produce compensating regulatory effects in the series resistance of the regulator device.

(b) As a clipping or voltage-limiting device it can be used to produce square waves from alternating sine waves.

(c) As a variable filter unit, when placed in series with a power-regulator transistor it reduces ripple voltage and improves regulation.

(d) As a nonlinear device it can be effectively applied to expanded-scale instrumentation. When used with a resistor-diode network in series with a milliammeter it produces upper-scale expansion.

(e) As a temperature-compensating device, when connected in series in opposite direction with a forward-biased PN junction (Fig. 15–17), the positive temperature coefficient of the Zener diode apposes the negative coefficient of the PN junction.

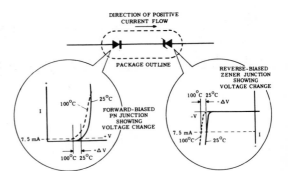

FIG. 15-17 Zener diode temperature compensation

(f) A double-limiting or slicing Zener-diode circuit is also used as a calibration source for oscilloscopes, delivering an accurate, symmetrical, clipped sine wave for visual comparison.

16 Microwave Measurements and Equipment

Microwave measurements, exclusive of antenna characteristics, are concerned basically with power and frequency. Frequency measurements are in a category by themselves (see Chapter 12), while power measurements depend upon sampling techniques and require accessory measurements—chiefly: (1) attenuation of the RF power being handled, (2) the determination of matching and terminating impedance.

It is when designing or checking transmission-line elements that we measure these quantities, in order to attain maximum power transfer; most particularly we measure reflections due to impedance mismatch since they are one of the chief sources of power loss in microwave transmission.

Other accessory measurements concern noise associated with a transmission system, the Q of various cavities and tuning elements, and sometimes the frequency-spectrum analysis of various microwave output generating devices. All of these measurements apply to both pulsed radar and modulated carrier signals.

Table 16–1 is a summary of the five types of microwave measurements described above. Note that coupling and directivity are a form of sampling by means of attenuation, and that reflections are simultaneously allied to power measurement since they represent losses in power transmission. This table also summarizes the important hardware used in measurement. The four most important kinds —i.e., meters, attenuators, and the slotted line—sampling devices and couplers, are treated successively in the text, and then the components and accessories are described.

High-power microwave measurements (chiefly transmitter output) also employ sampling procedures utilizing known attenuation; low-power measurements on receivers also use attenuated input power developed in the test signal generators.

METERS

Power meters generally fall into high- and low-power ranges—the former where there is enough power to dissipate or to measure by means of some sort of heat transfer. Low-power measuring or detecting devices usually require an amplifier to deliver readable meter indication.

Frequency meters for microwaves are exclusively built around some kind of resonant element, as described in Chapter 12, while impedance-measuring devices center around the slotted line.

ATTENUATORS

An attenuator is a sampling device placed in a transmission line in such a way that it picks off a reduced amplitude of the incident voltage and current wave. A load termination becomes a special form of attenuator representing conditions approaching short circuit.

Attenuators in present use may be classified as dissipative or nondissipative. The cut-off waveguide section, which passes only a limited band of frequencies, is a good example of the nondissipative attenuator; this attenuator merely rejects signals in proportion to the

Table 16-1 Summary of microwave equipment and measurement

Type of measurement	Input source and signal	Output measuring instrument	Accessories	Measuring techniques, ranges, comments
Power	Transmitter or equipt. tested	(1) Calorimeter } Power (2) Bolometer } meter	Attenuators, bolometer, mounts, bridges	(1) High power only—generally a complete set-up (2) Milliwatt power range
Frequency	Equipt. tested, signal generator	Cavity wavemeter, slotted line, and crystal frequency standard	Attenuators, directional couplers, stub tuners, mounts, frequency standard	Slotted line positioning less accurate than cavity reading, in turn less than crystal reference
Impedance or admittance	Variable-frequency signal generator	Slotted line, probe, and VSWR meter	Attenuator, frequency meter	Obtain reflection coefficient and read impedance from Smith Chart
Attenuation	Signal generator	Bolometer and power meter	Variable attenuator	Substitution procedures used with low accuracy due to poor resolution
Reflection coefficient and VSWR	Signal generator	Slotted line and VSWR indicator	Termination and calibrated attenuator	Calculation from slotted line positioning
Circuit Q	(1) Signal generator (2) Sweep-frequency sig. generator	(1) Slotted line, probe, VSWR meter (2) Wavemeter, crystal, oscilloscope	Attenuator, frequency meter	Reflection coeff. plus Smith chart / Frequency response at 3-db points
Frequency spectrum analysis	Spectrum analyzer	Crystal detector and oscilloscope display	Attenuators, directional coupler	Visual observation of oscilloscope pattern
Noise	Equipt. on test and noise generator	Power meter Broad-band voltmeter	Directional coupler, precision attenuator	Comparison of inherent noise signal to added noise signal
Antenna	Radiating auxiliary antenna	Antenna under test, receiver, and indicator	Standard gain horn, directional couplers, attenuators, crystal, meter	Pattern plotting from received and detected signal
Radar	Pulsed source equipment itself	Radar display	Echo box, couplers, attenuators	Inspection of reflected signal power, recovery, and other quantities

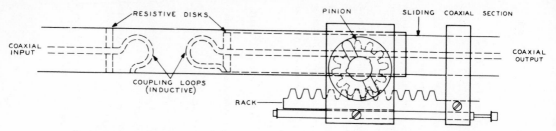

FIG. 16-1 Non-dissipative, cut-off, waveguide-type attenuator

length of waveguide section remaining *outside* its normal frequency-acceptance band instead of converting them into heat. In this sense it is *not* considered to be a filter. (See Fig. 16–1.)

The properties of an attenuator (or any lossy device) may be defined by the ratio of the power generated within a device (P_1) to the power delivered to a load or arbitrary impedance (P_2). In order to conveniently measure low-value replicas of the actual power we introduce an attenuator into a transmission line or measuring circuit to produce power or insertion loss (L), which is usually stated in logarithmic terms:

$$L = 10 \log \frac{P_1}{P_2}$$

The insertion loss represents power reflection due to impedance mismatch plus that due to dissipation in the device. Hence, the properties of the device are not uniquely defined unless its impedance relative to the generator of the source signal and that relative to the load power dissipation are both known. However, if the generator and the load each are matched to a line of its own impedance (these do not have to be the same), then P_1 becomes the maximum power available to the load.

Thus, a good attenuator or termination requires fairly precise impedance match over a wide range of frequencies, and variation in the nominal attenuation (indicated by the VSWR) must be kept within reasonable limits for broadband devices. For utmost accuracy, calibration curves are furnished with precision attenuators, which vary for low-power terminations from a VSWR of less than 1.01 (for a reference standard in a magic T) to a VSWR of 1.20 in the secondary arm of a directional coupler. (Note: A minimum of 30 db of attenuation is necessary to reduce the input VSWR of a short circuit to 1.01.) Another significant factor in the design of an attenuator or termination is the maximum power capacity. Too high an average power can produce excessive temperature in the resistive elements and materially alter their characteristics. Burn-out may also result from sustained corona ("arcing" or "sparking") under high peak pulse powers. Thus entirely different structures are used in low- and high-power attenuator structures.

DISSIPATIVE WAVEGUIDE ATTENUATORS (non-coaxial) consist of strips of resistance material placed inside a waveguide, parallel to the electrostatic field. Where accurate attenuation is not necessary, the strip is often made of bakelite or fiber, with an aquadag coating on one side, as shown in Fig. 16–2(a). Calibrated attenuators are usually of the metallized glass variety; an example is shown in Fig. 16–2(b). In this example, as the movable resistance element driven by a calibrated dial-and-cam arrangement approaches the center of the waveguide the power loss is greater. By shaping the cam surface we may arrange any desired spacing of the decibel calibration marks. Tapering of the ends of the resistive element produces a minimum of reflection over a wide band of frequencies.

Most waveguide attenuators have a limited frequency range, so it is common design practice to use two attenuators in cascade, making the total attenuation equal to the sum of the individual readings. In some designs, both attenuators are made continuously variable, and in other cases only one attenuator is continuously variable and the other adjusted in steps. Adjustable attenuation ranges of 5 to 50 db are common; fixed ranges may be in 20-db steps.

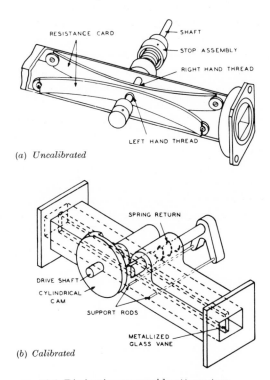

(a) *Uncalibrated*

(b) *Calibrated*

FIG. 16-2 Dissipative waveguide attenuators

To prevent the possibility of power burnout, dissipative attenuator set-ups often sample the power being measured by use of a directional coupler. Even with such a protective device damage may result from application of too much RF power; periodic inspection is recommended in any power-carrying installation for such signs as blistering, peeling, or discoloration of the resistive element.

DISSIPATIVE COAXIAL ATTENUATORS (sometimes called pads) are manufactured in short fixed coaxial sections, using resistive material for a center conductor; one typical design uses a glass center conductor rod, coated with a thin deposit of resistive metal or aquadag. Coaxial attenuators are made variable by constructing the resistive section in two telescoping sections so that the section length, and therefore the attenuation, may be varied.

A TYPICAL NONDISSIPATIVE CUT-OFF WAVEGUIDE ATTENUATOR is described in Fig. 16–1. It uses a circular pipe, too small to act normally as a waveguide, and having an adjustable section which acts as a short circuit at any position. When this short-circuiting section assembly (operated by a calibrated rack-and-pinion gear) is telescoped to make the cut-off section longer, greater attenuation results, since attenuation depends upon the cross section of the waveguide and the distance between the coupling loops at each setting. The resistive discs within the cavity provide impedance match over a wide range of frequencies.

SLOTTED LINE

The slotted line is the simplest and most direct laboratory means of measuring relative impedance in a transmission-line system; in practical usage it determines all desired quantities by measuring the *voltage standing-wave ratio* (VSWR). This measurement determines the wavelength in the guide by observing physical positions of the voltage minima or maxima. As the name implies, a thin longitudinal slot is cut in the outer wall of a transmission line so as not to interrupt current flow, and a thin wire probe is inserted in a region of high electric-field intensity. Figure 16–3 is a typical slotted line assembly for rectangular waveguide plus its associated probe and crystal. A small portion of the electric-field energy travelling down the line is coupled to the probe tip, forming the start of the probe-line center conductor which in turn feeds a crystal detector converting the energy at microwave frequency to direct

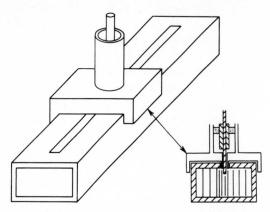

FIG. 16-3 Slotted line section and probe for waveguide

current or some low audio frequency. An audio modulation of 400 to 1,000 cycles applied to the microwave signal allows for amplification of detected audio modulation voltage, and provides greater output sensitivity.

In order to match the RF impedance of the crystal to the line impedance, tuning stubs are provided, usually of the order of several hundred ohms.

Figure 16–4, pictures a typical slotted line, assembly for use with coaxial lines. Details of the movable calibrated carriage, the probe assembly, together with a crystal mount and stub tuning section, are shown. Figure 16–5 gives details of an typical RF probe.

In typical measurements the probe depth is adjusted to the minimum that will supply an adequate signal to the detecting system, since too great a probe insertion will distort the symmetry of the electric-field configuration and consequently vary the minimum or residual mismatch of the transmission line. An RF by-pass capacitor, such as a coupling capacitor or a half-wavelength stub line, is usually provided to isolate the RF energy in the crystal from the d-c path to the indicating meter.

The crystal itself is a "square-law" device which yields a current output proportional to the square of the applied voltages, a condition which means that the output meter directly reads power. Sensitive models can

deliver crystal currents of as high as 20 milliamps to indicate an RF power input of only 30 microwatts; most crystal detectors of this sensitivity must be individually calibrated for absolute power measurements.

Higher power levels, up to tens of milliwatts, detect power thermally by the use of sensitive resistive elements (described later) and can be substituted directly for crystals in probe-type mounts. They have a much slower response time and require some form of auxiliary bridge and associated bias-voltage circuitry to measure variation in resistance. Details of power-bridge measurements appear in Chapter 18 under transmitter testing. Characteristics of the basic types of thermal low-power detectors used as sensing devices are listed in Table 16–2.

General VSWR measurement technique calls for the slotted line to be inserted in the microwave circuit preceding the device to be measured and then to be adjusted to a minimum ratio. Search for voltage maxima and minima is accomplished by moving the probe assembly longitudinally along the line by

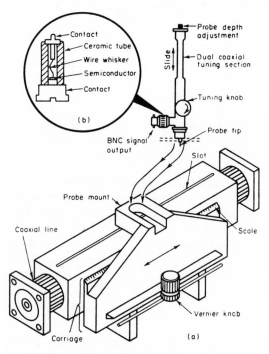

FIG. 16-4 Typical slotted line assembly for coaxial line

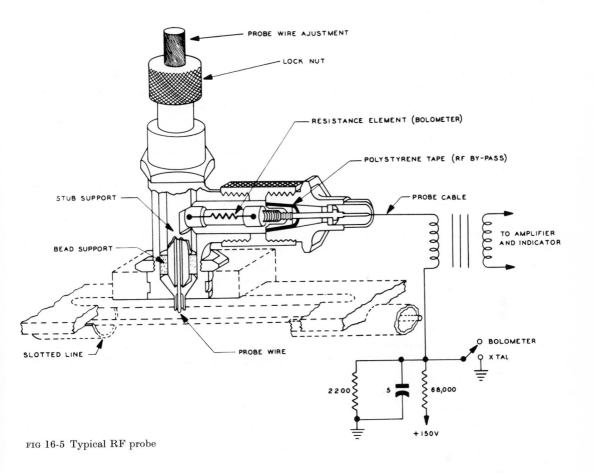

FIG 16-5 Typical RF probe

Table 16–2   Summary of low-power detectors

Type	Construction	Resistance	Power	Properties
Wire bolometer or barreter	Fine platinum wire several microinches in diam. (Wollaston wire)	50–200 ohms, positive coeff.	Range: 5–500 mw Coeff.: 3–12 ohms/mw	Rapid response time; nearly linear over range; delicate; small overload capacity
Film bolometer	Molecularly thin resistance film baked on a thin strip of glass or mica	200 ohms, positive coeff.	Range: 1–100 mw Coeff.: 50 ohms/mw	Sluggish response time; highest burnout rating; quite linear over range
Thermistor	A bead of semiconductor material placed between two thin parallel wires or in coaxial disc form	50–5,000 ohms, negative coeff.	Range: 50–400 mw Coeff.: 4–50 ohms/mw	Comparatively poor linearity and interchangeability
Thermocouple	Direct-heated two-wire systems, or enhanced by a carbon bridge on resistance bead	5–500 ohms	.5–10 mv/mw	Poor sensitivity; limited in frequency due to larger size; low resistance levels

means of a precisely calibrated carriage. Voltage peaks and valleys are thus a function of probe position. The ratio of the peak to valley voltages determines the VSWR (and, hence, the impedance mismatch), and the distance of the minima or maxima from the mismatch determines the phase angle of the reflection coefficient. A rough measurement of frequency is possible with the slotted line since the distance between pairs of either minima or maxima is half the guide wavelength. If the slotted line is long enough to compare the magnitude of successive voltage peaks or valleys, a crude measure of the attenuation is also possible.

COMPONENTS IN SAMPLING AND MEASURING TECHNIQUES

As noted at the beginning of the chapter, this section describes the accessory devices (exclusive of attenuators) that are needed in power measurement. Note that for convenience Table 16–1 lists attenuators along with impedance-matching devices, directional couplers, probes, etc.

SAMPLING DEVICES

The sampling devices used in power-testing procedures are roughly categorized in three common types of devices: (1) pickup test antennas, (2) RF probes, (3) couplers, and (4) attenuators.

PICKUP TEST ANTENNA

The test or pickup antenna consists of a portable directional antenna array broadly tuned to the frequency band to be used. This antenna, when placed in the radiation field of the transmitting antenna, picks up and samples a certain percentage of the radiated signal. In radar it is common practice to locate the pickup antenna at least one diameter of the reflector away from the radar antenna and to orient the two antennas for maximum pickup so that the space attenu-

ation is approximately 30 db. A convenient position for the pickup antenna is about 10 feet aboveground, so that its directional properties will minimize the effect of reflection from ground and nearby objects. The usual type consists of a dipole and parabolic reflector enclosed in a Plexiglass housing and of suitable size to be placed at a certain distance from the radar antenna. It is common practice to orient it directly at the main antenna and then adjusting its polarization to agree with that of the main radiator.

Another method is to clamp the pickup antenna to the edge of one reflector element and direct it toward the antenna feed array. This positioning uses antenna leakage power rather than direct radiation and has the advantage of enabling us to regulate the amount of pickup power received. Also, with this method the antenna does not require careful orientation.

If a pickup antenna is placed outside a system using a radome, the tests can then indicate operating efficiency, with all controllable factors included.

The pickup-antenna method of sampling power has four primary disadvantages: (1) the placement of the antenna is critical; (2) antennas are critical to frequency changes; (3) tests are difficult, particularly during radar scanning; (4) reflections caused by nearby objects may introduce errors in the received signal.

RF PROBE

The RF probe used in early radar testing consists of a small capacitive conductor or loop of wire inserted into the electrostatic field of an RF transmitter power line. (See Fig. 16–5.) It is common practice to adjust the probe penetration into the waveguide so that it provides 20 db or more attenuation between the main line and the probe output. In practical application the probe itself must be fitted with a coaxial connector to facilitate connection to an indicating meter. Although this use has become relatively obsolete, being superseded by use of the directional coupler, the RF probe is now used extensively as a power-extracting device in conjunction with directional couplers. The probe should be adjusted to extract a minimum of power so that normal radar operation during test will not be affected. *Used by itself* it has the following disadvantages: (1) its attenuation figure is particularly sensitive either to reflections from nearby objects or to those due to mismatch in the RF line; (2) the penetration adjustment is very critical; (3) the entire arrangement is very sensitive to frequency; (4) the attenuation figure depends not only upon characteristics of the main load but upon the load presented by the probe itself.

COUPLERS

Couplers may in general be termed directional or bidirectional. Subcategories go deeper into details of the actual coupling mechanism and briefly may be listed under single-, two-, and three-hole coupling systems.

Directional couplers serve as stable, accurate, and relatively broadband devices, which can be inserted into a transmission line so as to sample either incident or reflected power. In most cases, however, a directional coupler is built in as part of the entire system and is connected so as to sample the transmitted RF signal. In addition to reflections produced by mismatched impedances those due to undesired reflection from nearby objects are eliminated. Such reflections are an uncommon occurrence but one which sometimes causes errors; the directional coupler virtually eliminates intermediate or noise frequencies as a source of error in power measurements. Directional couplers are also made for use with coaxial transmission lines, and operate in a manner very similar to the two-hole coupler.

DIRECTIONAL COUPLERS

The directional coupler, as the name implies, couples, or samples, energy in the waveguide from a wave travelling only in one particular direction. By the proper use of one or more directional couplers, reflected signal power (travelling in the opposite direction) can be

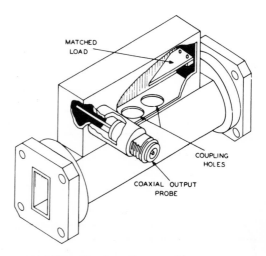

FIG. 16-6 Directional coupler assembly

prevented from affecting the accuracy of power measurements.

Figure 16-6 shows the assembly of a common type of directional coupler, which consists of a short section of waveguide coupled to the main-line waveguide by means of two small holes. It contains a matched load in one end and a coaxial output probe in the other. The degree of coupling between the main-line waveguide and the auxiliary guide is determined by the size of the two holes.

The action of this type of waveguide is explained by the diagrams in Figs. 16–7(a)(b). In Fig. 16–7(a) power is shown flowing from left to right, and two small samples are extracted or "coupled" out at points C and D with the probe connected to point F and the load connected to point E. Since the two paths, represented by C-D-F and E-E-F, to the coaxial probe are the same length, the two samples arrive at point F in phase and are picked up by the coaxial probe to give a power output reading. If, however, path C-D-F-E is one-half wavelength longer than path C-E, because the two holes are one-quarter wavelength apart, then the two samples will arrive at point E 180 degrees out of phase, producing cancellation, and absorbing no directly transmitted power flowing in the left-to-right direction.

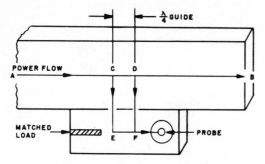

(a) *Directional coupler, showing direct power flow*

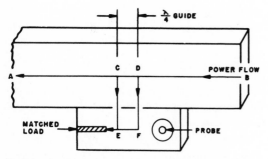

(b) *Directional coupler, showing reversed power flow*

FIG. 16-7 Details of sampling in directional couplers

Figure 16–7(b) shows the same coupler with reflected power flowing in the reverse direction. Again samples are removed at points *C* and *D*. The two paths *D-F-E* and *D-C-E* are the same length, and the two samples of reflected power arrive at point *E* in phase and are absorbed by the load. However, path *D-C-E-F* to the probe is a half wavelength longer than path *D-F* and the resulting 180-degree phase shift causes cancellation at point *E* so that no power indication results.

The result is that the coaxial probe and its rectifier meter measure power only from a wave travelling from left to right in the main line, and any reflections causing power to flow from right to left have no effect upon the output reading. All reflected power (travelling from right to left) is absorbed in the load.

In practice, the nominal attenuation or coupling factor between the coaxial output and the main line for power flowing from left

to right is usually adjusted to be over 20 db. The ability to reject power in the reverse direction is called the *directivity attenuation* or simply the *directivity;* it is usually greater than 20 db.

If a certain coupler has a nominal attenuation of 20 db and a directivity of 20 db, the forward attenuation is thus 20 db and the reverse attenuation 40 db. If the main line carries a 50-kw pulse the forward output would be 500 watts pulse power and the reverse output would be 5 watts pulse power. The five watts extracted for measurement purposes compared with 500 watts total power can be neglected in power measurements.

Forward, or nominal, attenuation in the two-hole coupler does not vary rapidly with frequency but the directivity does. Broadband couplers with less sensitive directivity will be discussed further on.

In attempting to improve the directive frequency range the three-hole coupling mechanism is used. This design consists of two directional couplers one-quarter wavelength apart using three holes one-quarter wavelength apart. This means that the three-hole coupler uses the action of two directional couplers, and the center hole serves as a common coupling to the two end holes.

The reverse type of broadband directional coupler is shown in Fig. 16–8. In this unit, the elongated coupling holes are on opposite halves of the main waveguide and spaced one-quarter wavelength apart. This causes a 180-degree phase shift between the coupled signals. This phase shift reverses the direction of coupling, so that when power enters at

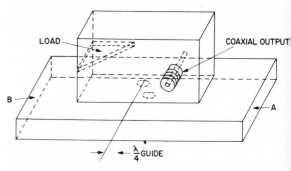

FIG. 16-8 Reverse directional coupler

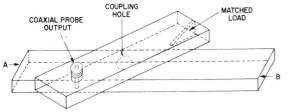

FIG. 16-9 Single-hole directional coupler

point A, the two signals arrive in phase at the coaxial output, but when (reflected) power enters at point B, the two signals arrive in phase at the load and are absorbed. The result is that this coupler's operation is the reverse of that in Fig. 16–7 and the directivity becomes relatively independent of frequency. The coupling factor does, however, vary rapidly with frequency.

Another type of directional coupler, shown in Fig. 16–9, uses a single hole as the coupling element. This is called the Bethe-hole coupler. Waves in the auxiliary guide are generated through a single hole owing to effects produced by *both* the electric and the magnetic fields in the main guide. Because of the phase relations involved in the coupling process, the waves generated by the two types of coupling cancel in the forward direction, but reinforce in the reverse direction. Therefore, power entering at point A is coupled to the coaxial output, while power entering at point B is absorbed in the dummy load. If the two waveguides were parallel, the magnetic component would be coupled to a greater degree than the electrostatic, and the directivity would be poor. By our placing the auxiliary waveguide at the proper angle, the amplitude of the magnetically excited wave is made equal to that of the electrostatically excited wave (without changing the latter), and good directivity is obtained. The angle required depends upon the frequency of operation.

BIDIRECTIONAL COUPLERS

A bidirectional coupler is used to measure direct as well as reflected power. As shown in Fig. 16–10, it consists of two enclosed sections

attached to each side of a straight section of waveguide and along its narrow dimension. Each enclosed section contains an RF pickup probe at one end and an impedance termination or matched load at the other end, consisting of a tapered resistance card. The sections are supplied with energy from within the main waveguide through three openings spaced one-quarter wavelength apart. Energy from the transmitter going toward the antenna enters the enclosed sections through the three openings on each side so that the RF probe farthest away from the transmitter is used to measure direct power, and the one nearest the transmitter is used to measure reflected power. Because the openings in each section are spaced one-quarter wavelength apart, the energy travels a quarter wavelength between each of the three openings and is coupled into the enclosed sections by a predetermined attenuation below that within the waveguide.

As shown, the center opening in each of the enclosed sections is larger than each of the holes on either side, thus allowing twice as much energy to enter through that opening. The transmitted energy entering section A, because of the location and dimensions of the openings, combines properly in phase and amplitude to make it measurable by the indicating meter connected to the direct

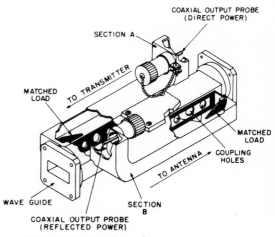

FIG. 16-10 Bidirectional coupler

power probe. The transmitted energy that enters section B will produce zero power because of the phase displacement of the three openings coupling energy into this enclosed section. The reason is that the energy passing the first opening will be 180 degrees out of phase with that of the center opening, and will be in phase with the energy at the third opening. Because the center opening is sufficiently large to supply twice the magnitude of energy as that supplied by either of the other two, the reflected energy is cancelled.

The end of the enclosed section is terminated in a matched load. Section B thus measures reflected energy due to either standing waves or energy received from targets, and acts in exactly the same manner as section A when it is making direct power measurements.

Since the direction of energy flow is reversed, the energy will now appear at the reflected power probe in section B. Reflected energy, upon entering section A, will of course be cancelled out in the same manner that section B cancels the transmitted power when performing direct power measurements.

MICROWAVE MEASUREMENT TECHNIQUES

ATTENUATION

Microwave measurements are by nature substitution or modified substitution methods. The signal source, whether it be a signal generator or output from a transmitter, is connected through an attenuator to a detector mount after passing through a length of the transmission line (either waveguide or coaxial line) into which the unknown device will be inserted. A suitable signal is then applied to give some low, attenuated detector output.

The unknown device to be measured is inserted into the line and the same signal again applied.

Measurement consists of adjusting the attenuator until the same detector output is obtained. Direct *change* in attenuator settings represents the loss in the device being tested.

A number of precautions must be observed, many of which are purely physical and concern the "plumbing" used in the set-up. All fittings and connections must be firm and must deliver a minimum of reflection loss so that they do not alter the true, final measurement. The detector mount, for instance, must be impedance-matched to the transmission line, which in turn must match the attenuator mount and the signal-generator output fitting (if used).

The frequencies of the signal generator, of the attenuator, and of the detector mount must also be in the proper range. Calibration charts for deviation in each of these components may be necessary and compensation may be required for total equipment attenuation above and over that in the device being measured.

IMPEDANCE

All impedance measurements except those at low transmission frequencies (below 500 mc) indirectly use the phenomenon of standing waves caused by reflections due to discontinuity in the transmission line or its terminations. Any mismatch causes a voltage standing-wave ratio of more than unity which can be translated into its corresponding reflection coefficient, both quantities yielding a means of measuring impedance.

There are accordingly three methods of measuring impedance:

1. By use of slotted line for coaxial-line related equipment.

2. By use of the reflectometer.

3. By use of the VHF bridge (for frequencies below 500 mc).

Using a slotted line in coaxial systems we create a set-up similar to that in Fig. 16–11, following all precautions previously referred to concerning matched interconnections, and following the general procedures concerning the slotted line given earlier in this chapter. It should be particularly noted that the slotted line's probe extracts measurement power since it, too, acts as an admittance, shunting the line so that the measured VSWR

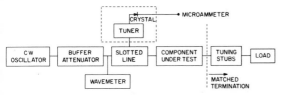

(a) Slotted line measurement of VSWR using unmodulated signal

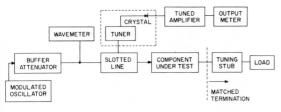

(b) Standing wave test set using slotted line, modulated source

FIG. 16-11 Test applications of the slotted line

is always lower than the true VSWR. The probe may also introduce minor reflections, which generally can be neglected. As noted previously, the probe penetration should be as shallow as possible.

The block-diagram set-ups of Figs. 16–11 (a)(b) illustrate two sampling methods, one using modulated microwave test signal input and one using CW or unmodulated signal.

Actual measurement calls for first measuring the VSWR and recording the position of the maxima and minima of the voltages measured with respect to the load's location; next, the load is replaced by a short circuit and the *shift* in the voltage minimum noted (in terms of wavelength). Third, by entering this change of position on the Smith Chart (see Appendix D2) the actual impedance and reflection coefficient can be established both in magnitude and in phase.

When measuring VSWR's of 10: 1 and over, the probe losses may cause inaccuracies; in this case the *twice-minimum-power method* may be used. This method, when using the slotted line, first establishes the electrical distance between two points that occur physically located at *twice* the amplitude of the

power existing at the minimum detected power point. The VSWR ratio can then be calculated from the following equation:

$$R_{swr} = \sqrt{1 + \frac{1}{\sin^2\left(\dfrac{\pi d}{\lambda g}\right)}}$$

where R_{swr} = VSWR of the load,
λ = wavelength of the waveguide,
d = the electrical distance (in terms of wavelength) between "twice-minimum-power" points.

In obtaining power-point readings, correct, direct amplitude readings will result if a square-law detector and a linear voltage indicator are used. With a linear detector, voltage readings should be 2.8: 1 for the correct double-power ratio.

THE REFLECTOMETER measures impedance in waveguide transmission systems by determining the reflection coefficient. It uses directional couplers which sample the input wave and the reflected wave. These couplers in turn feed two separate detectors whose outputs are applied to a ratio meter. Meter readings directly determine the reflection coefficient. Such meters are available at popular waveguide frequencies and can accurately read reflection coefficients as high as .5 (VSWR = 3.0.).

POWER MEASUREMENT

Details of power-measurement circuitry for components and techniques appear in Chapter 18 on transmitter testing and in Chapter 19 under radar power measurements. Since most radars operate at microwave frequencies, the latter treatment is pertinent to the present chapter.

Microwave power measurements can be divided into two ranges: between .1 and 10 milliwatts, and above 10 watts. In the former range measurements customarily are made with a bolometer which operates a bridge circuit. In the latter, direct power measurements are usually made with conventional calorimeters.

Electrically and physically bolometers require correct mounting hardware plus various devices for complete impedance matching such as double-stub tuners, stub-line stretchers, E-H tuners or slide-screw tuners.

Bolometer mounts have been designed for both coaxial and waveguide systems of frequencies between 10 mc and 40 kmc. In various applications bolometers may be described as *barretters* or as *thermistors*—either type utilizes similar mounts and matching provisions.

RECEIVER NOISE

Noise measurements generally concern receiver performance. Built-in amplification or pure gain is practically boundless, but the amount of usable gain is limited by noise. Gain is thus always given along with the corresponding noise factor, which turns out to be a figure of merit telling how many decibels the noise that the receiver generates by itself in the process of amplification is above the normal thermally generated noise at the receiver input.

Since any resistance generates its own thermal noise, we usually express the thermal noise input of a receiver as the noise generated across its conventional resistive input impedance—say across 50 or 100 ohms.

NOISE CALCULATIONS

In any conductor, this random electron motion due to thermal agitation produces a voltage, e_n, within the conductor. It is expressed in watts, being generated by the square of the individually generated noise voltages, e_{n1} across the generating resistance R_n.

Thus:

$$P_n = \frac{e_n^2}{R_n}$$

Since this voltage is a pure noise voltage, it will produce signals that contain frequencies randomly distributed throughout the entire RF spectrum. So when amplified by a receiver of a given band width, ΔF they will produce output only in proportion to its band width and its temperature. Thus $e_n^2 = 4KTR_n\,\Delta F$.

The input power, in watts, represented by this form of noise is therefore given by the formula:

$$P_n = \text{noise power} = 4KT\,\Delta F$$

where K = Boltzmann's constant (1.37
$\times$ 10^{-23} watt-seconds per degree Kelvin),

T = temperature in degrees absolute (Kelvin scale = degrees centigrade + 273),

ΔF = range of frequencies involved (band width) in cycles per second.

Summarizing these factors and cancelling out R_n in the power expression, this formula shows thermal agitation noise power dependent on band width and temperature. The constant K merely serves to convert the noise units into units of power. Since decrease of temperature causes less random electron motion, at absolute zero all motion and noise would theoretically cease.

NOISE MEASUREMENT

In practice, the actual noise developed in a receiver is greater than the calculated value because of the generation of other types of noise *within* the receiver circuits. For example, a carbon-type resistor, which is made up of fine particles of carbon, will generate additional noise power when current flows through the resistor, because of small changes in the contact area of the particles. Various resistor types have widely varying noise levels, and those that are used in the input circuits of a receiver must be chosen for as low a noise level as possible.

Electron tubes also generate noise signals, because of random variations in electron emission from the cathode, random variations in the current division between the plate and screen grid, etc. Since electron tubes produce noise in proportion to the number of electrodes employed, it follows then that triode rather than pentode tubes are generally used where noise limitation is an important consideration.

NOISE FIGURE (NF) is defined as the ratio of measured noise to calculated noise, expressed as a power ratio or in decibels.

In the microwave range of operation, virtually all of the noise originates within the receiver since atmospheric and man-made noise or static is normally too small to be considered. The three main sources of noise are: (1) the crystal mixer; (2) the IF preamplifier (usually the first two IF stages); and (3) the local oscillator.

MEASUREMENT USING A NOISE GENERATOR

A typical noise generator producing random noise signals uses a temperature-limited diode, operated at saturation. When one diode is operated under these conditions the noise produced is proportional to the d-c input power and affords convenient conversion to obtain the true noise power.

The procedure consists of monitoring receiver output under normal gain and comparing it with output using generated noise-signal input. This is conveniently done by employing some kind of linear output indicating meter, say a milliammeter in series with the second detector diode.

When the output meter's indication of normal signal output has been increased 1.4:1 with some particular noise-generator signal increase, the generated input noise is equal to the receiver noise power.

We then calculate the noise figure by

$$NF_{(\text{in db})} = 10 \log \frac{P_{\text{measured}}}{P_{\text{calculated}}}$$

where P_{measured} is the amount of noise measured as a base (generally in microwatts) and $P_{\text{calculated}}$ is the figure arrived at by using the conventional formula on p. 256.

As an example, to calculate the noise figure of a receiver having a band width of 4 megacycles (4×10^6) and operating at an ambient temperature of 20°C. ($T = (20 + 273)$):

$$
\begin{aligned}
NF &= 4KT \times F \\
&= 4 \times (1.37 \times 10^{-23}) \times (20 + 273) \\
&\quad \times (4 \times 10^6) \\
&= 6422.56 \times 10^{-17} \\
&= .06423 \quad \text{micromicrowatts}
\end{aligned}
$$

If the measured noise power being fed to the receiver under test turns out to be 1.018 micromicrowatts, then using the formula above, the noise figure of the receiver is

$$
\begin{aligned}
NF_{(\text{db})} &= 10 \log \frac{1.018}{.0642} \\
&= 10 \log 15.85 \\
&= 10 \times 1.2 \\
&= 12 \quad \text{db}
\end{aligned}
$$

17 Receiver Testing and Measurement

GENERAL CHARACTERISTICS

Five essential processes are involved in the reception of radio waves. *Primarily* receivers must provide a means for *extracting signal* energy from the radio carrier wave bearing the desired intelligence. This pickup or capture function exists in the antenna itself and its associated circuitry, which in turn also provides means for transferring minute amounts of captured energy to the first or "head-end" radio receiver circuits.

Secondly, the minute, resultant carrier wave or signal energy must be *amplified* through the successive receiver stages. Concurrent with this it undergoes a *third* process in the receiver circuits which supply *selectivity* along with the amplifier function in order to "weed out" or separate the desired radio wave from all other existing or interfering carrier waves. High frequency carrier or intermediate frequency amplifiers accomplishing this use *selective* resonant circuits both in the antenna and in following stages in the receiver.

The *fourth* function is that of separating or *detecting* the desired intelligence components from the received and amplified radio carrier wave. Since the carrier is *modulated* in response to speech, telegraph signals, or other information, the amplified energy extracted from the ether can not be utilized directly but must be *demodulated* or *detected*—which in one sense is the inverse of the modulation process. This process, in other words, separates the audio-frequency or speech components from

the radio-frequency carrier-wave components, and is called the demodulation function. It is performed by circuits variously described as detectors, frequency converters, or demodulators.

After the audio-frequency intelligence has been extracted by detection, it must be *amplified* and then finally *reproduced* into sound power. The headphone set or loudspeaker accomplishing this is a *reproducer*.

Excluding antenna action, each of these receiver functions uses a section of the receiver; they will next be described along with their particular design attributes or performance requirements. These functions are diagrammatically described in a typical receiver block diagram, Fig. 17–1.

GENERAL RECEIVER ORGANIZATION

Receivers in all categories employ the super-heterodyne circuit which converts, for efficiency in amplifying, the signal carrier into an *intermediate carrier frequency* signal (IF). In low-frequency, simple broadcast receivers the overall circuit organization follows single conversion as laid out in the block diagram of Fig. 17–2(a).

In a microwave radar receiver the organization follows an arrangement shown in Fig. 17–2(b). Here provision is made to automatically control both the local oscillator frequency and the gain of the intermediate frequency stages.

VHF and UHF receivers require double heterodyne conversion—that is, two sets of

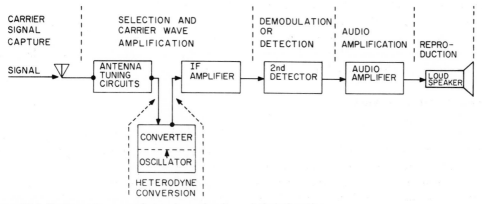

FIG. 17-1 Basic receiver superheterodyne circuits and their functions

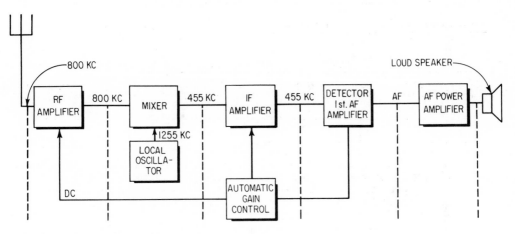

(a) *Single-conversion circuit organization*

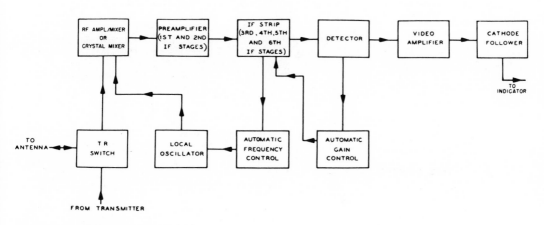

(b) *Microwave radar receiver organization*

FIG 17-2. Receiver circuit organization

IF amplifiers, two local oscillators and two mixers are used. Figure 17–3 blocks out circuit arrangements in a double-conversion FM communication receiver together with accessory noise, audio amplifier, and filter circuits.

PERFORMANCE CHARACTERISTICS

SENSITIVITY

The total amount of amplification or gain through all the stages of a receiver determines its overall sensitivity. This, in turn, is a measure of the weakest, uniformly modulated signal to which the receiver will respond by producing a given audio power output. This requirement is expressed in volts (or micro-

volts) and describes whether a reciever is capable of receiving signals of the order of 10, 100, or 500 microvolts. These levels assume delivery at the receiver's output of *standard sound power output* levels—usually 50 milliwatts when the input signal is modulated 30 percent.

NOISE FIGURE

The low limit of signals to which a receiver will respond is determined by the amount of noise accompanying the carrier wave or added to it by noise generated internally within the receiver. The *internal noise level* represents a signal originating from thermal agitation noise in the receiver; thus when a noise-free external signal is much less than the equiva-

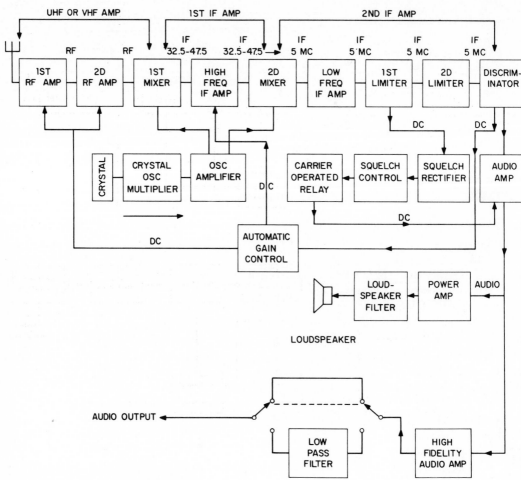

FIG 17-3. Double conversion FM receiver

lent noise generated by the first-circuits, reception is unsatisfactory or impossible. Therefore, the noise in a receiver's first or "head-end" circuits is the factor limiting the *usable* amplification or sensitivity that should be designed into its amplifying circuits. Noise ratings are generally expressed as the number of decibels above thermal noise level that is measured or being generated in the receiver's first circuits.

Externally a limit on gain and sensitivity is imposed by the *signal interference noise level* in the region of the receiver and antenna. The only way in which receiver design can influence this kind of noise is by adequate shielding against external fields, filtering of power-supply leads, and the inclusion of noise limiters to discriminate against certain types of impulse noise.

SELECTIVITY

Two head-end characteristics must be considered simultaneously in determining the desired selectivity of a receiver: (1) the resonant amplifier circuits must be so designed as to suppress adjacent or certain other (image) channel interference plus other spurious signal responses arriving simultaneously at the antenna, and (2) they must present an RF carrier response that is broad enough to pass, without excessive attenuation, the highest modulating frequency (audio or video) and still preserve receiver selectivity. In nearly every case it is desirable in these amplifier circuits to have a constant absolute bandwidth rather than a constant percentage bandwidth. A superheterodyne receiver lends itself very well to this requirement, since this type of *internal* receiver circuitry (namely the IF amplifier stages) provides the major part of overall selectivity. Most low-frequency receivers up through the HF band utilize two or more fixed tuned IF amplifier stages. Figure 17–4(a) shows a typical IF response characteristic curve of a broadcast receiver IF stage. Figure 17–4(b) shows overall response of a double superheterodyne FM receiver with a 5-mc second IF.

SIGNAL-NOISE CHARACTERISTIC

As noted above, the problem of first-circuit noise affects the choice of the kind of RF amplifier tube, the antenna coupling circuit, and other factors aimed to give the most efficient utilization of the signal picked up from the antenna.

POWER OUTPUT

Most commercial receivers do not require large power outputs such as used for driving loudspeakers. Thus high, undistorted audio-frequency output power within the receiver itself is of minor importance.

For military use, where interphone or headphones are used, power outputs of 10 to 100 milliwatts are usually satisfactory although for aircraft receivers pilot fatigue often requires 500 to 1,000 milliwatts. Certain fixed stand-by receivers utilize loudspeakers, and 2 to 3 watts is the usual maximum they require. Powerful, high-quality audio output systems are usually provided when needed as separate adjuncts to a receiver.

SPURIOUS RESPONSES

A superheterodyne receiver has a number of frequencies at which interfering signals may be troublesome. These spurious-response frequencies are a consequence of the double or triple frequency conversion essential to this type of receiver. Examples may be given with the oscillator or the first converter operating *above* signal frequency.

1. An image response occurs at a frequency $f_{rf} = 2f_{if}$ or at twice the intermediate frequency. This is ordinarily the strongest spurious response.

2. There is also some response to a signal directly at the *intermediate frequency* applied to the antenna frequency or at f_{if}.

3. If two signals, the desired one and an interfering one, f_{rf_1} and f_{rf_2} respectively, differ in frequency by the intermediate fre-

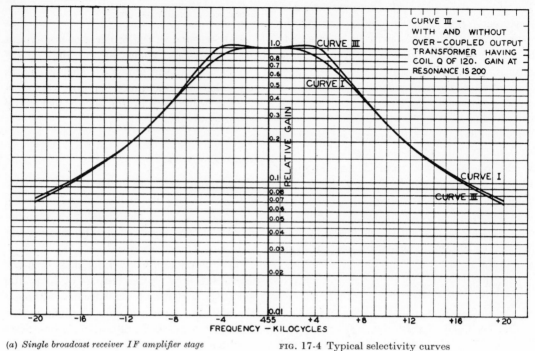

(a) Single broadcast receiver IF amplifier stage

FIG. 17-4 Typical selectivity curves

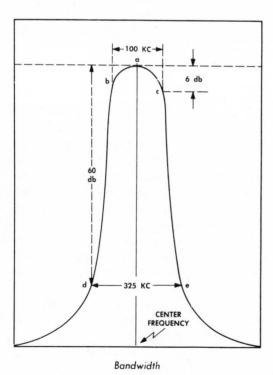

(b) Response curve of double superheterodyne FM receiver

quency, the spurious response known as *cross-modulation* is obtained, i.e.,

$$(f_{rf_1} - f_{rf_2}) = f_{if}$$

4. *Higher-order image* responses are obtained at frequencies $(2f_{osc} \pm f_{if})$—that is, at $(2f_{rf} + 3f_{if})$, $(2f_{rf} + 4f_{if})$, etc.

5. *Harmonic beat note* interference or "tweets" are obtained at $2f_{if}$, $3f_{if}$, etc., if these frequencies lie within the tuning range of the receiver.

OVERLOAD AND AVC

All communication receivers utilize automatic volume or gain control and in addition provide a manual sensitivity control for adjustment of output volume. In addition, it is always required that the receiver should not "block" with a strong signal input when the adjustment is made for maximum sensitivity and with strong antenna signal input. Typical levels may be inputs to the antenna of 0.1, 1, or even 2 volts. In the case of aircraft receivers

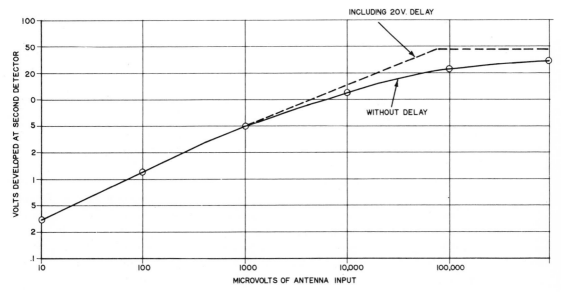

FIG. 17-5 Receiver AVC control curve

for the reception of radio range signals, where the pilot must distinguish by intensity between *A* and *N* code signals, it is further required that at all settings of the sensitivity control, for normal listening levels, the receiver output must *increase* with an *increase* in carrier input. This levelling action, known as the avc control characteristic, is pictured in Fig. 17–5.

FREQUENCY STABILITY

Receivers operating under field conditions must be designed to withstand such conditions as variations in ambient temperature, humidity, barometric pressure, voltage and frequency of the power supply, plus varying degrees of mechanical shock or vibration. Two sections of receiver circuitry which are particularly sensitive to temperature changes are the RF and IF amplifier tuning elements and those of the signal heterodyne oscillator. In the former, selectivity and image rejection ratio may be lost, while in the latter the entire receiver may become mis-tuned. Resettability of the oscillator tuning must also be preserved, for when the receiver is once tuned to a desired point, it must always be possible to reproduce

the setting of the tuning adjustment with a high degree of precision—in other words, without a significant amount of dial or tuning backlash.

AUDIO OR VIDEO FIDELITY

Good reception primarily requires that speech or telegraphic transmission be intelligible. The audio-frequency range for speech reception is generally limited enough to reduce extraneous noise but not enough to impair intelligibility. In multichannel telegraph, facsimile, or television receivers other characteristics of linearity and phase distortion must be considered; in commercial sound equipment the audio fidelity or frequency-response characteristic requirements are of primary importance and usually much *more* severe than in military service. Figure 17–6(a) is a typical "flat" audio response curve (300–5,000 cps) plotted from point-to-point measurements across a resistive load in the receiver's output stage. Figure 17–6(b) is the AF response curve of a low-quality, audio output transformer (flat from 200 to 3,000 cps).

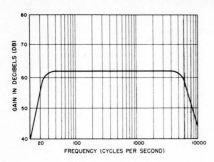

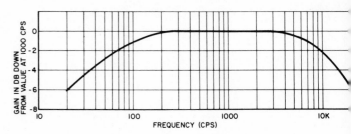

(a) *Amplifier response characteristic*
(*flat from 30–5000 cps*)

(b) *Audio response curve of a low-cost replacement audio transformer*

FIG. 17-6 Typical audio frequency response curves

CIRCUIT ISOLATION

Requirements concerning adequate shielding and isolation of the various stages in a receiver from each other, from the power supply, and from external disturbance usually accompany receiver specifications. The prevention of stray feedback is often necessary for stability of gain and selectivity; in the case of direction-finder receivers this is particularly important because of the severe minimum-error requirements in measured bearings.

Table 17–1   Summary of receiver characteristics and measurement techniques

Characteristic	Measuring equipment	Measuring units
Sensitivity	Signal generator	Microvolts for standard output
	Dummy antenna	Tuning range—kc or mc
	Output meter	Microphonics
	Noise generator	Db gain above thermal noise
		Signal-to-noise ratio
Selectivity	Signal generator	Bandwidth at 3 and 6 db down
		Image ratio
		Spurious responses
Power and audio	Signal generator	Power output capabilities
	VTVM	Audio-frequency response
	Wave analyzer	Distortion
		Hum level
		Audio stability
Stability	Counter	Local oscillator drift in cycles/1,000 hr.
	Frequency standard	
	Oscilloscope	
Control	Signal generator	Flatness of avc curve
	Output meter	Range of volume control
		Squelch circuit efficiency
		Hum modulation
Miscellaneous:		
Intermodulation	Signal generators (2)	Equiv. modulation percentage
Tuning resettability	Wave analyzer	Watts
Power consumption	Wattmeter	Degrees rise
Chassis heating	Thermocouples	Oscillator instability
Mechanical stability:	Shake table	
vibration, shock	Drop stand	
Reliability	Records	Failure rate

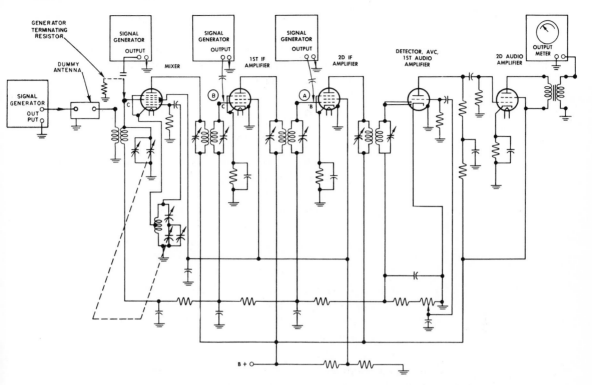

FIG. 17-7 Typical receiver measurement setup

RECEIVER TESTING TECHNIQUES

The following material describes the important measurements and techniques that must be employed in receiver analysis or testing. The approach is tailored to the handbook level and is intended primarily for field checking a receiver but may apply equally as well to basic laboratory set-ups. The material is merely a guide, not a complete dissertation, since detailed testing or precise measuring procedures require lengthy instructions. Some items in this category appear in Chapter 19, where they are applicable to radar receivers. Table 17–1 is a summary of overall receiver characteristics and their measurement.

PRELIMINARY APPROACH

Before any tests with a signal generator, the receiving equipment should be checked to ascertain that all transistors, vacuum tubes, rectifiers, and other replaceable elements with limited life capability are in good condition.

All plug-in or friction-contact type connections should be checked for noise and contact, by removal and replacement a number of times or by working them back and forth (as in the case of variable gain controls). Also, power-line voltage and frequency, battery condition, and the like should be checked before proceeding with the measurements. The signal generator used should be of a type recommended by the equipment instruction book or other qualified source. Output should be some standard power level.

SENSITIVITY

Inasmuch as the sensitivity measurement provides maximum information about the overall receiver condition, accurate simulation of operating conditions must be set up. (See Fig. 17–7.) This requires the application of an accurately calibrated variable input signal voltage from a suitable generator to various key points in a receiver's circuitry. After examining successive IF stages (points *A*, *B*) the generator is applied to the receiver's antenna terminals through an impedance which approximates that of the antenna with which the receiver is designed to be used. This simulated impedance is known as a *dummy antenna*. It insures that the signal current in the input circuit of the receiver is the same as would appear with the known signal induced in an ideal receiving antenna, and it also insures that the input circuit of the receiver is "loaded" the same as it would be by an ideal antenna.

DUMMY ANTENNAS

In the 15- to 30,000-kc range, a typical standard dummy antenna for high-impedance-input receivers consists of a 20-microhenry inductor shunted by a series-connected 400-micromicrofarad capacitor and a suitable 400-ohm resistor, with the shunt combination in series with a 200-micromicrofarad capacitor. Figure 17–8 schematically pictures this assembly. This unit should be enclosed within a properly designed and grounded shield-case and used with a signal generator having a resistive output impedance not exceeding 50 ohms. This dummy antenna "looks," impedancewise, like a 200-micromicrofarad capacitance at low frequencies, say in the 1-mc region, and "looks" like a 400-ohm resistance at frequencies of 2 to 30 mc. For the measurement of low-impedance-input receivers of 50 to 70 ohms nominal impedance, a signal generator with a 50-ohm output may be directly connected, without the use of an external dummy antenna. Other generator impedances may require special dummy-

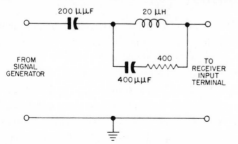

FIG. 17-8 Standard dummy antenna circuit schematic

antenna networks to properly load the generator and the receiver and to insure that the equivalent induced antenna voltage is accurately produced at the dummy output terminals.

CONDITIONS FOR SENSITIVITY MEASUREMENT: TYPES OF MODULATION

For measurement of sensitivity the receiver is adjusted for the type of reception desired, and facilities such as tone controls or audio filters, agc, silencer, noise limiter, and so on are placed in or out of operation as required or are set at appropriate control positions, as discussed later. The power-line voltage applied to the receiver should be well within the normal recommended operating range. The receiver output terminals should be properly loaded. At the headphone or audio-line terminals, *unless otherwise specified in the instruction book for the equipment*, the load should be a 600-ohm noninductive resistor (such as one of the composition type), capable of continuously dissipating the maximum receiver audio power output that can be produced at these terminals. High-impedance headphones may be used in shunt with such a load for monitoring the output. Low-impedance phones may load the output appreciably and should be removed when data is being taken.

The output voltage should be measured with a high-impedance audio voltmeter capable of accurate indication from 0.1 volt to 100 volts, and one that will not appreciably load the output circuit. Although some receivers are equipped with audio-output meters, they may not have suitable high frequency response to indicate required standard noise levels with sufficient accuracy.

The following descriptions cover testing procedures applicable to the various types of transmitted modulation. The commonly used transmissions are defined in Fig. 18–2.

C-W (A-1) AND FACSIMILE (A-4) SENSITIVITY

For c-w (A-1) reception sensitivity measurements, some means must be provided to set the output beat note of the receiver to the standard 1,000-cps frequency with reasonable accuracy (about 1,000 cps ± 50 cps).

In some receivers a 1,000-cps "sharp" audio filter is provided which has a bandwidth narrow enough to allow satisfactory adjustment of the beat note by centering the tone in the passband. The 1,000-cps internal tone modulation frequency of most signal generators is also accurate enough and can provide zero-beat against the output beat note. Alternatively, the output of a calibrated audio oscillator and that of the receiver may be fed independently to the deflection amplifiers of an oscilloscope to give the Lissajous pattern typical of synchronous waves for establishing the output frequency.

For determination of both keyed c-w and facsimile reception (A-1 and A-4) sensitivity, the c-w (beat-frequency) oscillator should be "on" and the receiver audio gain should be set at maximum, with agc, silencer, noise limiter, and output limiter turned *off*. If not otherwise specified in the receiver instruction book, audio filters or tone controls should be set for maximum audio range. The antenna trimmer normally should be peaked at the high-frequency end of each band, and not reset at other frequencies. The signal generator is used unmodulated.

Following these initial adjustments, the RF gain control is adjusted to produce 60 microwatts of noise (.19 volt across 600 ohms) with the receiver tuned to the desired frequency but with no input signal applied from the signal generator.

The signal (carrier only) is then applied, and is tuned as nearly as possible to center on the noise of the overall RF passband of the receiver, with the c-w oscillator frequency control adjusted to the side of zero beat that produces the higher output with a 1,000-cps beat note. The input-signal voltage is then adjusted to produce 6 milliwatts output (1.0 volts), resulting in +20 db output signal-to-noise ratio within .1 db. The receiver sensitivity, in terms of input-signal voltage, is then read from the signal-generator voltage calibration (see signal-generator instruction book to interpret voltage readings).

M-C-W(A-3) SENSITIVITY

M-c-w (A-3) reception sensitivity measurement requires the application of a carrier modulated 30 percent at 1,000 cps. The RF gain control should be set at maximum, with agc *on* and the c-w (beat-frequency) oscillator *off*, unless this condition is automatically established by a reception selector control (provided on some receivers). All other controls except the AF gain should be set as indicated for c-w (A-1) reception. Both the input-signal level and the AF gain control are then progressively adjusted until the receiver output noise level is 6 milliwatts (.6) volt with signal-generator modulation *off*, and the signal-plus-noise output is 6 milliwatts with modulation on, producing +10 db ratio of output signal-plus-noise to noise (10.4 db signal-to-noise ratio). The receiver sensitivity, in terms of input voltage, is then read from the signal-generator voltage calibration.

M-C-W (A-2) SENSITIVITY

Tone modulation (A-2) reception sensitivity should be measured under the above conditions and using the same procedure as for A-3 reception sensitivity, except that the AF gain is set at maximum with agc off, and the RF gain control and signal-generator output voltage varied to produce standard sensitivity conditions. Also, the generator should be modulated 100 percent at 1,000 cps, with standard output of 6 milliwatts signal plus noise and noise output of 60 microwatts for generator modulation off (20 db output signal-to-noise ratio).

If the available signal generators can not be modulated at 100 percent because of excessive frequency modulation or because of other limitations, an approximate sensitivity measurement may be made by employing 30 percent modulation to produce 6 milliwatts output with 10 db output signal-plus-noise to noise ratio. This procedure may give somewhat erroneous results, as detector modulation distortion or modulation clipping by built-in noise limiters do not always act linearly and may be much less at 30 percent than at 100 percent modulation.

FREQUENCY SHIFT KEYING (FSK)

The receiver and teletypewriter must operate satisfactorily to produce proper copy in FSK operation. If the receiver checks satisfactorily for c-w (A-1) sensitivity, then as far as it is concerned, only two factors could cause performance to deteriorate: (1) the additional switching for FSK reception, and (2) failure within the special FSK filters. Therefore, the receiver may be checked for FSK sensitivity by initially checking its standard c-w sensitivity. If this proves to be normal, switching to FSK operation will allow the output beat frequencies and audio output level to be checked to insure that they meet the requirements of whatever audio-type FSK converter is employed.

The output which the receiver can produce for an IF-type converter (if this facility is provided) may be checked with an electronic voltmeter capable of good accuracy at the intermediate frequency, with a range of .001 volt to at least 10 volts. The receiver and converter instruction books should be consulted for standards of receiver output in this case.

RESERVE GAIN

Reserve gain for all types of reception may be determined by measuring the ratio of noise output at standard gain (the gain condition used in measuring standard sensitivity) to noise output at maximum gain, provided maximum gain does not produce any substantial degree of output overload or saturation. If saturation is approached or reached at maximum gain, the setting for standard gain should be noted, and the reserve gain determined with the aid of a gain-control calibration curve, which can be obtained by subsequent measurement.

Gain variation over each band for any condition of reception may be determined by adjusting for standard gain (as for sensitivity measurements) at the high-frequency end of each band, and then noting the input-signal voltage required at various frequencies over the band to produce the same 6-milliwatt 1,000-cps output.

SELECTIVITY

The term "overall selectivity" usually refers to the frequency-selecting qualities of a receiver as measured from (and including) the antenna to the input terminals of the final detector. It does not normally include any elements of the audio system.

The overall selectivity of a superheterodyne receiver may be quite difficult to measure accurately with the equipment likely to be available in most field operating installations, especially at frequencies above 1 mc. However, if the lowest signal frequency is only several times that of the intermediate frequency the overall selectivity is very likely to be practically the same as the IF selectivity, and an accurate IF selectivity curve may suffice.

NARROW-BAND RECEIVER SELECTIVITY

For receivers with RF or IF bandwidth of less than about 5 kc at 6 db or less (e.g. VLF and LF receivers), the measurement can be made as follows: The receiver should be adjusted for standard m-c-w (A-2) sensitivity conditions (agc off), with a high-impedance d-c voltmeter connected to read the voltage across the final-detector diode load. (It may be necessary to connect a 1-megohm isolating resistor between the "high" end of the diode load and the "high" lead of the voltmeter to prevent regeneration or other undesirable effects.)

With unmodulated signal-generator antenna input the signal voltage is increased from standard input in successive steps of about 1.4, 2, 3, 5, 10, 100, and 1000 times the standard input, while at each step the frequency of the generator is simultaneously adjusted to off-center tuning to produce a constant detector-diode voltage (the value previously obtained with standard input at on-center tuning). The signal-generator frequency-vernier dial reading is taken for each step at both sides of resonance. The reading recorded should always be obtained by approaching from the same direction of dial rotation in order to minimize error resulting from signal-generator dial backlash. The signal-generator frequency dial can be calibrated with higher precision than afforded by its markings by using calculated kilocycles per division. This is done by taking ranges of limit frequencies from the selectivity curve data and then dividing the differences in frequency by the corresponding number of vernier divisions.

A curve on semilog paper (see Fig. 17–4) is then plotted using ordinates or "times resonant input voltage" (or "db above resonant input" on linear paper) versus abscissae (linear scale) of "kc off resonance." The points of greatest interest are usually those defining the 6 db down and 60 db down kilocycle bandwidths covering both sides of resonance. The db ratio of bandwidths at these attenuation points is a good index of overall selectivity since it defines the steepness exhibited by the overall selectivity curve.

Selectivity measurements may conveniently be made using a modulated carrier, provided that the rate of attenuation at the skirts of the curve is not too high (not more than about 6 db per kc). This means that relatively broad TRF and single-conversion superheterodyne receivers (designed for operation above 500 kc) may be measured with a carrier modulated 30 percent by a 400- or 1,000-cps tone.

For unmodulated carrier selectivity, the measurement procedure is the same as above using the same receiver conditions, except that the output measurement is made at the receiver audio output terminals. Other conditions such as for m-c-w (A-2) sensitivity (agc *off*) the audio output is maintained at

standard level while the input-signal frequency is varied by adjustment of the signal-generator carrier output voltage.

IF SELECTIVITY

IF selectivity may be measured with signal-generator input applied to the mixer grid using the same procedure as in measuring overall selectivity. In a double superheterodyne it may be desirable to disconnect the input-signal circuit from the preceding frequency converter to prevent that circuit from loading the signal generator. Also, it is usually necessary to provide a grid-return resistor for the mixer (about 10,000 ohms), as well as a coupling capacitor (about 1,000 $\mu\mu$f) from the mixer input grid to the signal-generator output, in order to prevent d-c return through the generator system. (See Fig. 17–7.) The oscillator should be disabled (by removing the oscillator tube or transistor or its supply voltages) if it appears to produce interference with the measuring signal. In doing this the mixer output impedance may be changed somewhat, but the resultant effects on selectivity are usually of a minor nature.

PRIMARY IMAGE REJECTION

The primary image rejection ratio provides a simple criterion of the preselector (front-end) inherent selectivity and its alignment condition. To determine the primary image ratio, the receiver is first adjusted for standard m-c-w (A-2) sensitivity conditions. The signal generator is then tuned to produce maximum

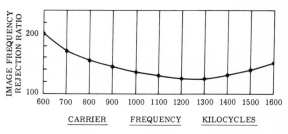

FIG. 17-9 Image rejection curve for broadcast receiver

response at the primary image frequency (twice the IF, away from resonance, on the same side as the oscillator) with the input-signal voltage adjusted to produce standard output. The ratio of the image-frequency input voltage to the standard sensitivity input (usually expressed in db) is the image rejection at that desired signal frequency. If the values obtained for this ratio over each band are within 3 db of the instruction-book values and the sensitivity is normal, the front-end alignment is probably correct. Figure 17–9 shows a typical image rejection curve.

TUNING-DIAL CALIBRATION

Tuning-dial frequency calibration can be checked against any signal whose frequency is accurately known, such as those of radio station WWV and standard AM, FM, and TV broadcast stations. Some receivers have built-in crystal calibrators which give harmonic signal tweets spaced throughout the working range of the receiver. If none of these signals is available, one must obtain a heterodyne frequency meter the output of which may be fed to the receiver antenna terminals and tuned in as an unmodulated c-w signal. With any of these means, the tuning dial error should be carefully observed. If the error is excessive (more than about ± 1 percent) and shows a definite progression with frequency, the receiver may require realignment.

TUNING-DIAL BACKLASH

Tuning-dial backlash is usually best determined in the c-w (A-1) reception condition, by first tuning in a c-w signal to receiver resonance with rotation of the dial in one direction, and adjusting the beat-frequency oscillator, on the side of zero beat that gives the greater output, until a 1,000-cps beat note accurate within ± 5 cps is obtained. The vernier tuning dial (if provided) is then read as accurately as possible, or the tuning knob is marked in some suitable way. Following this, the signal is again tuned in, approaching

it this time from the *opposite* direction of dial rotation, until the same 1,000-cps indication is obtained on the same side of zero beat as before. The difference in vernier-dial divisions or in angular position of the tuning knob is the backlash.

Zero-beat output from the receiver might be used as a reference for this measurement instead of 1,000 cps, which would dispense with the oscilloscope and audio oscillator. However, the audio response of most receivers at very low frequencies is not good, which usually makes quite difficult the accurate determination of zero beat by ear or output meter.

RESONANT OVERLOAD

The resonant overload characteristic (desired output versus signal carrier input voltage) should be determined with the receiver adjusted for standard sensitivity conditions for the type of reception desired (A-1, A-2, etc.). The receiver output voltage is first recorded for increasing values of signal-generator input from .1 microvolt to maximum. Next m-c-w operation should be recorded using the output noise level at each input-signal level with modulation off but with carrier on. These readings, when plotted on log-log paper, can be interpreted to indicate linearity of receiver gain, residual hum and hum modulation, etc.

If resonant overload curves are obtained for different audio-gain-control (agc on) and output-limiter-control (agc off) settings, respectively, the capabilities of the agc system and of the limiter may be determined (for steady-state signal conditions). If resonant overload curves are obtained at different silencer or squelch control settings over the working range, silencer characteristics and effectiveness of operation may be determined. These may be compared with reported or instruction-book data on these characteristics.

FREQUENCY STABILITY

Frequency stability of a receiver under mechanical stress caused by inclination, shock, or vibration may be noted by observing zero-beat output against a frequency-standard oscillator. Various surfaces of the receiver may be pressed upon or pounded with the hands to produce instability in bench tests. In either case, the effect of mechanical displacement of the receiver on the pitch of the output beat note at various receiver frequencies should be observed under c-w (A-1) conditions. Relative comparisons can be made between different receivers of the same model by this procedure, if it is suspected that a defect has developed in one of them. Similar simple tests can be made for microphonic elements.

Warm-up frequency drift may be measured (in A-1 reception condition) when the receiver is first turned on by setting a frequency meter to give a 1,000-cps beat-note output from the receiver. Then, as the receiver drifts, the frequency meter is retuned at intervals to produce this same beat note, and the new frequency reading is recorded each time until the drift has essentially stopped. If the drift is small, the frequency meter may be left fixed, and the change in beat-note frequency observed instead. If the receiver is not designed for A-1 operation, a signal that will heterodyne with the crystal frequency may be coupled into the final detector and the frequency meter used as described above.

Frequency stability with change in gain may be determined by feeding the maximum unmodulated carrier output of the signal generator to the receiver, as adjusted for c-w (A-1) or FSK (agc off) reception, and then turning the RF gain control from maximum gain down until the output signal can just be heard. The change in output beat-note frequency should be less than 100 cps with a well-designed receiver intended for signals below 30 mc, and less than 10 cps below 1 mc. A similar test for receivers not designed for the above modes of operation can be made by using a heterodyning voltage injected into the second detector. For such receivers, greater frequency changes are usually tolerable (up to 10 percent of the 6-db attenuation bandwidth of the overall selectivity curve).

Frequency stability with input-signal voltage change may be determined by noting the beat note during resonant overload measure-

ment using a c-w (A-1) or FSK (agc) signal. Conventional stability limits apply here. On receivers without beat-frequency oscillators auxiliary signal injection at the second detector is used.

NOISE (INTERFERENCE) MEASUREMENTS

Because of the increased number of electronic and electromechanical equipments required to meet modern military needs, the elimination or suppression of noise and radio interference produced by these equipments has assumed greater importance. Interference, it should be remembered, not only may restrict or prevent vital communications, but also may divulge to the enemy the position of a task unit during periods of radio silence.

Various test equipments called radio test sets or noise meters are available to aid in measuring and locating interference. However, a systematic and logical procedure must be followed to locate the offending noise.

If the receiver antenna system is introducing the interference, disconnecting the antenna at the receiver input terminals will generally cause the noise to disappear or abate considerably.

Noise being conducted through the power line will, of course, not be affected by the above procedure, except for that type of interference that requires cross modulation with a carrier to make itself evident. Also, noise generated within the receiver itself will not be altered. The above test is important when the sound of the interference appears similar to tube noise or power-supply hum. Caution must be observed when using this method on receivers that operate on the higher frequencies since a short length of antenna lead (or even an unshielded circuit) may be sufficient to pick up considerable interference when the source is close to the receiver.

When it is established that the antenna is picking up interference, it is necessary to determine the exact source. An effective method is to turn off all equipment operating in the vicinity; if the interference ceases, the individual equipments can then be restarted one at a time until the one that causes the interference to reappear is located. Because of the possibility that a weak source may be masked by a stronger source, it is better to begin with all equipments shut down than to stop individual equipments with others running.

A common method of locating a noise source using a field-intensity or noise meter is to move about the suspected area with the instrument operating and observe the intensity or listen to the audio level with a headset. Since noise signals attenuate rapidly with distance from the source it is often possible to find the origin of interference by walking in the direction of increasing signal strength. The particular part of the offending equipment may be located by the use of probe antennas.

Two types of probe antennas are available; the magnetic type, consisting of a small loop for magnetic pickup, and the electrostatic type, consisting of a length of shielded cable with about 5 inches of the insulated (but with shield stripped) inner conductor extending from the shielded portion. In using the latter the shield covering the leads to the probe should be connected to the case of the noise meter.

The conventional equipment used to measure noise and radio interference is essentially a sensitive portable receiver covering a specified range. A meter of this sort can usually be used as an RF voltmeter for direct measurement of voltage between two points. In terms of circuits this instrument differs from a conventional receiver in three respects: (1) a time delay is introduced into the avc circuit so that the output meter indicates the noise voltage in terms of the peak (or quasi-peak) value, which is more significant than the average, (2) the gain (not AF output) of the receiver is adjustable to previously calibrated levels, to ensure uniformity of measurement on all frequencies, and (3) a self-generated noise source is included to provide a calibrating signal. Briefly this source consists of a diode operating at saturation which generates by shot-effect noise a sufficiently constant source for calibration purposes. A controllable amount of generated noise is used and a filament-control rheostat is provided to maintain space current in the diode at saturation.

NOISE SOURCES

In crowded or shipboard installations or in complicated aircraft structures there are many noise sources, particularly among rotating or vibrating machinery. All commutators, slip rings, brushes, and brush holders are potential sources. All normal ground connections to frame or housings, and all movable contacts such as switch points and relay contacts which might produce arcing are likewise possible noise sources.

Transmitter Testing and Measurement **18**

TRANSMITTER FUNCTION

A transmitter's basic function is to:

1. Generate stable RF carrier energy.

2. Modulate or "key" the desired information into the carrier wave.

3. Power-amplify the generated RF energy.

4. Apply the amplified power to a suitable electromagnetic radiator.

Important transmitter auxiliary equipment sections are: (a) the modulators and associated amplifiers, (b) power supplies for modulators and the main RF generator, (c) control circuits for all the above, and (d) cooling equipment.

The auxiliary equipment to transmitters plays a far more improtant role than does that to receivers, which consists, chiefly of the power supply. Figure 18–1, a generalized block diagram covering a transmitter's main sections, shows basic layout of typical AM and FM transmitters.

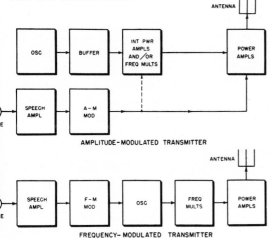

FIG. 18-1 Functional organization of transmitter circuitry

TRANSMITTER CLASSIFICATIONS

Transmitters may be classified according to: (1) operating carrier frequency, (2) the military or commercial service which they render, (3) radiated power, (4) type of modulation.

The operating carrier frequencies, their designations, and the various transmission services are listed in Tables 18–1, 18–2, and 18–3. Radar transmitters are assigned a considerable number of frequency bands, each one having several subfrequency ranges as shown in Table 18–4.

CATEGORIES OF TRANSMITTER USE

Broad "use" categories list transmitters as follows.

NAVIGATION: Low-frequency A-N range; VOR—VHF omnirange; ILS—instrument landing system using localizer and glide path; LORAN—long-range navigation; TACAN—navigational system; DME—distance measurement equipment.

RADAR (radio detection and ranging): Search, shipboard, mobile, and early warning; aircraft approach, height-finder, and weather; navigation.

GROUND COMMUNICATION: Direct, point-to-point; microwave links; scatter (ionosphere and troposphere).

MOBILE: commercial and police; marine; commercial aircraft.

BROADCAST: FM and AM radio; facsimile; television.

Table 18–1   Transmission bands

| Frequency | | Designation | Abbreviation |
KC	MC		
10–30		Very low	VLF
30–300		Low	LF
300–3,000		Medium	MF
3,000–30,000	3–30	High	HF
30,000–300,000	30–300	Very high	VHF
300,000–3,000,000	300–3,000	Ultra high	UHF
3,000,000–30,000,000	3,000–30,000	Super high	SHF

MODULATION CLASSES

Information appearing as modulation upon a carrier may be generally classified as: (1) *amplitude* (AM—for telephone, broadcast, television, and various types of pulse modulations), (2) *keyed* (continuous-wave—c-w on-off) or *frequency shift* (FSK); (3) frequency or phase (broadcast FM).

For coded listing of the types of modulation see Table 18–3.

POWER RANGES

High *average* power (10 to 50 kw) is most frequently transmitted at broadcast radio and television frequencies. High *peak* powers

Table 18–2   Frequency allocations

Fre-quency	Wavelength (in meters)	Uses
Up to 400 mc	0.75	Experimental
400–106 mc	2.83	Government, aircraft, police, television
108–88 mc	3.41	Frequency modulation
88–50 mc	6.82	Television
50 mc–1600 kc	187.5	Ship-to-shore, aircraft, police, foreign, government, point-to-point, experimental
1600–550 kc	545.45	Commercial broadcast
550–20 kc	15,000	Government, commercial, maritime, ship-to-shore, aircraft, point-to-point, high power government, transoceanic

(up to 10 megawatts) are employed in radar systems where the duty cycle is relatively small. Other services, chiefly communication links, use smaller power depending upon the range and character of the transmitted information.

TESTING AND MEASUREMENT TECHNIQUES

Six groups of measurements necessary in evaluating the performance of a transmitter: (1) power output, (2) modulation characteristics, (3) field strength and antenna characteristics, (4) frequency stability, (5) audio and pulse signal measurements concerning the transmitted information, (6) miscellaneous control adjustment and detailed performance tests.

POWER OUTPUT MEASUREMENTS determine a transmitter's capability to generate and efficiently transfer signals to the antenna. Besides the determination of pure power generation the indications produced by voltage standing-wave ratio (VSWR) measurements are an important factor in this transfer of energy. VSWR chiefly concerns impedance matching of the elements carrying power to the antenna, and at microwave frequencies it attains great importance. The general approach to these measurement techniques is described in this chapter. Special microwave techniques appeared in Chapter 16, while some areas are covered in Chapter 19 on radar testing.

MODULATION TESTING TECHNIQUES determine the amount and quality of the information superimposed on a transmitter's carrier wave. They concern FM, AM, and keying systems; they are applied to radiotelephone, television, and entertainment broadcast transmitters. These measurement techniques also concern audio response, distortion, waveform, and a number of other less important factors.

FIELD-STRENGTH ANTENNA MEASUREMENTS include consideration of impedance matching of transmitter output to antenna coupling devices. They are detailed in the latter part of this chapter.

FREQUENCY-MEASURING techniques and associated details concern the measurement of a transmitter's basic crystal-oscillator frequency. For the most part these have been covered in Chapter 12. Details for special transmitter applications appear below.

CONTROL, TESTING AND PROTECTIVE CIRCUITS

Interleaved throughout high-power transmitter layouts is the somewhat complicated network of circuits used to control, test, and protect the unit and its components from self-destruction. These circuits may be categorized as follows:

1. Power-control circuits for turning the transmitter on and off.

2. Functional sequencing and interlocking circuits.

3. Performance-indicating, testing and failure-alarm circuits.

4. Automatic recycling circuits (in some units) which operate the "off" and "on" function when slight or partial failures or slippages in performance occur.

5. Remote-control circuits provided for the convenience of operating personnel or for safety.

6. Automatic tuning circuits.

POWER-CONTROL CIRCUITS

These control the application of power to the main transmitter—primarily to the power supplies. They utilize relays, circuit breakers, and contactors (remote or locally operated)

Table 18–3   Transmission assignment codes

Bandwidth, kc	Type of modulation or emission	Type of information	Supplementary characteristics
System bandwidth required for proper reproduction at the receiver *Examples:* A3a voice–3 kc A3 voice–6 kc A5 VSB television–6,000 kc For frequencies below 10 kc, a maximum of two significant figures may be given after decimal: *Examples:* A1 telegraphy, 25 wpm–0.1 kc F1 telegraphy, 100 wpm–1.25 kc	A–Continuous wave including all types of AM B–Damped wave (spark) F–Angular modulation (frequency or phase) P–Pulsed emission	0–No keying or modulation 1–Telegraphy without other modulation 2–Telegraphy using modulated carrier (carrier may or may not be keyed) 3–Telephony 4–Facsimile 5–Television 6–Multiplex telegraphy 9–Composite and cases not covered above	No letter given for full carrier AM or any type of FM a–Single-sideband, reduced carrier (ssb) b–Independent sideband, reduced carrier (isb) c–Other types of reduced carrier d–Pulse amplitude modulation (PAM) e–Pulse width modulation (PWM) f–Pulse position modulation (PPM)

Table 18–4   Radar frequency bands and code-letter designations

Band P		Band S			Band X			Band K			Band Q		
Freq	λ	Sub	Freq	λ	Sub	Freq	λ	Sub	Freq	λ	Sub	Freq	λ
0.225	133.3	E	1.55	19.3	A	5.20	5.77	P	10.90	2.75	A	36.00	0.834
0.390	76.9		1.65	18.2		5.50	5.45		12.25	2.45		38.00	0.790
		F	1.65	18.2	Q	5.50	5.45	S	12.25	2.45	B	38.00	0.790
			1.85	16.2		5.75	5.22		13.25	2.26		40.00	0.750
		T	1.85	16.2	Y	5.75	5.22	E	13.25	2.26	C	40.00	0.750
			2.00	15.0		6.20	4.84		14.25	2.10		42.00	0.715
		C	2.00	15.0	D	6.20	4.84	C	14.25	2.10	D	42.00	0.715
			2.40	12.5		6.25	4.80		15.35	1.95		44.00	0.682
		Q	2.40	12.5	B	6.25	4.80	U	15.35	1.95	E	44.00	0.682
			2.60	11.5		6.90	4.35		17.25	1.74		46.00	0.652
		Y	2.60	11.5	R	6.90	4.35	T	17.25	1.74			
			2.70	11.1		7.00	4.29		20.50	1.46			
		G	2.70	11.1	C	7.00	4.29	Q	20.50	1.46			
			2.90	10.3		8.50	3.53		24.50	1.22			
		S	2.90	10.3	L	8.50	3.53	R	24.50	1.22			
			3.10	9.68		9.00	3.33		26.50	1.13			
		A	3.10	9.68	S	9.00	3.33	M	26.50	1.13			
			3.40	8.83		9.60	3.13		28.50	1.05			
		W	3.40	8.83	X	9.60	3.13	N	28.50	1.05			
			3.70	8.11		10.00	3.00		30.70	0.977			
		H	3.70	8.11	F	10.00	3.00	L	30.70	0.977			
			3.90	7.69		10.25	2.93		33.00	0.909			
		Z	3.90	7.69	K	10.25	2.93	A	33.00	0.909			
			4.20	7.15		10.90	2.75		36.00	0.834			
		D	4.20	7.15									
			5.20	5.77									

Band L				Band V		
Sub	Freq	λ		Sub	Freq	λ
P	0.390	76.9		A	46.00	0.652
	0.465	64.5			48.00	0.625
C	0.465	64.5		B	48.00	0.625
	0.510	58.8			50.00	0.600
L	0.510	58.8		C	50.00	0.600
	0.725	41.4			52.00	0.577
Y	0.725	41.4		D	52.00	0.577
	0.780	38.4			54.00	0.556
T	0.780	38.4		E	54.00	0.556
	0.900	33.3			56.00	0.536
S	0.900	33.3				
	0.950	31.6				
X	0.950	31.6				
	1.150	26.1				
K	1.150	26.1				
	1.350	22.2				
F	1.350	22.2				
	1.450	20.7				
Z	1.450	20.7				
	1.550	19.3				

which can carry several times the rated load current without dangerously overheating the contacts and which can withstand initial surge currents and voltage arcing. When surge currents are too high many contactor systems use time-delay relays. These apply a reduced voltage first; then the voltage is gradually increased until the surge condition has passed. These are known as step-starters.

SEQUENCING AND INTERLOCK CIRCUITS

These must apply power to the system in the following general order:

1. Self-generate or apply self-actuating power to its own control circuits such as relays, indicators, control voltages, etc.

2. Apply power to all cooling or heat-absorbing units, such as water pumps, blowers, high-voltage relay and interlock circuits.

3. Turn on power-amplifier filament supplies —readying these tubes for application of plate voltage.

4. Energize grid-bias supplies.

5. Turn on high-voltage supplies and those associated with screen voltages on pentode output amplifiers. Many of these functions can be programmed to operate automatically and often require time-delay circuits inserted within the sequence.

The primary indicator lamps used here indicate the presence of power delivered by the various power supplies. Many of these circuits employ indirect energization or are actuated by a relay which is in turn connected with the circuit being monitored.

Alarm monitor lamps indicate degree of failure in important units, such as rise in the cabinet air-supply temperature, of the high-power tube coolant temperature and its level, or of below normal RF output and input. Alarms for the latter two items would be simultaneously connected with the power amplifier's plate circuits and under abnormal conditions would open plate current contactors.

RECYCLING CIRCUITS

These are "turn-off" circuits used when temperature breakdown, flashovers, excess modulation, etc., occur. These networks are inserted within suitable (mostly high-voltage) power-supply switching circuits and are often event-sensitive, so that a failure must occur two or three times before the alarm-connected circuit finally turns off the main or attending supply. Stepping relays with progressive lock-up provisions and with time-delay circuits are added here.

REMOTE-CONTROL CIRCUITS

These circuits must comply with the Federal Communication Commission requirements aimed to ensure that a commercial transmitter is operating within legally assigned power limits and is at all times under the operator's control. The FCC specifies that control must be able to: (1) Completely control filament power. (2) Turn off the transmitter if the control circuits fail in any way. (3) Control the final amplifier plate supply. (4) Measure antenna current or give suitable indication of radiated power. (5) Monitor the frequency and modulation level. (6) Control and monitor tower beacon and obstruction lights.

Designing, installing, and operating remote-control systems obviously must tie in with the basic control provisions discussed above; the specific mechanism for such systems is not specified by FCC.

AUTOMATIC TUNING

Automatic tuning of transmitter circuits becomes necessary when multichannel switching operation is desired as in mobile, marine, or aircraft applications. Some transmitter designs utilize fixed, pretuned settings for channel selection. In others variable tuning of controlled transmitter circuits is accomplished by a sensing device which controls a servomechanism linked to the variable tuned transmitter elements. The sensing may be based on transmitter frequency, amplitude of tuned circuit voltages, or RF matching of impedance in the sensitive tuned circuits. Variable or dynamic tuning during automatic sensing and comparison operations is tailored to observe the basic transmitter-control switching sequences.

POWER MEASUREMENTS

RF POWER METERS

For low power (up to 500 watts) and relatively low RF ranges (3 to 300 mc), compact RF power meters are used to furnish direct readings of transmitter output. The sampling principle employed dissipates and measures, by wattmeter methods, a small, known portion of the total output that has been generated in a suitable resistance.

Figure 18–2 shows the representative circuit making up a typical RF power meter; this type utilizes a load resistor capable of dissipating the entire RF energy which is shunted directly across the output terminals. Low-power meters of this type frequently employ carbon piles or stacks of carbon discs mounted on a suitable rod.

The sampling circuit in Fig. 18–2 shows capacitors C_1 and C_2 forming a voltage divider,

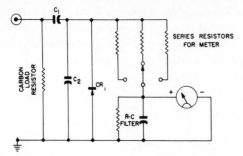

FIG. 18-2 Typical RF power meter and sampling circuit

where C_1 is made small so that it maintains a high capacitive reactance shunted across the load and consequently has little effect on the standing-wave ratio. The small voltage drop appearing across C_2 is applied to the crystal diode CR_1 which provides, when rectifying the incoming signal, a positive voltage for deflecting the indicating meter; it in turn is calibrated to read directly in watts. Suitable meter range resistances and an RF filter are used as shown. The upper frequency limit of the device is determined by the size of the capacitive voltage divider, since inaccuracies in measurements would result if it constituted enough parallel reactance to disturb the output line termination.

INDIRECT RF POWER MEASUREMENTS

Because direct methods of measuring RF power are ineffective when the frequency of the RF energy becomes high, many indirect methods have been devised. These methods usually convert the RF power under test into a secondary form of energy, such as light or heat, which can be conveniently measured and which is proportional to or directly related to the RF energy. In some cases it is also necessary to consider the thermal sluggishness of the measuring device, so that an associated time interval between readings is provided.

LAMP-LOAD METHOD. This method is not used at frequencies above 100 mc, since such loads vary enough so that the proper ter-

mination of the line delivering the power can not be accurately controlled during measurement. An example of this type of termination is seen in the use of two sets of three 28-volt, 4-watt lamps connected in parallel to provide approximately a 65-ohm, 12-watt termination (Fig. 18–3). Hot resistance variations cause some slight mismatch in this arrangement but since the inherent resistance of the lamps decreases as they are dimmed, mismatch is minimized when conditions are arranged to operate under less than full brightness.

This method is a substitution measurement which converts power into light intensity for visual comparison. It uses a pair of identical lamp combinations as shown in Fig. 18–3, where one lamp load is energized by the RF source, and the other by a 28-volt d-c power source. With the two banks of lamps located adjacent to each other and with the potentiometer across the 28-volt d-c source adjusted for equal intensity it is possible to judge equal power rather accurately, since the eye is reasonably sensitive to *relative brilliance*. Thus at equal brightness, the RF power is equal to the product of the d-c voltmeter and ammeter readings.

When greater accuracy is desired a photoelectric cell measurement is sometimes used.

RESISTOR-LOAD METHOD. A noninductive resistor acting as a load for the RF power source can be used for indirectly measuring power by observing temperature rise under load. This temperature rise is derived from thermocouple readings arranged to sample

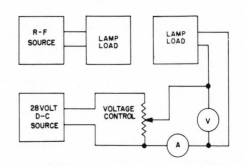

FIG. 18-3 Lamp load method of power measurement

temperature (due to RF power dissipation) in a stream of air around the load resistor. Figure 18–4 diagrammatically illustrates this method.

RECTIFIED RF METHOD. RF power may be measured by sampling and rectifying a transmitter's RF voltage and applying the d-c output to a meter calibrated in watts. In radar transmitters conversion of average power meter readings to peak power is usually made by this method in order to calculate the equipment's duty cycle.

BOLOMETER METHODS

In the UHF range, test equipments usually employ a bolometer, which is a low-power sampling and loading device that undergoes changes of resistance when subjected to changes in dissipated power. The sampled RF energy is usually obtained through an attenuator in conjunction with a directional coupler.

power increases. In either device, resistance is measured before and after the application of RF power. If the same change in resistance is then produced by a known variable d-c source of power, the RF power is equal to the variable d-c power. Bolometers so used make this relationship possible, particularly when they are calibrated for use in automatically adjustable bridge circuits where indications are directly read in units of power.

BARRETTER APPLICATION. The structure of a typical barretter is shown in Fig. 18–5. The fine wire (usually tungsten) making up the sensing element is extremely small in diameter, so that it is possible for the RF current to penetrate to the center and thereby minimize skin effect. The barretter resembles

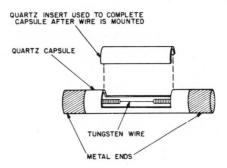

FIG. 18-5 Typical barretter construction

a cartridge-type fuse; it is supported in an insulating quartz capsule between two metallic ends, which also act as connectors. At low levels of power, the resistance-versus-power curve of the barretter is characterized by a square-law relationship.

THERMISTOR APPLICATION. A high degree of precision is made possible by using a thermistor in RF power measurements. Thermistor material is a semiconductor having a negative temperature coefficient. Figure 18–6 shows a common type of construction. A simple thermistor measuring circuit is shown in Fig. 18–6(b).

Thermistor bridge circuits frequently in-

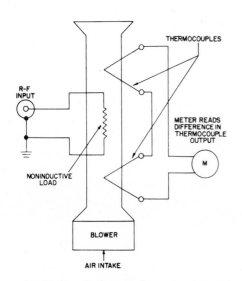

FIG. 18-4 Resistor load set-up for power measurement

There are two types of bolometers, each using substitution measuring techniques. They are the barretter and the thermistor. The barretter increases in resistance with temperature or as the dissipated power rises, while the thermistor decreases in resistance as the

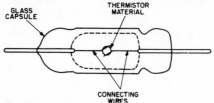

(a) Bead-type thermistor

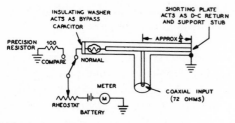

(b) Simple thermistor power measurement

FIG. 18-6 Thermistor construction and measuring circuit

clude compensating thermistor elements which respond to fluctuations in ambient temperature which could otherwise disturb bridge balance. The use of these is covered in Chapter 19.

The negative-resistance temperature coefficient of thermistors provides some degree of self-indicating overload protection since, when excessive power is applied and reduces the resistance of the thermistor, a pronounced RF mismatch results. Also the resulting decrease in power transfer reduces the likelihood of burnout.

LIMITATIONS. Barretters and thermistors are inherently low-power devices. A rating of 1 milliwatt has been standardized, although some models can be operated at power up to 10 or 20 milliwatts.

In high-power measurements a number of attenuating devices may be employed. These are briefly listed and described below; more detailed explanations appear in Chapter 16 and Chapter 19. For convenience the common attenuator types are again listed:

1. *The cut-off waveguide attenuator* is deliberately tailored for operational losses at a frequency below the physical size intended for its maximum efficiency.

2. *The directional coupler waveguide attenuator* cancels most of a sampled bit of main power flow and utilizes a reflected portion of this power for measurement.

3. *The resistive waveguide attenuator* utilizes a movable, absorptive, metallized glass strip mounted within the power-carrying section of waveguide.

4. *The RF probe attenuator* uses a power-extracting piece of wire located within an operating waveguide. If we know what proportion of the main stream of power the probe absorbs, detected energy measured across it gives us means of calculating the main power.

5. *The pickup antenna*, having a known attenuation due to its spacing from the main antenna, gives an output power low enough so that we can use the above power-detecting devices.

DIRECT POWER MEASUREMENT

When sampling methods are not accurate enough, power must be measured directly. Methods of measuring the entire power of the transmitter output by indicating the total amount being dissipated may be summarized as follows.

WATER-LOAD METHOD. The water-load method illustrated in Fig. 18–7(a) utilizes circulating distilled water retained by a dielectric partition within the water-tight waveguide section. Any waveguide reflections are minimized by presenting a tapered surface to the power flow by means of a slant-mounted partial partition across the waveguide. An adjustable matching section provides a minimum standing-wave ratio.

Temperature-sensitive elements located at both the intake and outlet valves sample the temperature of water pumped through the load section of waveguide at a carefully measured rate. RF power dissipated in the load element and transferred to the water is computed from differences in temperature of the input and output of the water-load.

GAS-LOAD METHOD. A simple measuring method dissipates RF power in the gas sealed

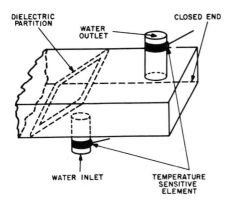

(a) *Water-load power testing*

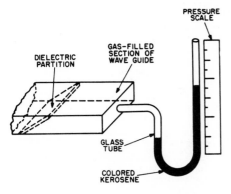

(b) *Diagrammatic set-up for gas-load power testing*

FIG. 18-7 Water- and gas-load power measuring set-ups

off by a dielectric window within a section of waveguide similar to the one shown in Fig. 18–7(b). When power is applied, energy is transferred to the gas, usually ammonia, and its temperature rises causing a corresponding increase in pressure measurable by a mano-meter tube attached to the waveguide. As power dissipated in the gas increases, its pressure forces colored liquid from the bottom of the manometer upward along the accompany-ing scale. This rise is calibrated in terms of applied RF power.

SAND-LOAD METHOD. The sand-load method of high-power measurement is similar in many respects to the resistor-load method. Em-ployed at lower frequencies, it dissipates RF heat-power within the waveguide by a sand load surrounding a temperature-sensitive ele-ment. In order to maintain correct match the sand is mixed with an appropriate proportion

of aquadag; a selected amount of energy is transferred to the surface of the mixture by tapering and slanting the sand-mixture sepa-rator. Temperature rise in the sand, measured by some heat-sensitive element, is then con-verted to watts of power output.

MODULATION MEASUREMENTS

AMPLITUDE MODULATION

A typical amplitude-modulated carrier wave is pictured in Fig. 18–8, a composite trans-mitted RF broadcast signal. This representa-tion is what the composition of a complicated alternating-current waveform would look like if we could instantaneously view it in an oscillo-scope. In this instance the composite wave is transmitting at what we call 40-percent modulation and is represented by the speech-modulating waveform shown in Fig. 18–8(b).

The composite wave breaks down as shown into the carrier wave itself, first without (c) and then with audio-frequency modulation (d) using sine-wave modulating voltage.

The pure carrier wave as received without modulation and viewed on an oscilloscope located, say, on one of the grids of a receiver's IF amplifier tubes, would be a pure sine wave of constant amplitude (Fig. 18–8(c)). This waveform in the usual broadcast radio receiver (with an intermediate frequency of 455 kc) would be a replica of the unmodulated a-c wave which is generated at radio frequencies of the transmitter and which exists at the receiver's antenna coil as well. As pictured, for full power transmission, the waveform peaks are at the mean average level, and $I_p = I_o$. The percentage modulation is, of course, zero, since no audio information or power is being transmitted.

Even when modulated, with higher and lower peak currents, this current I_o is always proportional to the average value of voltage or current delivered by the signal *without modulation*. (See the dotted average line in Fig. 18–8(d),(f).) This observation is signifi-cant, for when modulation is applied we must

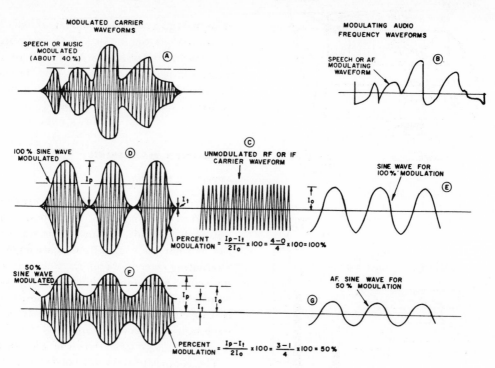

FIG. 18-8 AM carrier wave and modulation

consider the *ratio* of the peak power (as represented by the tips and troughs of the carrier sine waves when they are modulated) to the average value of the carrier power when it is *unmodulated*.

Modulation, the second component of the composite broadcast signal wave, is represented by the audio-frequency currents or voltages which are superimposed or *carried* on the carrier wave. (See Figs. 18–8(b), (e), and (g).) The modulation currents or voltages act on each and every carrier sine-wave cycle so as to vary their tips in amplitude above and below the mean value of the unmodulated carrier.

When, for instance, this carrier wave is modulated at the transmitter by a single pure audio-frequency note, represented by the sine waves of Figs. 18–8(e) or (g), and the tips of the carrier alternations are correspondingly varied in amplitude as in Figs. 18–8(d) or (f), the peaks are thus varied in height equal a-mounts above and below the mean carrier value I_o. Inspection shows that although the

amount of variation or modulation can vary, depending on the amount of audio voltage used to modulate, resulting modulation *does not vary the mean value of the carrier sine wave.*

In order to define the amount or percentage of modulation we must therefore calculate the relationships between the modulation tips at their highest or peak value (I_p) to the value of their tips in the trough (I_t) and compare these values numerically to the average peak carrier level (I_o). This calculation, when carried out from waveform measurements, constitutes the essence of modulation percentage.

The relationship is mathematically:

$$M = \frac{I_p - I_t}{2I_o} \times 100$$

where M = the percentage modulation.

If we consider each division marked off vertically on Fig. 18–8 as one unit of current, we may calculate modulation percentages on the examples shown.

Take Fig. 18–8(f), for instance, demonstrating 50 percent modulation. The lowest swing that the modulation has caused here is $I_t = 1$. The modulation peaks $I_p = 3$ can be entered in the equation with the mean carrier current $I_o = 2$. Thus

$$\frac{I_p - I_t}{2I_o} \times 100 = \frac{3 - 1}{2 \times 2} \times 100 = 50 \text{ percent}$$

Likewise in Fig. 18–8(d) we have:

$$M = \frac{I_p - I_t}{2T_o} \times 100 = \frac{4 - 0}{4} \times 100$$

$$= 100 \text{ percent}$$

Actually, when many audio frequency tones are modulating a carrier wave at the same time, the modulation envelope looks something like Fig. 18–8(a) where the modulation is a combination of many frequencies varying at all percentages during the process of modulation. Note the changes in modulation level, where the composition of the sound changes.

In broadcasting speech or music the *average* level of these depths of modulation must be closely controlled by operators at the transmitter station in order to maintain a constant mean value. In radio and television this percentage is continuously monitored for constancy of output, and for absence from over- or undermodulation; sound-energy output is also monitored. Commercial broadcast transmitters are, in fact, required by law to maintain a fixed 30 percent *average percentage* of modulation and also a *fixed average carrier level*. The *transmitted* carrier as it leaves the station thus remains extremely constant; and any change in *received* carrier at the antenna is due to some transmission factor encountered while the signal is in transit between the transmitter and the receiver.

Thus we see that signal modulation is purely a carrier amplitude variation, while the only quantity concerning *energy* that remains constant for relatively long periods of time is the carrier itself. No matter how much the carrier *peaks* of modulation vary, say in the heavily modulated signal of Fig. 18–8(d) or in the moderately modulated signal of Fig. 18–8(b), signal energy or the *average* carrier level remains the same.

MODULATION MEASUREMENT TECHNIQUES

DETECTION METHODS

Modulation measuring methods, of course, stem from detection. To illustrate these principles the rectifying action and the conditions surrounding a simple detector are shown in Fig. 18–9. This circuit is conventional in receivers and has the secondary of the last IF transformer connected directly to one plate of the detector diode rectifier tube; it uses a series load resistor R_1 returning from ground to the bottom side of the transformer coil and has a parallel-connected load capacitor C_1 and filter capacitor C_2. R_1 and C_1 are the load network across which are developed the d-c control voltage and the output audio voltages. C_1 must, therefore, be large enough to be a short circuit to IF voltages but small enough to be considerable impedance to audio frequencies.

The rectified carrier in Fig. 18–9 shows two conditions: (1) the results of detection of an unmodulated carrier and (2) the products of rectifying a 70 percent modulated signal. Details of the detection operation show normal rectifier action when positive carrier voltages appear across the diode plate. These produce conduction for the positive period of a carrier cycle. When this occurs a charge is passed to the load capacitors C_1 and to C_2, which are large enough for it to be held there for the time interval of the negative carrier swing, during which time there is no conduction. The carrier swing then returns to the positive condition. This holding of charge reflects the storage effects (time constant) of the capacitors and resistor network.

Since the diode does not conduct and effectively presents an open circuit on the carrier's negative excursion, the whole lower half of the modulated signal is actually removed, or literally thrown away, so that only the positive top half of the carrier excursion remains in either the modulated or the unmodulated case.

During the unmodulated interval, where no audio variations exist upon the carrier half-cycles, average rectified d-c is the only resulting product. This is equal to a little less than half the peak value of the maximum carrier wave amplitude and represents the average of the carrier level. This current flow, when converted into its corresponding voltage drop across the load resistor R_1, gives carrier-proportional meter readings.

In the modulated case a similar action takes place, and the charge on C_2 due to carrier half-cycles is again held over the period between IF peaks. Here, however, the rectified peaks of the carrier follow AF sound or music variations since the load capacitor C_1 presents

relatively great impedance to audio frequencies. These AF voltages vary in accordance to the modulation and in effect represent "extraction" of modulation in appearing as voltages across the load network. C_1, being of low impedance to RF, is of course sensitive to changes in carrier frequencies. Thus, AF voltages, superimposed upon the rectified d-c generated from the carrier, make the average of the combination of these two components, as measured by a d-c meter, still proportional to half the carrier peak.

The AF component is passed on through the coupling capacitor C_3 and completes the extraction of audio voltages; note that variations in modulation have not affected the

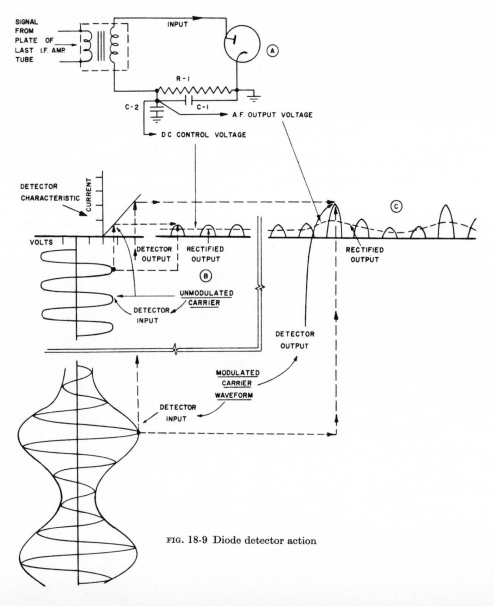

FIG. 18-9 Diode detector action

average value of the current flowing through the diode and have consequently produced no difference in the developed d-c voltage, although wide variations in AF voltage may simultaneously exist. With very low modulation frequencies, the recovered a-c level changes may be relatively slow; therefore the value of C_2 must be large enough so that, in conjunction with the filter resistor R_2, no average carrier level is lost.

It should be emphasized again that, although capacitor C_1 is a short circuit to IF voltages (in a receiver) and has a relatively long time constant compared to these frequencies, it is of high impedance to audio voltages. Consequently, the AF variations in the modulator appear across it and can be used for receiver output. This is the same as saying that the combination of R_2 and C_2 is, in effect, a low pass filter interposed between the IF and audio voltage sources and so designed as to keep these voltages from the grids of the controlled tubes.

AM WAVE-COMPONENT SEPARATION METHOD

Summarizing detector processes we see that measuring modulation percentages may be divided into four parts if we refer to the modulated and unmodulated RF waves: (1) the overall wave must be rectified or detected; (2) the RF portion of the sine-wave components must be filtered out; (3) the resultant d-c must be extracted for average-level measurement; (4) the modulating AF must be extracted for amplification and measurement purposes.

As a first approach we may functionally refer to a *wave-separation method* since the RF component is selected (and suppressed), the AF component is built up or *accepted* for use (a selective filter can be used if necessary), and the d-c component (derived from the carrier wave) is allowed to pass on as a measurable component. Note (in Fig. 18–8(d)) that the mean carrier level I_o when translated into a d-c component of the wave form is proportional to the carrier and is *independent* of the percent of modulation (since the modulation signal is symmetrical) and simi-

larly, the amplitude of the a-c is a replica of the envelope of the modulating signal.

CIRCUIT ANALYSIS. Figure 18–10 shows a basic circuit using the wave-component separation method for the measurement of modulation percentages. To sample the received signal this circuit uses a short antenna variably coupled to the measuring circuit by transformer T_1 and so arranged that inductor L and capacitor C comprise a resonant circuit tuned to the frequency of the radio wave under test. Variable coupling is provided in the antenna transformer to widen the range of meter readings. A diode detector, coupled to the tuned circuit by a capacitor C_1, rectifies the radio wave on positive excursions and produces average carrier indication on M_1 which is blocked off by L_5 from any residual RF coming from the output filter or from modulating a-c developed across C_1 and C_2. The

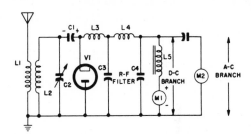

FIG. 18-10 Modulation measurement by wave-component separation

positive half-cycles passed on to the remainder of the circuit are filtered by L_1, L_4, C_3, and C_4, the latter being of sufficient value to develop an a-c component which is applied to M_2. The first of the two final metering branches of the circuit beyond the RF filter receiver delivers: (1) the a-c component, in the form of a fluctuating d-c signal which is a replica of the modulating signal, and (2) a d-c component which represents the average carrier value. Meter M_1 thus reads current which is directly proportional to the carrier; meter M_2, being a fairly high-resistance a-c meter, reads currents proportional to the original modulating signal.

INTERPRETATION OF READINGS. Since, for complete 100 percent modulation, the peak value of the carrier envelope (shown in Fig. 18–8(d) is equal to twice the average value, the minimum peak of the modulating a-c must be zero. If the length and position of the antenna were such that for 100 percent modulation there was full-scale deflection of 100 volts on meter M_1, then meter M_2 (being an a-c meter) would indicate 70.7 v. For 50 percent modulation (with the antenna coupling appropriately readjusted so that meter M_1 will still read 100 volts), meter M_2 would now indicate deflection of 35 volts (.707 × 50).

For convenience, then, by always adjusting the antenna for a reading of 100 volts on meter M_1, modulation percentage is directly calculated by using the voltage reading on meter M_2 multiplied by 1.4.

Reasoning in the same manner, it is apparent that if meter M_1 is adjusted to 141.4 volts, meter M_2 readings will directly equal the percentage value.

Circuit details concerning this set-up approximate the following: (1) the resistance in the d-c branch should be high—say, over 100,000 ohms; (2) a high-resistance a-c meter should be used to measure the a-c component. With such a meter, the component method yields an average modulation percentage and is not capable of disclosing either a positive or negative percentage of modulation since an a-c meter measures the effective, or rms, value of an a-c signal and not the peak value. Furthermore, the readings obtained this way are valid only when the modulating signal is a sine wave, as has been assumed through this discussion.

When the modulating signal is a complex wave, it is advisable to use a peak-reading electronic voltmeter to measure the a-c component. In this case, both the a-c and d-c meter readings will be alike when the modulation is complete. If the voltmeter responds quickly to continuous variations of the peak value of a signal, the instantaneous percent-ages of modulation, positive or negative according to the voltmeter, will be indicated.

DOUBLE-RECTIFIER METHOD—AM

Figure 18–11 illustrates a measurement method which, up to points A and B, is similar to the circuit shown in Fig. 18–10. Note, however, that diode V_1 has its cathode grounded so that negative half-cycles are developed across points A and B. Meter M_1 therefore receives pulsating voltage such as the waveform shown in Fig. 18–8(c).

In series with the voltage across M_1 is a variable d-c voltage, which is determined by the setting of potentiometer R_1 connected to the battery. Switch S is provided to prevent discharge of the battery when M_1 is not in use. M_2 is another d-c meter which indicates the amount of voltage effective between points B and C. The polarity of this voltage is opposite to that of the pulsating direct voltage indicated by M_1, causing the difference of the two voltages to appear between points A and C. These points are connected to a reversing switch.

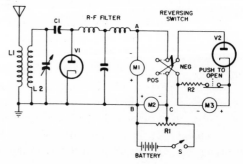

FIG. 18-11 Double rectifier method of modulation measurement

The second rectifier circuit, consisting of diode V_2, meter M_3, and the push-button shunting circuit, is energized by the difference voltage present between points A and C. With the reversing switch in the position indicated by the dotted lines, point C must be positive with respect to point A for current to flow through meter M_3. This condition occurs when the pulsating direct voltage exceeds the battery voltage during any portion of the cycle. If potentiometer R_1 is adjusted carefully until the current flow through meter M_3 just begins, the reading of meter M_2 closely equals the maximum value of the rectified modulated wave. This is the positive modulation peak.

When the reversing switch is in the second position, there can be a deflection of meter M_3 only if point A becomes positive with respect to point C. This condition is most likely to occur at the smallest absolute value of the negative rectified signal, or, in other words, at the instant of a negative peak of the modulating signal. Therefore, the negative modulation peak can be read on meter M_2 provided the potentiometer is adjusted so that current just begins to flow through meter M_3.

Meter M_1 thus provides a reading of the carrier voltage while M_2 provides a reading of the battery voltage. The different percentages of modulation can then be calculated from peak and through readings of M_2 and the average reading of M_1.

Thus:

positive modulation percentage
$$= 100(E_p - E_c)/E_c$$
negative modulation percentage
$$= 100(E_c - E_n)/E_c$$
average percentage
$$= 100(E_p - E_n)/2E_c$$

where E_p = positive modulation peak voltage indicated on meter M_2,

E_n = negative modulation peak voltage indicated on meter M_2,

E_c = carrier voltage indicated on meter M_1.

TEST LIMITATIONS. It is important to realize that the values obtained by this method are slightly inaccurate since contact potential in V_1 can cause negative or trough measurements to be slightly high and positive peak measurements to be slightly low.

These errors become smaller as the sensitivity of meter M_3 increases and the amplitude of the rectified carrier voltage increases, and an accuracy of 2 percent can be attained by using a meter with a 200-microampere movement in the presence of a 50-volt rectified

carrier. As a precautionary measure, the microammeter M_3 should be protected by a heavy shunt so that after a preliminary adjustment, it can be removed by the push-button switch. The double-rectifier method of modulation measurement can not deliver continuous indication of the modulation and is therefore not suitable for monitoring methods.

MONITOR METERS IN AM MEASUREMENT

DOUBLE-RECTIFIER CIRCUIT

In monitoring, a modulation meter should indicate the percentage of modulation directly and continuously. The circuit of Fig. 18–12 presents a double-rectifier circuit modified by the addition of a capacitor, a resistor, and a more sensitive microammeter calibrated directly in percentage of modulation. In this circuit, potentiometer R_1 is adjusted until meters M_1 and M_2 indicate the same readings. Since the battery voltage opposes the recti-

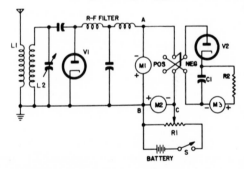

FIG. 18-12 Modulation measurement using the monitor method

fied voltage, the voltage across points A and C alternates in accordance with the modulation signal. The negative half-cycles between points A and C correspond to the negative modulation peaks, while the positive half-cycles correspond to the modulation (negative) peaks. Consequently, positive modulation peaks cause conduction in diode V_2 when the reversing switch is thrown in the left-hand position, and conduction is caused by the negative peaks when the switch is in the right-hand position. V_2 and its associated circuit constitute a peak detector for, during conduction in V_2, capacitor C_1 charges quickly to the peak of the modulation signal, since the diode impedance is small compared to the load presented to the voltage source. When diode V_2 is open, C_1 must discharge through M_3 and resistor R_2 so that the voltage across C_1 nearly equals the peak of the modulation except for a small loss between conducting peaks.

SLIDE-BACK ELECTRONIC VOLTMETER

The slide-back type of electronic voltmeter is a common type of modulation meter. A typical circuit arrangement is shown in Fig. 18–13, where excitation is derived from a tuned circuit suitably coupled to the transmitter across C_1.

The circuit operates as follows:

1. With no signal, potentiometer R_1 is adjusted so that M_1 indicates zero.

2. Potentiometer R_2 is adjusted so that the milliammeter M_2 indicates zero plate current through the tube.

3. With unmodulated input, the tuned circuit is adjusted so that the amplitude of the unmodulated carrier signal is sufficiently great to cause a convenient deflection of milliammeter M_2.

4. Potentiometer R_1 is adjusted so that the tube is again cut off, as indicated by zero deflection of meter M_2. This means that the

reading of meter M_1 now equals the peak voltage of the RF signal in the tuned circuit. This voltage, in turn, is proportional to the unmodulated carrier current E_1.

5. Without disturbing the tuned circuit, a modulated carrier signal is applied and R_1 again adjusted until the tube is just cut off. The new reading of meter M_1 (E_{max}) is proportional to the peak value of the modulated current.

6. The percentage of modulation can now be computed from the following formula:

$$\text{Percentage of modulation} = 100(E_{max} - E_1)/E_1$$

where E_{max} = second reading of meter M_1,
E_1 = first reading of meter M_1.

NEGATIVE-PEAK OVERMODULATION INDICATOR

To measure negative-peak overmodulation, a simple arrangement (Fig. 18–14) uses a diode and a milliameter connected as shown by means of a transformer across the plate-circuit modulation network of an RF amplifier. When the amplitude of the signal developed by the modulator is excessive, overmodulation occurs and the cathode of the diode swings negative, since ordinarily the cathode potential of the diode is positive while the RF amplifier tube is cut off. Under these conditions alarm is immediately indicated by deflection of M.

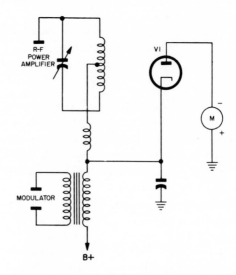

FIG. 18-14 Negative-peak overmodulation measurement

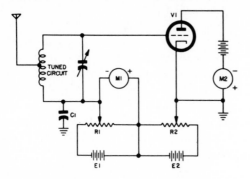

FIG. 18-13 Modulation measurement by slide-back voltmeter method

When the positive and negative peaks of a modulated carrier are unequal, there is an effective shift in its amplitude. When the positive peaks are disproportionate, this shift is upward; the shift is downward when the negative peaks predominate. Under these circumstances, the average value of the

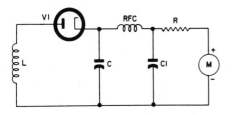

FIG. 18-15 Carrier shift measurement of modulation

RF half-cycles is not truly proportional to the carrier as we have previously assumed under the separation measuring methods discussed above. To indicate this shift a simple diode-detector circuit shown in Fig. 18–15 can be used. With a modulated carrier input and using appropriate tuning and antenna coupling, symmetrical modulation produces no change in meter reading. Higher readings indicate positive carrier shift; a

lower reading indicates negative carrier shift.

Although less accurate, a d-c milliameter connected in the plate circuit of a modulated RF amplifier is also capable of revealing carrier shift. This occurs because in most Class C plate-modulated amplifiers the plate-supply current varies in proportion to the effective plate-supply voltage, so that with no amplitude change due to unsymmetrical modulation this voltage and current relationship is preserved.

OSCILLOSCOPE TECHNIQUES IN AM MODULATION MEASUREMENTS

TRAPEZOIDAL PATTERNS

A common method in utilizing the cathode-ray oscilloscope for monitoring modulation measurements is by the trapezoidal-pattern method. Such patterns are obtained by applying a modulated carrier wave to the oscilloscope vertical deflection plates and the modulating signal to the horizontal deflection plates. Figure 18–16 shows a typical set-up for this measurement. From the resulting shape of the stationary pattern, we can calculate the percentage of modulation.

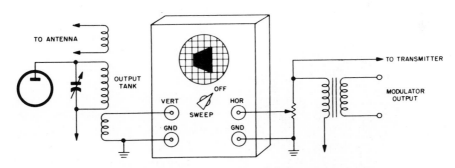

FIG. 18-16 Oscilloscope set-up for modulation measurement

FIG. 18-17 Trapezoidal patterns for various percentage modulations

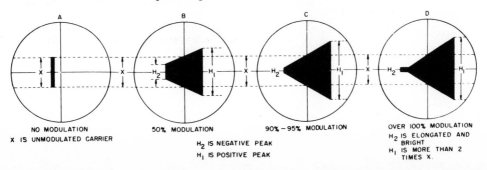

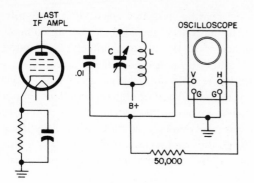

FIG. 18-18 Set-up for modified Lissajous figures for modulation measurement

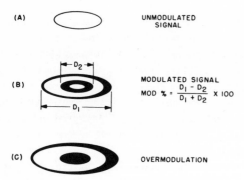

FIG. 18-19 Modulation measurement for modified Lissajous waveforms

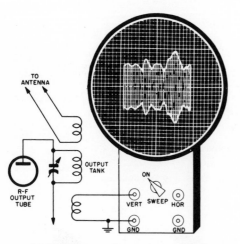

FIG. 18-20 Wave envelope measurement set-up

Figure 18-17 shows an example of a trapezoidal pattern with no modulation, 50 percent, 90 percent, and overmodulation.

MODIFIED LISSAJOUS FIGURES FOR MODULATION MEASUREMENT

Another method requires the use of a receiver tuned to the transmitter frequency. Oscilloscope connections made as shown in Fig. 18-18 (it may be necessary to retune the IF stage to compensate for the additional loading effect) give an elliptical oscilloscope pattern having a single sharp trace which is the result of a phase difference between the vertical and horizontal deflection voltages fed to the oscilloscope. This phase difference is produced by the horizontal amplifier input capacitance and the 50,000-ohm resistor.

The unmodulated elliptical pattern (Fig. 18-19(a)), having a single sharp trace, with modulation, broadens to a ribbon. For 100 percent, the dark area in the center of the pattern decreases to zero.

Overmodulation goes beyond this point and a bright spot appears in the center of the pattern. The modulation percentage may be calculated by the formula given in Fig. 18-19(c).

WAVE-ENVELOPE PATTERNS

For relatively low-frequency RF signals another useful procedure for monitoring AM modulation is to utilize the conventional internal sawtooth sweep voltages generated for the horizontal-deflection system while simultaneously applying RF signal directly to the vertical plates. For sine-wave modulation this method delivers displays which are replicas of the AM wave. The sweep frequency should be equal to, or a multiple of, the modulation frequency; a typical modulation envelope pattern is illustrated in Fig. 18-20.

FREQUENCY-MODULATION MEASUREMENTS

The concept of percentage modulation commonly used in connection with amplitude modulation does not apply to frequency modulation. FM transmissions using constant carrier amplitude deliver information by "swinging" or "wobbling" the carrier. The amount of carrier swing is called *frequency deviation;* it gives us a measure or index of modulation.

The *modulation index* is thus the ratio of the carrier's frequency deviation to the modulating frequency, namely:

$$M = \frac{F_d}{F_m}$$

where m = modulation index,

F_d = frequency *deviation* of the carrier,

F_m = frequency of the highest modulating signal.

The term *frequency deviation* has a key significance in that it is descriptive of the basic FM function. Specifically, it is the amount of "swing" or deviation (in kilocycles or megacycles) in the main carrier caused by its being modulated with audio voltages. For ranges of mean carrier excursion it is logical to specify the amount of deviation by expressing it as the ratio noted above, since such a ratio describes a modulation's greatest effects in terms of how far, in *maximum* number of kilocycles, it can move the carrier about its mean center frequency.

Thus the FCC allows a maximum deviation of 75 kc on the entertainment broadcast frequency bands up around 100 mc, and in terms of percent we can only refer to this as a limit and say that 75 kc is 100 percent modulation when the carrier is allowed to swing up to this maximum. Overmodulating, or overdeviating, will occur if the maximum carrier swing is exceeded. In this case transmission is not particularly affected but audio distortion may result. Also the bandwidth or "slice" of the communication frequency band occupied by a particular carrier exceeds, in this case, the limits assigned to it by law.

Commercial broadcast FM stations must not exceed a frequency deviation of 75 kc and the sound transmission of television stations is restricted to a deviation of 25 kc. A common method of measuring FM carrier deviation is described below.

BESSEL ZERO MEASUREMENT

For FM modulation measurements, a technique known as the Bessel zero method offers a simple method for determining frequency deviation. It utilizes the following equipment (see Fig. 18–21): a variable-frequency (low-distortion) audio oscillator, a communications receiver tunable to the carrier frequency of the FM transmitter, and a beat-frequency oscillator (sometimes included in the receiver).

As in AM, the modulation index M determines a relationship between carrier and modulation frequencies. In FM, however, the modulation index concerns *sideband spacing* rather than amplitude differences. Definite relationships of these spacings with respect to the carrier offer a method of determining the degree or percentage of modulation.

Specifically, the carrier sideband components vary cyclically in amplitude the farther they progress from the center frequency; they actually disappear completely for certain values of M, such as 2.405, 5.52, 8.654, etc. At these points none of the transmitted power is contained in the sidebands. This fact and the

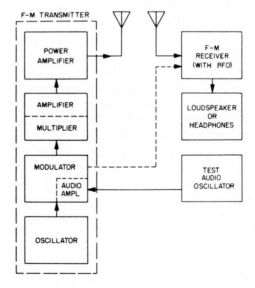

FIG. 18-21 Bessel zero method for measuring FM deviation

distribution of energy of other sideband frequencies are disclosed by a mathematical series known as Bessel functions, hence the name Bessel zero.

The technique of measurement calls for increasing the amplitude of the modulating signal until the carrier of the FM signal disappears. The first disappearance point occurs where 2.405 is substituted for M in the previously given equation. The frequency deviation can then be calculated: $F_d = 2.405F_m$.

MEASUREMENT TECHNIQUE TO FIND THE ZERO POINTS. To measure and adjust an FM wave, the carrier being analyzed must first be monitored by a receiver so that disappearance of the received sidebands can be detected as the amplitude of the modulating signal is increased, as shown in Figure 18–20.

This procedure involves the following steps:

1. The receiver is lightly coupled to the transmitter carrier and center-tuned under unmodulated conditions.

2. The receiver's beat frequency oscillator (BFO) is adjusted until some selected tone, such as 500 cps, is plainly heard in the output of the receiver. Once the pitch of this note is set, the BFO adjustments should be fixed so that the ear may become accustomed to this particular pitch.

3. Apply an audio signal from a suitable oscillator to the audio-amplifier input section of the transmitter so that an adjustable amplifier output may be fed to the modulating stage of the transmitter.

4. Vary the frequency deviation by changing the amplitude of this modulating signal until the selected 500-cycle tone first disappears. In making the measurement, conflicting modulating tones may be eliminated by use of a low-pass filter.

EXAMPLE

For purposes of discussion suppose we desire to limit a transmitter to a maximum frequency deviation of 25 kc. The modulating frequency

that will produce carrier disappearance at an index of 2.405 equals 10,395 cycles ($F = 25,000/2.405 = 10,395$). An audio signal of this frequency, when applied to the FM modulator and gradually increased in amplitude, will eventually extinguish the carrier. In the audio measurement set-up this adjustment produces a steady lessening of the beat note until it becomes inaudible. It is this audio amplitude, then, that produces 25 kc deviation, and this value must be constantly maintained through constant carrier operation for maximum efficiency and confinement within prescribed limits.

If a large frequency deviation such as 75 kc is to be established, we repeat the above computation and find that $F_m = 75/2.405 = 31.2$ kc. Since this frequency is too high for transmitter audio stages, we utilize the second carrier disappearance point, equalling 5.52, which leads to the relationship $F_m = 75/5.52 = 13.583$ kc and provides a frequency within the audio bandpass of most FM transmitters.

If the audio frequency (13.586 kc) is too high, we have recourse to the fact that a frequency-multiplying stage increases both the carrier center frequency and the frequency deviation by the same factor. For example, in a transmitter the reactance tube producing modulation of the generated frequency in an 8:1 multiplication system would require a frequency deviation of only 9.375 kc of the oscillator, which would correspond to a final frequency deviation of 75 kc in the final carrier. In adjusting such a set-up, a portion of the oscillator signal should be coupled to the receiver as indicated by the dotted lines shown in Fig. 18–21; then it is necessary only to find the amplitude of audio signal that produces a frequency deviation of 9.375 kc. At this circuit point the frequency of the modulating signal is determined by the relationship $F_m = 9.375/2.405 = 3.9$ kc.

AUDIO AND PULSE SIGNAL MEASUREMENTS

DISTORTION

The faithful reproduction of the audio components of a transmitted wave is achieved only when the overall distortion is a relatively low percentage. Although the FCC allows the harmonic distortion of a commercial AM transmission to be as high as 10 percent when the modulation level is 85 percent, the distortion produced by many transmitters is as low as 2 percent.

Distortion is present to some degree in any audio amplifier, not merely in those associated with a transmitter or receiver. In order to eliminate modulator influences, distortion components are first analyzed and measured in the audio amplifying system used in conjunction with a transmitter's modulator. Actually modulator distortion components are negligible because modern transmitters use carefully balanced modulating circuits and eliminate minor distortion caused by unbalanced operation, such as small changes in tube characteristics or in values of critical parts. Most distortion analysis concerns the harmonic content of the fundamental sine waves used in modulation. The important types of harmonic measurement techniques are covered in the following descriptions.

HARMONIC CALCULATIONS

The measured distortion represented by a particular harmonic is simply the ratio (expressed as a percentage) of a particular harmonic's amplitude to that of the fundamental frequency. When a number of harmonics of an individual frequency are measured, the total harmonic amplitude is expressed as the root-mean-square sum of the measured amplitude of the harmonics present in the signal. If, for example, the second harmonic contributed 4 percent distortion, the third harmonic 6 percent, and the fourth harmonic 5.5 percent, the total would be as follows:

$$\sqrt{16 + 36 + 30.25} = \sqrt{82.25}$$
$$= 9.07 \text{ percent}$$

The figure 9.07 percent represents the total rms harmonic distortion.

Four general types of test equipments are used for the measurement of the harmonic distortion contained in a signal. They are: (1) the tuned-circuit analyzer, (2) the hetero-

dyne analyzer, (3) the dynamometer analyzer, and (4) the fundamental-suppression analyzer.

TUNED-CIRCUIT HARMONIC ANALYZER

The harmonic contents of an AF wave can be extracted by using tuned circuits as shown in Fig. 18–22. Here we select, by tuning, the series-resonant currents at a specific harmonic frequency, coupling them by means of transformer T to an amplifier, and rectifying them to obtain indication on a d-c meter. Total harmonic output is derived from successively tuning L and C to all harmonics and summing these readings as described above.

Compensation for the variation in the a-c resistance of the series circuit, and for the variation of the amplifier gain over the frequency range of the instrument, is arranged through the network consisting of L_1, R_1, and C_1. This compensation also provides equal measurement sensitivity over the frequency range of the equipment.

The tuned-circuit method necessitates the use of electrically and physically large components in tuned circuits at lower audio frequencies. This, together with the difficulty in separating low-frequency harmonics, reduces the convenience of this method.

HETERODYNE HARMONIC ANALYZER

The heterodyne type of analyzer avoids using a plurality of highly selective, fixed-

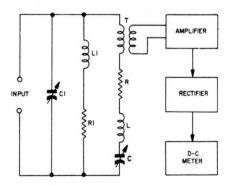

FIG. 18-22 Tuned-circuit harmonic analyzer

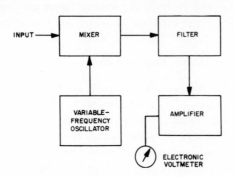

FIG. 18-23 Block diagram of heterodyne type harmonic analyzer

frequency filters necessary in the tuned-circuit method. In the subject type the output of a variable-frequency oscillator is heterodyned successively with each harmonic of the input signal, and either the sum or difference frequency is made equal to the frequency of the filter. As a result of converting each harmonic to a constant frequency, it is possible to use extremely selective filters (often quartz-crystal type); thus the circuit passes only the constant-frequency signal corresponding to the particular harmonic under test.

The essentials of a heterodyne type of harmonic analyzer are shown in Fig. 18–23. The balanced mixer modulator offers a simple means of lessening the amplitude of undesired components. Also, the low harmonic distortion generated by a balanced modulator produces high accuracy while the quartz-crystal or inverse-feedback filters provide good selectivity against unwanted responses. Most heterodyne analyzers provide direct readings and utilize automatic comparison of the harmonics to the impressed signal, which is in turn calibrated against a reference voltage.

DYNAMOMETER-TYPE ANALYZER

This instrument, although limited in usefulness, utilizes the same principle employed in a dynamometer-indicating ammeter (see Chapter 10), which compares the resultant magnetic force between current-carrying coils. The conventional design simultaneously applies composite and harmonic currents being compared in various combinations and sequences to moving and to stationary coils of a dynamometer meter movement.

The dynamometer principle is, in general, restricted to analyzing low-frequency waveforms—say, below 3 kc. In practice the complex wave, after suitable amplification, is applied to one fixed coil of the dynamometer, and the output of a variable-frequency (search) oscillator is applied to the other. When the frequency of the search oscillator is extremely close to a harmonic of the fundamental waveform being measured, the moving coil and the indicator attached to it oscillate at the difference frequency. The resultant currents produce a deflection proportional to the product of the currents in the two coils, that is, to that of the oscillator current and of the harmonic component. By holding the oscillator current constant (with the aid of a meter), the deflection of the pointer can be made proportional to the magnitude of the harmonic current alone.

A wave is analyzed, therefore, by varying the frequency of the search oscillator and noting both the amplitude and frequency at which the indicator oscillations occur.

FUNDAMENTAL-SUPPRESSION ANALYZER

The fundamental-suppression method of measuring distortion is used when the principal consideration is the total harmonic distortion, rather than knowledge of individual signal components. In this method (see Fig. 18–24)

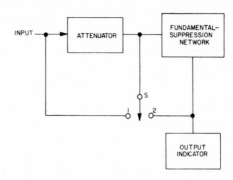

FIG. 18-24 Block diagram of fundamental suppression analyzer

the input waveform is applied to a network that suppresses the fundamental component and passes (with negligible attenuation) all of the harmonic frequencies. If a thermocouple or a square-law electronic voltmeter measures output, the rms value of the combined harmonic components will be indicated.

Removal of the fundamental frequency is by high-pass filters, some form of the Belfils bridge, or by bridged-T circuits.

Distortion meters operating on the principle of fundamental suppression are simpler and less expensive than instruments of the heterodyne type; of course they do not extract the amplitudes of the individual distortion components.

Fundamental-suppression networks are useful in other types of analyzers in that they reduce the amount of harmonic distortion generated in the analyzer itself. They also reduce selectivity requirements in measurement processes where frequency drift of the waveform is being analyzed.

Distortion analysis by means of an oscilloscope can also be accomplished quite accurately when using fundamental suppression since extracted harmonic components can be easily identified by visual observation.

INTERMODULATION DISTORTION MEASUREMENT

The quality of an audio signal may prove unsatisfactory even when the measured harmonic distortion of a single frequency is low. We meet such objectional conditions when a heterodyne or audio beating effect exists between the various frequency components of a waveform. This beating produces appreciable sum- and difference-frequency components which are not harmonically related to the original frequencies.

Intermodulation can be determined by simultaneously applying to the modulation amplifier under test two sine waves of different frequencies (for example, 400 cps and 1,500 cps), and then measuring the amplitude of the difference-frequency component (1,100 cps) appearing in the output. If all signals except the 1,100-cps component are suppressed by means of a suitable filter, we may directly measure the results of our induced intermodulation. Percentages under 8 or 10 percent are considered good. Such tests may be applied to the input of an entire audio recording and reproducing system, in order to obtain an index of the overall quality of the system.

PHASE DISTORTION—SQUARE-WAVE TESTING

Unsatisfactory reproduction may be due to poor phase response despite low harmonic distortion. This type of distortion appears in amplifiers and reproducers when impulse signals of a sudden or transient nature are transmitted. Such signals, being essentially rectangular in waveform, correctly fall under our discussion of square-wave testing and the interpretation of associated wave patterns referred to in Chapter 13.

FIELD-STRENGTH MEASUREMENTS

The magnitude of an electric field of a radio wave *at a given point* is known as the field strength or intensity of that wave. Field-strength measurements use the RF voltage induced in a receiving or pickup antenna. Noise measurements can also be made by this method.

Several types of test equipments for the measurement of field strength and noise are available in a number of frequency ranges. These instruments are classified by various labels: radio test sets, field-strength meters, or radio noise meters. They measure either the *relative* or *absolute* magnitude of field intensity produced by a transmitter-excited antenna and can be used to determine antenna efficiency, directivity characteristics, and signal coverage, or to provide information useful in selecting transmitter antenna sites, making field surveys, and checking spurious harmonic radiation.

The simplest test set uses a grid-dip meter, in conjunction with a pickup antenna, a diode (or crystal), and a microammeter. The meter is calibrated to indicate the relative strength of the field acting on the pickup antenna, although in the case of this particular circuit it is not directly proportional to the field intensity because of the nonlinearity of the crystal.

More elaborate test equipments measure absolute field intensity by comparing the voltage induced in a pickup antenna with a voltage generated by a self-contained calibrated oscillator. The antenna voltage is amplified in a sensitive receiver where two calibrated attenuators, one between the antenna and mixer stage and the other in the first-cathode follower amplifier, allow comparisons to be used. The indicating meter in this test equipment uses the diode current in the second detector.

Field-intensity measurements require careful checking of pickup antenna placement because objects or persons near either the radiating source or the meter may cause shadows or reflections and consequent errors in final results. In general, the antenna should always be extended to its full length to ensure proper operation within the tuning range of the adjustment circuits. For detecting and locating interference or noise, audio response through a telephone headset is preferable in order to identify the type of signal.

MEASUREMENT DATA

FIELD STRENGTH is measured and expressed in *volts per meter*. It represents at any receiving location the *change in*, or the *electric potential gradient* produced by, a radiated or transmitted radio wave. Since the field of the wave represents a dynamic or changing condition this gradient is proportional to the separation of the receiving elements, and also to the height of the antenna intercepting the field which must be maintained constant during a measurement. For this reason we express field strength in terms of a standard, one-meter high antenna and since most field intensities are very small, it is convenient to employ the terms *millivolts* or *microvolts* per meter. Thus, a 1-millivolt-per-meter field produces a 1-millivolt potential when using an antenna

of 1 meter effective height assuming that the antenna is oriented in the direction of the greatest rate of potential change. Similarly, an antenna with an effective height of 5 meters which is subjected to a field intensity of 20 millivolts per meter would develop a 100-millivolt signal. Obviously, in addition to effective height, the length or size of an antenna has a relationship to the amount of voltage it develops.

TRANSMITTING ANTENNA EFFICIENCY in practical usage is usually stated in such terms as *power gain* and *field gain*. Since the maximum reception is obtained in antennas of one-half wavelength, these terms are based on the field intensity produced by a half-wave antenna in free space. Relative field-strength measurements are usually taken at a distance of one mile under conditions where there are no reflected waves.

POWER GAIN is thus defined as the ratio of the power required by a half-wave antenna to produce a particular field strength at a distance of one mile, to the power required by the antenna under test to produce the same field strength.

In equation form this is expressed as:

$$\text{power gain} = \frac{\text{power required with vertical half-wave antenna}}{\text{power required with antenna under test}}$$

ANTENNA FIELD GAIN is the ratio of field strength produced at a distance of one mile by 1-kilowatt antenna power to 137.6 millivolts per meter. This assumes the antenna to be radiating vertically polarized waves (a vertical antenna), that the distance is measured horizontally over flat terrain, and that there are no reflections or obstructing structures.

$$\text{field gain} = \frac{\begin{array}{c}\text{field intensity of antenna at} \\ \text{1 mile for 1-kw input}\end{array}}{137.6 \text{ millivolts per meter}}$$

Since power is proportional to voltage squared, the relationship between field gain and power gain is:

$$\text{field gain} = \sqrt{\text{power gain}}$$

A power increase of four is thus required in order to double a transmitter's radiating ability. Power gain can be obtained by using multi-elements in an antenna, which is a more economical measure than using higher-power output tubes.

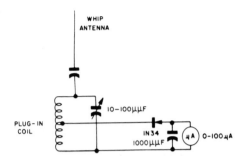

FIG. 18-25 Circuit of simple field-strength meter

SIMPLE METER APPLICATION

A simple instrument which produces relative measurements of field intensity is shown in Fig. 18–25. The arrangement employs a crystal diode connected similarly to the grid-dip circuit shown in Fig. 18–27. This instrument uses plug-in coils for wide frequency range, a whip antenna for pickup, and a sensitive microammeter as the indicating device.

ADVANCED METER APPLICATION

When greater sensitivity is necessary, field-strength meters employ a specifically designed, high-gain receiver which uses a calibrated attenuator at the input of its first IF amplifier and so arranged that the output of the mixing stage is always exactly proportional to the RF signal voltage present in the grid circuit. (See Fig. 18–26.) For proper mixing and calibration an auxiliary adjustable RF oscillator and an electronic voltmeter are provided to enable substitution-type measurements.

Using a loop antenna to pick up and develop the input RF signal it is possible to verify by calculation as well as to measure input field-strength conditions with this more advanced type of instrument. For receiver operation its local oscillator is coupled to the loop by means of a transformer, or applied directly across a coupling resistor in series with the loop and so arranged that its output does not vary as a result of tuning. With this circuit the input circuit can be metered by an electronic voltmeter, or the plate circuit of the mixer can be metered by a milliammeter calibrated against a 1-volt signal at the grid. The calibrated attenuator preceding the IF amplifier allows for normalized input and permits control of signal so as to avoid saturation of the IF stages. Precaution must also be taken by proper coupling to prevent overloading of the mixer stage. Final indication is through a detector and metering circuit following the IF amplifiers.

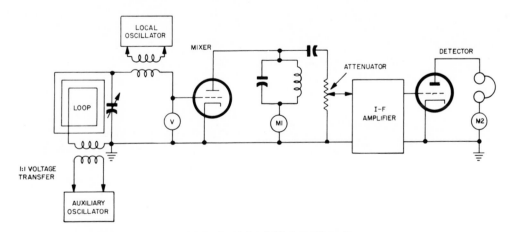

FIG. 18-26 Sensitive field-strength meter

The grid-dip meter is another commonly used circuit in relative field-strength measurements. In using this meter the plate voltage must be turned off, and a loop antenna must be connected to the coil terminals of the instrument. When tuned to the selected transmission frequency and using appropriate plug-in coils, signal input produces current flow in the grid-cathode circuit. Rectified and amplified signals produce directly proportional meter deflection. Description and applications of the grid-dip meter appear at the end of this chapter.

TYPICAL TEST PROCEDURE

Field-strength measurements described above are based on substitution procedures using various inputs from the auxiliary oscillator and comparing them with a 1-volt signal at the grid of the mixer by means of attenuator settings and output meter readings. From the three attenuator readings necessary under these adjustment steps we can also calculate the resonant voltage rise in the loop antenna.

ALTERNATE TEST PROCEDURE

A more convenient signal substitution method of measuring field strength is possible when a standard signal generator is available. With this method a sensitive radio receiver is tuned to the signal—the loop antenna being adjusted for maximum reception. The gain of the receiver is then set to provide a convenient deflection, noted on the meter in its detector output circuit.

Next, with the loop oriented so that the received signal is not being picked up, a voltage from the signal generator is introduced into the antenna circuit, and its amplitude adjusted so that the deflection of the meter in the detector circuit is the same as noted above. This induced signal amplitude, divided by the voltage-transfer ratio, gives us enough data to calculate the field strength produced by the loop, which in turn equals the signal initially picked up.

GRID-DIP METER APPLICATIONS

Stated in simple terms, a grid-dip meter is a multiple-range, tunable oscillator which includes a milliammeter in its grid circuit to indicate the strength of oscillation. When an external circuit absorbs energy from plug-in coils making up the oscillator tuned circuit, the grid circuit receives less excitation, less grid current flows and consequently produces a distinct "dip" in the meter indication.

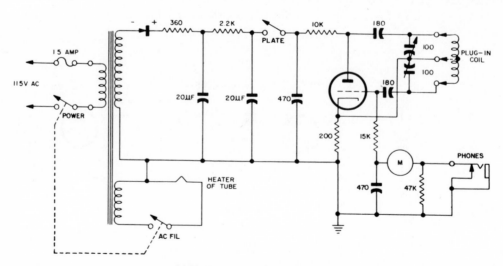

FIG. 18-27 Typical grid-dip meter circuit

Figure 18–28 shows a representative circuit of this meter. The plug-in coils are tuned over various ranges by means of variable capacitors; direct frequency calibration appears on a dial connected to the shaft operating the tuning capacitors C_1 and C_2.

METER CIRCUIT ANALYSIS. The oscillator shown in Fig. 18–27 is a conventional Colpitts type. The low-frequency plug-in coils are center-tapped to preserve inductive balance regardless of tuning, a feature used to stabilize oscillations and maintain constant amplitude throughout the frequency band of the coil. Self-bias is employed to prevent excessive tube current when a plug-in coil is not in use; the meter, being in series with the d-c path to ground, indicates the flow of grid current. The supply voltage is applied by means of a separate switch so that in the off position the oscillator is de-energized and the grid-cathode portion of the tube can then function as a diode detector.

CHECKING TUNED CIRCUITS. The grid-dip meter can also determine the resonant frequency of a tuned circuit that is de-energized. Here d-c voltage to the plate is used and the plug-in coil, which simulates a probe, is brought near the tuned circuit under test and oriented for maximum energy transfer. Next the tuned-circuit frequency is slowly changed until a dip in the grid meter appears. This indicates that energy is being absorbed by the external circuit from the tank circuit made up of the plug-in oscillator coils, and the resonant frequency of the external circuit and the frequency of oscillation must be the same.

OTHER APPLICATIONS. Although less well-known than the preceding application, there are three other basic ways of using the grid-dip meter: (1) It can be employed as a signal generator where suitable coupling can be made with its tuning coils to the circuit under test. (2) The instrument can serve as an oscillating detector for determining the fundamental or harmonic frequencies of unknown but operating RF circuits. This technique calls for the connection of headphones into the grid circuit of the oscillator by means of the phone jack. When an external source of RF power is coupled to the probe, there will be an audible beat note in the phones each time the adjustable frequency of the test instrument is made nearly equal to the fundamental or a harmonic frequency of the RF source. At zero beat, the setting of the calibrated grid-dip dial specifies the unknown frequency. (3) A grid-dip meter can be operated as an absorption-type frequency meter when the grid-cathode portion of the tube acts as a diode. As in the operation of a conventional wavemeter, the meter reading will increase perceptibly when the instrument is closely coupled and tuned to a source of RF energy.

MISCELLANEOUS USES. The grid-dip meter has a large number of applications. To mention a few it can be used to: (1) align superheterodyne receivers and determine whether the local oscillator is functioning, (2) tune the tank circuits of a transmitter and neutralize any of the stages, (3) detect parasitic oscillations and determine their frequency, (4) adjust shunt and series traps, (5) make antenna and transmission-line adjustments, (6) measure Q, inductance, and capacitance, (7) measure relative field strengths.

19 Radar System Testing and Power Measurement

In analyzing and maintaining a piece of radar equipment the average technician must first understand the fundamental principles: how radiated waves of electromagnetic energy can detect distant moving and stationary objects. In principle radar measures distance and direction by determining the elapsed time between the instant of transmitting a pulse or burst of radiated energy and the instant of echo reception from these same pulses as they return from the object. Figure 19–1 is a simplified block diagram explaining the basic radar principle. Radar testing therefore concerns: (1) transmitters, which generate and transmit pulses of energy outward from a movable antenna, (2) receivers, which amplify echoes of the reflected pulses as they arrive back through the original antenna, and (3) cathode-ray tube displays, which through their scanning mechanism indicate the presence, distance, and direction of the target reflecting the initiating pulses.

The use of the oscilloscope and a thorough knowledge of pulse techniques are particularly important in this type of measurement inasmuch as the scanning action in a cathode-ray tube gives measurable indications of the travel time of pulses sent out by the transmitter and of the reflected echoes. This indication of elapsed time is possible because the pulses travel at the speed of light, which is a constant known value. Also, most radars utilize a movable antenna which continually sweeps horizontally over selected angular sectors in order to locate targets in a definitely determined direction of the transmitted and reflected wave paths. Thus an angularly adjustable transmitting and receiving antenna can in effect "track" an object having a given bearing "azimuth" by positioning itself so that the strongest reflection is produced.

RADAR SYSTEMS

Figure 19–2 is a block diagram showing more detailed interrelationships of six basic parts of a radar system, which may be described as follows:

1. A *transmitter system*, which generates periodically interrupted or "pulsed" high-frequency energy—usually at microwave frequency. This includes a modulator for pulse generation and processing plus a UHF or a VHF transmitter for development of the ultimate power output.

2. An *antenna and positioning system* which radiates this energy at various bearings and angular positions into the atmosphere.

3. A *receiver*, which detects, amplifies, and processes the reflected echoes coming back from the target.

4. A *duplexer*, serving in effect as a switch, which automatically routes received antenna signals to the receiver after it has allowed

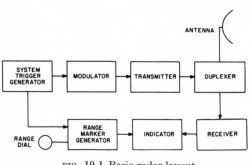

FIG. 19-1 Basic radar layout

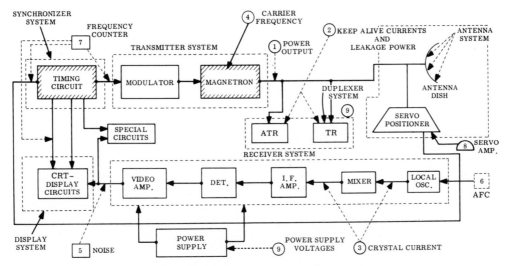

FIG. 19-2 Functional radar system showing measurement points

outgoing radiated energy to be transmitted from the same antenna.

5. A *display unit*, which is a visual means of showing, in terms of their distance and direction, the received echoes in the form of spots or "blips" of light appearing on the face of a cathode-ray tube.

6. A *synchronizer system*, which controls the original pulse timing and sends proper signals to the receiver and display system for the measurement of direction and distance.

The display allows an operator to watch spots or "blips" of light move (on the face of the cathode-ray tube) with respect to fixed calibrated distance circles and within angular markings showing calibrated azimuth.

SYSTEM CHARACTERISTICS AND KEY MEASUREMENTS

Figure 19–2 also shows key measurement points in a typical radar system giving details of a number of the interleaving functions. Discussion of these key points covers the full operation of basic radar equipment. Briefly, these monitoring points determine: (1) operational frequency of the transmitter carrier, (2) pulse power output, (3) receiver gain, selectivity, image rejection, etc., (4) synchronizer performance indicated by timing, gating, elapsed time intervals, and other miscellaneous dependent factors, (5) microwave performance of antenna and associated plumbing, (6) modulation characteristics, (7) receiver noise measurements and their effects on the overall performance, (8) display characteristics, (9) duplexer operation as indicated by TR and ATR leakage power and keep-alive currents.

DETAILS OF KEY MEASUREMENTS

In the following discussion of functional details and of related key measurements the respective paragraphs refer to encircled numbers on Fig. 19–2.

1. Power output at the magnetron. This test is a basic transmitter measurement and is described under microwave techniques and measurements.

2. TR leakage power and keep-alive currents. Measurement of switching-tube current is a specialized operation. A brief description of these tubes and details of checking them is given below.

3. Mixer crystal current furnishes a combined index of operation of the local receiver oscillator and the received signal. See radar receiver testing.

4. Carrier frequency. The frequency of the fundamental radiated energy is of vital

importance and must be continually monitored by a high-frequency wavemeter type of instrument as described in Chapter 12.

5. Noise. Overall operation of the echo receiver is usually indicated by noise measurement taken at the IF amplifier output. This is a complicated and vital measurement allied to receiver characteristics. Noise measurements are described under receiver testing.

6. AFC voltages. The direct-current voltage measurement of these circuits is a dynamic operating indication showing overall receiver performance.

7. Timing frequency. Frequency of the pulse, or repetition-rate timing as determined by the synchronizing circuits, is a measurement which directly determines the distance-measurement accuracy of the whole system. This procedure falls under counter techniques in frequency measurement. (See Chapter 12.) The source of these self-generated voltages and waveforms is in the *synchronizer* which is allied to both the modulating and the display system (Fig. 19–2).

8. Servo-amplifiers. Inasmuch as these amplifiers drive the antenna, its positioning accuracy is directly proportional to their operating efficiency. This type of testing is covered in Chapter 20.

9. Power-supply voltages. Since these values are applied to every section of a radar they are of primary importance. Some common measurements are listed below since no special techniques are involved. Power-supply design, however, is covered in Chapter 21.

POWER MEASUREMENT DEFINITIONS

PEAK PULSE POWER, AVERAGE PULSE POWER, AND DUTY CYCLE

Power measurements are classified as either peak pulse power or average pulse power. The usable transmitter output occurs at peak level, but most modern test methods measure the heating value of the RF energy, obtaining the average value. It is correct to use either value for reference as long as they are consistently defined. Frequently, it is necessary to convert from peak pulse power to average pulse power, or vice versa; therefore the relationship between the two must be understood.

The average-power-level axis presenting the actual heating value of typical pulse trains is at a height somewhere between the zero-axis level and the pulse peak value. It is defined and located as that level where the pulse area above its own average level equals the area that exists *between pulses* below the average axis.

More simply, if the pulse areas are evened off *above the measurement axis* in such a way as to fill in the space *between pulses below this axis*, its true level is then the average value, as shown in Fig. 19–3.

In the same figure, simple peak pulse power is proportional to the area of its width (in time) multiplied by its height (which is proportional to power). The area representing total *average power* is thus equal to the average pulse power level multiplied by the pulse period (t). Since we have, by definition, made the two areas equal, it is permissible to express the equation as follows:

(1)   pulse width × peak pulse
$$= \text{average pulse power} \times t$$

Transposing terms in the equation produces:

(2) $\dfrac{\text{average pulse power}}{\text{peak pulse power}} = \dfrac{\text{pulse width}}{t}$

and since $t = 1/PRF$, where PRF = pulse repetition frequency (per second), t = time between pulses,

(3) $\dfrac{\text{avg pulse power}}{\text{peak pulse power}} = \text{pulse width} \times PRF$

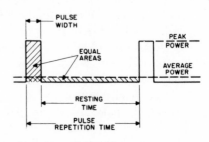

FIG. 19-3 Transmitter pulses showing peak and average power

DUTY CYCLE. From the above we see that a key relationship exists between pulse width and pulse occurrence (the time between pulses). This relationship is known as the *duty cycle* and is synonymous with the two expressions (2) and (3) above. This expression is also the ratio of average power to peak power and thus represents the degree of *usefulness* of a radar's transmission characteristic. It is also the percentage of time that effective pulse power, of voltage, or of current, is effectively "on."

EXAMPLE

If a certain radar has a pulse width of $\frac{1}{2}$ microsecond and a pulse recurrence frequency of 2,000 pulses per second, the duty cycle is $\frac{1}{2} \times (10^{-6}) \times 2,000$ or .001 (.1 percent). If the peak pulse power is 200 kw, the average pulse power is 200 kw $\times$ .001, or 200 watts, or if the pulse current is 10 amp, then the average pulse current is .01 amp.

Figure 19–4 is a nomograph for converting peak pulse power to average pulse power when an ideal square pulse is used.

RADAR SYSTEM TESTING

Any radar, regardless of the excellence of its component sections, is worthless unless, as a system, it performs functionally (1) to a high degree of accuracy and (2) with good legibility of display.

So far as performance goes, specific radar tests must concern: (1) the radiation of power out into the atmosphere, (2) switching input and output signals, (3) receiving and amplifying the echoes coming back from the target, and (4) displaying an accurate distance and azimuth presentation of the echo reflections on a suitable picture tube.

From a performance-measurement standpoint operation is dependent upon the following key quantities: (1) transmitter output pulse power, frequency, and spectrum content, (2) receiver sensitivity bandwidth for minimum detectable signal, (3) TR and receiver recovery time, (4) pulse timing, gating, and AFC efficiency.

The following description of radar system

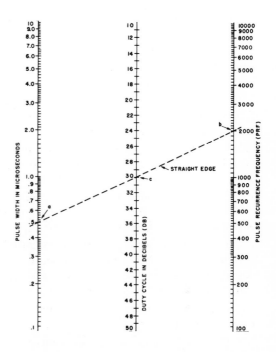

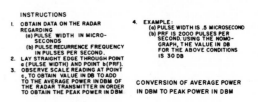

INSTRUCTIONS

1. OBTAIN DATA ON THE RADAR REGARDING
   (a) PULSE WIDTH IN MICROSECONDS
   (b) PULSE RECURRENCE FREQUENCY IN PULSES PER SECOND.
2. LAY STRAIGHT EDGE THROUGH POINT a (PULSE WIDTH) AND POINT b(PRF).
3. OBSERVE SCALE READING AT POINT c, TO OBTAIN VALUE IN DB TO ADD TO THE AVERAGE POWER IN DBM OF THE RADAR TRANSMITTER IN ORDER TO OBTAIN THE PEAK POWER IN DBM

4. EXAMPLE:
   (a) PULSE WIDTH IS .5 MICROSECOND
   (b) PRF IS 2000 PULSES PER SECOND. USING THE NOMOGRAPH, THE VALUE IN DB FOR THE ABOVE CONDITIONS IS 30 DB

CONVERSION OF AVERAGE POWER IN DBM TO PEAK POWER IN DBM

FIG. 19-4 Nomograph for duty cycle conversion

testing will be limited to the specialized procedures peculiar to good radar performance. Inasmuch as most of the basic radar components are common to other equipment, they must utilize and sometimes overlap similar procedures employed in routine tests and measurements applied to similar, generalized measurements on transmitters and receivers appearing in other sections.

TRANSMITTER TESTS

Transmitter output pulse power is a routine test applied to any pulse-modulated transmitter (see Chapter 18). Transmitter carrier-frequency stability is determined or measured the same way in all power transmitters; details appear in Chapter 12.

PULSE SPECTRUM ANALYSIS of a transmitted pulse is a special procedure which provides a wide range of information about a radar transmitter's output section, and particularly so in designs using an output magnetron. A spectrum analyzer, using an oscilloscope display samples the magnetron's output and in addition to rough power output indication, tells whether the shape of the output pulse has been properly preserved in the modulating process. More specifically, it tells whether the pulsed carrier contains unwanted amplitude or frequency modulation, whether its main frequency mode is jumping about or "double-moding," and whether the basic modulating pulse width has been affected. These measurements also indicate both the receiver band-width necessary to pass all frequency components generated in pulsing the output tube and stability data concerning the local oscillator frequency, since most spectrum analyzers have built-in frequency meters.

Figure 19–5(a) shows the block diagram of a spectrum analyzer, in effect a high-gain narrow-band panoramic receiver. In operation, a sawtooth generator operates on the receiver's local oscillator to produce a swept variable frequency, which is centered about that of the radar magnetron's output tuned circuitry.

The sawtooth acts simultaneously on the horizontal deflection plates of the built-in cathode-ray indicator so that receiver output over the swept range is synchronously displayed. A reaction-type frequency meter is usually coupled to the magnetron input so as to indicate local oscillator frequency.

A conventional spectral display in Fig. 19–5(b); shows typical amplitude distortion plus a frequency marker pip. The envelope of a similar display in Fig. 19–5(c) shows irregular side lobes due to combined FM and AM modulation. A normal display has symmetrical side lobes which are some 20 db below the amplitude of the main lobe.

Generally, the irregular side lobes in a spectral display are due to poor distribution of side-band frequencies which are generated during the pulse waveform modulation process. On the CRT display all of these simultaneously generated side bands show up as finely divided vertical lines filling in the main envelope area. The individual side-band lines are usually not distinguishable within the envelope and are spaced apart by the repetition frequency. When modulation is incorrect, or the magnetron defective, these side-band components produce the irregular spectral displays noted above.

Some common output and modulation troubles include: (1) defective magnetron, (2)

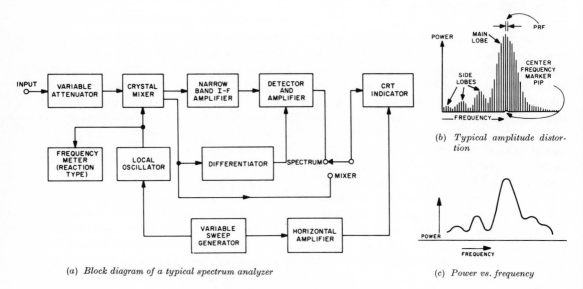

(a) Block diagram of a typical spectrum analyzer

(b) Typical amplitude distortion

(c) Power vs. frequency

FIG. 19-5 Spectrum analyzer and typical displays

defective magnet, (3) mismatch in modulator section, (4) improper pulse shape applied to modulator, (5) reflections from nearby objects, (6) improper klystron operating voltages, (7) poor input pulse transformer characteristics, and (8) mismatch of input impedance to klystron impedance.

RECEIVER SENSITIVITY AND BANDWIDTH

Microwave radar receivers are exceptionally high-sensitivity amplifiers utilizing overall gains in the range of 90 to 105 db. Being superheterodynes and usually employing IF's in the 30-mc or 60-mc range, the major portion of the overall amplification is in the IF amplifier which has been maximized to fit in with the noise limitations of the preamplifier, the crystal mixer, and the local oscillator.

Usable, realizable sensitivity, however, is solely dependent upon the ability of the combination of these three sections to pass recognizable signal through their inherent, self-generated noise; any increase of gain in the main IF amplifier following them (assuming its noise to be negligible) merely amplifies *both* noise and signal so that recognition of the signal is not improved.

Besides the noise produced by these three sections the electrical input circuits of the receiver itself also possess inherent or thermal noise which is readily calculable. This type of noise is called "thermal" because it is due to the heat-dependent, molecular agitation within the very substance of the resistive material within the input circuitry itself. Any resistor, for instance, has a directly measurable and calculable noise voltage existing across its terminals. Since it is an inherent characteristic, input noise (exclusive of noise picked up from space, static, and so on) is proportional to the effective resistive impedance existing across the antenna terminals.

Inherent input noise is random in nature; that is, it generates measurable voltages at *all* alternating current frequencies. Consequently, for comparison it must be measured over a specified bandwidth of frequencies. These voltages also depend upon the operating temperature of the resistance so that inherent

noise power (usually in microwatts) when calculated must assume some particular temperature; normally, 25°C. is used. In a receiver "head-end," total measured noise includes the three sources stated above.

THE NOISE FACTOR (NF) of a receiver equals ten times the ratio of the logarithms of the measured receiver noise power to the calculated thermal noise power. The following is an example of a typical calculation taken at 40°C. with a receiver with a bandwidth of 6 mc.

The thermal noise power (in watts) across any resistance may be stated as

$$P_n = 4 \times K \times T \times F$$

where K is Boltzmann's constant (1.37×10^{-23}), T is absolute temperature (degrees Kelvin = degrees centigrade plus 273), and F is the bandwidth (cps).

In our example,

$$P_n = 4 \times (1.37 \times 10^{-23}) \times (40 + 273)$$
$$\times (6 \times 10^6)$$
$$= .06423 \text{ micromicrowatts}$$

P_n for the receiver in question measured $.82 \times 10^{-12}$ watts.

$$NF = 10 \log 10 \frac{P_m}{P_n}$$
$$= 12 \text{ db}$$

The above method is a standard calculation and may be applied to any type of receiver. Seven- to 12-db noise figures are common in many radars; in communication or TV receivers operated at lower frequencies the figure may be under 5 db.

THE MINIMUM DISCERNIBLE SIGNAL

In most radars the pulse transmission feature gives rise to a direct noise measurement that is more applicable to performance and indirectly linked to the true measured noise figure. This is the *minimum discernible signal* (*MDS*) measurement, which, in brief, measures the ability of a receiver on its display to distinguish or discern a pulse above and over the noise voltages existing on the same display.

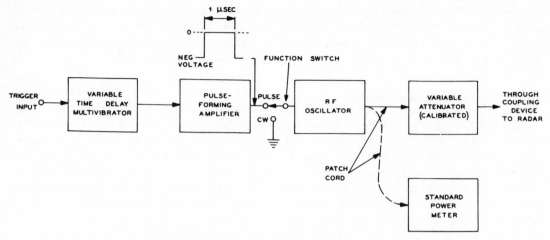

FIG. 19-6 Pulsed RF signal generator for MDS measurement

The MDS is readily measured on the "A" scope —which is a common adjunct to most PPI radar or other types of display.

The method calls for using a pulse RF signal generator (see Fig. 19–6) in which the general procedure is to apply the transmitter's main "bang" pulse to a variable, start-stop multivibrator which in turn triggers a pulse-forming amplifier suitably arranged to modulate the oscillator of an RF signal generator. This results, in effect, in the production of a controlled and variable, delayed pulse which modulates the signal generator. This pulse produces an *artificial echo* which can be positioned and adjusted in amplitude.

Details of the measurement consist of the following steps:

1. Apply transmitter main bang pulse output to the input of the overall signal generator.

2. Apply calibrated signal-generator attenuator output (c-w switch position) through a suitable coupling device to produce pickup antenna input.

3. Using the c-w mode of operation *tune* the RF oscillator to the radar receiver frequency.

4. Adjust the receiver gain (using low c-w input) to produce a moderate noise output on the "A" scope.

5. Set the RF oscillator output to 1 milliwatt by means of the *uncalibrated* attenuator using the thermistor bridge power meter.

6. Apply pulsed output to the receiver input and position the artificial echo pulse in a clear space on the noise area of the display.

7. Attenuate the pulse signal, reducing the displayed echo until it is just visible above the noise.

8. The total MDS is the reading on the calibrated attenuator plus zero attenuation loss, plus cable loss, plus space loss between the signal-generator output and the pickup antenna.

RECEIVER BANDWIDTH AND MDS MEASUREMENTS USING AN FM SIGNAL GENERATOR

An FM, RF signal generator presents a number of advantages over the usual pulsed-signal generator used in radar receiver measurements. It overcomes the main problem that arises with the use of pulse modulation—that of accurately tuning the signal generator to the receiver frequency. By using a periodically swept RF oscillator centered about the radar frequency, and by triggering by the "main bang" pulse, the receiver response is automatic at its tuned frequency. In addition, its output is displayed as an artificial echo.

Figure 19–7(a) is the basic block diagram of an FM signal generator showing connection of the transmitter triggering pulse followed by feeding of the sawtooth sweep-generator output to the RF oscillator. The remainder of the signal generator is identical to the pulsed type. The sawtooth sweep voltage, lasting for about 50 microseconds, is linear; it is controlled by a signal-width control which determines the amplitude of the sawtooth voltage and a phase control which determines the level at which the voltage is applied to the klystron RF oscillator's repeller, thus fixing the operating point of the swept frequency.

Figure 19–7(b) shows how the transmitter pulse triggers the sweeping sawtooth voltage waveform, which in turn varies the receiver input frequency over its passband. Observing the receiver's output scope display we, in effect, plot receiver output versus the periodic sweeping frequency, and obtain a pulse very similar to the simulated artificial echo referred to above.

The width of the simulated pulse depends upon the receiver bandwidth and the rate at which the signal frequency is swept. For example, if the receiver bandwidth is 10 mc and the signal-generator frequency is swept at the rate of 10 mc per microsecond (the slope of the RF sawtooth) the signal will be within the receiver passband for only one microsecond and we shall have displayed a one-

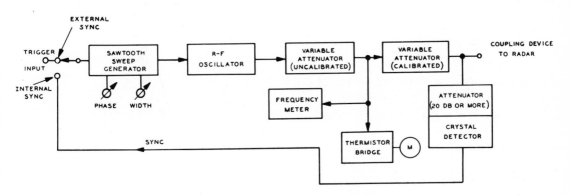

(a) *Basic block diagram for FM signal generator*

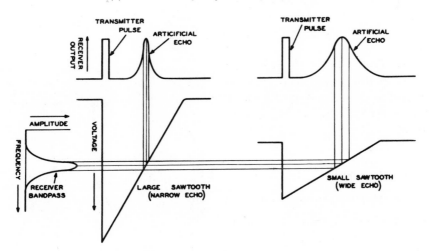

(b) *Sawtooth sweep in simulation of artificial echo*

FIG. 19-7 FM signal generator and pulse testing

microsecond pulse. The illustration shows how sawtooth sweeping voltage which is regulated by the width control delivers a wider and smaller pulse. By varying the phase control we can position the simulated, echo-like response to the desired range with respect to the trigger pulse.

With an FM signal generator, MDS and recovery-time measurements are conducted in the same way as with a pulsed-signal generator. Of course, care must be taken to maintain the correct pulse width (usually the echo pulse is adjusted to the width of the transmitter pulse) and to use correct amplitude control so that spurious modes of RF klystron operation do not occur.

RECEIVER BANDWIDTH MEASUREMENT

This measurement set-up and a typical resonance curve (with frequency marker) is shown in Fig. 19–8(a)(b). Receiver bandwidth (in kc, mc, etc.) is the frequency spread between the half-power points on its frequency response curve. During the conventional MDS measurement, if at readable oscilloscope response display, we couple in the absorptive effect of a frequency meter and observe the resultant pip, frequencies may be compared at these points on the curve; bandwidth is simply the difference between frequencies at the two settings.

In the scope display of Fig. 19–8(c), bandwidth is the frequency difference between points A and B as determined by the marker pip when it coincides with the 70.7 percent response point.

RECOVERY TIME MEASUREMENT

COMBINED TR AND RECEIVER RECOVERY TIME

A number of factors can limit the minimum range of a radar. For instance, if the TR switching action is slow—in other words, if the TR tube takes too much time to de-ionize—a short-range echo may arrive too soon after the main "bang" transmitter pulse and

consequently not be displayed before the receiver has become unblocked. Again, unblocking is also dependent upon receiver recovery time and on receiver sensitivity.

Before discussing details of receiver and TR circuitry, note that both measurements can be combined into an overall recovery time (see Fig. 19–9(b)) which can be defined as

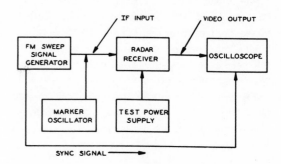

(a) *Test set-up for receiver bandwidth measurement*

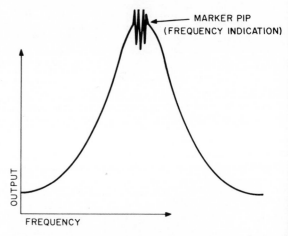

(b) *Response marker pip at mid-frequency point*

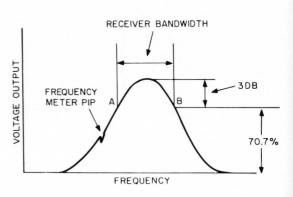

(c) *Receiver response curve*

FIG. 19-8 Receiver bandwidth measurements

the total interval following the transmitter pulse until the receiver has returned to within about 6 db of normal sensitivity (some specifications call for 3 db). In various radar sets this may vary from 2 to 10 microseconds.

DETAILED TR TUBE RECOVERY MEASUREMENTS

The useful life of a tube, as indicated by its recovery time, may be measured by receiver sensitivity procedures or indirectly by the condition of its keep-alive current. This current is deliberately passed through a tube by applying a small voltage which is just enough to maintain partial ionization and thus insure proper firing. It so happens that the magnitude of the keep-alive current is directly proportional to the recovery time, so that any increase should be a warning that the tube must be replaced.

In particular, *TR recovery time* is most simply

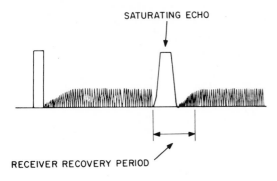

SATURATING ECHO

RECEIVER RECOVERY PERIOD

(a) *Display for total receiver recovery time*

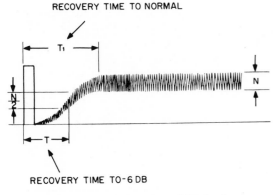

RECOVERY TIME TO NORMAL

T_1

N

$\frac{N}{2}$

T

RECOVERY TIME TO -6 DB

(b) *TR recovery time display using a C-W signal*

FIG. 19-9 TR tube and overall receiver recovery time measurement displays

measured by using a c-w signal generator. The procedure is to:

1. Adjust the receiver gain to a minimum amount of noise on the dispay—say $\frac{1}{4}$ inch on the "A" scope.

2. Apply the signal-generator output (modulated by the transmitter main bang pulse) to the antenna input coupling device and tune to the receiver frequency.

3. Adjust the signal-generator output attenuator until the transmitter pulse just barely produces receiver saturation.

4. The display will appear as in Fig. 19–9(a), showing the signal recovery slope between the main bang and normal "between pulse" noise.

5. Measure recovery time as the distance in microseconds from the start of the main bang pulse to the *midpoint* of the recovery-time slope. This halfway point (6 db) is the reference level for recovery-time measurements.

In using a signal generator with simulated echo provisions the TR recovery time is obtained by measuring the effective *transmission* time difference between the front edge of the main bang pulse and the point at which the echo pulse (when moved by the generator phase control) has been reduced 2:1 (6 db) by the recovery effects of the TR tube.

RECEIVER RECOVERY TIME

The determination of overall receiver recovery time utilizes receiver sensitivity measurements based on the MDS procedure described earlier in this chapter. The general procedure is to use a signal generator by comparing the c-w noise response and the pulse-modulated response of a receiver under high gain adjustment when using signals modulated by an *adjustable artificial echo*.

Recovery measurements in greater detail are shown in the block diagram of Fig. 19–7.

The procedure calls for first applying a calibrated unmodulated (c-w) signal to a receiver and TR system as follows:

1. Adjusting and observing noise response on the receiver for barely usable high gain for this input.

2. Modulating the carrier with the trigger plus the artificial echo until pulse input is reduced by a calibrated attenuator.

3. Attenuating the pulse input and measuring when the pulse is just observable above the noise. This is a brief procedure for the minimum discernible noise measurement described later on.

Finally, the artificial echo is adjusted for saturation (see Fig. 19–9(b)) and moved to some point on the display that is free of other echoes or reflections.

The receiver recovery time (distance T) is distance in microseconds from the start of the echo pulse to the average c-w noise level.

OVERALL SYSTEM TESTING TECHNIQUES

Overall a radar system must fundamentally (1) possess accurate range characteristics, and (2) deliver to the antenna all possible power that the output magnetron indicates that it is generating. Therefore, independently over and above all the other normally inherent characteristics of total specified power, expected sensitivity, and adequate legible display, we are concerned with the factor of range measurement and voltage standing-wave ratio (VSWR). These two characteristics are dependent upon the correct electrical assembly of the basic radar-system building blocks. In brief, they form the framework of overall performance, not apparent in subsystem characteristics: they must be measured and determined on the system operating as a whole.

RANGE MEASUREMENT

The accuracy of distance measurement depends upon full knowledge and compensation for the delays in a radar system. The transmitted pulse is subject to many of these, all of which must be accounted for in range calibration. These delays occur: (1) in the modulator, where the output pulse occurs later than the trigger pulse, (2) in the output magnetron, where the output pulse requires time to build up after application of the modulator pulse, (3) in the microwave plumbing system, where the transmitted pulse must travel from the magnetron to the antenna dish and the receiver pulse must travel from the dish back to the receiver terminals, (4) in the receiver, where the acquired pulse must thread its way through the various amplifier, detection, and conversion sections up to the display tube.

These delays may show up as discrepancies of several hundred yards when the range indication shows zero; therefore, they are labeled *zero errors*.

ZERO ERRORS. Delays making up zero error may be determined by four measurement techniques using: (1) a fixed target, (2) double echoes from multiple reflections, (3) an external range calibrator, (4) a synchroscope.

FIXED-TARGET REFLECTIONS may be obtained from a good reflecting structure such as a steel building, a metal tower, or gas tanks, whose distance has been accurately determined by surveyors or optical range-finding instruments. Portable reflectors may be more convenient in some cases.

The indicated range should be greater than the actual known range, the difference being the zero error.

DOUBLE ECHOES produced by a pair of targets with suitable reflective properties, both within the range of a *single sweep* distance of a radar scan provide a convenient means for measuring zero errors. (See Fig. 19–10.) If the true distance *between the two targets A and B* is known (checked by optical or surveying instruments) and since echoes from both include the same zero errors we may use the known range

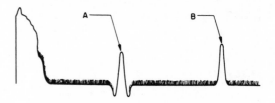

FIG. 19-10 Zero error by double echo display

and compare it to the indicated range for determining zero error (See Fig. 19–9). We determine the actual zero error physically by slipping the range-counter mechanism enough to compensate for it (in yards) as determined by the distance apart (in yards) of the known targets.

EXTERNAL RANGE CALIBRATORS produce accurate, crystal-controlled markers, (on the scope display) which can be coupled into the range-indicator marker amplifiers and used to adjust the calibration circuits of the unit under test. Adjustable delays and convenient calibrator trigger pulses make it simple to synchronize range-indicator distances to the true distance markers generated on the calibrator.

THE SYNCHROSCOPE (see detailed description in Chapter 13) utilizes accurately calibrated and triggered linear sweeps to establish true range. By observation and comparison of received targets on the calibrated synchroscope sweep, and with sweeps triggered by the range-indicator marker circuits, zero error can be measured and compensated for by adjustment on the various ranges in the range-marker circuitry.

STANDING-WAVE RATIO, when viewed solely as a microwave measurement technique, may logically belong in Chapter 16, but as a vital quantity related to transmitter output efficacy it will be discussed in condensed form at this point.

As an index of mismatch in the entire transmission system this ratio is primarily indicative of losses between the magnetron and the antenna. In addition, however, it gives many other valuable facts:

1. It may indicate the cause of magnetron pulling.

2. It gives a key to arc-over in the RF line which may occur at points of maximum voltage.

3. It can indicate the existence of mistuned or mismatched elements connected with the TR and ATR switches.

4. It keys investigation of dirt or moisture in the RF transmission line.

5. It shows up dented or bent transmission lines or elements.

6. Burrs, poor joints or connections, and faulty grounds produce high VSWR's.

7. Mismatch of the antenna is a major VSWR indication.

VSWR TESTING. The key equipment in this measurement is the slotted line, which, as seen in Chapter 16, is a coaxial or waveguide section of transmission line, at least a wavelength long and having a longitudinal slot cut in its outer conductor which permits insertion of an RF probe anywhere over the length of the waveguide. Positioning the probe and sampling energy picked up by it permits exploration of the voltage field existing within the waveguide and gives a direct index of reflections, mismatch, and other valuable quantities. Impedance relationships can be determined by using marked and calibrated positions of the probe so that voltage maximum can be related to wavelength dimensions.

Most radars have a permanently built-in slotted line tailored for minimum losses and mismatch. If no slotted line is provided one should be inserted (using adapters) in the transmission line as near the magnetron as possible. With the RF probe properly adjusted for penetration within the waveguide and its output connected to a probe amplifier, the simplest approach is to observe maximum and minimum voltage points as they are encountered by moving the probe through its normal travel. When the ratio of these maximum to minimum points becomes unity, the system has attained perfect match or the VSWR = 1. Excessively high VSWR's (1.5:1 or higher) indicate that adjustment must be made in the stubs or in any of the areas mentioned above.

Slotted-line measurements can contribute information on many more factors than just impedance mismatch; they permit measurement of impedances (the amount of mismatch), they give an indirect method of calculating power, and they indicate physical location of possible failures or mismatches in a system.

DIRECTIONAL-COUPLER AND MAGIC-T TESTING METHODS. VSWR can be calculated from measurements taken with a directional coupler. This somewhat inaccurate method compares the incident power to the reflected power (with the coupler reversed).

Using a bidirectional coupler, consisting of two directional couplers mounted on the same line, no reversing is needed and rapid direct readings of both transmitted and reflected power can be made with good accuracy. Details of these components and measuring techniques are covered in Chapter 16. The magic-T coupler next described is, however, a specialized device warranting discussion here.

The magic-T is a special type of directional coupler, using three-dimensional construction, arranged so that polarization effects can be used to isolate specific measurement quantities. Figure 19–11 shows four waveguides in a typical arrangement which couples arm *A* to *B* and *C* (independent of *D*) and couples *D* to *B* and *C* (independent of *A*). No power interchange occurs between *A* and *D* *unless there are reflections*.

The procedure consists of applying power through a matched signal generator to arm *A* and inserting an *RF* detector in arm *D*. With

arm *C* matched to a load and absorbing all the generator power, when the device being tested at *B* is correctly matched no indication appears at *D*. With mismatch of the unit attached to *C*, reflections appear back at the waveguide junction and deliver output to *D*. VSWR then becomes a comparison of the power in arm *A* compared to that in arm *D*.

SYSTEM TESTING EQUIPMENT

In addition to the components used in microwave measurements such as bolometers, couplers, and loads (see Chapter 16), radar microwave testing uses a number of handy adjuncts peculiar to this type of transmission. They are: (1) the echo box, (2) the resonant cavity, (3) the cavity resonator, (4) microwave filter and tunable stubs.

THE ECHO BOX

The echo box is a type of resonant cavity or chamber. (See Fig. 19–12(a).) It is tuned by a calibrated plunger and tuning dial to the radar frequency being used and is coupled to radar energy by a pickup dipole or coaxial horn placed in the radiation field. The functional set-up is shown in Fig. 19–12(b). Actuating energy can also be extracted by a cable suitably connected in on a directional coupler. For indication of relative power measurements an output meter consisting of a crystal and a microammeter is used, and an attenuator is usually included in the instrument set-up (Fig. 19–12(c)).

The operation depends upon signal to the radar receiver *sent back* by the *tail end of* the energy envelope generated by continued resonant oscillations (ringing) of the box after it has been excited by the main bang pulse. (See Fig. 19–12(d).) This ringing time extends for yards (or microseconds) past the main bang and produces an envelope on the "A" scope from which information can be gathered. (See Fig. 19–12(e).) Equivalent waveform configurations are also obtainable on the "J" scope and on a PPI.

Echo-box indications are purely relative and

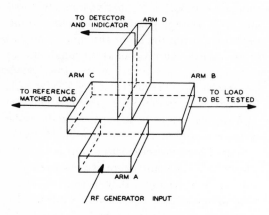

FIG. 19-11 Magic-T directional coupler assembly

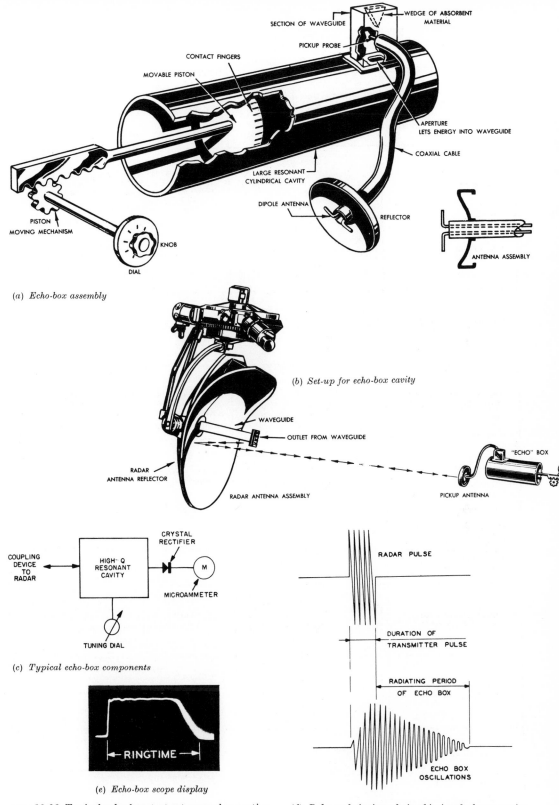

SECTION OF WAVEGUIDE

WEDGE OF ABSORBENT MATERIAL

PICKUP PROBE

CONTACT FINGERS

MOVABLE PISTON

APERTURE LETS ENERGY INTO WAVEGUIDE

COAXIAL CABLE

LARGE RESONANT CYLINDRICAL CAVITY

DIPOLE ANTENNA

REFLECTOR

ANTENNA ASSEMBLY

PISTON MOVING MECHANISM

KNOB

DIAL

(a) *Echo-box assembly*

(b) *Set-up for echo-box cavity*

WAVEGUIDE

OUTLET FROM WAVEGUIDE

RADAR ANTENNA REFLECTOR

RADAR ANTENNA ASSEMBLY

"ECHO" BOX

PICKUP ANTENNA

CRYSTAL RECTIFIER

COUPLING DEVICE TO RADAR

HIGH-Q RESONANT CAVITY

M

MICROAMMETER

TUNING DIAL

(c) *Typical echo-box components*

RADAR PULSE

DURATION OF TRANSMITTER PULSE

RADIATING PERIOD OF ECHO BOX

ECHO BOX OSCILLATIONS

RINGTIME

(e) *Echo-box scope display*

FIG. 19-12 Typical echo-box test set-up and operation

(d) *Pulse and ringing relationship in echo-box operation*

313

EFFECT	APPEARANCE ON		PROBABLE CAUSE
	RADAR INDICATOR	ECHO BOX METER	
RINGTIME AND TEST SET OUTPUT SATISFACTORY			RADAR PERFORMANCE SATISFACTORY
RINGTIME LOW, OUTPUT READING SATISFACTORY			RECEIVER TROUBLE: DETUNED MIXER OR LOCAL OSCILLATOR, BAD CRYSTAL, EXCESSIVE I-F NOISE, ADJUSTMENT OF PROBES IN MIXER CAVITY. DETUNED T-R BOX.
RINGTIME LOW, TEST SET OUTPUT VERY LOW.			LOW POWER OUTPUT. CHECK SPECTRUM.
RINGTIME LOW, TEST SET METER READING LOW.			TROUBLE PROBABLY IN TRANSMITTER AND RECEIVER AND/OR TROUBLE IN TRANSMISSION LINE.
RINGTIME ERRATIC, TEST SET METER READING STEADY.			TEST SET DETUNED. BAD PULSING, DOUBLE MODING TRANSMITTER, OR LOCAL OSCILLATOR POWER SUPPLY TROUBLE. CHECK SPECTRUM.
RINGTIME ERRATIC, TEST SET OUTPUT READING ERRATIC.			FAULTY TRANSMISSION LINE OR CONNECTION — CONDITION WORSE WHEN LINE IS RAPPED
END OF RINGTIME SLOPES GRADUALLY, PERHAPS EVEN EXCESSIVE RINGING. GRASS APPEARS COURSE. TEST SET OUTPUT READING STEADY AND SATISFACTORY.			OSCILLATING I-F AND/OR NARROW BAND RECEIVER.
PRONOUNCED DIP IN RINGTIME AT END OF PULSE.			FAULTY TR OR DUE TO RECEIVER GATING ACTION
RINGTIME VERY SLIGHTLY LOW, POOR OR BAD SPECTRUM.		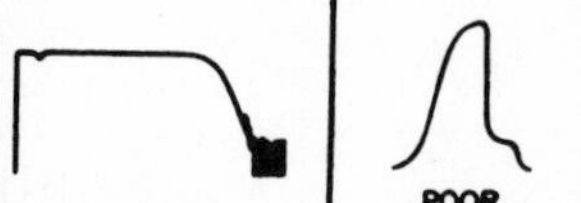 POOR SPECTRUM	TRANSMITTER TROUBLE.
BLANK SPACES OR ROUGH PATTERN ON PPI RINGTIME INDICATOR, TEST SET OUTPUT READING VARIES AS RADAR ANTENNA IS ROTATED.			FREQUENCY PULLING OF TRANSMITTER DUE TO BAD ROTATING JOINT OR TO REFLECTING OBJECT NEAR RADAR ANTENNA.

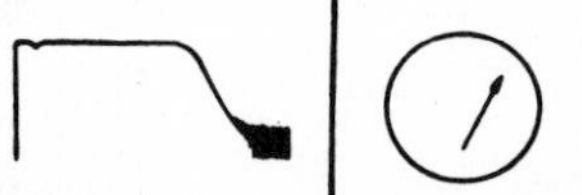

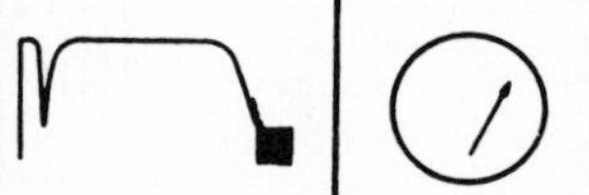

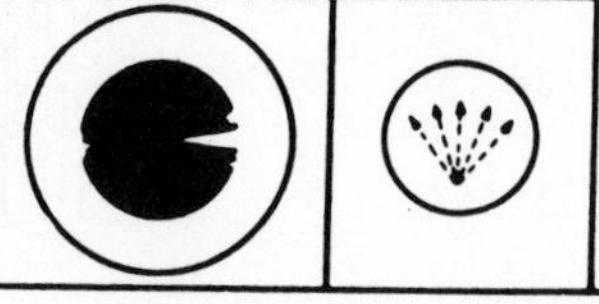

FIG. 19-13 Echo-box trouble indications

for comparison measurements must be made with the same connections, couplings, etc. Correctly used, however, an echo box is a simple way of checking peak transmitter power, receiver sensitivity, recovery time, and spectrum analysis.

All measurements with the echo box are a combination of the ringing time (see distance T in Fig. 19–12(e)) and the power output meter. Various combinations of these as given in Fig. 19–13 indicate specific trouble symptoms. We might say in general that echo-box readings can generally separate transmitter troubles from receiver failure. The former are indicated by low-power meter readings, the latter by reduced ringing time.

An echo box's ringing time is generally correlated with the sensitivity of a particular system in terms of ringing-time difference per db change in sensitivity. A common figure of this nature is about 100 yards per db. Thus if a radar has lost 1,000 yards of ringing time, its sensitivity has decreased about 10 db.

RADAR POWER MEASUREMENTS

Power measurements on a radar are, for the most part, taken at relatively low levels compared to its transmitter's full capabilities. In other words, devices for sampling the normal maximum power flow are used; these devices divert for measurement proportional amounts of the total power through an accurately calibrated attenuator, a directional coupler, or through a space-calibrated device such as the pickup antenna. Description of these measurement, merely supplements the general description and low-power approach used in Chapter 18.

Power measurements using sampling methods may be divided into those using heat as a sensing factor and those using direct measurement of the radar pulse characteristics—that is, the height, width, and repetition rate.

In heat-sampling measurements output indicators use the thermistor as the actuating element in one circuit form or another; in direct sampling we use crystal rectification and measurement of the radar's pulse characteristics by means of a synchroscope.

CALIBRATION

Occasionally, however, it is necessary for calibration purposes to accurately determine the actual total power being generated by a particular transmitter. In principle the methods and techniques are described under transmitter power testing in Chapter 18. A refinement of the water-load method is given in the following explanation since it describes some details of the physical relationship in a typical radar microwave system.

Figure 19–14 is a block arrangement of a typical water-load power-measurement system. By correctly proportioning the terminating waveguide to form a non-reflecting load and circulating water through it the total system power absorbed in the circulating water can be measured as follows.

If we measure the input and output temperatures of the circulating water and know the rate of water flow, the total power absorbed can be easily calculated:

$$\text{power (in watts)} = 4.18m \times C_p \times t$$

where m = water flow in grams per second,

C = specific heat of water in calories/ gram °C.,

T = input and output temperature differences, °C.

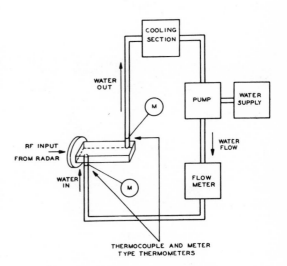

FIG. 19-14 Water-load power test measurement set-up

By comparing the absolute power reading this method yields with other sampling methods described further on, we may calibrate the thermistor bridge, attenuator, or coupler.

THERMISTOR POWER MEASUREMENTS

In microwave measurements a thermistor used to terminate a transmission line offers a convenient way to measure transmitted power. Waveguide power converted into heat when absorbed in the terminating element produces a measureable change in the thermistor's resistance.

Figure 19–15(a) shows two types of thermistors in current use. We may broadly classify them as: (1) the disc type, which is used more often for temperature compensation, and (2) the bead type, which is used exclusively for measurements.

In the bead type the active material located at the junction of two fine wires is in the form of a very small encapsulated bead. The unit is supported by heavy pigtail leads imbedded in the glass capsule which provide external electrical connections. The fine inner wires, which support the bead inside the capsule, are small enough to prevent significant heat from being carried away from the bead by thermal conduction. In addition, the bead's size prevents high-frequency skin effect from causing resistance errors because RF current flow can penetrate to the center material. Bead resistance varies with temperature from about 10 to about 1,000 ohms, centering about common radar waveguide impedances.

SIMPLE THERMISTOR POWER METER

The power-measurement arrangement shown in Fig. 19–15(b) uses the thermistor mounted in one of the legs of a "T" terminating stub

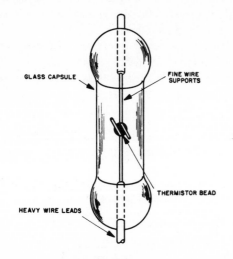

Bead type

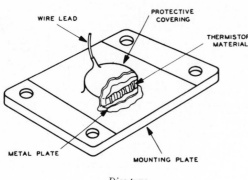

Disc type

(a) *Typical thermistors*

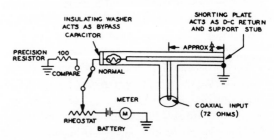

(b) *Simplified diagram of thermistor power meter*

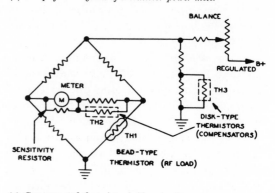

(c) *Compensated thermistor bridge circuit*

FIG. 19-15 Types of thermistors and power measurement set-ups

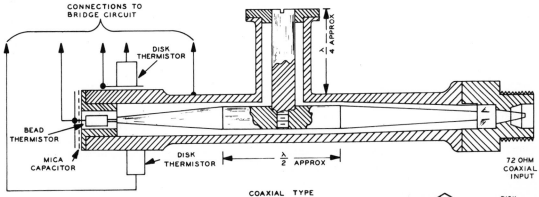

COAXIAL TYPE

located at the end of the coaxial line from which power is sampled. One short-circuited, quarter-wave stub serves as a d-c path for the thermistor current while the other end uses the thermistor as a load in series with the center conductor. The low end of the thermistor is brought out through an insulating washer that acts as a short circuit to radio frequencies but which allows direct current to flow. The thermistor resistance of 100 ohms provides an impedance match in order to absorb full transmitted power. A precision 100-ohm resistor can be switched in and out to provide a comparison load impedance to check the thermistor's value under mean operating conditions. Measurements are made by comparison of meter readings.

In using this set-up the rheostat is adjusted until the meter indicates the same current for the thermistor under various power input conditions as for the 100-ohm resistor. In other words, the comparison switch should produce equal currents in either position. Note that this adjustment allows for calibration at different ambient operating temperatures.

THERMISTOR BRIDGE

The thermistor bridge provides an indirect method of power measurement with good accuracy and with provision for temperature compensation. The compensated thermistor-bridge circuit, shown in Fig. 19–15(c), incorporates a Wheatstone arrangement, three of whose legs are precision resistors, the fourth being a bead-type thermistor. When the

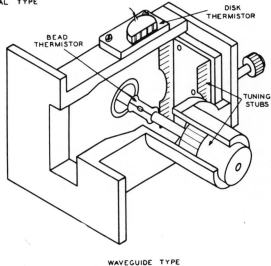

WAVEGUIDE TYPE

FIG. 19-16 Construction of waveguide thermistor mounts

bridge is balanced the latter acts as a matched load for a particular RF line being measured. Two temperature-compensating disc-type thermistors function by being mounted in thermal contact with the section of the RF line containing the bead thermistor. Figure 19–16 shows the construction of the coaxial and the waveguide types of thermistor mounts.

In actual testing the bridge is adjusted through the balancing potentiometer by electrically setting the output meter to a point where one milliwatt of RF power will produce zero meter current. A zero-centered type meter is used, with a factory-adjusted sensing resistor arranged so that with full-scale meter reading one milliwatt of RF power is required to restore the reading to mid-scale. Thermistor bridges measure only the average power level,

317

owing to the thermal time lag of the sensing element which is in turn a function of the slow rate of thermistor resistance change. Since heat transfer is a relatively slow process, the time required for an appreciable resistance change is great compared to the period between pulses in the average radar. Measurements must thus include a great number of radar pulses in order to give stabilized readings over a period of minutes. Erratic or sudden variations in power level occur too rapidly to be detected by the thermistor bridge.

THERMISTOR BRIDGE TEMPERATURE COMPENSATION is necessary: (1) bridge balance must be maintained at all ambient temperatures; (2) indicating sensitivity must remain constant under varying temperature conditions. In Fig. 19–15(c) the thermistor TH_1 together with its associated resistors compensates for any unbalance due to temperature variation; TH_2 compensates for temperature effects on sensitivity.

Considering TH_1 as the ambient temperature rises and with no compensation, an unbalanced condition occurs since the resistance of the bead thermistor drops. With compensation, however, the resistance of TH_1 also decreases, causing a reduction in the d-c voltage applied to the bridge. This in turn reduces d-c bridge power, causing the resistance of the bead thermistor to return to normal and thus maintain bridge balance. Since RF is applied only to the bead thermistor, compensation does not depend upon RF power.

At high ambient temperatures without compensation the value of d-c applied to the

bridge is low, resulting in reduced bridge sensitivity. Compensation at high temperatures provided by TH_2 (effectively in series with the indicating meter) restores bridge sensitivity since TH_2 presents a lower series resistance to the meter and allows more current to flow.

CRYSTAL-SYNCHROSCOPE POWER MEASUREMENTS

Power measurements center around the crystal-detector sampling and attenuation techniques described under microwave components (Chapter 16). The actual measurements typified in Fig. 19–17 are made by a crystal-synchroscope set-up following attenuation of the sampled power through a pickup antenna and a calibrated attenuator.

The crystal (suitably mounted in a matched stub built into the attenuator output) rectifies or detects the RF pulse envelopes and converts them into video pulses which are replicas of the transmitter output power. The peak transmitter power is thus simulated by the pulse height, repetition rate, and its width and shape when they are directly examined on a synchroscope.

Knowing these characteristics and the total attenuation existing in the pickup antenna (space loss), in the antenna cable, and knowing the attenuator zero loss and the actual indicated attenuator loss, we can calculate the actual radar output power. The synchroscope is, of course, the key measurement device in the above procedure since it permits the examination of all details of pulse characteristics.

THE SYNCHROSCOPE

The synchroscope widely used in radar testing is a triggered-sweep oscilloscope producing a trace only upon initiation by an input trigger. As contrasted with the continuous sawtooth sweep provided in old-style oscilloscopes, synchroscope circuits are otherwise similar except for the signal channel and the sweep channel. A typical triggered-sweep synchroscope is shown in block diagram form in Fig. 19–18. Triggered-sweep oscilloscopes

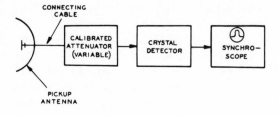

FIG. 19-17 Crystal-synchroscope set-up for power measurements

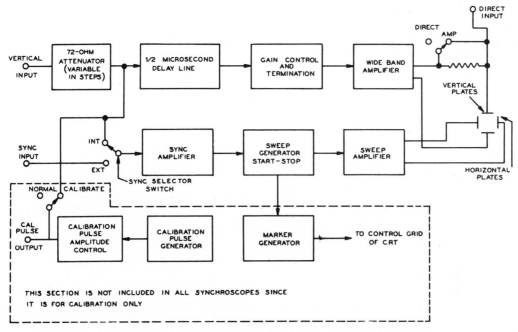

FIG. 19-18 Block diagram of a typical triggered-sweep synchroscope

have three outstanding advantages: (1) they permit exact examination of the input pulse; (2) they are useful in displaying nonperiodic pulses; (3) they can provide a wide range of sweep speeds not possible with the conventional oscilloscope. The signal-channel input circuit is usually in the form of a 72-ohm adjustable-step attenuator. Its function is to ensure that all signals, regardless of amplitude, deliver about the same input level to the vertical amplifier. The artificial delay line following the attenuator delays the signal under observation until the sweep trace is under way, since it also has been triggered by the input signal. This line is a low-pass filter with a cut-off frequency higher than the highest video frequency to be passed; it has an input and output impedance of 72 ohms. If the delay line were not used, the initial portion of the displayed waveform might not appear on the trace if too much time were required before the input signal voltage could rise to the level needed to trigger the sweep circuits. Modern oscilloscopes with triggered

sweeps use a variable, manually adjustable delay line arranged so that the signal can be positioned on the display to meet various conditions that may be encountered in the triggering pulse.

The delay line can also provide means for self-calibration. If reflections are deliberately induced by mismatch in the line termination, a series of accurately spaced pulses appear which provide sweep marker points.

The synchroscope provides horizontal sweep circuits with a sync switch for either internal or external sync, the usual sync amplifier, and a gain control in order to control the start-stop sweep generator when it is fed triggering pulses. Amplifier control circuits have calibration provisions including a sweep time marker generator plus auxiliary circuits which are similar to those in conventional oscilloscopes. Variable sweep speeds are also provided ranging from a very few microseconds to about 250 microseconds. Further description of the synchroscope-type oscilloscope is given in Chapter 13.

20 Synchros and Servomechanism Testing

The material in this chapter deliberately emphasizes the characteristics and testing of *synchros*, since they constitute the main building blocks within any servo system and since they also provide the major portion of the control function actuating a mechanical system. Factual, tabulated data are supplemented by simplified textual information concerning overall servo systems. Typical descriptions include variations in error-detecting circuits, voltage and power amplifiers, testing and trouble-shooting techniques, etc.

A servomechanism or servo is an angularly controlled, power-driven, electronic-mechanical system. (See Fig. 20–1.) To transmit, control, and convert the flow of power it employs synchros, electronic control circuits, electronic voltage amplifiers, servo power amplifiers, and finally, servo motors. Functionally, since most servos are angularly oriented their outputs are mostly derived from motor or rotational power. Purely mechanical servos do exist, however. They may consist of gear trains, levers, valves, pumps, or the like, all basically functioning in exactly analogous manner to their electronic counterparts and all being, of course, directly linked and servoed to a mechanical load. Electrical systems, although more complex, generally afford greater flexibility, higher-speed operation, and the potentiality of greater precision.

Briefly, a basic servo system consists of: (1) low-power, error-detecting circuitry chiefly handling small voltages, (2) the synchro devices (usually a pair) which transduce or angularly interpret the error signals, and (3) the servo power amplifier which it feeds and controls; (4) the final output motor or other device which really "puts out" the necessary controlled power.

A servomechanism or servo system (not necessarily all electronic) must deliver continuously controlled and instantaneously regulated amounts of output power, angularly synchronized at all times with small amounts of input power. (See Fig. 20–2(a).) This controlled power transfer is generally *angular* in nature; that is, it concerns movements of a few degrees in such output devices as radar antennas, gun turrets, rudders, etc. The synchronization of input and output is a key function performed chiefly by the appropriately named "*synchros*" which continuously follow input signals originated by human control, such as the helmsman in the case of a ship's rudder.

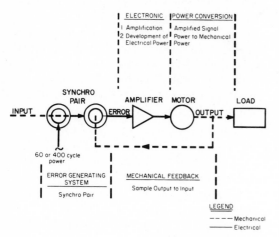

FIG. 20-1 Basic servomechanism system

At rest, or when in a stabilized position, the input and output signals have been synchronized (or zeroed) and no further change occurs either angularly in a mechanism's output device or electrically in the input or in other signals going through a system.

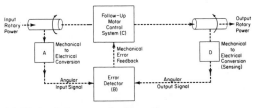

(a) *Mechanical servomechanism action*

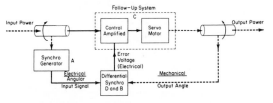

(b) *Electrical servomechanism action*

FIG. 20-2 Mechanical and electrical servomechanism action

When the output or load is changed, however—say, due to unpredictable external forces (such as cross winds against a ship) or input alterations (say, when the helmsman decides to make a turn and rotates the steering wheel)—an *error signal* is generated within the servomechanism which in turn instructs the input or output power devices to change their power relationships so as to correct the error. Figure 20–2(b) shows the electrical analog to the generalized mechanical arrangement of Fig. 20–2(a). Similarly lettered blocks perform like functions except that sensing and error-detection are simultaneously performed in the differential synchro (B and D).

Error-detection is usually performed in electronic sensing circuits or in a type of servo called a *differential*. (See block B and D in Fig. 20–2(b).) Thus we see that a complete servo system must:

1. Accept mechanical input commands and electrically pass them directly through the system in order to cause the output device or

load to "follow" or position itself accordingly (Block A).

2. Sense changes in output power (Block D).

3. Compare existing or past conditions with changes in input or output. This is the purpose of the error-detecting section (Block B).

4. Send on through the system loop the error-generated, compensating or correcting signal which restores balanced or zeroed input-output relationships. This is represented in Block C, and is sometimes called the controller, the control system, or the "follow-up" arrangement.

A mechanical example of servo action is seen in a steam engine where speed is controlled by a centrifugal ball-type governor. Figure 20–3 illustrates this; errors or changes are sensed by the ball governor when, say, steam pressure goes up or the load is lightened. This error signal (increased speed) is sensed by the governor balls in terms of their upward motion (by speed-instituted centrifugal force) and generates error-correction through movement of the rocker arm and linkage connected to the governor. This error-correcting action by means of the governor to input-valve linkage consists of cutting down the steam flow at the input valve until speed is lowered and equilibrium is established.

The feedback or correcting loop for controlling power output is thus an automatic device which "servoes" power output just as an automatic servo-actuated steering mechanism on a ship, when keyed into the navigational compass, will keep it automatically on course.

SYNCHROS AND THEIR FUNCTION IN BASIC SERVO SYSTEMS

A synchro may be considered basically as either an a-c motor or its analogous generator. It has a stator (composed of windings imbedded in a slotted magnetic structure) and a rotating, shaft-mounted rotor likewise accommodating, on its cylindrical magnetic core, windings which may be sometimes slot-wound, sometimes layer-wound. All types of synchros

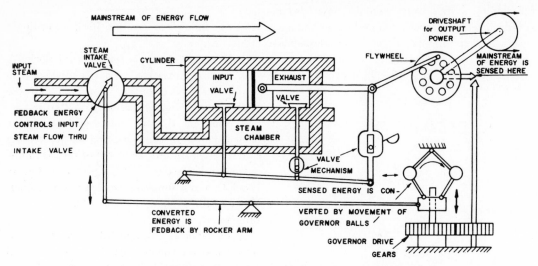

FIG. 20-3 Mechanical servo action in a steam engine

have brushes riding on slip rings in order to transfer a-c power to the rotor.

There are no physical connections in a synchro between the stator and rotor winding; the torque of movement developed in a motor-type synchro is the result of attractive and repulsive magnetic forces developed by currents in the stator acting upon those in the rotor. In the generator type, rotor movement generates, by magnetic induction, correct positioning currents in the stator windings. When the stator windings of a generator are connected to those of a motor these positioning currents cause the motor's rotor to rotate exactly in angular sychronism with the movement of the generator rotor.

To provide energy for the magnetic fields so that positioning can be effected, standard 60-cycle or 400-cycle alternating current must be supplied to the rotors of synchro motors or generators. These varying sine-wave currents produce an effect equivalent to the substitution of permanent magnets for the generator and motor rotors.

Therefore, all synchro motors and generators have *five leads* for external connection—three leads coming from the stator windings which carry positioning current information and two leads from each rotor to which is applied the 115-volt a-c. One type of synchro (the

control transformer) uses a similar arrangement of five leads but does not require that 115-volt power be applied to the rotor. A final synchro type, the differential motor or generator (to be discussed later), uses the conventional three-lead stator arrangement but uses *three leads* coming from a balanced, three-section rotor structure. Figure 20–4 summarizes and describes the magnetic and electrical characteristics of basic synchro types.

SYNCHRO TYPES AND FUNCTION

The *synchro generator transmits* from its stator winding, positioning current information telling how many degrees its rotor has been moved. (See Fig. 20–4(a).) Schematically and in type designations this unit bears the identifying letter "G." Stator leads are marked S_1, S_2, S_3 and rotor leads R_1, R_2.

The *synchro motor* (symbolically designated "M") *receives* (Fig. 20–4(b)) positioning current information through its stator winding and transforms it into *mechanical positioning* of its rotor. A motor therefore delivers a certain amount of torque through its shaft. When teamed up with a generator it constitutes an elementary remote-control servo system, suitable for moving dials, small controls, or instrument elements that require light torque.

Synchro motors (M, Fig. 20–4(b)), although electrically equivalent to a generator in reverse, must have a mechanical adjunct known as an *inertial damper*. This device is in effect a small flywheel and brake assembly mounted on the rotor shaft opposite the slip ring which prevents the rotor from spinning or oscillating when power is suddenly applied.

The *synchro differential generator* or motor (respectively DG or D, Fig. 20–4(c)) angularly adds or subtracts mechanical and/or electrical inputs to give mechanical and/or electrical outputs. A generator, for instance, will accept an angular shaft position (say 15°), and additively combine it with angular currents

in its stator calling for 11° angular positioning to deliver output positioning currents which will move a motor shaft 26° (15° + 11°). Subtractively this same combination, with proper connections, can deliver positioning currents equal to 4° (15° − 4°).

When using a differential motor we can apply two sets of positioning currents (15° and 11°) each to the differential's stator and rotor which will cause its shaft to move 26° or 4°, depending upon whether the connections have been made additively or subtractively.

The *synchro control transformer* (CT, Fig. 20–4(d)) is electrically similar to a synchro generator. It has a slotted, distributed stator input winding but utilizes a distributed rotor winding (in slots) instead of a concentrated or bunched layer winding used in the conventional motor.

In addition, both stator and rotor windings of a CT consist of many turns of fine wire— both are of high-impedance. The rotor's winding, being distributed, delivers no output shaft torque; its useful output consists of positioning voltages developed when it is moved by hand or by a follow-up mechanical force. In the latter case its output is fed into an amplifier which in turn serves to actuate a power servo output.

In other words, the rotor of a control transformer acts as a high-impedance output generator which produces voltages in-phase with those existing between R_1 and R_2 on the generator rotor which feeds it. Exact angular coincidence will exist between the two rotors provided the CT rotor currents are maintained at minimum—that is, when the CT rotor feeds a similar high-impedance load.

Synchro capacitors (Fig. 20–4(e)) are triple-unit condenser assemblies which when connected across the stator leads of a CT or a differential increase its accuracy. These assemblies are tailored for size and accuracy to match the type CT or DG being used; they increase shaft-positioning accuracy by cancelling the magnetizing current drawn by the stator windings.

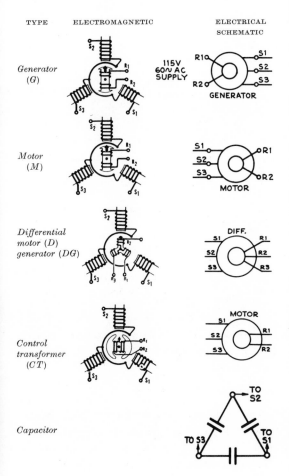

FIG. 20-4 Summary of synchros and wiring layout

SYNCHRO TYPES, SIZES AND MARKINGS

The five basic types of synchros may bear either old or new style marking or lettering. Many systems will probably cling to their historic original nomenclature. These are:

G = generator
M = motor
D = differential motor
DG = differential generator
CT = control transformer

However, modern military specifications and more definitive written descriptions use the designations given below. Table 20–1 gives data concerning mounting, speed, and power supply.

Table 20–1   New style designation

Control transmitter	Cx
Torque transmitter	Tx
Receiver	TR
Control differential transmitter	CDX
Torque differential transmitter	CTX
Differential receiver	TDR
Control transformer	CT
Bearing-mounted stator	B (suffix)
60-cycle	6
400-cycle	4

Data on size, weight, and physical dimensions of the various models commonly used under the older specification MIL-S-2335 and under the later specification MIL-S-2078A appear in Table 20–2.

It should be noted that unless specified by the suffix "B" all synchros are flange mounted —that is, by means of an end plate which is integral with the motor frame. Special mountings are sometimes used; an example is the nozzle mounting which is a clamp completely encircling the body of a unit.

SYNCHRO MAGNETIC AND ELECTRICAL CHARACTERISTICS

Since all synchro stator and rotor coils are wire-wound magnetic structures they can be described in electrical and magnetic terms. The basic characteristics, all of which enter testing and measurement, are: (1) exciting or magnetizing current, (2) exciting power (from loss current), (3) d-c resistances of stator and rotors. The specifications accompanying each and every size and type of synchro usually list these quantities in one form or another. In the case of differential units the exciting currents are given with and without an accompanying capacitor, which (as we have seen earlier) serves to reduce the exciting current.

Table 20–2   Size, weight, and dimensions of old and new size designations

Sizes covered by MIL-S-2335

Size	Weight, lb (approx.)	Length, in.	Diameter, in.
1	1½ to 2	3.9 to 4.2	2.25
3	2 to 3	5.2 to 5.51	3.10
5	5	6.0 to 6.8	3.39 to 3.63
6	8	6.4 to 7.5	4.5
7	18	8.9 to 9.2	5.75
8	60	13.13	8.63

Sizes covered by MIL-S-20708A

Size	Weight	Length, in. (w/o shaft)	Diameter, in.
08		1.240	0.750
11		1.732 to 1.789	1.062
12		2.692	1.125
15	Not	1.772 to 2.253	1.437
16	defined	2.593	1.537
18	by	2.520 to 2.670	1.750
19	spec	3.300	1.900
23		3.530 to 3.830	2.250
31		5.100 to 5.355	3.100
37		5.250 to 5.950	3.625

In the case of synchro generators and motors another characteristic is given.

MINIMUM UNIT TORQUE GRADIENT

This quantity in a motor (or in a similar generator used as a motor) is expressed in inch-ounces per degree. It is a measure of the motor strength or turning power necessary (when driven by its generator counterpart) to move its shaft forcibly away from some normally synchronized position. In other words, if a motor, connected stator-to-stator with its

GENERAL CONNECTION PRACTICE

The five wires of a synchro system are numbered in such a way that the shaft of a normal motor will turn counter-clockwise when an increasing reading (see Fig. 20–6) is sent over these wires, provided it is connected directly, as in Fig. 20–5(a). As in the figure, a direct connection is obtained by connecting R_1 to the middle, and S_3 to the high-numbered bus.

STANDARD GENERATOR CONNECTIONS:

Connect a generator to the bus as shown in each case if it is to transmit an increasing reading when its shaft is turned in the indicated direction (see Fig. 20–5(b)).

STANDARD MOTOR CONNECTIONS:

Connect a motor to the bus as shown in each case if its shaft is to turn in the indicated direction when it receives an increasing reading (see Fig. 20–5(c)).

STANDARD CONNECTIONS FOR DIFFERENTIAL GENERATORS:

Connect the stator leads of a differential to the generator circuit, and its rotor leads to the motor or control transformer circuit (see Fig. 20–5 (d)). Connect a differential generator to the busses as shown in each case if, with constant stator voltages, it is to transmit an increasing reading from its rotor leads when its shaft is turned in the indicated direction. In either case it will transmit an increasing reading from its rotor leads when it receives one on its stator leads with its shaft stationary.

STANDARD CONNECTIONS FOR DIFFERENTIAL MOTORS:

Connect a differential motor to the busses as shown in each case if, with constant voltages on one side, its shaft is to turn as indicated when it receives an increasing read-in from the other side (see Fig. 20–5(e)).

STANDARD CONNECTIONS FOR CONTROL TRANSFORMERS:

Connect the stator leads of a control transformer to the bus as shown in each case if its shaft is to turn as indicated when following an increasing reading (see Fig. 20–5(f)).

STANDARD CONNECTIONS FOR SYNCHRO CAPACITORS:

Whenever a differential or control transformer is used, mount a synchro capacitor of the proper size as close to it as possible, and connect as shown in Fig. 20–5(g).

FIG. 20-5 Summary of stator and rotor connections

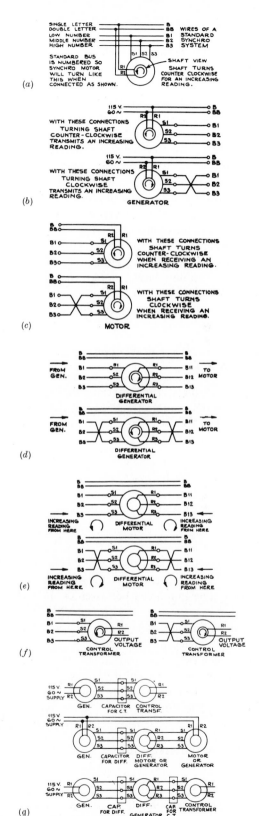

(a)

(b)

(c)

(d)

(e)

(f)

(g)

driving generator, had five inch-ounces applied against its normal shaft rotation, which in so doing moved the shaft five degrees, it would have developed a torque gradient of one inch-ounce per degree. This gradient or rate of change increases fairly uniformly up to 60° away from the synchronized position; from there on it increases less rapidly until it reaches maximum torque at 90°.

In utilizing synchros to produce torque it should be realized that accuracy is sacrificed. Also note that since current determines torque, the impedance of a motor or generator is inversely proportional to its torque-producing ability; in other words, a low-impedance motor will produce relatively high torque since it can inherently draw more current.

STANDARD SYNCHRO CONNECTIONS, VOLTAGES, AND ROTATION

Figure 20–5(a)-(g) summarizes the various stator and rotor connections used on all types of synchros. The diagrams use standard five-wire lead designations:

R_1, R_2 for rotors
S_1, S_2, S_3 for stators
B, BB for standard a-c bus, input
B_1, B_2, B_3 for stator bus-wire connections

In a two-speed system—where similar information is transmitted at different speeds—the low-speed bus uses the lower B numbers, B_1, B_2, B_3, while higher-speed signal currents flow on higher-numbered bus circuits, B_4, B_5, B_6.

Notes describing each type of circuit connection are given in Fig. 20–5.

A convenient picturization of the phase relationships between supply voltages on the leads in a standard five-wire synchro system is shown in Fig. 20–6.

TESTING AND TROUBLE-SHOOTING SYNCHRO CIRCUITS

In analyzing a synchro by itself within an overall system, the specific component-identi-

fied troubles fall within a few categories. Generally, a synchro by itself can have the following malfunctions:

OVERLOAD

Worn bearings or defective gears may cause a receiver to lag its transmitter. This condition produces abnormally high currents in one of

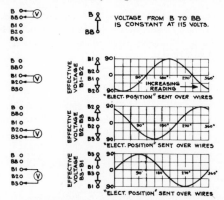

FIG. 20-6 A standard five-wire synchro system

the stator windings, but it is possible in some overload cases for zero current to exist in one particular lead while heavy currents exist in the other two. Therefore, measurement must be made by inserting an ammeter in two of the stator leads.

Since it is inconvenient to open up stator connections for such current measurements, overload indicators are often built into the synchro interconnections. This is accomplished by using two current transformers connected as in Fig. 20–7, the primary of each being connected in series with a stator lead. If the two secondary windings of these transformers are connected series-opposing, mechanical or electrical overload will develop enough voltage to light a neon bulb. This device can be ar-

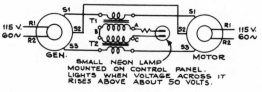

FIG. 20-7

ranged in the circuit so that the indicating bulb is located on the control panel; it also indicates unbalanced conditions in stator windings. Blown-fuse indicators can also be installed using the double-winding transformer circuit and in conjunction with the neon indicator.

SHORTED OR OPEN WINDINGS

Using the information given in specifications concerning stator and rotor resistances, many troubles can be analyzed by using simple resistance measurements.

Trouble can also be found by placing an a-c meter across the rotor winding of a normal motor or differential generator, while it is being driven by a generator, and then turning the shaft of the generator. A constant output voltage will result (while turning the generator shaft) if all generator and motor windings are balanced. Extending this technique further we may encounter a number of symptoms, categorized in Table 20–3.

OSCILLATION AND SPINNING

During switching, or in very abrupt change of rotational conditions, a servo system may oscillate or temporarily spin for a few seconds and then stop. Serious failures such as poor dampers or shorted or incorrectly wired stator leads can produce spinning. Such troubles are remedied in conventional manner.

If all electrical connections and components seem correct, there may be system or impedance-matching factors influencing abnormal spinning. The following are a few of the precautions that should be observed:

1. *Motor size.* All motors normally switched into a system should be of the smallest size that will operate and at the same time produce desired accuracy. Such tailoring will minimize switching disturbances.

2. The weight and consequently the *mechanical inertia* of loads attached to motor shafts should be as small as possible.

Table 20-3 Trouble-shooting with an voltmeter

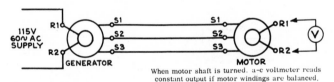

When motor shaft is turned. a-c voltmeter reads constant output if motor windings are balanced.

Voltage between:	Under normal conditions
S_1—S_2	Varies from 0 (at 120° and 300°) to 90 volts (at 30° and 210°).
S_2—S_3	Varies from 0 (at 60° and 240°) to 90 volts (at 150° and 330°).
S_1—S_3	Varies from 0 (at 0° and 180°) to 90 volts (at 90° and 270°).
R_1—R_2	On both generator and motor, is constant at 115 volts.

Any trouble except an open in the stator circuit will cause one or more of the voltages to be wrong, as follows:

Symptoms	Trouble
IF: Voltage between one pair of S leads is 0 for all generator positions. Voltage between other pairs of S leads varies from 0 to 78 volts. R_1—R_2 voltages are both 115 volts.	S LEADS ARE SHORTED (where 0 volts is read at all positions)
IF: S voltages vary from 0 to 55 volts, R_1—R_2 voltage on one unit is 115 volts, on the other unit is 0 volts.	R LEADS ARE SHORTED (on unit where 0 volts is read)
IF: S voltages vary from 0 to 75 volts, R voltage is 115 volts on both units.	ONE ROTOR IS OPEN INTERNALLY (see below)
IF: S voltages vary from 0 to 80 volts, R voltage is 115 volts on one unit and 90 volts on the other.	ROTOR SUPPLY LEADS ARE OPEN (on unit reading 90 volts)

3. The *driving generator* supplying a number of motors should be big enough to accommodate its accompanying load. Switching in a weak generator induces extraneous currents conducive to oscillation.

4. *Overload indicators*, improperly designed or used, can produce oscillation.

5. *Large currents* due to unbalanced capacitors can cause oscillation. Changing capacitors may cure such troubles.

INCORRECT WIRING generally gives immediate indication of trouble. Figure 20–8 may be used in order to isolate the simpler of these errors.

ZEROING

"Zeroing" a synchro means, in general, adjusting it mechanically so it will work properly in a system in which all the other synchros are zeroed. Doing this mechanically requires the loosening of the lugs that clamp

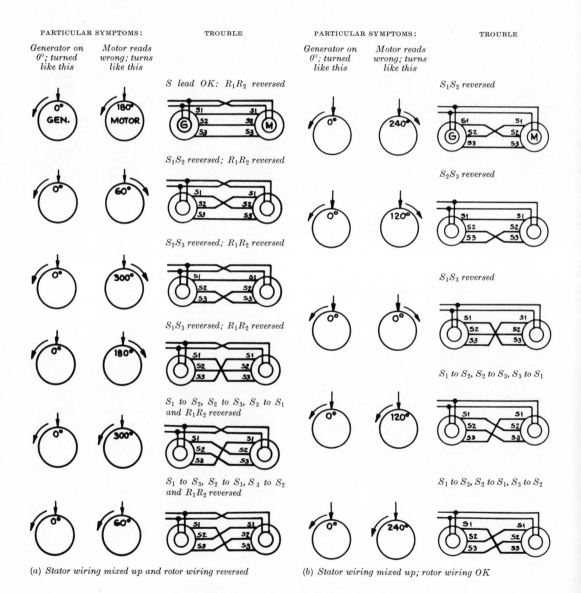

(a) *Stator wiring mixed up and rotor wiring reversed*

(b) *Stator wiring mixed up; rotor wiring OK*

FIG. 20-8 Causes of trouble in incorrect wiring

the flange and turning the whole case. In some cases it may be better to loosen the shaft coupling or some intermediate gear in order to turn the shaft.

Separate types of synchros require slightly different zeroing procedures and also involve the use of electrical zeroing measurements. All types are covered in the material that follows. (*Note:* An asterisk appearing against any of the steps means that during that step precautions should be taken *not to leave power connected* for more than the few minutes necessary to zero the instrument.)

ZEROING THE SYNCHRO MOTOR

In general this zeroing process requires that the dial or mechanical output mechanism must read zero when the electrical voltages are likewise zero. This requires that, since the shaft of a motor is free to turn, it may be slipped to zero if some zero electrical voltage can be accurately determined.

METHOD A. After the motor connections have been isolated and the 115-volt a-c supply reconnected across S_2 and a jumpered cross connection placed from S_1 to S_3 (see Fig. 20–9(a)) the shaft will immediately turn to zero. If the unit must be left connected for any time use a Variac to reduce the supply voltage applied to S_2.

METHOD B. When it is impossible to remove a motor's supply leads use a connection similar to Fig. 20–9(b) in conjunction with a correctly zeroed generator. With the generator in zero position connect a temporary jumper from S_1 to S_2 and adjust the motor dial mechanism, since the rotor will have automatically assumed zero position. Check the

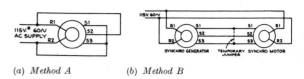

(a) *Method A*   (b) *Method B*

FIG. 20-9 Zeroing the synchro motor

adjustment by observing shaft movements as the jumper is touch-connected on and off.

ZEROING THE SYNCHRO GENERATOR

Procedures for generator zeroing are similar to those used for a motor. Connect as in Fig. 20–10(a).

METHOD A. When driving a motor which is correctly zeroed the generator being zeroed is mechanically unclamped and the rotor moved until the driven motor dial shows zero.

To check the adjustment (in the unclamped position) momentarily short-circuit S_1 to S_3; if the *motor shaft* moves the system is not zeroed. Then move the motor back to zero dial, adjust the generator position, and repeat until no shaft movement results.

METHOD B. Set the generator's rotor to zero using the calibrated motor and remove all generator stator leads. Then connect a sensitive a-c voltmeter or a pair of headphones across S_1 and S_3. Next, turn the generator rotor carefully until minimum sound or voltage is obtained. Clamp in this position and reconnect stator leads. *Caution:* be sure that the minimum position is at true zero, since the 180° position will likewise produce a minimum or null voltage reading.

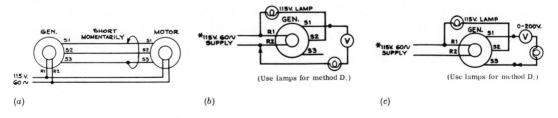

(a)   (b)   (c)

FIG. 20-10 Zeroing the synchro generator

METHOD c. When no calibrated motor is available and when zero position of the generator is fairly closely known, proceed as follows at this position (see Fig. 20–10(b)-(c)):

1. With a 115-volt a-c supply across the rotor connect R_1 to S_2 and place a voltmeter across S_1 to S_3. Fig. 20–10(b).

2. Unclamp generator and turn until motor reads zero.

3. With 115-volts a-c still across R_1, R_2, connect R_1 to S_2 and place meter from S_1 to R_2. It should now read around either 37 volts or 193 volts. Fig 20–10(c).

4a–1. *If the reading is around 37 volts*, remove all previous connections except the 115-volt supply across R_1 and R_2 and place the voltmeter across S_1 and S_3.

4a–2. Zero the generator by moving the rotor and using the lowest voltmeter scale. Clamp. The adjustment is then complete.

4b–1. If the meter reads around 193 volts start over with step 1.

4b–2. Follow step 2 above.

4b–3. Follow step 3 above, only now the a-c voltmeter should read 37 volts.

4b–4. Proceed as in steps 4a–1 and 4a–2.

METHOD d. This method is identical with Method C except that two 115-volt lamps and a pair of headphones are used instead of the a-c voltmeter. See Fig. 20–10(b)-(c). The steps are as follows:

1. With 115 volts a-c across R_1 and R_2 connect lamp 1 between R_1 and S_2 and lamp 2 between S_1 and S_3.

2. Unclamp generator and turn rotor until lamp 2 is extinguished.

3. With 115-volt a-c and lamp 1 still connected as in step 1, connect lamp 2 between S_1 and R_2. It will either be dim or extra bright.

4a–1. If lamp 1 is dim remove all connections except R_1 and R_2 and zero the generator with headphones across S_1 and S_2.

4b–1. If lamp 1 is bright, start over with step 1.

4b–2. Follow step 2.

4b–3. Follow step 3, only now lamp 2 is dim.

4b–4. Repeat step 4a–1 for final zeroing.

ZEROING THE DIFFERENTIAL MOTOR

In general these adjustments are similar to those performed on the ordinary motor, since the differential shaft is usually free to turn:

METHOD A. Connect the motor according to Fig. 20–11(a). The shaft will immediately turn

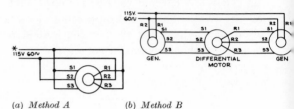

(a) *Method A*   (b) *Method B*

FIG. 20-11 Zeroing the differential motor

to zero, and the dial can then be correspondingly set. For safety, in case the adjustment consumes considerable time, a Variac should be used to reduce the rotor applied voltage to around 80 volts.

METHOD B.

1. If the differential is mechanically attached to other equipment leave the unit connected between its respective generators, being sure that they are correctly zeroed.

2. Connect temporary jumpers between S_1 and S_3 and from R_1 to R_3. (See Fig. 20–11(b).)

3. This should automatically produce motor zero so that the dial setting can be made.

If intermittently connecting and disconnecting the jumpers produces no movement in the differential shaft, zeroing has been correct.

ZEROING THE DIFFERENTIAL GENERATOR

Procedure in this case is very similar to that used for the differential motor.

METHOD A

1. With the DG connected normally between a correctly zeroed generator and a correctly zeroed motor (see Fig. 20–12(a)) the DG rotor automatically assumes zero position. The dial can then be set.

2. With a jumper across S_1 and S_3 of the common generator and DG leads, place a temporary short circuit across R_1 and R_3.

If the motor jumps at all, the DG must be readjusted for zero.

METHOD B

1. With the working combination of a zeroed generator and a zeroed motor, disconnect the DG under test.

2. Connect a pair of phones or a sensitive voltmeter across the DG terminals R_1 and R_3.

3. Turn the DG carefully until minimum sound or voltage exists. Clamp and set dial.

METHOD C

1. Set a zeroed generator feeding the DG under test accurately at zero position.

2. Disconnect the generator and connect

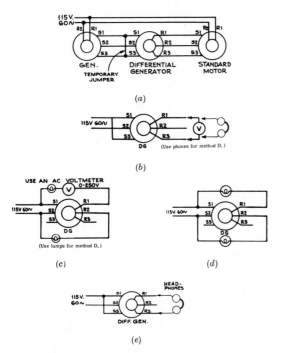

(a)

(b)

(c)   (d)

(e)

FIG. 20-12 Zeroing the differential generator

the various DG leads as in Fig. 20–12(b) with the voltmeter across S_1 and R_1.

3. Turn the DG until the meter reads zero. It will then be at approximately zero.

4. Reconnect as in Fig. 20–12(c) and now turn the DG carefully for minimum voltmeter reading. This is the final zero setting.

METHOD D. This procedure is similar to

that used in zeroing a generator with lamps and a pair of headphones. Fig. 20–12(d).

1. Set a zeroed generator driving the DG under test at its zero position.

2. Remove all DG connections and connect as in Fig. 20–12(c).

3. Unclamp the rotor and turn until *both* lamps are dimmest. The unit is now at approximately zero.

4. Reconnect as in Fig. 20–12(b).

5. Turn rotor carefully until phones deliver minimum tone level as in Fig. 20–12(e). This is the final zero condition.

ZEROING THE CONTROL TRANSFORMER.

METHOD A

1. Set the correctly zeroed generator driving the transformer under test to its zero position.

2. Isolate the CT and connect as in Fig. 20–13(a).

3. Turn the CT rotor until the meter reads minimum (about 40 v). The unit is now approximately on zero.

4. Reconnect as in Fig. 20–13(b) and turn carefully until meter reads minimum. This is the final zero position.

METHOD B

1. Set the correctly zeroed generator driving the CT under test to its zero position.

2. Isolate the unit and connect 6-watt, 115-volt lamps as shown in Fig. 20–13(c).

3. Turn CT rotor until lamps are both dimmest. CT is now approximately on zero.

4. Reconnect as in Fig. 20–13(d), and turn

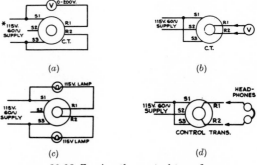

(a)   (b)

(c)   (d)

FIG. 20-13 Zeroing the control transformer

rotor carefully until minimum sound occurs in phones. This is the final zero position.

GENERAL REPAIR, MAINTENANCE, AND TROUBLE-SHOOTING

Synchro units are precision electromechanical devices which when demounted or adjusted require careful handling and usually require special lubricants, tools, jigs, etc., for disassembly.

The major portion of maintenance test time spent on any overall servo system occurs during the diagnosis process. No set rules can be stated on how to trouble-shoot a system—one can only list general areas of weakness and common operating and construction problems. A few that are common to systems that have been in service for some time are:

1. Opens, shorts, grounds, and misconnection through the various switches that accompany any system.

2. Oil or water leakage into the synchro framework.

3. Vibration failures such as loose lugs, terminal boards, fasteners, laminations, and the like.

4. Bearing trouble due to rust, corrosion, mechanical springing of a synchro frame, and so on.

5. Winding trouble due to such things as loose wires and corroded insulation.

6. Slip-ring troubles from wear, dirt, poor contact, and so on.

Power Supplies and Filter Circuits 21

Power-supply design techniques extend through every phase of electronic equipment; each equipment must have, or must include, a power supply that meets its own unique requirements. Early in electronic technology, power-supply design was regarded as a routine procedure because the requirements were minimal. Today, the complexion of electronic equipment has changed so that power-supply design is a highly specialized operation. For computer and complex circuitry, a power supply must not only deliver the correct output voltage and current with a minimum of ripple and with good regulation and high efficiency, but it must be unaffected by transients encountered in both input and output circuitry, must have provisions for delivering extremely precise output voltages, must be able to accept short-circuited terminal conditions, must be physically light in weight and mechanically rugged, and must deliver extremely reliable performance.

Many types and kinds of power supplies exist; they may be classified, as below, by function, by power, by application, by circuit, and in some cases by type of rectification. The oldest and most commonly used power supplies are those using vacuum-tube rectifiers. Modern, low-voltage types are solid-state transistorized units using semiconductor rectifiers.

Summarizing, we have:

By function: regulated or unregulated units.

By power: high-current, low-voltage supplies for transistorized equipment; or high-voltage, high-current power supplies for transmitter operation.

By circuit: power rectifiers using half-wave, full-wave, or bridge circuits.

By rectifier: vacuum-tube, silicon, selenium, copper-oxide diodes.

Fundamentally, the conventional power supply processes sine-wave a-c input in four basic steps (see Fig. 21–1): (1) It transforms the input a-c to the desired level. (2) It rectifies the stepped up (or down) supply energy in order to deliver direct current. (3) It filters the a-c from the rectified product. (4) It processes or regulates it for application to terminals suitable for attaching to an external load.

A small bleeder path is usually provided in parallel with the output terminals to stabilize the overall circuitry at no load.

The basic half-wave, full-wave, and bridge circuits, with important voltage waveforms, as commonly used, are illustrated in Table 21–1. Semiconductor rectifier elements are shown in these diagrams with the filter units intentionally omitted. Figure 21–2 shows two voltage-doubler circuits, a tripler, and quadrupler circuit using vacuum-tube rectifiers.

BASIC COMPONENTS AND DESIGN CHARACTERISTICS

Using Fig. 21–2 with normalized output-current conditions for the three basic circuit types, we may obtain the basic power-supply characteristics in terms of current and voltage ratios from the rectifier output. Details concerning rectifier definitions, ratings, and their performance characteristics are given at the end of the chapter.

Considering items onward from the rectifier output, we encounter ripple current and voltage, the filter networks used to reduce it, and regulation problems.

THE FILTER

The filter is an electrical network interposed between the rectifier output and the ultimate usable output terminals; it is designed to limit or filter out the ripple from reaching the output. Most filters are low-pass, π-type networks with antiresonant tuning, in order to

FIG. 21–1 Basic power-supply processes

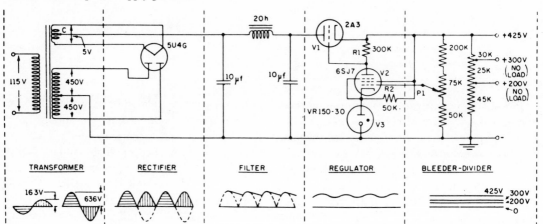

TRANSFORMER	RECTIFIER	FILTER	REGULATOR	BLEEDER-DIVIDER
Low voltage is stepped up by the transformer from 115 volts to 900 volts. Center tap provides a dividing point so that 450 volts are applied to each section of the 5U4G rectifier. The ends of the transformer alternately become positive and negative. Center tap C on heater winding is used to force plate current to divide equally in each filament lead. If there is no center tap, a voltage divider of two equal 50-ohm resistors may be put across the secondary to produce the same effect. Alternately positive and negative voltage is applied to the plates of the rectifier.	The two plates conduct alternately as each plate is made positive in turn by the secondary of the transformer. Pulses of current flow from the filament line to each plate in turn. The plates alternately become positive and negative with the applied a-c, but the filament line will show a one-directional flow.	Capacitors charge when the rectifier conducts, and they discharge through the bleeder resistor when the tube is not conducting. Choke builds up a magnetic field when the tube draws current. The field collapses as current decreases, tending to keep a constant current flowing in the same direction through the bleeder resistor and the load. Capacitor input (illustrated) gives higher voltage output with low current loads. Choke input gives steadier output with less ripple under load conditions.	If the load draws more current or if the a-c input voltage falls, the terminal voltage of the power supply falls. Resistor R_1, tube V_2, and gas-tube V_3 are in series across the rectifier terminals. V_3 holds the cathode of V_2 at a constant positive potential with respect to ground, and setting of P_1 determines bias on V_2. A fall in terminal voltage causes more negative bias on V_2, hence, less current through V_2, hence, less current through R_1. Less IR drop across R_1 causes less negative bias on V_1. V_1, then acts as a lower value resistor, and terminal voltage decrease is checked.	As a bleeder, the resistor is for safety to discharge the capacitors when power is removed. As a load resistor, it acts as a stabilizer to protect the voltage regulator at no load, and to improve the regulation. A voltage divider meets the requirements of a load resistor and a bleeder, but in addition has taps placed at intervals for voltage at less than the maximum. It is usually grounded at the lower end but may be grounded at any higher point to get a negative output.

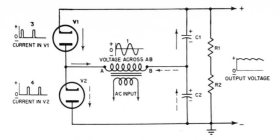

(a) Conventional voltage-doubler circuit using two half-wave rectifier tubes to provide full wave

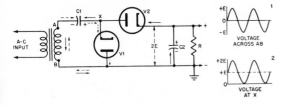

(b) Cascade voltage doubler with half-wave rectification

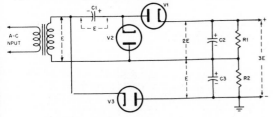

(c) Simple voltage-tripler circuit

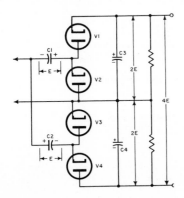

(d) Voltage-quadrupler circuit

FIG. 21–2 Voltage-multiplying circuits

eliminate the second harmonic ripple. As described later in this chapter, the performance of a filter can be calculated and predicted. Filters, in power supplies, may be roughly categorized as having either capacitive or choke input and are designed and rated with respect to their ability to reduce ripple voltage and their effects upon regulation, considering the three common power-supply types. The

categories are the capacitive input, the choke input, and the π-section filter. Their characteristics may be summarized as follows.

CAPACITIVE INPUT (see Fig. 21–3(a)). This circuit has: (a) high d-c output voltage at light loads, (b) good ripple reduction only at light loads, (c) poor voltage regulation, (d) high current surges which often necessitate addition of protective series surge resistance.

CHOKE INPUT, PLUS CAPACITOR (see Fig. 21–3(b)). This circuit combines the large-load effectiveness of the choke input filter with the light-load effectiveness of the capacitive-input filter.

π-SECTION FILTER. This section has: (a) higher open-circuit voltage and (b) poorer regulation. It can be analyzed as a series combination of capacitive and choke input filter.

FIG. 21–3 Rectifier currents and voltages

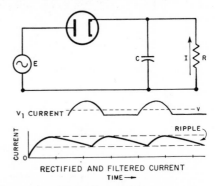

(a) Half-wave rectifier with capacitive input

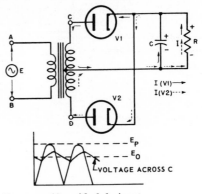

(b) Full-wave rectifier with choke input

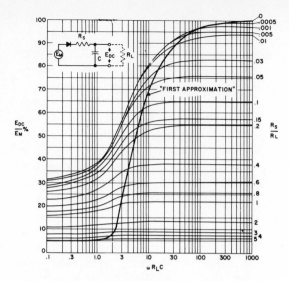

(a) *Percent ripple vs. filter and load*

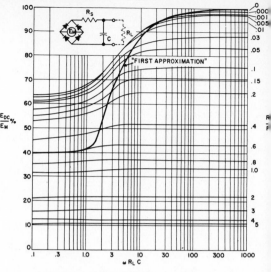

(b) *Percent ripple vs. load and input capacitor*

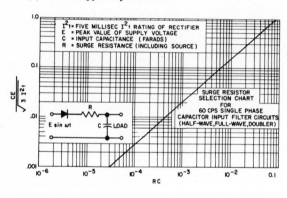

(c) *Surge resistor selector*

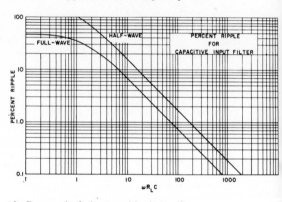

(d) *Percent ripple for capacitive input filter*

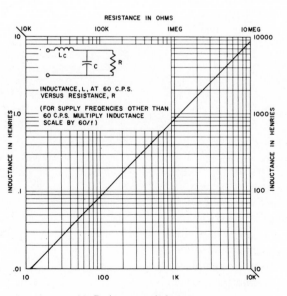

(e) *Resistance vs. inductance*

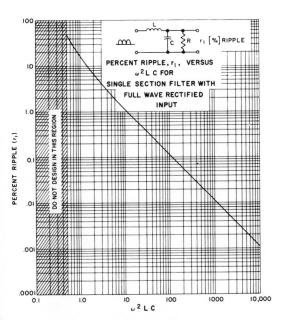

(f) Percent ripple for single-section filter

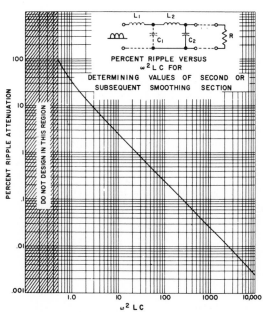

(g) Percent ripple attenuation for subsequent smoothing section

FIG.   21–4 Performance characteristics

PERFORMANCE CURVES—DESIGN FACTORS

Power-supply performance can be predicted or measurements checked if enough of the design parameters described below are known. With the aid of curves (Fig. 21–4(a)–(g)) applying to common circuit configurations, we may determine output voltages, ripple voltages, and so on, covering most operating conditions. Table 21–1 lists voltage and current ratios for the three basic circuits when values are referenced to a d-c output current (using a 1-ampere base figure).

OPERATING PARAMETERS

E_{dc} = d-c output voltage,

E_{ac} = rms value of alternating harmonic components in output voltage,

E_m = peak value of the a-c supply voltage ($E_m = 2V_{ac}$),

r = ripple; percent $r = E_{ac}/E_{dc}$,

r' = ripple with surge resistance, R_s, in circuit,

S_r = ripple attenuation factor,

R_s = surge resistance,

R_b = bleeder resistance,

R_L = load resistance; $R_L = E_{dc}/I_{dc}$,

ω = angular frequency = $2\pi \times$ supply frequency,

L = circuit inductance in henrys,

C = circuit capacitance in farads.

PERCENT RIPPLE is defined as the measured percentage of voltage or current referred to the normal d-c output, upon which it appears superimposed. Ripple voltage exists in progressively increasing amounts as measurements proceed from the output toward the rectifiers. Such a series of measurements is useful in trouble-shooting or in studying filter design.

Ripple voltages are a-c and consist predominantly of the second harmonic frequency of the supply line, although other harmonic frequencies may be present in various amounts. For instance, a 60-cycle power supply generates 120-, 180-, and 240-cycle ripple—the 120-cycle harmonic being predominant.

Care should be exercised to measure the ripple content of any additional or special voltage supplies which are adjuncts to the main source for bias or control purposes.

REGULATION—REGULATED SUPPLIES

The performance characteristics of regulated supplies are commonly plotted as curves showing how the output voltage varies as load currents are increased. If a single figure is quoted, it refers to the percentage change in output voltage encountered in going from no load to full load.

Regulated power supplies achieve output-voltage constancy through proper circuit design by inserting a series regulating tube or transistor (sometimes called a "pass element")

in the main path of rectified output current. Figures 21–5 and 21–6 show, respectively, a silicon transistor and a heavy-current-duty vacuum tube performing this function.

Functionally, improvement in regulation is obtained by causing the series resistance of the pass element or regulator to change as the load changes. This is done by sensing or measuring change in output voltage when load varies, amplifying the change, and feeding it back, in proper polarity, to alter the series regulator's internal resistance so that it can compensate, or allow passage of less or more current as the case requires. In effect, output voltage is restored to initial conditions where

Table 21–1   Common current and voltage relationships in basic rectifier circuits.

Type of circuit		Single phase half-wave	Single phase center-tap	Single phase bridge
Primary				
Secondary				
One cycle wave of rectifier output voltage (no overlap)				
Number of rectifier elements in circuit		1	2	4
RMS d-c volts output		1.57	1.11	1.11
Peak d-c volts output		3.14	1.57	1.57
Peak reverse volts per rectifier element		3.14	3.14	1.57
		1.41	2.82	1.41
		1.41	1.41	1.41
Average d-c output current		1.00	1.00	1.00
Average d-c output current per rectifier element		1.00	0.500	0.500
RMS current per rectifier element	Resistive load	1.57	0.785	0.785
	Inductive load	....	0.707	0.707
Peak current per rectifier element	Resistive load	3.14	1.57	1.57
	Inductive load	....	1.00	1.00
Ratio: Peak to average current per element	Resistive load	3.14	3.14	3.14
	Inductive load	....	2.00	2.00
% ripple $\left(\dfrac{\text{RMS of ripple}}{\text{average output voltage}}\right)$		121%	48%	48%
		Resistive load		Inductive
Transformer secondary RMS volts per leg		2.22	1.11 (To center-tap)	1.11 (Total)
Transformer secondary RMS volts line-to-line		2.22	2.22	1.11
Secondary line current		1.57	0.707	1.00
Transformer secondary volt-amperes per leg		3.49	1.57	1.11
Transformer primary RMS amperes per leg		1.57	1.00	1.00
Transformer primary volt-amperes per leg		3.49	1.11	1.11
Average of primary and secondary volt-amperes		3.49	1.34	1.11
Primary line current		1.57	1.00	1.00
Line power factor		....	0.900	0.900

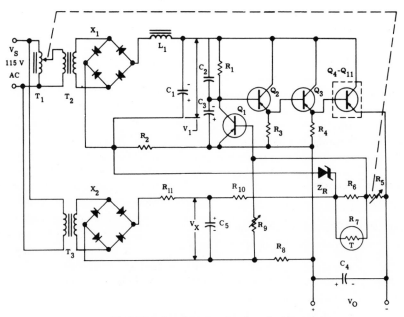

FIG. 21–5 Regulated power supply using transistors

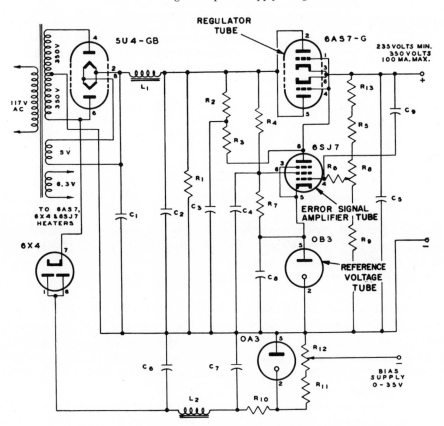

FIG. 21–6 Regulated power supply using vacuum tubes

it is compared for sensing to a reference voltage developed across a zener diode or reference vacuum tube.

In Fig. 21–5, Q_2, Q_3, Q_4 are the series-regulating power transistors, and the 6AS7G is the analogous regulator tube in Fig. 21–6. Note in each case that the feedback amplifier transmits sensed voltage differences back to the control elements of the regulator elements.

OTHER POWER-SUPPLY CHARACTERISTICS

In addition to the main performance factors described above, the following characteristics are important design features of a power supply.

1. *Fusing and automatic reset.* Protective circuit breakers, fuses, or other devices are the mark of good power-supply design. These eliminate the possibility of damage within the power supply or to circuitry serviced by it.

2. *Heating factors.* Since the major part of an equipment's supply current funnels through the power supply, its provisions for adequate cooling are important. This is particularly true in vacuum-tube equipment where the operating vacuum-tube filament circuits are usually supplied by a separate secondary winding on the main power transformer.

3. *Voltage-breakdown and overvoltage provisions.* All rectifiers and associated hardware must be rated and physically disposed to withstand the maximum peak inverse voltages normally encountered, plus those occurring under maximum excursions of input voltage. Many supplies provide line-voltage regulators to accomplish this.

In the case of transistorized equipment, extreme care is necessary to prevent switching or power-supply induced transient voltages from reaching the operating equipment, since transistor burnout can occur sometimes in a few milliseconds with moderate overvoltage. This characteristic is sometimes known as overshoot. Fast-dropout circuits are often used as a preventive measure.

AUTOMATIC SHORT-CIRCUIT PROTECTION

Automatic current-limiting circuits enable a power supply to continue operating at a limited current, and without damage, under any output overload including short circuits. The output voltage is restored to normal when the overload is removed, as distinguished from a fuse or circuit-breaker system which opens at overload and must be physically closed to restore power.

In high-power transmitter supplies certain further precautions are necessary:

1. Interlock switches are mandatory so that screen or access doors, when opened, automatically turn off the main a-c power.

2. Time-delay circuits are necessary to hold off application of plate voltage until power-tube filaments have fully warmed up. Otherwise the tube's internal structure may be damaged.

LIFE CHARACTERISTICS

Among the characteristics of rectifier units tested in Table 15–6, we note that solid-state rectifier power diodes have unlimited life. Selenium rectifier stacks, on the other hand, have a life expectancy of 60,000 to 100,000 hours, although they exhibit self-healing qualities under moderate breakdown voltages. Mercury-arc rectifier tubes have a life expectancy of approximately 20,000 hours. The electrolytic filter capacitors used in power supplies are probably weakest in longevity. Although sometimes self-healing, these units have a relatively short life—1,000–2,000 hours—and in many supplies are designed with plug-in bases for easy replacement.

SPECIAL POWER SUPPLIES

TRANSFORMERLESS SUPPLIES are frequently used in a-c, d-c radio and TV receiver circuitry for reasons of economy. Figures 21–7(a) and (b) are examples of this circuitry, the latter acting in the added role of a voltage doubler.

VOLTAGE-DOUBLING AND QUADRUPLING circuits are employed in specialized power and supply applications. Some economy is achieved,

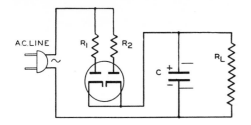

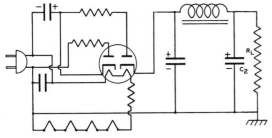

(a) *Simple half-wave circuit*

(b) *Balanced voltage doubler*

FIG. 21–7 Transformerless power-supply circuits

although with transformer input the extra circuitry is hardly worth the added complexity. See Fig. 21–2(d) for a typical transformer less supply.

VIBRATOR AND OSCILLATOR SUPPLIES. For mobile use a convenient method of obtaining several hundred volts from battery-supply voltages is to generate pulse-alternating voltages by means of a vibrator unit, step up the resultant voltage by a transformer, and rectify the delivered output. The vibrator with its contacts is in effect a rapidly acting switch which alternately sends battery current through two opposed primary windings of a transformer, thus inducing a square-wave a-c voltage in the secondary winding (Fig. 21–8(a)). To avoid the use of rectifier units, another set of contacts on the same vibrator armature is alternately and synchronously placed across the stepped-up secondary voltage to produce rectified d-c. Figure 21–8(b) shows a typical circuit.

Transistor oscillator power supplies fundamentally operate exactly like the vibrator-circuit power supply described above. In Fig. 21–8(c) the power transistors in the battery-primary transformer circuit constitute a free-running square-wave oscillator. Their output appearing across the primary is equivalent to the switching function performed

by the mechanical vibrator, while the stepped-up secondary voltage is converted to d-c by conventional rectifier diodes.

TESTING AND DESIGN

In addition to the obvious measurements associated with measuring and testing a power supply, a number of special conditions, characteristics, and instruments are important when analyzing performance.

COMPARISON BRIDGE. Measurements involving voltage comparison utilize circuits whose configuration and principle of operation resemble a four-arm electrical bridge. The elements are arranged so that there is zero error signal when balance exists in the circuit. Changes in output voltage in relation to a reference voltage create error signals which,

FIG. 21–8 Vibrator and oscillator power-supply circuits

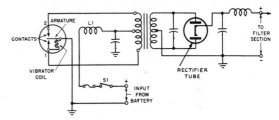

(a) *Simple interrupter circuit*

(b) *Synchronous self-rectifying circuit*

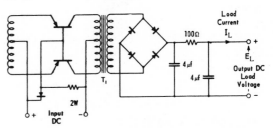

(c) *Transistor oscillator power supply (dc to dc conversion)*

by means of negative feedback, are used to correct the output so that bridge balance is restored. Comparison bridges are capable of measuring better than .01 percent regulation.

COMPLEMENTARY TRACKING. When two regulated supplies are interconnected in parallel, suitable interconnections must be made so that one supply (the master) operates to control the other (the slave). This mechanism causes the output voltages to vary in opposite polarity with respect to a common point.

COMPLIANCE VOLTAGE RANGE. On a constant-current power supply the compliance voltage is the voltage range required to sustain a given value of constant current throughout a range of load resistances.

A constant-current power supply is one which automatically varies the load voltage in order to constantly maintain a fixed ratio of V_{load}/R_{load}.

CONTROL RATIO. The control ratio expressed in ohms per volt is the required change in control resistance to produce a one-volt change in the output voltage.

AUTOMATIC VOLTAGE/CURRENT CROSSOVER. In some modern and sophisticated power supplies circuits exist which arrange for automatic switch-over between modes of regulation, that is, from constant voltage to constant current (or vice versa), as dictated by varying load conditions. The constant-voltage and constant-current levels can be independently adjusted within the specified voltage and current limits of the power supply. The regulation area common to both constant-voltage and constant-current operation is called the *crossover point*.

OUTPUT INPEDANCE. The effective dynamic output impedance of a power supply is the ratio of the measured peak-to-peak change in output voltage with respect to a measured peak-to-peak change in alternating load current. This impedance varies with frequency and is usually specified over a power supply's frequency range—say, from direct current to 100 kc.

RECOVERY TIME specifies in seconds the time needed for the output voltage or current to return to a value within the regulation specification after a step or abrupt load or line voltage change occurs.

RESPONSE TIME (TIME CONSTANT) is the time required after a step load or line change for the voltage or current excursion to be reduced to 37 percent of its peak value.

RECTIFIER RATINGS AND DEFINITIONS

Ratings are limiting values assigned by the manufacturer, which, if exceeded, may result in permanent impairment of performance. In order to establish safe ratings, the voltages, currents, polarities, and temperatures of the various rectifier characteristics must be specifically defined. These appear in Appendix B-6, where electrical conditions are compatible with thermal conditions.

ELECTRICAL FILTER CIRCUITS

A filter is a network primarily intended to discriminate against the passage of certain particular groups of frequencies while simultaneously passing other particular groups or portions of the frequency spectrum. Filters also serve as impedance-matching devices and functionally or electronically exist in sections, each consisting of two or more electrical components or sets of components. Sections can be connected in series or in tandem for refinement of filtering action or to improve impedance matching.

Filters may be classified according to the relative range of frequencies that they pass or reject and the type of circuitry employed. In terms of frequency, we thus have low-pass, high-pass, band-pass, or, conversely, frequency-band rejection filters; in terms of circuits we generally refer to "L," "T," or "π" sections: Basically, when filters have series capacitors schematically connected across the top of the configuration they are high-pass filters; with series-connected inductors they

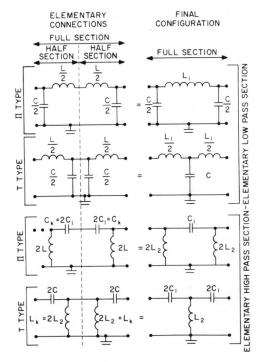

FIG. 21–9 Elementary filter circuits

are low-pass filters. In the high-pass case the leg or shunt (parallel to ground) connected elements are inductors; low-pass units have shunt-connected capacitor elements. (See Fig. 21–9.)

Full T or π filter sections are electrically assembled from elementary *half* or "L" sections, each element of which uses double-value shunt impedances or half-value series impedances according to their use respectively in high- or low-pass circuits. This means (as shown in Fig. 21–9(a)(b)) that low-pass sections use elementary $C/2$ shunt leg components while high-pass sections use elementary $2C$ series components. The inverse is true of the elementary inductances used. The equivalent full sections are shown when we combine the half and double impedance legs according to their series or parallel configuration to form the full C or L section value with which calculations are performed.

We see, then, that for constant impedance in an elementary section, the relationship between the basic L_k and C_k must always remain constant with change in frequency

since X_L increases with frequency and X_C decreases with frequency. Thus their ratio, L_k/C_k, must always be constant—hence the name constant-K filter. Going one step further, given the characteristic impedance Z_0 of the filter and its limiting or cut-off frequency (f_c) we can calculate the values of both elementary C_k and L_k elements as follows:

For low-pass:

$$C_k = \frac{1}{f_c Z_0}, \qquad L_k = \frac{Z_0}{f_c}$$

For high-pass:

$$C_k = \frac{1}{4 f_c Z_0}, \qquad L_k = \frac{Z_0}{4 f_c}$$

FILTER CHARACTERISTICS

Figure 21–10 shows the basic low-pass and high-pass constant-K types of filters plus circuit variations in what are known as M-derived configurations. The figure also graphically shows transmission characteristics (attenuation versus frequency) plus the basic equations describing inherent characteristics —impedance, cut-off frequency, attenuation, and phase shift. Note that in circuit configurations all *sectional* circuit elements bear subscripts designating whether they are series or shunt elements. Thus all top or series elements of both T and π sections are L_1 or C_1 while shunt legs are designated L_2 or C_2.

FILTER TERMINOLOGY

CHARACTERISTIC IMPEDANCE is expressed as the impedance, in ohms, which a filter's elements produce when connected as a section. In selecting and connecting filter elements, the designer usually aims to attain an impedance which matches some adjacent circuit's input or output impedance in order to produce maximum transfer of power. Using *sectional* filter elements L_1, L_2, C_1, C_2 (see Fig. 21–10), low-pass and high-pass characteristic impedances are respectively $Z_0 = L_1/C_2$ and $Z_0 = L_2/C_1$.

THE PASS BAND of a filter is the frequency spectrum that is transmitted with little or no loss.

THE STOP BAND is the area of a filter's frequency spectrum where deliberate attenuation exists. Attenuation may vary and is usually least near the cut-off frequency, rising as frequency departs from this value.

THE CUT-OFF FREQUENCY of a filter network is the point at the beginning or end of the pass-band characteristic where the attenuation is 6 db or more greater than the minimum or top amplitude point of the frequency characteristic curve.

ATTENUATION in a filter is the ratio of the output currents to the input currents when both ends of the filter network are terminated in their characteristic impedance.

THE PHASE SHIFT of a filter at a given frequency is the amount, in angular measure, or in radians, that the output currents in a filter lag behind the input currents. Curves showing this variation appear in Fig. 4–0.

RC FILTERS using series R followed by shunt C give low-pass performance with gradual frequency characteristics compared to LC filters; they are the simplest of all types and are often used in power supplies where regulation is of minor importance.

LR FILTERS using series L and shunt R elements have restricted usage and are found chiefly in impedance-matching circuits.

M-DERIVED FILTERS are a variety of the constant-K filter where, in order to obtain a sharper cut-off characteristic, either of the shunt or series elements is resonated with a reactance of the opposite sign. When the reactance is added to the series arm, the section is said to be *shunt derived;* if added to the shunt arm, it is called *series derived.*

FIG. 21–10 Summary of filter characteristics

TYPE	ATTEN-UATION	STRUCTURE π	STRUCTURE T	C_1	L_1	C_2	L_2	PASSBAND Z_0	$f\infty$	f_c	$\dfrac{f\infty}{f_c}$
"K"	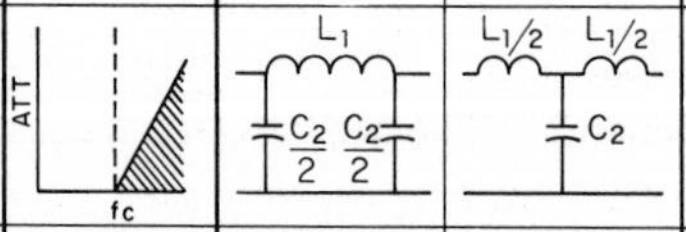	L_1 ; $\frac{C_2}{2}$ $\frac{C_2}{2}$	$\frac{L_1}{2}$ $\frac{L_1}{2}$; C_2		$\dfrac{Z_o}{\pi f_c}$ $-L_k-$	$\dfrac{1}{\pi f_c Z_o}$ $-C_k-$		$\sqrt{\dfrac{L_1}{C_2}}$	∞	$\dfrac{1}{\pi\sqrt{L_1 C_2}}$	∞
"m_1"	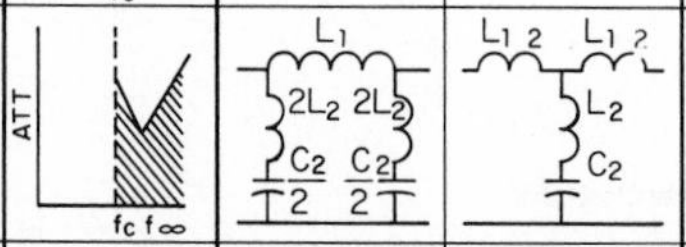	L_1 ; $2L_2$ $2L_2$; $\frac{C_2}{2}$ $\frac{C_2}{2}$	$\frac{L_1}{2}$ $\frac{L_1}{2}$; L_2 ; C_2		mL_k	mC_k	$\dfrac{1-m^2}{4m}L_k$	$\sqrt{\dfrac{L_1}{C_2}}$	$\dfrac{1}{2\pi\sqrt{L_2 C_2}}$	$\dfrac{1}{\pi\sqrt{C_2(L_1+4L_2)}}$	$\sqrt{1+\dfrac{L_1}{4L_2}}$
"m_2"		C_1 ; $\frac{C_2}{2}$ $\frac{C_2}{2}$ L_1	$2C_1$ $2C_1$; $\frac{L_1}{2}$ C_2 $\frac{L_1}{2}$	$\dfrac{1-m^2}{4m}C_k$	mL_k	mC_k		$\sqrt{\dfrac{L_1}{C_2}}$	$\dfrac{1}{2\pi\sqrt{L_1 C_1}}$	$\dfrac{1}{\pi\sqrt{L_1(C_2+4C_1)}}$	$\sqrt{1+\dfrac{C_2}{4C_1}}$
"K"	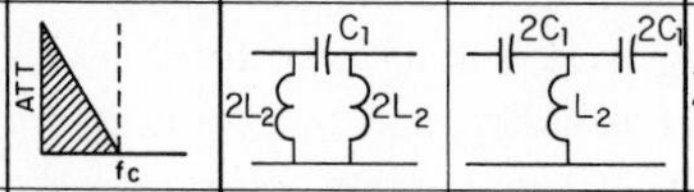	C_1 ; $2L_2$ $2L_2$	$2C_1$ $2C_1$; L_2	$\dfrac{1}{4\pi f_c Z_o}$ $-C_k-$			$\dfrac{Z_o}{4\pi f_c}$ $-L_k-$	$\sqrt{\dfrac{L_2}{C_1}}$	0	$\dfrac{1}{4\pi\sqrt{L_2 C_1}}$	∞
"m_1"	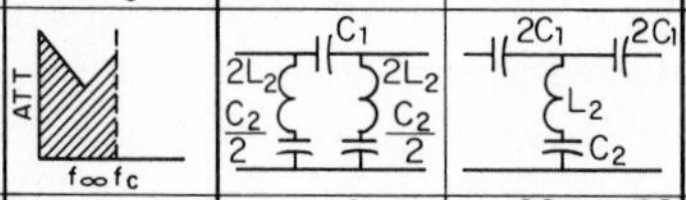	$2L_2$ C_1 $2L_2$; $\frac{C_2}{2}$ $\frac{C_2}{2}$	$2C_1$ $2C_1$; L_2 ; C_2	$\dfrac{C_k}{m}$	$\dfrac{4m}{1-m^2}C_k$		$\dfrac{L_k}{m}$	$\sqrt{\dfrac{L_2}{C_1}}$	$\dfrac{1}{2\pi\sqrt{L_2 C_2}}$	$\dfrac{1}{4\pi}\sqrt{\dfrac{1}{L_2 C_1}+\dfrac{4}{L_2 C_2}}$	$\sqrt{1+\dfrac{C}{4C_1}}$
"m_2"		C_1 ; L_1 ; $2L_2$ $2L_2$	$2C_1$ $2C_1$; $\frac{L_1}{2}$ $\frac{L_1}{2}$ L_2	$\dfrac{C_k}{m}$	$\dfrac{4m}{1-m^2}L_k$		$\dfrac{L_k}{m}$	$\sqrt{\dfrac{L_2}{C_1}}$	$\dfrac{1}{2\pi\sqrt{L_1 C_1}}$	$\dfrac{1}{4\pi}\sqrt{\dfrac{1}{L_2 C_2}+\dfrac{4}{L_1 C_1}}$	$\sqrt{1+\dfrac{L_1}{4L_2}}$

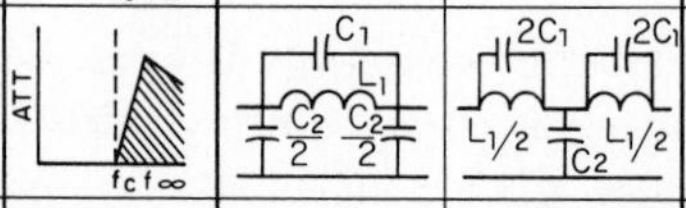

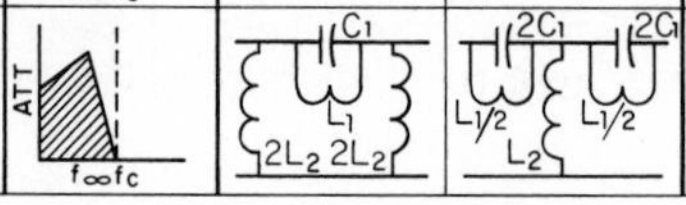

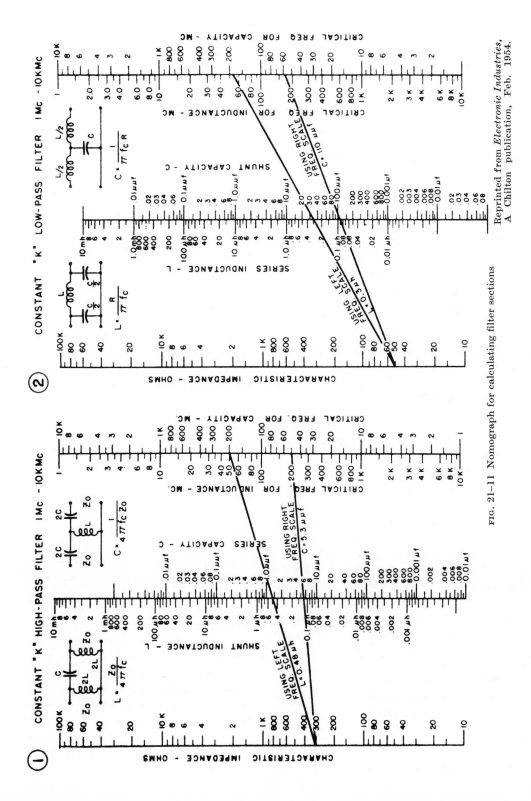

FIG. 21-11 Nomograph for calculating filter sections

Reprinted from *Electronic Industries*,
A Chilton publication, Feb. 1954.

Now in the resonating process the ratio of a resonated element's impedance to the impedance of its corresponding constant-K section is called its M factor—hence the name M-derived. In performance the ratio M turns out to be related to the ratio of cut-off frequency and the frequency of infinite attenuation. It is best fixed at a value between zero and one. For small values of M the sharpness of cut-off increases while the attenuation also increases. For a good trade-off, a value of $M = .6$ is optimum for most applications.

It should be noted that at resonance in M-derived filters we encounter an attenuation peak called the "notch" frequency which is directly dependent upon the Q of the resonant arm of the derived sections.

COMPOSITE FILTERS are made up of cascaded constant-K and M-derived sections in order to "tailor-in" specifically desired shapes of cut-off and attenuation characteristics.

FILTER APPLICATIONS

Tailored networks and filter design have wide usage in electronic applications. Among those most frequently encountered we might list the following:

1. Power-supply filters serve to reduce ripple voltage.

2. Telephone circuit band-pass selectors are used to match line or circuit impedances and to give specific response characteristics.

3. RFI or TVI reduction filters are low- or high-pass filters which are used with signal or communication equipment to reduce noise.

4. Transmitter output networks are used to give specific output frequency characteristics, to match impedances, or to reduce harmonic output or distortion.

5. Sideband splatter reduction filters are a form of transmitter output filters usable in specific types of transmission.

EXAMPLE OF FILTER CALCULATION

Design characteristics and element sizes can be readily calculated with the aid of the nomographs in Fig. 21–11.

For example, suppose we wish to design a rejection filter for antenna noise rejection in a TV receiver below 50 mc. If the antenna impedance is 300 ohms, we lay a straight edge between 300 on the left-hand scale and 50 mc on the inductance side of the right-hand scale. On the inductance side of the middle scale we cross at $L_k = .48$ microhenrys. Similarly a straight edge between 300 ohms and 50 mc on the capacity side of the right-hand scale tells us when intersecting the middle scale that $C_k = 5.3\ \mu\mu f$ will be required. The π filter having these values will have a series top element (C_1) of $5.5\ \mu\mu f$ since $C_k = C_1$ with shunt legs $(2L_2)$ of $.96\ \mu h$ each. If we had chosen a T filter, the series top elements would have each been $10\ \mu\mu f\ (2C_1)$ and the shunt leg L_2 or $.48\ \mu h$.

Another typical problem is to design a low-pass filter to cut off at 55 mc and match a 50-ohm input line. By employing the technique described in Nomograph 2 we obtain $C_k = 11\ \mu\mu f$ and $L_k = .3/\mu h$.

EXTENDING FREQUENCY RANGE

Since the reactive values are inversely proportional to the critical frequency, it is a simple matter to extend the frequency range by multiplying or dividing by a proportionality factor. An example using audio frequencies will illustrate this. Suppose, in the first problem above, we wanted to match a high-pass filter cutting off below 50 cps (instead of 50 mc) to 300 ohms. The same lines would be drawn on Nomograph 1, but the capacitive and inductive values would be multiplied by the ratio of the frequencies $(50 \times 10^6)/50$, or 1 million. Thus, the elements would be $C_k = 5.3\ \mu f$ and $L_k = .48$ henrys. The same rule applies to low-pass filters. Stated in other words, the reactive values increase in inverse proportion to the frequency. Conversely, as the frequency goes up in multiples of that shown on the nomographs, the L and C values are made smaller in the same ratio.

Appendices

Appendix

General Electronics A

Appendix A-1
Symbols for Electronic Diagrams

ANTENNAS

general

dipole

loop

counterpoise

ATTENUATORS

balanced

unbalanced

BATTERIES

d-c source;
general—one cell

multicell

CAPACITOR

general

shielded

adjustable

mechanically linked

variable differential

CORE

memory

toroidal

CRYSTAL UNIT, PIEZOELEC-
TRIC

EARPHONE, TELEPHONE
RECEIVER, HEARING AID

general

FUSE

general

fusible element

INDUCTOR WINDING

 OR

general

magnetic core

tapped

adjustable

continuously adjustable

LAMPS

ballast lamp or tube

a-c glow, cold cathode or
neon

incandescent

MICROPHONE

general

directional

PICKUP

mechanoelectric
(complete)

RECTIFIER, METALLIC

general

full-wave bridge

349

RELAY

basic

coil

2-pole, double make

polarized relay with
transfer contact

RESISTOR

general

tapped

adjustable contact
variable

SHIELDING

- - - - - - - -

electric or magnetic

SIGNALLING DEVICES

bell

buzzer

horn, loudspeaker,
siren, howler

sounder, telegraph

SWITCH

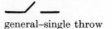

general–single throw

general–double throw

general–knife

pushbutton–circuit
closing (make)

pushbutton–circuit
opening (break)

SYNCHRO

may have letter symbol
to indicate type

transformer, receiver,
transmitter (complete)

differential receiver,
transmitter (complete)

TELEGRAPH KEY

(complete)

TERMINAL BOARD OR STRIP

(4 terminals shown)

THERMISTOR

general (complete)

with independent
integral heater (complete)

THERMOCOUPLE
(all symbols complete)

general

TRANSFORMER

general; in coaxial and
waveguide, taper or step
transformer without mode
change

magnetic core

shielded

adjustable inductance–
1 winding adjustable

mutual inductor,
adjustable inductance–
constant current trans-
former

autotransformer

VARISTOR

asymmetrical

symmetrical

VIBRATOR

shunt drive (typical)

separate drive (typical)

SEMICONDUCTOR DEVICES

PNP transistors;
arrow pointing up is NPN

P-type field-effects transistor; arrow pointing up
is N-type

PNPN transistor (hook or
conjugate-emitter connec-
tion); arrow reversed is
NPNP

breakdown PN diode (or
Zener diode)

varactor—voltage-
variable capacitor

tunnel diode
(letter may be T)

TUBE, ELECTRON

triode

pentode, equipotential cathode

twin triode, equipotential cathode

rectifier; d-c voltage regulator (d-c glow lamp is same)

phototube

photomultiplier

cathode-ray, electric field deflection (electrostatic)

cathode-ray, magnetic deflection

vapor rectifier, single-anode, pool type with ignitor

magnetron, tunable, aperture coupled

reflex klystron, integral cavity, aperture coupled

TRANSMISSION PATH

—— wire

air or space

shielded 5-conductor cable, separated for convenience on complete symbol

CHASSIS FRAME

(not necessarily at ground potential)

GROUND

COAXIAL CABLE

(used with recognition symbols at path ends and intermediate points)

ATTENUATOR, UNIDIRECTIONAL

(shown: attenuation in main direction, 1 db; opposite direction, 55 db)

CIRCULATOR

(arrow as shown indicates power flow to next arm, but not to others)

COUPLER, DIRECTIONAL

general; arrows indicate direction of power flow

aperture coupling, 30 db loss

loop coupling

probe coupling

resistance coupling

COUPLING

by loop to space

by loop to guided transmission path

by probe to space

by loop from coaxial to circular waveguide with d-c grounds connected

by probe from co-axial to rectangular waveguide with d-c grounds connected

FIELD POLARIZATION

rotator

amplitude modulator

FLANGES

→ plain

—< choke

HYBRID

general

rectangular waveguide and coaxial coupling

ISOLATION, D-C

of waveguide path (intentional)

RESONATOR

general

tunable, with adjustable Q coupled by probe to coaxial system

TERMINATORS

cable (line at left)

—— open circuit (not a fault)

short circuit (not a fault)

coaxial cable and waveguide—movable short

series capacitor, path open

series inductor, path shorted

TRANSDUCER, MODE

general

from rectangular to circular waveguide

WAVEGUIDE

circular

rectangular

ridged

Appendix A-2
Glossary of Electronic Terms

Agonic. An imaginary line of the earth's surface passing through points where the magnetic declination is 0°; that is, points where the compass points to true north.

Ammeter. An instrument for measuring the amount of electron flow in amperes.

Ampere. The basic unit of electrical current.

Ampere-turn. The magnetizing force produced by a current of one ampere flowing through a coil of one turn.

Amplification. The process of increasing the strength (current, power, or voltage) of a signal.

Amplification factor (μ). The ratio of a small change in plate voltage to a small change in grid voltage, with all other electrode voltages constant, required to produce the small change in plate current.

Amplifier. A device used to increase the signal voltage, current, or power, generally composed of a vacuum tube or transistor and associated circuit called a STAGE. It may contain several stages in order to obtain a desired gain.

Amplitude. The maximum instantaneous value of an alternating voltage or current, measured in either the positive or negative direction.

Anode. A positive electrode; the plate of a vacuum tube.

Aquadag. A graphite coating on the inside of certain cathode-ray tubes for collecting secondary electrons emitted by the screen.

Arc. A flash caused by an electric circuit ionizing a gas or vapor.

Armature. The rotating part of an electric motor or generator. The moving part of a relay or vibrator.

Atom. The smallest particle into which matter may be divided by chemical means.

Attenuation. The reduction in the strength of a signal.

Autotransformer. A transformer in which the primary and secondary are connected together in one winding.

Azimuth. The angular measurement in a horizontal plane and in a clockwise direction, beginning at a point oriented to north.

Ballast resistor. A resistor that has the characteristic of decreasing its resistance when current flow decreases.

Battery. Two or more primary or secondary cells connected together electrically. The term does not apply to a single cell.

Bias. Vacuum tube—the difference of potential between the control grid and the cathode; transistor—the difference of potential between the base and emitter and the base and collector; magnetic

amplifier—the level of flux density in the magnetic amplifier core under no-signal condition.

Bias winding. The winding on the core of a magnetic amplifier that controls the bias.

Breakdown diode. (*See* Zener diode.)

Breaker points. Metal contacts that open and close a circuit at timed intervals.

Brush. The conducting material, usually a block of carbon, bearing against the commutator or slip rings through which the current flows in or out.

Bus bar. A primary power distribution point connected to the main power source.

Capacitor. Two electrodes or sets of electrodes in the form of plates, separated from each other by an insulating material called the dielectric.

Cascade. In series, such as tuning circuits or amplifier stages used one after another.

Choke coil. A coil of low ohmic resistance and high impedance to alternating current.

Circuit. The complete path of an electric current.

Circuit breaker. An electromagnetic or thermal device that opens a circuit when the current in the circuit exceeds a predetermined amount. Circuit breakers can be reset.

Circular mil. An area equal to that of a circle with a diameter of 0.001 inch. It is used for measuring the cross section of wires.

Coaxial cable. A transmission line consisting of two conductors concentric with and insulated from each other.

Commutator. The copper segments on the armature of a motor or generator. It is cylindrical in shape and is used to pass power into or from the brushes. It is a switching device.

Conductance. The ability of a material to conduct or carry an electric current. It is the reciprocal of the resistance of the material, and is expressed in mhos.

Conductivity. The ease with which a substance transmits electricity.

Conductor. Any material suitable for carrying electric current.

Contact rectifier. Two different solids in contact, in which rectification is due to greater conductivity across the contact in one direction than the other.

Core. A magnetic material that affords an easy path for magnetic flux lines in a coil.

Coulomb. A unit of electrical charge; the quantity of electrical charge created by a steady flow of one ampere for one second.

Counter emf. Counter electromotive force; an emf induced in a coil or armature that opposes the applied voltage.

Counting circuit. A circuit which receives uniform pulses representing units to be counted and produces a voltage in proportion to their frequency.

Current limiter. A protective device similar to a fuse, usually used in high-amperage circuits.

Cycle. One complete positive and one complete negative alternation of a current or voltage.

Detection. The process of separating the modulation component from the received signal.

Dielectric. An insulator; a term that refers to the insulating material between the plates of a capacitor.

Diode. Vacuum tube—a two-element tube that contains a cathode and plate; semiconductor—a material of either germanium or silicon that is manufactured to allow current to flow in only one direction. Diodes are used as rectifiers and detectors.

Direct current. An electric current that flows in one direction only.

Distortion. The production of an output waveform which is not a true reproduction of the input waveform. Distortion may consist of irregularities in amplitude, frequency, or phase.

Doppler effect. An apparent change in the frequency of a sound or electromagnetic wave reaching a receiver when there is relative motion between the source and the receiver.

Duct. An atmospheric phenomenon consisting of two layers between which electromagnetic waves are channeled.

Eddy current. Induced circulating currents in a conducting material that are caused by a varying magnetic field.

Efficiency. The ratio of output power to input power, generally expressed as a percentage.

Electricity. The science which treats of the phenomena and laws of things electrical.

Electrode. A terminal used to emit, collect, or control electrons and ions; a terminal at which electric current passes from one medium into another.

Electrolysis. Corrosion caused by a current flowing in and out of the surface of a conductor.

Electrolyte. A solution of a substance which is capable of conducting electricity. An electrolyte may be in the form of either a liquid or a paste.

Electromagnet. A magnet made by passing current through a coil of wire wound on a soft iron core.

Electromotive force (emf). The force that produces an electric current in a circuit.

Electron. A negatively charged particle of matter.

Electron emission. The liberation of electrons from a body into space under the influence of heat, light, impact, chemical disintegration, or potential difference.

Electronic switch. A circuit which causes a start-stop action or switching action by electronic means.

Energy. The ability or capacity to do work.

Equivalent circuit. A diagrammatic arrangement of coils, resistors, and capacitors, representing the effects of a more complicated circuit in order to permit easier analysis.

Farad. The unit of capacitance.

Feedback. A transfer of energy from the output circuit of a device back to its input.

Field. The space containing electric or magnetic lines of force.

Field winding. The coil used to provide the magnetizing force in motors and generators.

Filter. A combination of circuit elements designed to pass a definite range of frequencies, attenuating all others.

Fluorescence. The property of emitting light as the immediate result of, and only during, electronic bombardment.

Flux field. All electric or magnetic lines of force in a given region.

Free electrons. Electrons which are loosely held and consequently tend to move at random among the atoms of the material.

Frequency. The number of complete cycles per second existing in any form of wave motion, such as the number of cycles per second of an alternating current.

Full-wave rectifier circuit. A circuit which utilizes both the positive and the negative alternations of an alternating current to produce a direct current.

Fuse. A protective device inserted in series with a circuit. It contains a metal that will melt or break when current is increased beyond a specific value for a definite period of time.

Gain. The ratio of the output power, voltage, or current to the input power, voltage, or current, respectively.

Galvanometer. An instrument used to measure small d-c currents.

Gas tube. A tube that gives certain electrical characteristics because it is filled with a certain type of gas.

Gating (cathode-ray tube). Applying a rectangular voltage to the grid or cathode of a CRT to sensitize it during the sweep time only.

Generator. A machine that converts mechanical energy into electrical energy.

Grid. A wire, usually in the form of a spiral, that controls the electron flow in a vacuum tube.

Grid detection. Detection by rectification in the grid circuit of a detector.

Grid leak. A high resistance connected across the grid capacitor or between the grid and the cathode to provide a d-c path from grid to cathode and to limit the accumulation of charge on the grid.

Ground. A metallic connection with the earth to establish ground potential. Also, a common return to a point of zero potential. The chassis of a receiver or a transmitter is sometimes the common return, and therefore the "ground" of the unit.

Harmonic. An integral multiple of a fundamental frequency. (The second harmonic is twice the frequency of the fundamental or first harmonic.)

Henry. The basic unit of inductance.

Heptode. A vacuum tube having seven electrodes.

Heterodyne. To beat or mix two signals of different frequencies.

Hexode. A vacuum tube having six electrodes.

Hole. In semiconductors, the space in an atom left vacant by a departed electron. Holes flow in a direction opposite to that of electrons, are considered to be current carriers, and bear a positive charge.

Horsepower. The English unit of power, equal to work done at the rate of 550 foot-pounds per second. Equal to 746 watts of electrical power.

Hysteresis. A lagging of the magnetic flux in a magnetic material behind the magnetizing force which is producing it.

Impedance. The total opposition offered to the flow of an alternating current. It may consist of any combination of resistance, inductive reactance, and capacitive reactance.

Incident wave. A wave striking an object.

Inductance. The property of a circuit which tends to oppose a change in the existing current.

Induction. The act or process of producing voltage by the relative motion of a magnetic field across a conductor.

Inductive reactance. The opposition to the flow of alternating or pulsating current caused by the inductance of a circuit. It is measured in ohms.

Inductor. A circuit element designed so that its inductance is its most important electrical property; a coil.

In phase. Applied to the condition that exists when two waves of the same frequency pass through their maximum and minimum values of like polarity at the same instant.

Intensity modulation. The control of the brilliance of the trace on the screen of a cathode-ray tube in conformity with the signal.

Inversely. Inverted or reversed in position or relationship.

Isogonic line. An imaginary line drawn through points on the earth's surface where the magnetic deviation is equal.

Joule. A unit of energy or work. A joule of energy is liberated by one ampere flowing for one second through a resistance of one ohm.

Kilo. A prefix meaning 1,000.

Klystron. A tube in which oscillations are generated by the bunching of electrons (that is, velocity modulation). This tube utilizes the transit time between two given electrodes to deliver pulsating energy to a cavity resonator in order to sustain oscillations within the cavity.

Knee. An abrupt change in direction between two fairly straight segments of a curve.

Lag. The amount one wave is behind another in time; expressed in electrical degrees.

Laminated core. A core built up from thin sheets of metal and used in transformers and relays.

Lead. The opposite of lag. Also, a wire or connection.

Linear. Having an output which varies in direct proportion to the input.

Line of force. A line in an electric or magnetic field that shows the direction of the force.

Load. The power that is being delivered by any power producing device. The equipment that uses the power from the power producing device.

Magnetic amplifier. A saturable reactor type device that is used in a circuit to amplify or control.

Magnetic circuit. The complete path of magnetic lines of force.

Magnetic field. The space in which a magnetic force exists.

Magnetic flux. The total number of lines of force issuing from a pole of a magnet.

Magnetize. To convert a material into a magnet by causing the molecules to rearrange.

Magneto. A generator which produces alternating current and has a permanent magnet as its field.

Magnetron. A vacuum-tube oscillator containing two electrodes, in which the flow of electrons from cathode to anode is controlled by an externally applied magnetic field.

Megger. A test instrument used to measure insulation resistance and other high resistances. It is a portable hand-operated d-c generator used as an ohmmeter.

Megohm. A million ohms.

Mho. The unit of conductance, which is the reciprocal of resistance.

Micro. A prefix meaning one-millionth.

Milli. A prefix meaning one-thousandth.

Milliammeter. An ammeter that measures in thousandths of an ampere.

Modulation. The process of varying the amplitude (amplitude modulation), frequency (frequency modulation), or phase (phase modulation) of a carrier wave in accordance with other signals in order to convey intelligence. The modulating signal may be an audio-frequency signal, video signal (as in TV), or electrical pulses or tones to operate relays, etc.

Molecule. The atom or group of atoms that constitute the smallest particle in which a compound or material can exist separately.

Motor-Generator. A motor and a generator with a common shaft used to convert line voltages to other voltages or frequencies.

Mutual inductance. A circuit property existing when the relative position of two inductors causes the magnetic lines of force from one to link with the turns of the other.

Negative charge. The electrical charge carried by a body which has an excess of electrons.

Neutron. A particle having the weight of a proton but carrying no electric charge. It is located in the nucleus of an atom.

Nonlinear. Having an output which does not vary in direct proportion to the input.

Nucleus. The central part of an atom, mainly comprised of protons and neutrons. It is the part of the atom that has the most mass.

Null. Zero, a minimum.

Octode. A vacuum tube having eight electrodes.

Ohm. The unit of electrical resistance.

Ohmmeter. An instrument for directly measuring resistance in ohms.

Oscilloscope. An instrument for showing, visually, graphical representations of the waveforms encountered in electrical circuits.

Overload. A load greater than the rated load of an electrical device.

Permalloy. An alloy of nickel and iron having an abnormally high magnetic permeability.

Permeability. A measure of the ease with which magnetic lines of force can flow through a material as compared to air.

Phase difference. The time in electrical degrees by which one wave leads or lags another.

Phosphorescence. The property of emitting light for some time after excitation by electronic bombardment.

Plate. The principal electrode in a tube to which the electron stream is attracted.

Plate current. The current flowing in the plate circuit of a vacuum tube.

Plate detection. The operation of a vacuum-tube detector at or near cut-off so that the input signal is rectified in the plate circuit.

Plate resistance (r_p). The internal resistance to the flow of alternating current between the cathode and plate of a tube. It is equal to a small change in plate voltage divided by the corresponding change in plate current, and is expressed in ohms. It is also called a-c resistance, internal impedance, plate impedance, and dynamic plate impedance. The static plate resistance (R_p), or resistance to the flow of direct current, is a different value.

Polarity. The character of having magnetic poles, or electric changes.

Pole. The section of a magnet where the flux lines are concentrated; also where they enter and leave the magnet. An electrode of a battery.

Polyphase. A circuit that utilizes more than one phase of alternating current.

Positive charge. The electrical charge carried by a body which has become deficient in electrons.

Potential. The amount of charge held by a body as compared to another point or body. Usually measured in volts.

Potentiometer. A variable voltage divider; a resistor which has a variable contact arm so that any portion of the potential applied between its ends may be selected.

Power. The rate of doing work or the rate of expending energy. The unit of electrical power is the watt.

Power factor. The ratio of the actual power of an alternating or pulsating current, as measured by a wattmeter, to the apparent power, as indicated by ammeter and voltmeter readings. The power factor of an inductor, capacitor, insulator is an expression of their losses.

Prime mover. The source of mechanical power used to drive the rotor of a generator.

Proton. A positively charged particle in the nucleus of an atom.

Push-pull circuit. A push-pull circuit usually refers to an amplifier circuit using two vacuum tubes in such a fashion that when one vacuum tube is operating on a positive alternation, the other vacuum tube operates on a negative alternation.

Ratio. The value obtained by dividing one number by another, indicating their relative proportions.

Reactance. The opposition offered to the flow of an alternating current by the inductance, capacitance, or both, in any circuit.

Reciprocal. The value obtained by dividing the number 1 by any quantity.

Rectifiers. Devices used to change alternating current to unidirectional current. These may be vacuum tubes, semiconductors such as germanium and silicon, dry-disc rectifiers such as selenium and copper oxide, and also certain types of crystal.

Relaxation oscillator. A circuit for the generation of nonsinusoidal waves by gradually storing and quickly releasing energy either in the electric field of a capacitor or in the magnetic field of an inductor.

Relay. An electromechanical switching device that can be used as a remote control.

Reluctance. A measure of the opposition that a material offers to magnetic lines of force.

Resistance. The opposition to the flow of current caused by the nature and physical dimensions of a conductor.

Resistor. A circuit element whose chief characteristic is resistance; used to oppose the flow of current.

Resonance. The condition existing in a circuit in which the inductive and capacitive reactances cancel each other.

Resonance curve. A graphical representation of the manner in which a resonant circuit responds to various frequencies at and near the resonant frequency.

Retentivity. The measure of the ability of a material to hold its magnetism.

Reverberation. The continuation of sound by excessive reflection.

Rheostat. A variable resistor.

Saturable reactor. A control device that uses a small d-c current to control a large a-c current by controlling core flux density.

Saturation. The condition existing in any circuit when an increase in the driving signal produces no further change in the resultant effect.

Self-induction. The process by which a circuit induces an emf into itself by its own magnetic field.

Series-wound. A motor or generator in which the armature is wired in series with the field winding.

Servo. A device used to convert a small movement into one of greater distance or force.

Servomechanism. A closed-loop system that produces a force to position an object in accordance with the information that originates at the input.

Solenoid. An electromagnetic coil that contains a movable plunger.

Space charge. The cloud of electrons existing in the space between the cathode and plate in a vacuum tube, formed by the electrons emitted from the cathode in excess of those immediately attracted to the plate.

Standing wave. A distribution of current and voltage on a transmission line formed by two sets of waves traveling in opposite directions and, characterized by the presence of a number of points of successive maxima and minima in the distribution curves.

Static. A fixed nonvarying condition; without motion.

Sweep circuit. The part of a cathode-ray oscilloscope which provides a time-reference base.

Synchronous. Happening at the same time; having the same period and phase.

Synchro system. An electrical system that gives remote indications or control by means of self-synchronizing motors.

Tachometer. An instrument for indicating revolutions per minute.

Tertiary winding. A third winding on a transformer or magnetic amplifier that is used as a second control winding.

Thermistor. A resistor that is used to compensate for temperature variations in a circuit.

Thermocouple. A junction of two dissimilar metals that produces a voltage when heated.

Trace. A visible line or lines appearing on the screen of a cathode-ray tube in operation.

Transformer. A device composed of two or more coils, linked by magnetic lines of force, used to transfer energy from one circuit to another.

Transmission lines. Any conductor or system of conductors used to carry electrical energy from its source to a load.

Triggering. Starting an action in another circuit, which then functions for a time under its own control.

Triode. A three-electrode vacuum tube, containing a cathode, control grid, and plate.

Tuned circuit. A resonant circuit.

Vacuum tube. An evacuated envelope containing two or more electrodes.

Vector. A line used to represent both direction and magnitude.

Video amplifier. A circuit capable of amplifying a very wide range of frequencies, including and exceeding the audio band of frequencies.

Volt. The unit of electrical potential.

Watt. The unit of electrical power.

Wattmeter. An instrument for measuring electric power in watts.

Waveform. The shape of the wave obtained when instantaneous values of an a-c quantity are plotted against time in rectangular coordinates.

Wavelength (λ). The distance, usually expressed in meters, traveled by a wave during the time interval of one complete cycle. It is equal to the velocity divided by the frequency.

Zener diode. A solid-state semiconductor that has voltage-regulation characteristics when subjected to reversed bias.

ELECTRONIC CIRCUIT AND COMPONENT ABBREVIATIONS

a-c	alternating current	kw	kilowatt
a	ampere	kw-hr	kilowatt-hour
A	area	H	magnetic field intensity
AF	audio-frequency	mmf.	magnetomotive force
C	capacitance	M	mega (10^6)
X_c	capacitive reactance	MΩ	megohm
c	centi (10^{-2})	μ	micro (10^{-6})
cm	centimeter	μa	microampere
G	conductance	μf	microfarad
Q	coulomb	μh	microhenry
cemf	counterelectromotive force	$\mu\mu$f	micromicrofarad
I	current (d-c or rms value)	μv	microvolt
i	current (instantaneous value)	m	milli (10^{-3})
d	deci (10^{-1})	ma	milliampere
dk	deka (10)	mh	millihenry
K, k	dielectric constant	mw	milliwatt
E	difference in potential (d-c or rms value)	M	mutual inductance
e	difference in potential (instantaneous value)	n	nano (10^{-9})
d-c	direct current	Ω	ohm
emf	electromotive force	p	pico (10^{-12})
f	frequency	pf	picofarad
G	giga (10^9)	P	power
h	hecto (10^2)	R	resistance
h	henry	rpm	revolutions per minute
hp	horsepower	rms.	root mean square
Z	impedance	T	tera (10^{12})
L	inductance	t	time
X_L	inductive reactance	T	torque
k	kilo (10^3)	v	volt
kv	kilovolt	w	watt
kv-a	kilovolt-ampere		

SOME ABBREVIATIONS USED IN ELECTRONIC ILLUSTRATIONS

A	ammeter	EQ	equalizer	OHM	ohmmeter
ADJ	adjust	F	frequency meter	OSC	oscillator
AMPL	amplifier	FILT	filter	OUT	output
AR	amplifier	FL	filter	PH	phasemeter
AT	attenuator	FREQ	frequency	PREAMP	preamplifier
AUTO	automatic	FUND	fundamental	PS	power supply
AUX	auxiliary	G	galvanometer	REC	receiver
BAL	balanced	GEN	generator	REG	regulat(or) (ed)
BP	band pass	GND	ground	RU	reproducing unit
CATH FOLL	cathode follower	HARM	harmonic	SEL	selector
CONV	converter	HOR	horizontal	SIG	signal
CPS	cycles per second	HP	high pass	SYNC	synchroniz(er) (ing)
CRO	cathode ray oscilloscope	IN	input	TAB	table
CRT	cathode-ray tube	LP	low pass	TEMP	temperature
DB	decibel meter	MAN	manual	TPR	teleprinter
DEFL	deflection	MIC	microphone	VERT	vertical
DET	detector	MOD	modulator	VIB	vibrator
DIFF	difference	MV	multivibrator	VTVM	vacuum tube voltmeter
DISC	discriminator	NET	network	W	wattmeter

Appendix A-4

ALTERNATING-CURRENT WAVEFORMS

1. SYMMETRICAL

Sinusoidal

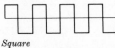

Square

Non-sinusoidal

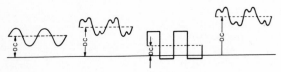

Triangular

2. NONSYMMETRICAL

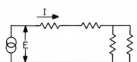

Saw-tooth

3. SUPERIMPOSED ON D-C

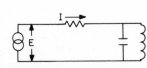

4. COMPOUNDED OF FUNDAMENTAL AND HARMONICS

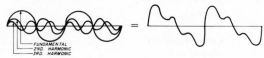

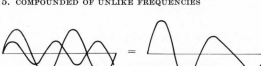

5. COMPOUNDED OF UNLIKE FREQUENCIES

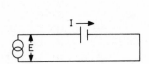 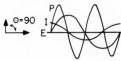

A-C CIRCUITS

RESISTIVE

$$\text{Impedance} = Z_R = R$$

Current is in phase with voltage.
Therefore, $\theta = 0$ and $\cos\theta = 1$
Power factor $= 1$
Power $= EI\cos\theta = EI$

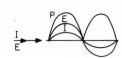

INDUCTIVE

$$\text{Impedance} = X_L = 2\pi f L$$

Current lags voltage by 90°.
Therefore, $\theta = 90°$ and $\cos\theta = 0$
Power factor $= 0$
Power $= EI\cos\theta = 0$

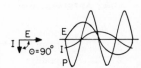

CAPACITIVE

$$\text{Impedance} = X_c = \frac{1}{2\pi f C}$$

Current leads voltage by 90°.
Therefore, $\theta = 90°$ and $\cos\theta = 0$
Power factor $= 0$
Power $= EI\cos\theta = 0$

RESISTIVE AND INDUCTIVE (CAPACITIVE)

$$\text{Impedance} = Z = \sqrt{R^2 + X^2}$$

Current lags (leads) voltage by less than 90°.
Therefore, θ is variable $= \tan^{-1} X/R$
Power factor $= \cos\theta$
Power $= EI\cos\theta$

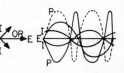

Resonance occurs when the effects of inductance and capacitance exactly oppose each other. This occurs at a single particular frequency: $f = 1/(2\pi\sqrt{LC})$

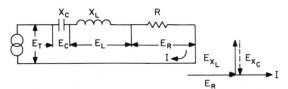

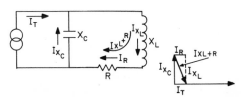

SERIES RESONANCE *occurs when:*

$$E_C = E_L \quad IX_C = IX_L \quad \text{or} \quad E_T = E_R = IR$$

A-c voltages (and sometimes reactances) are added *vectorially.* Voltage across inductor (or inductive reactance) opposes voltage across capacitor (or capacitive reactance).

Series resonance causes voltage step-up. Voltage step-up is the ratio of the voltage across either of the reactive elements to the voltage across the source. Its value is

$$\frac{E_{XC}}{E_T} = \frac{E_{XL}}{E_T} = Q = \frac{X_C}{R} = \frac{X_L}{R}$$

Impedance: $\quad Z = R$

PARALLEL RESONANCE *occurs when:*

$$IX_C = IX_L \quad I_T = I_R$$

Branch currents are added *vectorially.* Current through inductor opposes capacitor current.

Parallel resonance causes current step-up. Current step-up is the ratio of the current through either of the reactive branches to the total line current. Its value is:

$$\frac{I_{XC}}{I_T} = \frac{I_{XL}}{I_T} = Q = \frac{X_C}{R} = \frac{X_L}{R}$$

Impedance: $\quad Z = \dfrac{1}{CR}$

Appendix A-5
Nomenclature for Military
Communications-Electronics Equipment

AN nomenclature uses the following equipment indicator letters:

INSTALLATION

A   airborne (in aircraft)
B   underwater mobile, submarine
C   air transportable (inactivated)
D   pilotless carrier
F   fixed
G   ground, general use
K   amphibious
M   ground, mobile (vehicle carries only this equippment)
P   pack or portable
S   water surface craft
T   ground, transportable
U   general utility (two or three installations; airborne, shipboard, and ground)
V   ground, vehicular (vehicle has other functions besides carrying this equipment)

TYPE OF EQUIPMENT

A   invisible light, heat radiation
B   pigeon
C   carrier (wire)
D   radiac
F   photographic
G   telegraph or teletype
I   interphone and public address
K   telemetering
L   countermeasures (inactivated)
M   meterological
N   sound in air
P   radar
Q   sonar and underwater sound
R   radio
S   special types or combinations
T   telephone (wire)
V   visual and visible light
X   facsimile or television

FUNCTION

A   auxiliary assemblies (not complete operating sets)
B   bombing
C   communications (receiving and transmitting)
D   direction finder
G   gun or searchlight directing
H   recording (photographic, meterological, and sound)
L   searchlight control
M   maintenance and test assemblies (incl. tools)
N   navigational aids
P   reproducing (photographic and sound)
Q   special, or combination of types
R   receiving
S   detecting and/or range and bearing
T   transmitting
W   remote control
X   identification and recognition

Appendix A-6
Military Specifications

CONDENSED LIST OF STANDARD SPECIFICATIONS

MIL-STD-15A: electrical and electronic symbols

MIL-STD-16B: electrical and electronic reference designations

MIL-STD-103: abbreviations for electrical and electronic use

MIL-STD-108D: definitions of and basic requirements for enclosures for electric and electronic equipment

MIL-STD-122: color code for chassis wiring

MIL-STD-188: military communications system technical standards

MIL-STD-196: joint electronics-type designation system

MIL-STD-200D: electron tubes and semiconductor devices, diodes

MIL-STD-202A: test methods for electronic and electric component parts

MIL-STD-221A: color code for resistors

MIL-STD-243: types and definitions of models for communications equipment

MIL-STD-283: letter symbols for electrical and electronic quantities

MIL-STD-285: attenuation measurements for enclosures, electromagnetic shielding, for electronic test purposes

MIL-STD-442: telemetry standards for guided missiles and aircraft

GENERAL ELECTRONIC EQUIPMENT SPECIFICATIONS

MIL-E-5400A: aircraft electronic equipment

MIL-E-5272A: environmental testing, aeronautical and associated equipment

MIL-I-6181B: interference limits, tests and design requirements, aircraft

JAN-I-225: interference measurement, 150 kc to 20 mc

MIL-I-11748B: interference reduction

JAN-P-658: packaging and packing of electronic, electrical, and electromechanical equipment and spare parts

MIL-R-15668A: a radio-communication transmitting equipment, low-frequency, medium and high power

MIL-S-4473C: shielding of magnetron tubes, magnets, and components containing magnets, for air shipment

JAN-S-44: shock testing mechanism for electrical indicating instruments

MIL-S-901B: test for shipboard application class HI (high impact) shockproof equipment

MIL-T-945A: test equipment for use with electronic equipment

MIL-T-5422C: aircraft electronic equipment environmental testing

MIL-T-17113: electronic equipment shock, vibration, and inclination tests

MIL-T-20060: test equipment, shock and vibration, for navigational equipment, and test methods

MIL-T-152A: treatment, moisture and fungus-resistance, for communications, electronic, and associated equipment

DETAILED COMPONENT SPECIFICATIONS

Starred specifications (*) may have "slash" sheets which should be consulted for details on specific types, or supplements, or both.

Absorbers, RF radiation:
MIL-A-11052: metallized plates

Accelerometers, aircraft:
MIL-A-5885A

Adapters and spacers:
JAN-A-185: for electrical indicating instruments

Antennas, airborne Communication:
MIL-A-6224D: UHF
MIL-A-6271A: VHF

Attenuators, fixed:
MIL-A-3933: coaxial line and waveguide

Batteries:
*MIL-B-18C: dry
*MIL-B-10154B: water-activated, dunk-type primary
MIL-B-3549: battery power supply for diagnostic instruments

Cable:
MIL-C-3885A: cable and cord assemblies, electrical
JAN-C-76: insulated hookup wire, radio and instrument
MIL-C-342A: flexible and extra flexible, 300 and 600 v
*MIL-C-17B: RF, coaxial, dual coaxial, twin connector and twin lead

Capacitors:
*MIL-C-12889A: by-pass, radio interference reduction, paper, a-c and d-c
MIL-C-11693A: feedthrough, radio interference reduction, paper, a-c and d-c
MIL-C-11015A: fixed, ceramic, general-purpose
MIL-C-20C: fixed, ceramic, temperature-compensating
*MIL-C-3871: fixed, dry electrolytic, nonpolarized, a-c

MIL-C-62A: fixed, dry electrolytic, polarized, aluminum, d-c

*MIL-C-3965B: fixed, electrolytic, tantalum

*MIL-C-11272A: fixed, glass dielectric

*MIL-C-5B: fixed, mica

*MIL-C-10950B: fixed, mica, button sytle

*MIL-C-25A: fixed, hermetically sealed in metallic cases, paper, d-c

*MIL-C-91A: fixed, nonmetallic cases, paper

MIL-C-14157A: fixed, high-reliability, paper or paper-plastic, d-c

*MIL-C-92A: variable, trimmer, air-dielectric

MIL-C-81A: variable, ceramic

MIL-C-14409: variable, piston-type, tubular trimmer

Coils:

MIL-C-1898: cored, high permeability

*MIL-C-15305A: RF and transformers, IF and RF

Connectors:

*MIL-C-3767A: electrical power, bladed type

MIL-C-5015D: AN type

MIL-C-3608: BNC, for RF cable

*MIL-C-3989: coaxial, RF

MIL-C-3643: HN, for RF cables

MIL-C-3650: LC, for RF cables

*MIL-C-71A: N, for RF cables

MIL-C-3607: pulse, for RF cables

MIL-C-3655 twin for RF cables

Couplers, directional:

MIL-C-15370A: coaxial and waveguide

Crystals and units:

MIL-C-3687A: blanks, quartz

MIL-C-15729A: raw quartz

MIL-C-16C: units, quartz

CR-1A/AR: pressure-mounted

KIL-C-239C: units, quartz

CR-5/U

*MIL-C-3098B: units, quartz

MIL-C-12813A: units, quartz, wire mounted, metal-plated

Dummy loads:

*MIL-D-3954A: electrical, waveguide

Electron tubes and crystal rectifiers:

*MIL-E-1D

*MIL-E-75C: tubes packaging-marking (also listed as MIL-P-75C)

Holders, crystal:

*MIL-H-10056C

Jacks and knobs:

MIL-J-641B: telephone jacks

*MIL-K-3926: control knobs

Lampholders and lights, indicator:

MIL-L-3661: bayonet base, miniature, and candelabra

Lines, RF transmission:

*MIL-L-3890: coaxial, air dielectric

Meters, electrical:

MIL-M-16125A: frequency

*MIL-M-3823: indicating, basic (sealed panel-mounting types, $1\frac{1}{2}$ inch), and scaleplates

MIL-M-17275A: indicating, d-c, 1 inch

MIL-M-10304A: indicating, panel-type, ruggedized

*MIL-M-6B: indicating, panel-type, $2\frac{1}{2}$ and $3\frac{1}{2}$ inch, general spec.

Microphones:

MIL-M-2714A: carbon, hand-held

MIL-M-11101B: dynamic

Plugs, telephone:

MIL-P-642A

Rectifiers, metallic:

*MIL-R-11050A: selenium

Relays, armature:

MIL-R-5757C

Resistance wire:

QQ-R-175 (federal spec.)

Resistors:

*MIL-R-3080B: current regulating, ballast tubes

JAN-R-29: external meter, high-voltage, ferrule terminal type

*MIL-R-11C: fixed, composition, insulated

*MIL-R-10683A: fixed, composition film, VHF

*MIL-R-10509C: fixed, film, high stability

MIL-R-11804C: fixed, film, power type

MIL-R-14293A: fixed, high-megohm, hermetically sealed

*MIL-R-93B: fixed, wirewound, accurate

JAN-R-184: fixed, wirewound, low power

MIL-R-26C: fixed, wirewound, power type

*MIL-R-94B: variable, composition

*MIL-R-19A: variable, wirewound, low operating temperature, general spec.

*MIL-R-22A: variable, wirewound, power type

Sockets:

JAN-S-28A: electron tube and accessories

*MIL-S-12883A: for electronic components, and accessories

Switches:

*MIL-S-3928: coaxial, RF transmission line

MIL-S-3786: rotary, circuit selector, low current capacity

JAN-S-63: sensitive

JAN-S-23: toggle

JAN-S-57: vacuum

Synchros:

MIL-S-20708A: general spec.

Transformers and inductors:

*MIL-T-27A: audio, power and pulse

Transistors:

*MIL-T-19500A: general spec.

Twine and tape:

MIL-T-7131A: lacing and tying

Varnish:

MIL-V-173A: moisture and fungus-resistant

Vibrators:

MIL-V-95A: interrupter and self-rectifying

Waveguide:

*MIL-W-287A: assemblies, flexible
MIL-W-3970:   assemblies, rigid
MIL-W-85C: rigid, rectangular

Wire:

MIL-W-76A: electrical, insulated, hookup, and cable
MIL-W-3861:   electrical, bare copper
MIL-W-6370B: electrical, insulated, antenna
MIL-W-3795A: electrical, tinsel
MIL-W-583A: magnet
MIL-W-13169A: electrical, for instrument test leads

Appendix A-7
How to Use the Reactance Chart

The accompanying reactance charts provide a simple direct method for obtaining, at any frequency: (1) the reactance (in ohms) of any size inductance, (2) the reactance (in ohms) of any size capacitor, (3) the resonant frequency determined by any capacitor-inductance circuit combination.

Two charts, Fig. 1 and Fig. 2, are provided, Fig. 1 for rough calculations to obtain the *approximate range* of values needed and Fig. 2 for use as a magnified replica (7 : 1) of a single square area of Fig. 1 in order to obtain accurate values surrounding the point of interest.

Both charts have four sets of scale lines superimposed on one another. For explanation refer to Fig. 2.

One set of horizontal lines	Inductance scale	Extending *right to left* with number of ohms on left termination
One set of vertical lines	Frequency scale	Extending *from top to bottom* with numbers on bottom end of lines
One set of slant lines	Frequency scale	Extending *upward to right* from lower left to upper right. Numbered on outside border
One set of slant lines	Capacitance scale	Extending *downward to right* from upper left to lower right. Numbered on inside border

BASIC PROCEDURE

Correct use of the chart arrives at the desired electrical quantity by determining the intersection of two scale lines, each representing a given electrical quantity (inductance, capacitance, frequency, or reactance) and projecting this point along another line to the final value scaled on an edge of the chart.

EXAMPLE 1

Find reactance in ohms (see point + on rough scale) for 100 mmf at 720 kc

1. Locate intersection of 100-mmf capacitance line and 720-kc frequency line.

2. Draw horizontal line from intersection over to the left-hand reactance scale where it intersects the reactance scale at *2,200 ohms*—the answer.

3. On fine scale (Fig. 2) follow same procedure.

EXAMPLE 2

Find reactance of 500 microhenries (μh) at 720 kc

1. Locate intersection of 100-mmf capacitance line and 720-kc frequency line.

2. From this intersection draw horizontal line as above to 2,200-ohm point.

To determine the resonant frequency of a 100-$\mu\mu$f capacitor and a 500-μh coil select these two slant lines and locate their intersection at 720 kc.

GENERAL PROCEDURE

After locating an intersection on the rough scale chart, Fig. 1, notice in which part or general area of a heavy-line-bounded-square the intersection lies; they go to the same general area of Fig. 2 (fine scale) since it is an expanded equivalent of the single rough-scale square where the intersection was found. This precaution is necessary since two levels of slant scale lines appear in each square.

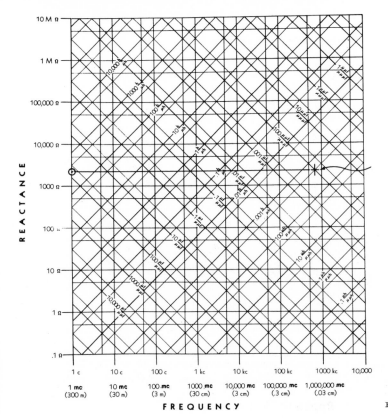

FIG. 1 Reactance chart—rough scale

FIG. 2 Reactance chart—fine scale (Always obtain approximate value from Fig. 1 before using Fig. 2.)

Printed with the permission of General Radio Company.

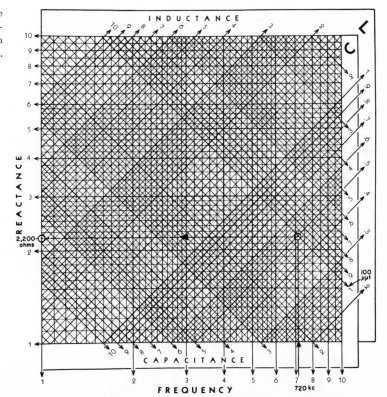

Appendix A-8
Summary of Ohm's-law Equations

Current = Amperes = $\dfrac{\text{Volts}}{\text{Ohms}}$ $\left(I = \dfrac{E}{R}\right)$

Potential = Volts = Amperes × Ohms ($E = IR$)

Resistance = Ohms = $\dfrac{\text{Volts}}{\text{Amperes}}$ $\left(R = \dfrac{E}{I}\right)$

Power: Watts = Volts × Amperes   ($W = EI$)

Watts = Volts squared divided by ohms

$$\left(W = \dfrac{E^2}{R}\right)$$

Watts = Amperes squared × ohms
($W = I^2 R$)

RESISTANCE IN SERIES:

R_s is total resistance; r_1, r_2, r_3, etc., are individual resistances.

$$R_s = r_1 + r_2 + r_3 + \cdots$$

RESISTANCES IN PARALLEL:

$$\frac{1}{R_p} = \frac{1}{r_1} + \frac{1}{r_2} + \frac{1}{r_3} + \cdots$$

or

$$R_p = \cfrac{1}{\dfrac{1}{r_1} + \dfrac{1}{r_2} + \dfrac{1}{r_3} + \cdots}$$

CAPACITY OF CONDENSERS IN PARALLEL:

$$C_p = c_1 + c_2 + c_3 + \cdots$$

CAPACITY OF CONDENSERS IN SERIES:

$$\frac{1}{C_s} = \frac{1}{c_1} + \frac{1}{c_2} + \frac{1}{c_3} + \cdots$$

or

$$C_s = \cfrac{1}{\dfrac{1}{c_1} + \dfrac{1}{c_2} + \dfrac{1}{c_3} + \cdots}$$

Appendix A-9
Circuit Q—Its Nature and Measurement

The letter Q when used in describing the qualities of a resonant circuit is widespread in its application to almost every phase of performance. Basically, it expresses a comparison, during one cycle of operation, giving the ratio of the total energy stored in a circuit versus the energy dissipated.

From Q measurements we can determine:

1. The damping effect when current is decaying in a resonant circuit.

2. Phase angle and power factor of tuned circuits.

3. Selectivity of a tuned circuit.

4. Radio-frequency resistance of a coil.

5. The loss angle of a capacitor at RF.

6. Dielectric constants.

7. Antenna characteristics.

8. Transmission-line parameters.

The Q-Meter operating in a circuit measures the resonant rise of voltage across either of the reactive elements in a tuned circuit. This measurement results from injecting a small, known radio-frequency voltage across a very small series resistor which is part of the resonant circuit. The magnified or resonant voltage rise is measured by a vacuum-tube voltmeter. Since the amount of injected voltage is accurately known, the resonant voltage rise or the circuit magnification factor can be directly calibrated in terms of the Q of the coil being measured.

Q *in series resonant circuits* is calculated using the effective series resistance (R_s), which is a fictitious value representing all losses including those of the resonant coil and capacitor. Algebraically, using R_s, we express it:

$$Q = \frac{\omega L}{R_s} = \frac{1}{\omega C R_s}$$

Thus we see $R_s = \omega L/Q = 1/Q\omega C$ and is usually a very *small* quantity.

Q *in a parallel resonant circuit* is calculated using the effective parallel resistance (R_p) which is a reflected fictitious value representing all losses (including those of the resonant coil and capacitor) and which is represented by a parallel resistor connected *across* the turned circuit. We express it:

$$Q = \frac{R_p}{\omega L} = \omega C R_p$$

Again we see $R_p = Q\omega L = Q/\omega C$ and represents a very *large* quantity.

Here we see that the impedance of a parallel resonant circuit is Q times the impedance of the reactive elements. Also, in the series case, the current flowing at resonance is Q times the normal current flow.

Q in a *damped oscillating circuit* tells us the logarithmic decrement δ of the circuit. Here:

$$\delta = \frac{\pi}{Q} = \frac{R_s}{2fL} = 2\pi^2 fCR_s$$

Now, $R/2L$ is the damping coefficient which tells the amount by which the amplitude of each successive cycle is lower than its predecessor. So δ, which multiplies this number by f, accounts for frequency and is logarithmic in nature since the equation for current decay is:

$$\frac{I_2}{I_1} = \epsilon^{-RT/2L}$$

Q and circuit phase angle. The vector relationship between the current and driving voltage in a resonant circuit is the familiar formula:

$$\tan\phi = \frac{\omega L}{R_s} = Q$$

where $\phi = $ the phase angle.

Q and power factor. Of similar nature is the power factor of an inductor or the ratio of the total effective resistance to the total circuit impedance.

$$Q = \frac{1}{\cos\phi}$$

Appendix A-10
EIA Microelectronics Terminology

The Electronic Industries Association has issued a bulletin which defines microsystem electronics as "that entire body of electronic art which is connected with or applied to the realization of electronic systems from extremely small electronic parts." Other definitions include:

Electrical element. The concept in uncombined form of any of the individual building blocks from which electronic circuits are synthesized. Examples of basic electrical elements are insulation, inductance, resistance, capacitance, and transistance.

Transistance. The electrical element which controls voltages or currents so as to accomplish gain or switching action in a circuit. Examples of the physical realization of transistance occur in transistors, diodes, saturable reactors, lumistors, and relays.

Component. A packaged functional unit consisting of one or more circuits made up of devices, which may be part of (in turn) an operating system or subsystem. A part of, or division of, the whole assembly or equipment. Examples of components are IF amplifiers, counters and power supplies.

Integrated circuit. The physical realization of a number of circuit elements inseparably associated on or within a continuous body to perform the function of a circuit.

Hybrid integrated circuit. An arrangement consisting of one, or more, integrated circuits in combination with one or more discrete devices. Alternatively, the combination of more than one type of integrated circuit into a single integrated component.

Packaging density. The number of devices or equivalent pack devices per unit volume in a working system or subsystem.

Module. A unit is a packaging scheme displaying regularity and comparable repetition. It may not be separable from other modules after initial assembly. Usually all major dimensions are in accordance with a prescribed series of dimensions.

Morphology, integrated. The structural characterization of an electronic component in which the identity of the current or signal modifying areas, patterns, or volumes has become lost in the integration of electronic materials in contrast to an assembly of devices performing the same function.

Morphology, translational. The structural characterization of an electronic component in which the areas or patterns of resistive, conductive, dielectric, and active materials in or on the surface of the structure can be identified in a one-to-one correspondence with devices assembled to perform an equivalent function.

MICROELECTRONIC GLOSSARY

Component part. The physical realization of an electrical circuit element as an independent body which cannot be further reduced or divided without destroying its stated function. Typical component parts have two to four connecting leads.

Passive component. Usually means a resistor, capacitor, inductor, transformer.

Active component. An electrical or electronic element which can control voltages or currents to produce gain or switching action in a circuit (e.g., transistor, diode, vacuum tube, or saturable reactor). The word "device" has a synonymous meaning.

Circuit. The interconnection of a number of component parts in one or more closed paths to perform a desired electrical function. Test circuits contain both active and passive component parts. The word "network" has the same meaning.

Substrate. The material upon which several component parts, or a circuit, are fabricated.

Passive substrate. An insulating substrate which provides only physical support and possibly acts as a thermal sink (e.g., glass or ceramic).

Active substrate. A substrate in which select areas are used to fabricate active components (e.g., a piece of semiconductor material within which transistors and diodes can be formed).

Microminaturization. A generic term implying very small size.

Microelectronics. A coined word used to describe the entire spectrum of approaches or techniques to physically realize microminiature electronic circuits. The generic word "microcircuit" has a synonymous meaning. Note: Small size, by itself, is not the goal of microelectronics; work objectives include: improved reliability; reduced size, weight, and power consumption; and lower total cost.

Microsystems electronics. That field of electronics which involves the realization of microminiature systems using microelectronics.

Module. One or more electronic circuit functions, assembled according to a standard set of dimensions and form factors, and used as building blocks in a packaging scheme for electronic equipment. In general, modules are considered expendable items and are not to be maintainable once the assembly is complete. The words "modular assembly" have the same meaning.

Thin-film circuit. One or more layers of conductive, insulative, semiconductive, or ferromagnetic film materials deposited in a pattern relationship by vapor deposition or electrochemical processes, usually on a passive substrate. At the present time, the production of thin-film circuits involves the addition of discrete active elements that have been fabricated by a separate process.

Functional electronic block (Sometimes abbreviated FEB). An individual block of material which can perform one or more electronic circuit functions (e.g., an amplifier, oscillator, gate, or counter). Performance for an FEB is most easily described on an input-output basis.

Integrated circuit. A functional electronic block wherein both active and passive component parts are produced integrally with, and inseparable from, an active substrate. Regions in each block behave like conventional circuit elements (e.g., resistors, capacitors, diodes, transistors); therefore, classical network analysis and synthesis techniques may be used to design and develop new integrated circuits.

Molecular electronics. A functional electronic block in which physical phenomena in materials are combined to perform a required circuit function without reference to electronic circuits for design analysis or synthesis. This term is frequently used interchangeably with "integrated circuit," although there is a subtle difference. In the true molecular electronic block, an equivalent circuit and its elements or component parts can not be identified. "Molectronics" is a coined word for molecular electronics.

Multiples and submultiples	Prefaces	Symbols
10^{12}	tera	T
10^{9}	giga	G
10^{6}	mega	M
10^{3}	kilo	k
10^{2}	hecto	h
10	deka	da
10^{-1}	deci	d
10^{-2}	centi	c
10^{-3}	milli	m
10^{-6}	micro	u
10^{-9}	nano	n
10^{-12}	pico	p
10^{-15}	femto	f
10^{-18}	atto	a

Appendix B-1
Resistance-coupled amplifier data

With the aid of the two reference diagrams and the accompanying equations for determining the size by-pass and coupling condensers, one should be able to build a good amplifier or check the design of one under repair.

Data are given for use under commonly used supply voltages. Values of gain are given for two different values of applied signal; the first for a typical small signal and the second for the maximum which can be used without exceeding the 5% distortion limit.

SYMBOLS USED

Symbol	Function	Unit
Rb	plate load resistor	megohms
Rc2	screen dropping resistor	megohms
Rcf	grid resistor of following tube	megohms
Ebb	plate supply voltage	volts
Eb	plate voltage at plate	volts
Ec or Ecl	grid to neg. fil. voltage	volts
Ec2	screen grid voltage	volts
E_{sig}	input signal	RMS volts
E_{out}	output to following grid	RMS volts
Ib	plate current	ma.
Ic2	screen grid current	ma.
Cc	coupling condenser	mfd.
Cc2	screen by-pass condenser	mfd.

Values of capacity are not specified since these are dependent mostly on the frequency characteristic required in each individual case.

For low frequency limit = f_1

$$Cc = \frac{1.6 \times 10^6}{f_1 Rcf} \text{ mfd.}$$

$$Ck = \frac{1.6 \times 10^6}{f_1 Rk} \text{ mfd.}$$

$$Cc2 = \frac{1.6 \times 10^6}{f_1 Rc2} \text{ mfd.}$$

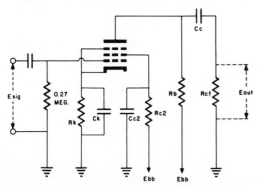

FIG. 1 Typical self-biased pentode circuit

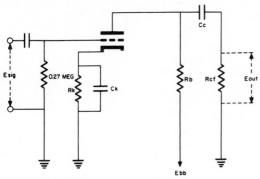

FIG. 2 Typical self-biased triode circuit

	Ebb = 100 volts							Ebb = 250 volts						
Rb	.1		.27			.47		.1		.27			.47	
Rc_2	.27		.68			1.2		.27		.68			1.2	
Rcf	.27	.47	.27	.47	1.0	.47	1.0	.27	.47	.27	.47	1.0	.47	1.0
Rk	1200	1200	2700	2700	2700	4700	4700	470	470	1000	1000	1200	1500	1800
Ib	.57	.57	.246	.246	.246	.143	.143	1.74	1.74	.74	.74	.72	.44	.42
Ic_2	.24	.24	.106	.106	.106	.063	.063	.68	.68	.30	.30	.29	.18	.175
Ec_1	−1.0	−1.0	−1.0	−1.0	−1.0	−1.0	−1.0	−1.1	−1.1	−1.0	−1.0	−1.2	−0.9	−1.1
Ec_2	41	41	28	28	28	25	25	66	66	46	46	52	34	40
Eb	46	46	34	34	34	33	33	76	76	50	50	55	43	52
E_{sig}	.05	.05	.05	.05	.05	.05	.05	0.1	0.1	0.1	0.1	0.1	0.1	0.1
E_{out}	5.8	6.0	5.6	6.9	8.3	6.4	8.5	19.0	20.0	20.5	25.0	29.8	25.1	31.0
Gain	116	120	112	138	166	128	170	190	200	205	250	298	251	310
% Dist.	3.6	3.7	3.9	3.3	2.4	4.7	3.5	2.7	2.5	3.4	1.1	0.8	2.2	0.7
E_{sig}[1]	.07	.07	.06	.09	.11	.05	.07	.32	.32	.26	.22	.29	.14	.22
E_{out}	8.0	8.0	6.6	12.0	16.5	6.4	11.5	54.0	56.0	37.0	47.7	67.0	34.0	57.5
Gain	114	119	110	133	150	128	164	169	185	185	217	231	243	261
% Dist.	5.1	4.9	4.7	4.9	3.5	4.7	4.7	4.9	3.3	5.1	2.6	3.3	3.5	3.7

[1]For self bias operation this is taken at the grid current point with less than $\frac{1}{8}$ microampere grid current.

	Ebb = 100 volts							Ebb = 250 volts						
Rb	0.1		0.27			0.47		0.1		0.27			0.47	
Rcf	0.27	0.47	0.27	0.47	1.0	0.47	1.0	0.27	0.47	0.27	0.47	1.0	0.47	1.0
Rk	4700	5600	8200	10,000	10,000	12,000	15,000	1800	1800	3300	3300	3900	4700	5600
Ib	.23	.204	.132	.117	.117	.092	.08	.84	.84	.45	.45	.41	.30	.28
Ec	−1.08	−1.143	−1.03	−1.17	−1.17	−1.10	−1.2	−1.51	−1.51	−1.49	−1.49	−1.59	−1.41	1.57
Eb	77.0	79.6	64.4	68.4	68.4	56.8	62.4	166.	166.	128.	128.	139.	109.	118.5
E_{sig}	0.1	0.1	0.1	0.1	0.1	0.1	0.1	0.1	0.1	0.1	0.1	0.1	0.1	0.1
E_{out}	3.6	3.8	4.2	4.35	5.0	4.7	5.2	5.4	5.7	6.1	6.6	6.9	6.6	7.1
Gain	36.0	38.0	42.0	43.5	50.0	47.0	52.0	54.0	57.0	61.0	66.0	69.0	66.0	71.0
% dist.	3.4	3.4	3.6	3.2	2.6	3.2	2.6	0.3	...	0.5	0.2	0.2	0.4	0.2
E_{sig}[1]	.14	.14	.11	.14	.17	.13	.17	.5	.5	.41	.45	.54	.38	.48
E_{out}	5.0	5.2	4.6	6.0	8.3	6.1	8.5	26.5	28.5	24.5	29.0	37.0	25.0	33.5
Gain	35.7	37.2	41.8	42.9	48.8	46.9	50.0	53.0	52.0	59.8	64.4	68.5	65.8	69.8
% dist.	5.0	5.1	4.1	4.9	5.1	4.4	5.0	5.0	4.4	4.95	4.4	4.8	4.1	4.2

[1]At grid current point, less than $\frac{1}{8}$ microampere grid current through 0.27 megohm grid resistor.

	Ebb = 100 volts						Ebb = 250 volts					
Rb	0.047		0.10		0.27		0.047		0.10		0.27	
Rcf	0.1	0.27	0.1	0.47	0.27	0.47	0.1	0.27	0.1	0.47	0.27	0.47
Rk	1800	2200	3300	4700	8200	10,000	1500	2200	2700	3900	6800	8200
Ib	1.05	0.97	0.57	0.50	0.24	0.22	2.79	2.4	1.49	1.31	0.61	0.58
Ec	−1.89	−2.13	−1.90	−2.35	−1.93	−2.19	−4.18	−5.28	−4.03	−5.11	−4.15	−4.74
Eb	50.6	54.4	43.0	50.0	36.5	40.9	119	137	101	119	85	94
E_{sig}	0.5	0.5	0.5	0.5	0.5	0.5	1.0	1.0	1.0	1.0	1.0	1.0
E_{out}	6.6	7.1	6.8	7.4	7.3	7.4	14.8	15.0	15.2	16.2	15.9	16.2
Gain	13.2	14.2	13.6	14.8	14.6	14.8	14.8	15.0	15.2	16.2	15.9	16.2
% distortion	1.9	1.8	2.4	2.0	2.0	1.7	1.4	1.4	1.8	1.3	1.6	1.3
E_{sig}[1]	0.95	1.13	0.95	1.3	0.95	1.20	2.70	3.50	2.55	3.30	2.64	3.05
E_{out}	12.5	15.5	12.9	19.2	13.7	17.7	39.9	52.5	38.4	53.0	42.0	49.4
Gain	13.1	13.9	13.6	14.7	14.4	14.7	14.7	15.0	15.0	16.1	15.9	16.2
% distortion	3.9	4.2	4.9	4.7	4.4	4.5	4.1	4.9	4.9	4.6	4.7	4.5

[1]For self bias operation this is taken at the grid current point with less than $\frac{1}{8}$ microampere grid current.

Appendix B-2
Typical Receiving Tube Characteristics and Basing Diagrams

Basing diagrams shown: 4D, 4R, 5BO, 4BU, 4M, 5AP, 6X, 4AJ, 4K, 4V, 6CB

TYPE	DESCRIPTION	FILAMENT VOLTS	AMPERES	TYPE OF CATHODE	APPLICATION	PLATE VOLTS	SCREEN GRID VOLTS	CONTROL GRID VOLTS (NEG.)	PLATE CURRENT MA	SCREEN CURRENT MA	TRANS. CONDUCTANCE µMHOS	AMPLIFICATION FACTOR	LOAD RESISTANCE OHMS	POWER OUTPUT WATTS	RECTIFIER MAX A.C. RMS VOLTS PER PLATE	RECTIFIER MAX D.C. OUTPUT MA	BULB DRAWING NO.	BULB STYLE	BASE EIA NO.	BASE STYLE
00A■	TRIODE	5	0.25	FIL.	DETECTOR	45		0	1.5		666	20					ST-14	78	MED. 4 PIN	4D
01A■	TRIODE	5	0.25	FIL.	CLASS A AMPLIFIER	135		9	3		800	8					ST-14	78	MED. 4 PIN	4D
01AA	TRIODE	5	0.25	FIL.	AMPLIFIER	90		4.5	3.0		800	8					ST-14	78	MED. 4 PIN	4D
01B	TRIODE	5	0.125	FIL.	AMPLIFIER	90		4.5	2.5		725	8					ST-14	78	MED. 4 PIN	4D
0A2	GLOW DISCHARGE DOUBLE DIODE			COLD	VOLTAGE REGULATOR	185 DC Min.		5 to 30	Ionization Voltage: 155 DC / Operating Voltage: 150 DC / Regulation: 5 Volts Between 5-30 Ma.								T-5½	5	MIN. 7 PIN	5BO
0A3/VR-75	GLOW DISCHARGE DIODE			COLD	VOLTAGE REGULATOR	105 DC Min.		5 to 40	Ionization Voltage: 100 DC / Operating Voltage: 75 DC / Regulation: 5 Volts Between 5-40 Ma.								ST-12	69	6 PIN OCTAL	4AJ
0A4G	GAS TRIODE			COLD	TRIGGER	Peak Cathode Current: 100 Ma. Max. / Normal Cathode Current: 25 Ma. Max. / Anode Drop: Approx. 70 Volts											ST-12	69	6 PIN OCTAL	4V
0A5	RELAY TUBE			COLD	CONTROL TUBE	Anode Operating Voltage: 750 / Grid 3 (Trigger) Bias Voltage: +90 / Grid 3 (Trigger) Resistance: 0.25 Meg. / Grid 2 (Shield) Floating / Discharge Condenser Capacitance: 0.25 µf / Grid 1 (Keep-Alive) Current: 50 µAmp. / Grid 3 (Trigger) Pulse Voltage: 85											T-5½	5	MIN. 7 PIN	5BO
0B2	GLOW DISCHARGE DIODE			COLD	VOLTAGE REGULATOR	133 DC Min.		5 to 30	Ionization Voltage: 115 DC / Operating Voltage: 105 DC / Regulation: 1 Volt Between 5-30 Ma.								T-5½	5	MIN. 7 PIN	5BO
0B3/VR-90	GLOW DISCHARGE DIODE			COLD	VOLTAGE REGULATOR	125 DC Min.		5 to 30	Ionization Voltage: 110 DC / Operating Voltage: 90 DC / Regulation: 8 Volts Between 5-40 Ma.								ST-12	69	6 PIN OCTAL	4AJ
0C3/VR-105	GLOW DISCHARGE DIODE			COLD	VOLTAGE REGULATOR	133 DC Min.		5 to 40	Ionization Voltage: 115 DC / Operating Voltage: 105 DC / Regulation: 2 Volts Between 5-40 Ma.								ST-12	69	6 PIN OCTAL	4AJ
0D3/VR-150	GLOW DISCHARGE DIODE			COLD	VOLTAGE REGULATOR	185 DC Min.		5 to 40	Ionization Voltage: 160 DC / Operating Voltage: 150 DC / Regulation: 4 Volts Between 5-40 Ma.								ST-12	69	6 PIN OCTAL	4AJ
0Y4■	GAS FILLED DIODE			COLD	HALF-WAVE RECTIFIER	Pins 7-8 Must be Connected / Peak Current: 500 Ma. Max. / Max. DC Starting Voltage: 95 V. / Tube Drop: Approx. 12 V.									40 to 75	300	MT-8	17	5 PIN OCTAL	4BU
0Y4G■	GAS FILLED DIODE			COLD	HALF-WAVE RECTIFIER	SAME CHARACTERISTICS AS 0Y4											T-7	12	5 PIN OCTAL	4BU
0Z4	GAS FILLED DIODE			COLD	FULL-WAVE RECTIFIER	Peak starting-supply voltage per plate: 300 min. / Peak plate-to-plate voltage: 1000 / DC output voltage: 300; peak plate current: 200 ma.									30 to 75		MT-8A	16	6 PIN OCTAL	4R
0Z4A/1003	DOUBLE DIODE			COLD	FULL-WAVE RECTIFIER	Tube Drop: 24 Volts									265 c	30 Min. 85 Max.	MT-8A	16	6 PIN OCTAL	4R
0Z4G	GAS FILLED DOUBLE DIODE			COLD	FULL-WAVE RECTIFIER	Tube Drop: 24 Volts / SAME CHARACTERISTICS AS TYPE 024									365 D	30 Min. 85 Max.	T-7	12	5 PIN OCTAL	4R*
1A3■	DIODE	1.4	0.15	HEATER	DETECTOR RECTIFIER	117			330							0.5	T-5½	4	MIN. 4 PIN	5AP
1A4P■	PENTODE	2	0.06	FIL.	CLASS A AMPLIFIER	180	67.5	3	2.3	0.8	750	Cutoff: 15 µmhos @ −15 V.	1000				ST-12	72	SMALL 4 PIN	4M
1A4T■	TETRODE	2	0.06	FIL.	CLASS A AMPLIFIER	180	67.5	3	2.3	0.7	750		960				ST-12	72	MED. 4 PIN	4K
1A5GT■	PENTODE	1.4	0.05	FIL.	CLASS A AMPLIFIER	90 / 85	90 / 85	4.5 / 4.5	4 / 4.5	0.8 / 0.7	850 / 800	25,000 / 25,000	300 / 300	0.115 / 0.100			T-9	35	7 PIN OCTAL	6X

■ Tube types not recommended for new equipment design.

* Pin #1 has no connection

c Single tube operation.

D Resistance parallel operation.

TYPE	DESCRIPTION	FILAMENT VOLTS	FILAMENT AMPERES	TYPE OF CATHODE	APPLICATION	PLATE VOLTS	SCREEN GRID VOLTS	CONTROL GRID VOLTS (NEG.)	PLATE CURRENT MA.	SCREEN CURRENT MA.	TRANS-CONDUCTANCE µMHOS	PLATE RESISTANCE KILOHMS	AMPLIFICATION FACTOR	LOAD RESISTANCE OHMS	POWER OUTPUT WATTS	RECTIFIER CONDENSER INPUT: MAX. A.C. RMS VOLTS PER PLATE	MAX. PEAK INVERSE VOLTS	MAX. D.C. OUTPUT MA.	BULB STYLE	BULB DRAWING NO.	BASE STYLE	BASE EIA NO.	TYPE
5AV8	TRIODE PENTODE	4.7	0.6*	HEATER	CLASS A AMPLIFIER B A	200 200	150	6 G	13 9.5	2.8	3300 6200	5.75 300	19	Cut-off: 10 µamp. @ −19 V. Cut-off: 10 µamp. @ −8 V.					T-6½	8	MIN. 9 PIN	9DZ	5AV8
5AW4	DIODE	5.0	4.0	FIL.	FULL WAVE RECTIFIER	Tube Voltage Drop: Ib = 250 Ma. DC per Plate: 46 V.										450 550		250 250	T-12	68	OCTAL 5 PIN	5T	5AW4
5AX4GT■	DOUBLE DIODE	5	2.5	FIL.	FULL-WAVE RECTIFIER	Max. Steady State Peak Plate Current per Plate: 525 Ma. Max. Transient Peak Plate Current per Plate: 3.5 Amp. Tube Voltage Drop at 175 Ma.: 65 V.										350	1400	175	T-9	37	5 PIN OCTAL	5T	■5AX4GT
5AZ4	DOUBLE DIODE	5	2	FIL.	FULL-WAVE RECTIFIER	Peak plate current per plate: 350 ma.										350	1400	125	T-9	30	5 PIN LOC.	5T	5AZ4
5B8	TRIODE PENTODE	4.7	0.6*	HEATER	CLASS A AMPLIFIER B A	200 200	150	6 G	13 9.5		3300 6200	5.75 300	19	Cut-off: 10 µa @ −19 V. Cut-off: 10 µa @ −8 V.					T-6½	8	MIN. 9 PIN	9EC	5B8
5BE8	TRIODE PENTODE	4.7	0.6*	HEATER	CLASS A AMPLIFIER B A	150 250	110	0H 0J	18 10	3.5	8500 5200	5 400	40	Cut-off: 10 µa @ −12 V. Cut-off: 10 µa @ −10 V.					T-6½	8	MIN. 9 PIN	9EG	5BE8
5BK7A	DOUBLE TRIODE	4.7	0.6*	HEATER	CLASS A AMPLIFIER	150		H	18		9300	4.6	43	Cut-off: 10 µa @ −11 V.					T-6½	8	MIN. 9 PIN	9AJ	5BK7A
5BQ7A	TWIN TRIODE	5.6	0.45*	HEATER	CLASS A AMPLIFIER	150		E	9		6400	6.1	39	Cut-off: 10 µa @ −10 V.					T-6½	8	MIN. 9 PIN	9AJ	5BQ7A
5BR8	TRIODE PENTODE	4.7	0.6*	HEATER	OSCILLATOR B MIXER A	150 250	110	H J	18 10	3.5	8500 5200	5.0 400	40	Cut-off: 10 µa @ −12 V. Cut-off: 10 µa @ −10 V.					T-6½	8	MIN. 9 PIN	9FA	5BR8
5BS8	TWIN DIODE	5.6	0.45*	HEATER	CLASS A AMPLIFIER	150		E	10		7200	5	36	Cut-off: 10 µa at −7 V. (Section 2 Only)					T-6½	8	MIN. 9 PIN	9AJ	5BS8
5BT8	TWIN DIODE PENTODE	4.7	0.6*	HEATER	GENERAL PURPOSE	200	150	G	9.5	2.8	6200	300		Cut-off: 10 µamp. @ −8 V.					T-6½	8	MIN. 9 PIN	9FE	5BT8
5BW8	DOUBLE DIODE PENTODE	4.7	0.6* ±6%	HEATER	HORIZONTAL PHASE DETECTOR AMPLIFIER	250	110	J	10.0	3.5	5200	250		Cutoff: 10 µa @ −10 V. Average Diode Current, Each Diode With 5 V. DC Applied = 20 Ma.					T-6½	8	MIN. 9 PIN	9HK	5BW8
5BZ7	TWIN TRIODE	5.6	0.45*	HEATER	CLASS A AMPLIFIER	150			10		6800	5.6	38						T-6½	8	MIN. 9 PIN	9AJ	5BZ7
5CG8	TRIODE PENTODE	4.7	0.6*	HEATER	CONVERTER B A	100 250	150	M N	8.5 7.7	1.6	5800 4600	6.9 750	40	Cut-off: 10 µamp. @ −10 V. Cut-off: 10 µamp. @ −10 V.					T-6½	8	MIN. 9 PIN	9FA	5CG8
5CL8	TRIODE TETRODE	4.7	0.6*	HEATER	CLASS A AMPLIFIER B D	125 125	125	H 1.0	15 12	4.0	8000 5800	5.0 100	40	Cut-off: 10 µamp. @ −9 V. Cut-off: 10 µamp. @ −10 V.					T-6½	8	MIN. 9 PIN	9FX	5CL8
5CL8A	TRIODE TETRODE	4.7	0.6*	HEATER	OSCILLATOR D MIXER B	125 125	125	1 H	12 15	4.0	6400 8000	100 5	40	Cut-off: 10 µamp at −10 V. Cut-off: 10 µamp at −9 V.					T-6½	8	MIN. 9 PIN	9FX	5CL8A
5CM6	PENTODE	4.7	0.6*	HEATER	VERTICAL DEFLECTION AMPLIFIER	250 250	250	12.5 12.5	45 49.5	4.5	4100 5000	50 19.6	9.8	Cutoff: 0.5 Ma. @ −37 V. Cutoff: 0.5 Ma. @ −37 V.					T-6½	9	MIN. 9 PIN	9CK	5CM6
5CM8	TRIODE PENTODE	4.7	0.6*	HEATER	CLASS A AMPLIFIER B D	250 200	150	2 G	1.8 9.5	2.8	2000 6200	50 300	100	Cut-off: 10 µamp. @ −8 V.					T-6½	8	MIN. 9 PIN	9FZ	5CM8
5CQ8	TRIODE TETRODE	4.7	0.6*	HEATER	CLASS A AMPLIFIER B D	125 125	125	H 1	15 12	4.2	8000 5800	5 140	40	Cut-off: 100 µamp at −7 V.					T-6½	8	MIN. 9 PIN	9GE	5CQ8
5CR8	TRIODE PENTODE	4.7	0.6*	HEATER	CLASS A AMPLIFIER B A	125 125	125	2 0	12 13	3	4000 7700	5.5 300	22	Cut-off: 10 µamp at −13 V. Cut-off: 20 µamp at −6.5 V.					T-6½	8	MIN. 9 PIN	9GJ	5CR8
5CZ5	BEAM PENTODE	4.7	0.6*	HEATER	CLASS A AMPLIFIER	250	250	14	46F	103F				7500K	21.5L				T-6½	11A	MIN. 9 PIN	9HN	5CZ5
5DH8	TRIODE PENTODE	5.2	0.6*	HEATER	CLASS A AMPLIFIER B A	250 125	125	C H	7.3 13.5	3.8	4400 8600	12 150	53	Cut-off: 10 µamp at −10 V. Cut-off: 20 µamp at −6 V.					T-6½	8	MIN. 9 PIN	9EG	5DH8
5EA8	TRIODE PENTODE	4.7	0.6*	HEATER	OSCILLATOR B MIXER A	150 125	125	H 1	18 12	4.0	8500 6400	5 800	40	Cut-off: 10 µamp at −12 V. Cut-off: 10 µamp at −9 V.					T-6½	8	MIN. 9 PIN	9AE	5EA8
5EH8	TRIODE PENTODE	4.7	0.6*	HEATER	CLASS A AMPLIFIER B A	125 125	125	1 1	13.5 12	4.0	7500 6000	170	40	Cut-off: 20 µamp at −9 V. Cut-off: 20 µamp at −10 V.					T-6½	8	MIN. 9 PIN	9JG	5EH8
5FV8	TRIODE PENTODE	4.7	0.6*	HEATER	VERTICAL DEFLECTION OSCILLATOR B CLASS A AMPLIFIER A	125 125	 125	1.0 1.0	14.0 12.0	 4.0	8000 6500	5 200	40	Cutoff: 20 µa @ −9 V. Cutoff: 20 µa @ −9 V.					T-6½	8	MIN. 9 PIN	9FA	5FV8

* Thermal characteristics of the heater are controlled such that heater voltage surges during the warm-up cycle are minimized provided the tube is used with other types which are similarly controlled. Heater warm-up time: 11.0 seconds.

■ Tube types not recommended for new equipment design.

A Pentode section. B Triode section.
D Tetrode section. F Zero signal.
K Plate to plate. L Maximum signal.

G Bias obtained through 180 ohm cathode resistor.
H Bias obtained through 56 ohm cathode resistor.
J Bias obtained through 68 ohm cathode resistor.
E Bias obtained through 220 ohm cathode resistor.
M Bias obtained through 100 ohm cathode resistor.
N Bias obtained through 200 ohm cathode resistor.
C Bias obtained through 390 ohm cathode resistor.

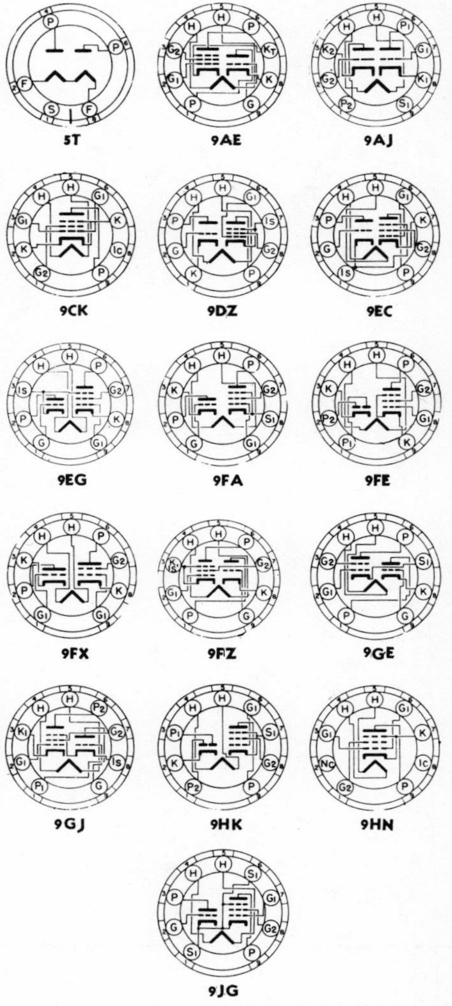

Tube Base Diagrams

Basing diagrams (socket connections viewed from bottom):

5BS · 6K · 7S · 9AH
4CG · 6J · 7R · 9B
4AC · 5D · 6S · 7V · 9AK

TYPICAL OPERATING CONDITIONS AND CHARACTERISTICS

TYPE	DESCRIPTION	FIL. VOLTS	FIL. AMP.	CATHODE	APPLICATION	PLATE VOLTS	SCREEN GRID VOLTS	CONTROL GRID VOLTS (NEG.)	PLATE CURRENT MA.	SCREEN CURRENT MA.	TRANS CONDUCTANCE μMHOS	PLATE RESISTANCE OHMS	AMP. FACTOR	LOAD RESISTANCE OHMS	POWER OUTPUT WATTS	RECT. MAX A.C. VOLTS RMS	RECT. MAX PEAK INVERSE VOLTS	RECT. COND. INPUT D.C. OUTPUT MA.	BULB STYLE	DRAWING NO.	BASE STYLE	EIA NO.	TYPE
6V6GTA	BEAM PENTODE	6.3	0.45*	HEATER	CLASS A AMPLIFIER / CLASS AB AMPLIFIER	315 / 180 / 285 / 250	225 / 180 / 285 / 250	13.0 / 8.5 / 15	34ᵛ / 29ᵛ / 70ᵛ / 70ᵛ	2.2ᵛ / 3ᵛ / 4.0ᵛ / 5ᵛ	3750 / 3700 / 2600 / 3750	80 / 58 / 70		8500 / 5500 / 8000 / 10000 (Load Is Plate-to-Plate)	5.5 / 14				T-9	35	7 PIN OCTAL	7S	6V6GTA ■
6Y7G ■	DOUBLE DIODE TRIODE	6.3	0.3	HEATER	CLASS A AMPLIFIER	250 / 180		20 / 13.5	8 / 6	1.0 / 0.8	1100 / 975 / 750	58 / 54	7.5 / 8.5						ST-12	71	7 PIN oc. AL.	7V	6Y7G ■
6V8	TRIPLE DIODE TRIODE	6.3	0.45	HEATER	CLASS A AMPLIFIER	250 / 100		3 / 1	3 / 1		1200 / 1300	58 / 54	70 / 70		0.35 / 0.16 / 0.075				T-6½	8	MIN. 9 PIN	9AH	6V8 ■
6W4GT	DIODE	6.3	1.2	HEATER	HALF-WAVE RECTIFIER / DAMPER SERVICE	Peak Plate Current: 600 ma. max. Hot-Switching Transient Plate Current for 0.2 sec. max.: 3.5 amp. max.										1250	1250	125	T-9	35	6 PIN OCTAL	4CG	6W4GT
6W5G ■	DIODE	6.3	0.9	HEATER	FULL-WAVE RECTIFIER	Peak Plate Current: 600 ma. max.										325	3500	125	ST-12	69	6 PIN OCTAL	6S	6W5G ■
6W6GT ■	TETRODE	6.3	1.25	HEATER	CLASS A AMPLIFIER	200 / 100	125 / 110		46ᵛ / 49ᵛ	2.2ᵛ / 4.0ᵛ	8000 / 8000	28 / 13		5000 / 2000	3.8 / 2.1				T-9	35	7 PIN OCTAL	7S•	6W6GT ■
6W7G ■	PENTODE	6.3	0.15	HEATER	CLASS A AMPLIFIER	250	100	3	2	0.5	1225	1500							ST-12	71	7 PIN OCTAL	7R	6W7G ■
6X4	DOUBLE DIODE	6.3	0.6	HEATER	FULL-WAVE RECTIFIER	Max. Peak Plate Current per Plate: 210 Ma.										325	1250	70	T-5½	5	MIN. 7 PIN	5BS	6X4
6X5	DOUBLE DIODE	6.3	0.6	HEATER	FULL-WAVE RECTIFIER	SAME CHARACTERISTICS AS TYPE 6X5GT													MT-8B	20	6 PIN	6S	6X5
6X5GT	DOUBLE DIODE	6.3	0.6	HEATER	FULL-WAVE RECTIFIER											325	1250	70	T-9	35	6 PIN OCTAL	6S•	6X5GT
6X8	TRIODE PENTODE	6.3	0.45	HEATER	CONVERTER / TRIODE UNIT / PENTODE UNIT	150 / 150 / 100 / 250	150 / 150	13 (Osc. Grid #1 Current: 2 Ma.) / 8.5 / 7.7	6.2 / 1.8 / 8.5 / 7.7	3.5 / 1.8 / 1.6	150 / 5800 / 4600	6.9 / 750	40		0.5 watt (Osc.)				T-6½	8	MIN. 9 PIN	9AK	6X8
6X8A	TRIODE PENTODE	6.3	0.45*	HEATER	CHARACTERISTICS IDENTICAL TO 6X8														T-6½	8	MIN. 9 PIN	9AK	6X8A ■
6Y3G ■	DIODE	6.3	0.7	HEATER	HALF-WAVE RECTIFIER								5000				1250	7.5	ST-12	71	8 PIN OCTAL	4AC	6Y3G ■
6Y5 ■	DOUBLE DIODE	6.3	0.8	HEATER	FULL-WAVE RECTIFIER								350				1250	50	ST-12	70	SMALL 6 PIN	6J	6Y5 ■
6Y6G	BEAM PENTODE	6.3	1.25	HEATER	CLASS A AMPLIFIER	200 / 135	135 / 135	14 / 13.5	61ᵛ / 58ᵛ	2.2ᵛ / 3.5ᵛ	7100 / 7000	18.3 / 9.3		2600 / 2000	6 / 3.6				ST-14	77	SMALL 7 PIN	7S	6Y6G ■
6Y6GA	BEAM PENTODE	6.3	1.25	HEATER	CLASS A AMPLIFIER	200	135	14	61ᵛ	2.2ᵛ	7100	18.3		2600	6	Signal: 9.5 V. RMS			T-12	60	7 PIN OCTAL	7S	6Y6GA ■
6Y7G ■	DOUBLE TRIODE	6.3	0.6	HEATER	CLASS B AMPLIFIER	250 / 180		0 / 0	10.6ᵛ / 7.6ᵛ	Current and Output for Both Sections / Peak Plate Current per Plate: 180 Ma.		14,000 / 7000		14,000 / 7000	8.0 / 5.5				ST-12	69	8 PIN OCTAL	8B	6Y7G ■
6Z4 (84/6Z4)	DOUBLE DIODE	6.3	0.5	HEATER	FULL-WAVE RECTIFIER	Peak Plate Current per Plate: 180 Ma.							450				1250	60	ST-12	70	SMALL 5 PIN	5D	6Z4 (84/6Z4)
6Z5 (6Z5/12Z5)	DOUBLE DIODE	6.3 / 12.6	0.8ᴮ / 0.4ᴶ	HEATER	FULL-WAVE RECTIFIER	Current and Output for Both Sections							230					60	ST-12	70	SMALL 6 PIN	6K	6Z5 (6Z5/12Z5)
6Z7G ■	DOUBLE DIODE TRIODE	6.3	0.3	HEATER	CLASS B AMPLIFIER	180 / 135		0 / 0	8.4ᵛ / 6ᵛ	Current and Output for Both Sections		12,000 / 9000		12,000 / 9000	4.2 / 2.5				ST-12	69	8 PIN OCTAL	8B	6Z7G ■
6ZY5G ■	DOUBLE DIODE	6.3	0.3	HEATER	FULL-WAVE RECTIFIER	Peak Plate Current per Plate: 120 Ma.							450				1250	40	ST-12	69	6 PIN OCTAL	6S	6ZY5G ■

Oscillator Grid Resistor: 2700 Ohms. Grid Current: 3.6 Ma. (6X8 triode unit)
Oscillator Voltage at Mixer Grid #1: 2.6 V. rms. Mixer Grid #1 Circuit Resistance: 120000 Ohms. (6X8 pentode unit)
Cutoff: 10 μa at −10 V. Cutoff: 10 μa at −8 V.
Signal: 6 V. RMS

* Thermal characteristics of the heater are controlled such that heater voltage surges during the warm-up cycle are minimized provided the tube is used with other types which are similarly controlled. Heater warm-up time: 11.0 seconds.

■ Tube types not recommended for new equipment design.

• Pin #1 has no connection.

ᴮᴬ Triode unit as 250 mc osc.

ᴮᴮ Pentode unit as mixer.

ᴬᶠ Bias obtained through 100 ohm cathode resistor.

ᴬᴿ Bias obtained through 200 ohm cathode resistor.

ᵛ Zero signal.

Base connection diagrams (top of page): 5A · 4Z · 4D · 5AM · 5AL · 5AA · 5C · 5BT · 5BQ · 6AD · 5F · 5E · 7S · 7Q · 6B · 9JE

TYPICAL OPERATING CONDITIONS AND CHARACTERISTICS

TYPE	DESCRIPTION	FIL. VOLTS	FIL. AMPERES	TYPE OF CATHODE	APPLICATION	PLATE VOLTS	SCREEN GRID VOLTS	CONTROL GRID VOLTS (neg.)	PLATE CURRENT (ma.)	SCREEN CURRENT (ma.)	TRANS CONDUCTANCE (μmhos)	PLATE RESISTANCE (ohms)	AMP. FACTOR	LOAD RESISTANCE (ohms)	POWER OUTPUT	RECTIFIER MAX AC VOLTS PER PLATE	MAX PEAK INVERSE VOLTS	MAX DC OUTPUT MA	BULB STYLE	DRAWING NO.	BASE STYLE	EIA NO.	TYPE
35CD6GA	BEAM PENTODE	35	0.45*	HEATER	HORIZONTAL DEFLECTION AMPLIFIER	175 / 60	175 / 100	30 / 0	Cut-off: 1.0 ma. @ -55 V.							•			T-12	62	8 PIN OCTAL	5BT	35CD6GA
35DZ8	TRIODE PENTODE	35.0	0.15	HEATER	CLASS A AMPLIFIER (C/D)	120 / 145	120	0 / 0	0.8 / 6		Cutoff: 20 μa @ -2.5 V.	7.2	100	2500	2.0				T-6½	10B	MIN. 9 PIN	9JE	35DZ8
35L6GT	BEAM PENTODE	35	0.15	HEATER	CLASS A AMPLIFIER	200 / 110	125 / 110	0 / 7.5	43F / 40F				5000 / 2500	2500	3.0 / 1.5				T-9	35	7 PIN OCTAL	7S	35L6GT
35W4	DIODE	35A0	0.15	HEATER	HALF-WAVE RECTIFIER	Without Panel Lamp / With Panel Lamp					Signal: 5.3 V. RMS					330 / 330		100 / 80	T-5¼	5	MIN. 7 PIN	5BQ	35W4
35Y4	DIODE	35	0.15	HEATER	HALF-WAVE RECTIFIER	Max. Peak Plate Current: 600 Ma.										235	700	100	T-9	25	8 PIN OCTAL	5AL	35Y4
35Z3	DIODE	35	0.15	HEATER	HALF-WAVE RECTIFIER	Max. Peak Plate Current: 600 Ma.										235	700	100	T-9	30	8 PIN LOC.	4Z	35Z3
35Z4GT	DIODE	35	0.15	HEATER	HALF-WAVE RECTIFIER	Peak Plate Current per Plate: 600 Ma.										235	700	100	T-9	35	6 PIN OCTAL	5AA	35Z4GT
35Z5GT	DIODE	35	0.15	HEATER	HALF-WAVE RECTIFIER											235	700	60	T-9	35	6 PIN OCTAL	6AD	35Z5GT
35Z6G	DOUBLE DIODE	35	0.3	HEATER	HALF-WAVE RECTIFIER	With plate current passing through pilot lamp and tapped heater section										235	700	110	ST-14	77	7 PIN OCTAL	7Q	35Z6G
36	TETRODE	6.3	0.3	HEATER	CLASS A AMPLIFIER	250	90	3	3.2	1.7	1080	550	595						ST-12	72	SMALL 5 PIN	5E	36
36AM3	DIODE	36A0 / 32F	0.10	HEATER	HALF-WAVE RECTIFIER	DC Output Voltage = 105 V. Input Capacitor = 40 μf. Tube Voltage Drop @ I_B = 150 Ma.: 20 V.										117		75	T-9		MIN. 7 PIN	5BQ	36AM3
37	TRIODE	6.3	0.3	HEATER	CLASS A AMPLIFIER	250		18	7.5		1100	8.4	9.2						ST-12	70	SMALL 5 PIN	5A	37
38	PENTODE	6.3	0.3	HEATER	CLASS A AMPLIFIER	250	250	25	22	3.8	1200	100	120						ST-12	72	SMALL 5 PIN	5F	38
39/44	PENTODE	6.3	0.3	HEATER	CLASS A AMPLIFIER	250	90	3	5.8	1.4	1050	10,000	2.5		Cutoff: 2 μmhos @ -42.5 V.				ST-12	72	SMALL 5 PIN	5F	39/44
40	TRIODE	5	0.25	DC FIL.	CLASS A AMPLIFIER	180		3	0.2		200	150	30	Load Resistance: 0.25 Megohm					ST-14	78	MIN. 4 PIN	4D	40
40Z5GT	DIODE	45	0.15	HEATER	HALF-WAVE RECTIFIER											235	700	100	T-9	32	6 PIN OCTAL	6AD	40Z5GT
41	PENTODE	6.3	0.4	HEATER	CLASS A AMPLIFIER	315	250	21	25.5F	4.0F	2100	110		9000	4.5	Signal: 12.7 V. RMS			ST-12	70	SMALL 6 PIN	6B	41
42	PENTODE	6.3	0.7	HEATER	CLASS A AMPLIFIER	285 / 250	285 / 250	20 / 16.5	38 / 34	7 / 6.5	2550 / 2500	78 / 80		7000 / 7000	4.8 / 3.2	Signal: 11.6 V. RMS			ST-14	78	MED. 6 PIN	6B	42
43	PENTODE	25	0.3	HEATER	CLASS A AMPLIFIER	160 / 95	120 / 95	18 / 15	33 / 20	6.5 / 4	2375 / 2000	42 / 45		5000 / 4500	2.2 / 0.9	Signal: 12.7 V. RMS / 10.6 V. RMS			ST-14	78	MED. 6 PIN	6B	43
45	TRIODE	2.5	1.5	FIL.	CLASS A AMPLIFIER	275 / 180		56 / 31.5	36 / 31		2050 / 2125	1.70 / 1.65	3.5 / 3.5	4600 / 2700	2.0 / 0.825				ST-14	78	MED. 4 PIN	4D	45
45Z3	DIODE	45	0.075	HEATER	HALF-WAVE RECTIFIER											117	350	65	T-5½	4	MIN. 7 PIN	5AM	45Z3
45Z5GT	DIODE	45	0.15	HEATER	HALF-WAVE RECTIFIER											235	700	60	T-9	35	6 PIN OCTAL	6AD	45Z5GT
46	TETRODE	2.5	1.75	FIL.	CLASS A AMPLIFIER (AF) / CLASS B AMPLIFIER (AN)	250 / 400	33	22 / 12F	2350	2.38	5.6		6400 / 5800	1.25 / 20	Grid bias measured from filament center; Current and output for 2 tubes; Load in plate-to-plate				ST-16	84	MED. 5 PIN	5C	46

■ Tube types not recommended for new equipment design.
A0 Without pilot lamp; with lamp 32 v., 0.15 amp.
O Between pins #3 and #4.
P Between pins #3 and #6.
F Zero signal.
AF Grid tied to plate.
AN Grid tied together.
AN Two grids tied together.
D Pentode section.
C Triode section.

Base connection diagrams (EIA designations): 4C, 4E, 5D, 6H, 8AO, 4B, 4D, 5AA, 6G, 8AA, 8AV, 4AD, 4CB, 5A, 6F, 7Q

TYPICAL OPERATING CONDITIONS AND CHARACTERISTICS

TYPE	DESCRIPTION	FIL. VOLTS	FIL. AMPERES	TYPE OF CATHODE	APPLICATION	PLATE VOLTS	SCREEN GRID VOLTS	CONTROL GRID VOLTS (NEG.)	PLATE CURRENT MA.	SCREEN CURRENT MA.	TRANS. CONDUCTANCE μmhos	PLATE RESISTANCE OHMS	AMPLIFICATION FACTOR	LOAD RESISTANCE OHMS	POWER OUTPUT WATTS	MAX A.C. RMS VOLTS PER PLATE	MAX PEAK INV. VOLTS	D.C. OUTPUT MA.	BULB STYLE	DRAWING NO.	BASE STYLE	EIA NO.	TYPE
70L7GT	DIODE PENTODE	70	0.15	HEATER	BEAM POWER UNIT AS CLASS A AMPLIFIER; HALF-WAVE RECTIFIER	110	110	7.5	40	3	7500			2000	1.8	117	350	70	T-9	41	8 PIN OCTAL	8AA	70L7GT
71A∎	TRIODE	5	0.25	FIL.	CLASS A AMPLIFIER	180		40.5	20		1700	1.75	3	4800	0.79				ST-14	78	MED. 4 PIN	4D	71A
75∎	DOUBLE DIODE TRIODE	6.3	0.3	HEATER	CLASS A AMPLIFIER	250		2	0.9		1100	91	100						ST-12	72	SMALL 6 PIN	6G	75
75S∎	DOUBLE DIODE TRIODE	6.3	0.3	HEATER	CLASS A AMPLIFIER	250		2	0.9		1100	91	100						ST-12	72	SMALL 6 PIN	6G	75S
76∎	TRIODE	6.3	0.3	HEATER	CLASS A AMPLIFIER	250/100		13.5/2	5/2.5		1450/1150	9.5/12	13.8						ST-12	70	SMALL 5 PIN	5A	76
77∎	PENTODE	6.3	0.3	HEATER	CLASS A AMPLIFIER	250	100	3	2.3	0.5	1250	1000							ST-12	72	SMALL 6 PIN	6F	77
78∎	PENTODE	6.3	0.3	HEATER	CLASS A AMPLIFIER	250/90	125/90	3/3	10.5/5.4	2.6/1.3	1650/1275	600/300							ST-12	72	SMALL 6 PIN	6F	78
79∎	DOUBLE TRIODE	6.3	0.6	HEATER	CLASS B AMPLIFIER	250		0	10.6					14,000	8				ST-12	72	SMALL 6 PIN	6H	79
80	DOUBLE DIODE	5	2	FIL.	FULL-WAVE RECTIFIER											350	1400	125	ST-14	78	MED. 4 PIN	4C	80
81∎	DIODE	7.5	1.25	FIL.	HALF-WAVE RECTIFIER											700	2000	85	ST-16	89	MED. 4 PIN	4B	81
82∎	MERCURY FILLED DOUBLE DIODE	2.5	3	FIL.	FULL-WAVE RECTIFIER											450	1550	115	ST-14	78	MED. 4 PIN	4C	82
83	MERCURY FILLED DOUBLE DIODE	5	3	FIL.	FULL-WAVE RECTIFIER											450	1550	225	ST-16	84	MED. 4 PIN	4C	83
83V∎	DOUBLE DIODE	5	2	HEATER	FULL-WAVE RECTIFIER											375	1400	175	ST-14	78	MED. 4 PIN	4AD	83V
84/6Z4∎	DOUBLE DIODE	6.3	0.5	HEATER	FULL-WAVE RECTIFIER											325	1250	60	ST-12	70	SMALL 5 PIN	5D	84/6Z4
85∎	DOUBLE DIODE TRIODE	6.3	0.3	HEATER	CLASS A AMPLIFIER	250		20	8		1100		8.3	20,000	0.35				ST-12	72	SMALL 6 PIN	6G	85
89∎	PENTODE	6.3	0.4	HEATER	CLASS A AMPLIFIER	250	250	25	32	5.5	1800	70	125	6750	3.4				ST-12	72	SMALL 6 PIN	6F	89
99V	TRIODE	3.3	0.063	FIL.	CLASS A AMPLIFIER	90		4.5	2.5		425	15.5	6.6						T-8	13	SMALL 4 NUB	4E	99V
99X	TRIODE	3.3	0.063	FIL.	SAME CHARACTERISTICS AS TYPE 99V														T-9	47	SMALL 4 PIN	4D	99X
115-A	TRIODE	5	0.25	FIL.	CLASS A AMPLIFIER	180		13.5	7.7		1800	4.7	8.5	10,650	0.285				ST-14	78	MED. 4 PIN	4D	115-A
117L7/M7GT∎	DIODE BEAM PENTODE	117	0.09	HEATER	BEAM POWER UNIT AS CLASS A AMPLIFIER; HALF-WAVE RECTIFIER	105	105	5.2	43	4	5300			4000	0.85	117	350	75	T-9	41	8 PIN OCTAL	8AO	117L7/M7GT
117N7GT∎	DIODE BEAM PENTODE	117	0.09	HEATER	BEAM POWER UNIT; CLASS A AMPLIFIER; HALF-WAVE RECTIFIER	100	100	6	51	5	7000			3000	1.2	117	350	75	T-9	41	8 PIN OCTAL	8AV	117N7GT
117P7GT∎	DIODE BEAM PENTODE	117	0.09	HEATER	PENTODE CLASS A AMPLIFIER; HALF-WAVE RECTIFIER	105	105	5.2	43	4	5300			4000	0.85				T-9	41	8 PIN OCTAL	8AV	117P7GT
117Z3	DIODE	117	0.04	HEATER	HALF-WAVE RECTIFIER				Peak Plate Current per Plate: 540 Ma.							117	330	90	T-5⅞	5	MIN. 7 PIN	4CB	117Z3
117Z4GT	DIODE	117	0.04	HEATER	HALF-WAVE RECTIFIER											117	350	90	T-9	28	6 PIN OCTAL	5AA	117Z4GT
117Z6GT	DOUBLE DIODE	117	0.075	HEATER	HALF-WAVE RECTIFIER				DC current for each section							235	700	60	T-9	35	7 PIN OCTAL	7Q	117Z6GT
183∎	TRIODE	5	1.25	FIL.	CLASS A AMPLIFIER	250		60	25		1800	1.8	3.2	4500	2				ST-14	78	MED. 4 PIN	4D	183

Rectifier condenser input, D.C. output MA. — Signal: 5.3 V. RMS

∎ Tube types not recommended for new equipment design.

373

Appendix B-3
Typical Registered JEDEC Transistor Types

JEDEC No.	Type	Use	MAXIMUM RATINGS Pc mw @ 25°C	BVce / BVcb*	Ic ma	Tj°C	ELECTRICAL PARAMETERS MIN. hfe-hfe*	@ Ic ma	MIN. fhfb mc	MIN. Ge db	MAX. Ico (μa)	@ Vcb
2N22	Pt		120	−100	−20	55	1.9α					
2N23	Pt		80	−50	−40	55	1.9α					
2N24	Pt		120	−30	−25	50	2.2α					
2N25	Pt		200	−50	−30	60	2.5α					
2N26	Pt		90	−30	−40	55						
2N27	NPN		50	35*	100	85	100		1			
2N28	NPN		50	30*	100	85	100		.5			
2N29	NPN		50	35*	30	85	100		1		15	30
2N30	Pt	Obsolete	100	30	7	40	2.2α		2T	17T		
2N31	Pt	Obsolete	100	30	7	40	2.2α		2T		150	25
2N32	Pt	Obsolete	50	−40	−8	40	2.2α		2.7	21T		
2N32A	Pt	Obsolete	50	−40	−8	40	2.2α		2.7	21T		
2N33	Pt	Obsolete	30	−8.5	−7	40						
2N34	PNP	Obsolete	50	−25	−8	50	40		.6	40T		
2N34A	PNP	Obsolete	50	−25	−8	50	40		.6	40T		
2N35	NPN		50	25	8	50	40		.8	40T		
2N36	PNP		50	−20	−8	50	45T			40T		
2N37	PNP		50	−20	−8	50	30T			36T		
2N38	PNP		50	−20	−8	50	15T			32T		
2N38A	PNP		50	−20	−8	50	18T			34	−12	−3
2N41	PNP		50	−25	−15	50	40T			40T	−10	−12
2N43	PNP	AF	240	−30	−300	100	30	1	.5		−16	−45
2N43A	PNP	AF	240	−30	−300	100	30	1	.15		−16	−45
2N44	PNP	AF	240	−30	−300	100	25T	1	.5		−16	−45
2N45	PNP	Obsolete	155	−25	−10	100	25T		.5	34	−16	−45
2N46	PNP		50	−25	−15	50	40T			4T	−10	−12
2N47	PNP		50	−35*	−20	65	.975α				−5	−12
2N48	PNP		50	−35*	−20	65	.970α				−5	−12
2N49	PNP		50	−35*	−20	65	.975				−5	−12
2N50	Pt		50	−15	−1	50	2α		3T			
2N51	Pt		100	−50	−8	50	2.2α					
2N52	Pt		120	−50	−8	50					−350	−7
2N53	Pt			−50	−8							
2N54	PNP		200	−45	−10	60	.95α			40T		
2N55	PNP		200	−45	−10	60	.92α			39T		
2N56	PNP		200	−45	−10	60	.90α			38T		
2N59	PNP		180	−25*	−200	85	90T*	−100		35T	−15	−20
2N59A	PNP		180	−40*	−200	85	90T*	−100		35T	−15	−20
2N59B	PNP		180	−50*	−200	85	90T*	−100		35T	−15	−20

JEDEC No.	Type	Use	MAXIMUM RATINGS Pc mw @ 25°C	BVce / BVcb*	Ic ma	Tj°C	ELECTRICAL PARAMETERS MIN. hfe-hfe*	@ Ic ma	MIN. fhfb mc	MIN. Ge db	MAX. Ico (μa)	@ Vcb
2N744	NPN-EM		300	25	200	300S	80T*					
2N753	NPN-PEP	Sw	300	25		175J	80T		750			
2N754	NPN-M		300	60	50	175J	50T		45.0		1.0	
2N758	NPN-M		500	45	100	200A	50T		50.0			
2N759	NPN-PL	AF	500	45	100	200A	65T		50.0			
2N760	NPN-PL	AF	500	45	100	200A	150T		50.0			
2N761	NPN-M		500	45	100	200A	35T*		50.0			
2N762	NPN-M		500	45	100	200A	70T*		50.0			
2N768	PNP-MD		35	12	100	100	40T*		175		25	
2N769	PNP-M		35	12	100	100J	55T*		900		3.0	
2N779	PNP-MD		60	15	50	100	90T*		480		25	
2N779A	PNP-MD		60	15	100	100	60T*		450		3.0	
2N780	NPN-M		300	45		175J	20T		30.0			
2N781	PNP-EM		150	15	200	100	25T*				3.0	
2N782	PNP-EM		150	12	200	100	20T				3.0	
2N783	NPN-EM		300	40	200	175	40T				.25	
2N784	NPN-EM		300	30	200	175	25T				.25	
2N796	PNP-M		150	13	100	85A	75T*		80.0		3.0	
2N815	NPN-FA		75	25	200		80T*		8.00	14	10	
2N816	NPN-FA		75	25	200	100J	80T*		8.00	14	10	
2N818	NPN-FA		75	30	400	85J	25T		2.50		10	
2N819	NPN-FA		75	30	400	85J	30T		5.00		10	
2N820	NPN-FA		75	30	400	85J	30T		5.00		10	
2N821	NPN-FA		75	30	400	85J	70T*		10.0		10	
2N822	NPN		75	30	400	85J	70T*		10.0		10	
2N823	NPN		75	25	400	85J	40T		12.0		5.0	
2N824	NPN		75	25	400	85J	40T		12.0		5.0	
2N828	PNP-D		150	15	200	150S	40T*		400		3.0	
2N834	NPN-PEP	Sw	300	40	200	175J	40T*		500		.50	
2N835	NPN-M		300	25	200	175	40T*		450		.50	
2N839	NPN-M		300	45	50	175J	35T		30.0		1.0	
2N840	NPN-M		300	45	50	175	70T		30.0		1.0	
2N841	NPN-M		300	45	50	175	140T		40.0		1.0	
2N844	NPN-M		300	60	50	175	80T*		50.0	14	1.0	
2N845	NPN-M		300	100	50	175	80T*		50.0	14	1.0	
2N846	PNP-MD		60	15	50	100S	35T*		450		25	
2N849	NPN-M		450	25		175J	40T*				10	
2N850	NPN-M		450	25		175J	80T*				10	
2N870	NPN-PL		500	100		200J	70T*		110		.01	
2N871	NPN		500	100		200J	120T*		130		.01	
2N909	NPN-D		400	60		175J	55T		160		1.0	
2N910	NPN-PL		500	100		200J	100T		60.0		.025	

JEDEC No.	Type	Use	MAXIMUM RATINGS				ELECTRICAL PARAMETERS					
			Pc mw @ 25°C	BVce BVcb*	Ic ma	Tj°C	MIN. hfe-hfe*	@ Ic ma	MIN. fhfb mc	MIN. Ge db	MAX. Ico (μa)	@ Vcb
2N1781	NPN		100	25*	100	100	60*		6.0		20	
2N1785	PNP		45	10*	50	85	60*		125		10	
2N1786	PNP		45	10*	50	85	60*		125		10	
2N1787	PNP		45	15*	50	85	60*		125		10	
2N1808	NPN		150	25*	300	100S	60*		4.0		5.0	
2N1889	NPN-PL		800	100*		200J	70*		110		.01	
2N1890	NPN-PL		800	100*		200J	120*		130		.01	
2N1893	NPN-PL	Sw	800	120*		200J	85*		110		.01	
2N1924	PNP	AF	225	−60*	−500	85	30*	−100	1.0		−10	45
2N1925	PNP	AF	225	−60*	−500	85	47*	−100	1.3		−10	45
2N1926	PNP	AF	225	−60*	−500	85	65*	−100	1.5		−10	45
2N1954	PNP		200	60*	1.0 Amp	100J	120				20	
2N1955	PNP		200	60*	1.0 Amp	100J	200				20	
2N1956	PNP		200	60*	1.0 Amp	100J	120				20	
2N1958	NPN		600	60*	500	175	45				.50	
2N1959	NPN		600	60*	500	175	80				.50	
2N1960	PNP		150	15*	200	100	25				3.0	
2N1961	PNP		150	12*	200	100	20				3.0	
2N1969	PNP		150	30*	400	100	125		10		5.0	
2N1973	PNP		800	100*		200J	100		60		.025	
2N1974	PNP		800	100*		200J	50		50		.025	
2N1975	PNP		800	100*		200J	30		40		.025	
2N1986	NPN		600	50*		150J	150*		50.0		5.0	
2N1987	NPN		600	50*		150J	50*		50.0		5.0	
2N1997	PNP		250	45*	500	100S	75*		3.0		6.0	
2N1998	PNP		250	35*	500	100S	100*		6.50		6.0	
2N2022	PNP		150	15*	50	100J	35				3.0	
2N2042	PNP		200	105*			50		.50			
2N2042A	PNP		200	105*	200	100	50		.50		25	
2N2043	PNP		200	105*			113		.75			
2N2043A	PNP		200	105*	200		113		.75		25	
2N2049	NPN-PL		800	75*		200J	60*		50		.01	
2N2060	NPN-PL		500	100*		200J	35*				2.0	
2N2085	NPN		150	33*	500	100	100		8.0		5.0	
2N2086	NPN		600	120*	500	300S	70*		225		2.0	
2N2087	NPN		600	120*	500	300S	65*		225		2.0	
2N2106	NPN-M	AF	125	60*		150J			15MC		.20	30
2N2107	NPN-M	AF	125	60*		150J			15MC		.20	30
2N2108	NPN-M	AF	125	60*		150J			15MC		.20	30
2N2169	PNP		60	15*		100S	85*				3.0	
2N2192	NPN-PEP	Sw	800	60	1.0 Amp	300S	100*	150			10 mμa	30
2N2192A	NPN-PEP	Sw	800	60	1.0 Amp	300S	100*	150			10 mμa	30

JEDEC No.	Type	Use	MAXIMUM RATINGS				ELECTRICAL PARAMETERS					
			Pc mw @ 25°C	BVce BVcb*	Ic ma	Tj°C	MIN. hfe-hfe*	@ Ic ma	MIN. fhfb mc	MIN. Ge db	MAX. Ico (μa)	@ Vcb
2N2193	NPN-PEP	Sw	800	80	1.0 Amp	300S	40*	150			10 mμa	30
2N2193A	NPN-PEP	Sw	800	80	1.0 Amp	300S	40*	150			10 mμa	30
2N2194	NPN-PEP	Sw	800	60	1.0 Amp	300S	20*	150			10 mμa	30
2N2194A	NPN-PEP	Sw	800	60	1.0 Amp	300S	20*	150			10 mμa	30
2N2195	NPN-PEP	Sw	600	45	1.0 Amp	300S	20*	150			100 mμa	60
2N2195A	NPN-PEP	Sw	600	45	1.0 Amp	300S	20*	150			100 mμa	60
2N2196	NPN	Power	2W	80*		175	10*		15T		75	80
2N2197	NPN	Power	2W	80*		175	20*		15T		75	80
2N2201	NPN	Power	15W	120*		175J	30*		15MC		50	120
2N2202	NPN	Power	15W	120*		175J	30*		15MC		50	120
2N2203	NPN	Power	15W	120*		175J	30*		15MC		50	120
2N2204	NPN	Power	15W	120*		175J	30*		15MC		50	120
4D20	NPN	Sw	150	40*	25	150J	33*			1.0		
4D21	NPN	Sw	150	40*	25	150J	88*			1.0		
4D22	NPN	Sw	150	40*	25	150J	185*			1.0		
4D24	NPN	Sw	125	15*	25	125J	33*			1.0		
4D25	NPN	Sw	125	15*	25	125J	88*			1.0		
4D26	NPN	Sw	125	15*	25	125J	133*			1.0		
4C28	NPN	Sw	150	40*	25	125J	15		12.0	2.0		
4C29	NPN	Sw	150	40*	25	125J	30		12.0	2.0		
4C30	NPN	Sw	150	40*	25	125J	55		12.0	2.0		
4C31	NPN	Sw	150	40*	25	125J	115		12.0	2.0		
7B1	NPN	Power	15W	80*		175	12*		15T		50	80
7C1	NPN	Power	15W	80*		175	12*		15T		50	80
7D1	NPN	Power	15W	80*		175	12*		15T		50	80
7E1	NPN	Power	15W	80*		175	12*		15T		50	80
7F1	NPN	Power	7W	80*		175	12*		15T		50	80
7B2	NPN	Power	15W	80*		175	30*		15T		50	80
7C2	NPN	Power	15W	80*		175	30*		15T		50	80
7D2	NPN	Power	15W	80*		175	30*		15T		50	80
7E2	NPN	Power	15W	80*		175	30*		15T		50	80
7F2	NPN	Power	7W	80*		175	30*		15T		50	80
7B3	NPN	Power	15W	120*		175	12*		15T		50	120
7C3	NPN	Power	15W	120*		175	12*		15T		50	120
7D3	NPN	Power	15W	120*		175	12*		15T		50	120
7E3	NPN	Power	15W	120*		175	12*		15T		50	120
7F3	NPN	Power	7W	120*		175	12*		15T		50	120

ABBREVIATIONS

AF Audio Frequency Amplifier and General Purpose
AF Out High current AF Output
AF Sw Low frequency switch
GD Grown Diffused
IF Intermediate Frequency Amplifier
J Operating Junction Temperature
lo IF Low IF (262 Kc) Amplifier
NPN-A NPN Alloyed

NPN-D NPN Diffused
NPN-EM NPN Epitaxial Mesa
NPN-FA NPN Fused Alloyed
NPN-G NPN Grown
NPN-GD NPN Grown Diffused
NPN-M NPN Mesa
NPN-PL NPN Planar
NPN-PEP NPN Planar Epitaxial Passivated

NPN-PM NPN Planar Epitaxial Mesa
Osc High gain High frequency RF oscillator
PNP-A PNP Alloyed
PNP-D PNP Diffused
PNP-EM PNP Epitaxial Mesa
PNP-M PNP Mesa
PNP-MD PNP Micro-Alloyed Diffused
Pt Point contact types

Pwr Power output 1 watt or more
RF Radio Frequency Amplifier
S Storage Temperature
Si Silicon High Temperature Transistors (all others germanium)
Sw High current High frequency switch
T Typical Values
UNI Unijunction Transistor

Appendix B-4
Typical JEDEC Transistor Outlines

With three numbered terminals:
1 emitter
2 base
3 collector

With four-numbered terminals:
1 emitter
2 base
3 shield or ground
4 collector

With two-numbered terminals:
1 emitter
2 base
Case collector

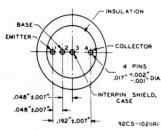

JEDEC NO. TO-45

.360" MAX. DIA.

.375" MAX.

.187" ±.015"

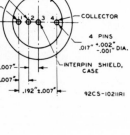

INSULATION

BASE

EMITTER

COLLECTOR

4 PINS
.017" +.002" -.001" DIA.

INTERPIN SHIELD, CASE

.048" ±.007"
.048" ±.007"
.192" ±.007"

92CS-10211R1

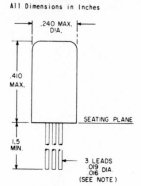

JEDEC No. TO-1
All Dimensions in Inches

.240 MAX. DIA.

.410 MAX.

SEATING PLANE

1.5 MIN.

3 LEADS
.019 DIA
.016
(SEE NOTE)

2
1 3

.081 DIA.
.061

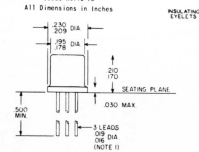

JEDEC No. TO-36

.610" MIN.
.710" MAX.

.312" MAX.

.140" MAX.

INDEX PIN OF INSULATING MATERIAL .140" DIA MAX.

EMITTER

.345"R.

COLLECTOR (CONNECTED TO CASE)

INSULATING EYELETS

BASE

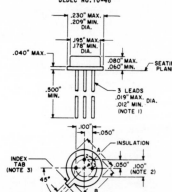

JEDEC No. TO-46

.230" MAX.
.209" MIN. DIA.

.195" MAX.
.178" MIN. DIA.

.040" MAX.

.080" MAX.
.060" MIN.

SEATING PLANE

.500" MIN.

3 LEADS
.019" MAX. DIA.
.012" MIN.
(NOTE 1)

.100"
.050"

INDEX TAB (NOTE 3)

INSULATION

A

.050" .100"
(NOTE 2)

45°

.046" MAX.
.036" MIN.

B

(NOTE 4)

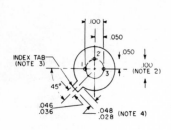

JEDEC No. TO-18
All Dimensions in Inches

.230 DIA
.209

.195 DIA
.178

.210
.170

SEATING PLANE

.500 MIN.

.030 MAX.

3 LEADS
.019 DIA
.016
(NOTE 1)

.100

.050

.050

INDEX TAB (NOTE 3)

2
1 3

.100
(NOTE 2)

45°

.046
.036

.048
.028 (NOTE 4)

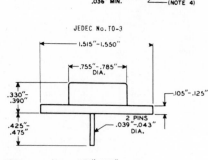

JEDEC No. TO-3

1.515"-1.550"

.755"-.785" DIA.

.330"-.390"

.105"-.125"

.425"-.475"

2 PINS
.039"-.043" DIA.

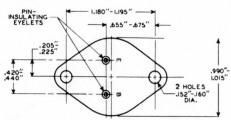

PIN-INSULATING EYELETS

1.180"-1.195"

.655"-.675"

.205"-.225"

.420"-.440"

.990"-1.015"

2 HOLES
.152"-.160" DIA.

376

Appendix B-5
Registered JEDEC Silicon and Germanium Rectifiers

Definitions and abbreviations are given on pages 342–43.

JEDEC TYPE NO.	CYCLICAL PRV	MAX I$_{DC}$
1N91	100	350 ma
1N92	200	375 ma
1N93, USN 1N93	300	400 ma
1N151	100	1200 ma
1N152	200	1000 ma
1N153	300	750 ma
1N158	400	400 ma
1N248	50	16 A
1N248A, B, C	50	30 A
1N249	100	16 A
1N249A, B, C	100	30 A
USA 1N249B	120	30 A
1N250	200	16 A
1N250A, B, C	200	30 A
USA 1N250B	250	30 A
1N253 JAN 1N253	95	1.5 A
1N254 JAN 1N254	190	1.5 A
1N255 JAN 1N255	380	1.5 A
1N256 JAN 1N256	570	1.5 A
1N315 (USAF 1N315)	300	75 ma
1N332	400	1300 ma
1N333	400	975 ma
1N334	300	1300 ma
1N335	300	975 ma
1N336	200	1300 ma
1N337	200	975 ma
1N339	100	1300 ma
1N340	100	975 ma
1N341	400	1300 ma
1N342	400	975 ma
1N343	300	1300 ma
1N344	300	975 ma
1N345	200	1300 ma
1N346	200	975 ma
1N348	100	1300 ma
1N349	100	975 ma
1N368	200	200 ma
1N440	100	300 ma
1N440B	100	750 ma
1N441	200	300 ma
1N441B	200	750 ma
1N442	300	300 ma
1N442B	300	750 ma
1N443	400	300 ma
1N443B	400	750 ma
1N444	500	300 ma
1N444B	500	750 ma
1N445	600	300 ma
1N445B	600	750 ma
1N536	50	750 ma
1N537	100	750 ma
1N538 USAF 1N538	200	750 ma
JAN 1N538	240	750 ma
1N539	300	750 ma
1N540 USAF 1N540	400	750 ma
JAN 1N540	480	750 ma
1N547 USAF 1N547	600	750 ma
JAN 1N547	720	750 ma
1N550	100	800 ma
1N551	200	800 ma
1N552	300	800 ma
1N553	400	800 ma
1N554	500	800 ma
1N555	600	800 ma
1N560	800	600 ma
1N561	1000	600 ma
1N562	800	700 ma
1N563	1000	700 ma
1N599	50	600 ma
1N599A	50	600 ma
1N600	100	600 ma
1N600A	100	600 ma
1N601	150	600 ma
1N601A	150	600 ma
1N602	200	600 ma
1N602A	200	600 ma
1N603	300	600 ma
1N603A	300	600 ma

JEDEC TYPE NO.	CYCLICAL PRV	MAX I$_{DC}$
1N604	400	600 ma
1N604A	400	600 ma
1N605	500	600 ma
1N605A	500	600 ma
1N606	600	600 ma
1N606A	600	600 ma
1N607	50	1.5 A
1N607A	50	1.5 A
1N608	100	1.5 A
1N608A	100	1.5 A
1N609	150	1.5 A
1N609A	150	1.5 A
1N610	200	1.5 A
1N610A	200	1.5 A
1N611	300	1.5 A
1N611A	300	1.5 A
1N612	400	1.5 A
1N612A	400	1.5 A
1N613	500	1.5 A
1N613A	500	1.5 A
1N614	600	1.5 A
1N614A	600	1.5 A
1N645, A USAF 1N645	225	400 ma
1N646 USAF 1N646	300	400 ma
1N647 USAF 1N647	400	400 ma
1N648 USAF 1N648	500	400 ma
1N649 USAF 1N649	600	400 ma
1N676	100	200 ma
1N677	100	400 ma
1N678	200	200 ma
1N679	200	400 ma
1N681	300	200 ma
1N682	300	400 ma
1N683	400	200 ma
1N684	400	400 ma
1N685	500	200 ma
1N686	500	400 ma
1N687	600	200 ma
1N689	600	400 ma
1N1095	500	750 ma
1N1096	600	750 ma
1N1100	100	750 ma
1N1101	200	750 ma
1N1102	300	750 ma
1N1103	400	750 ma
1N1115	100	1.5 A
1N1116	200	1.5 A
1N1117	300	1.5 A
1N1118	400	1.5 A
1N1119	500	1.5 A
1N1120	600	1.5 A
1N1191	50	25 A
1N1192	100	25 A
1N1193	150	25 A
1N1194	200	25 A
1N1195	300	25 A
1N1195A	300	30 A
1N1196	400	25 A
1N1196A	400	30 A
1N1197	500	25 A
1N1197A	500	30 A
1N1198	600	25 A
1N1198A	600	30 A
1N1199, A	50	21 A
1N1200, A	100	21 A
1N1201, A	150	21 A
1N1202, A	200	21 A
1N1203, A	300	21 A
1N1204, A	400	21 A
1N1205, A	500	21 A
1N1206, A	600	21 A
1N1341, A	50	11.5 A
1N1342, A	100	11.5 A
1N1343, A	150	11.5 A
1N1344, A	200	11.5 A
1N1345, A	300	11.5 A
1N1346, A	400	11.5 A
1N1347, A	500	11.5 A

JEDEC TYPE NO.	CYCLICAL PRV	MAX I$_{DC}$
1N1348, A	600	11.5 A
1N1487	100	750 ma
1N1488	200	750 ma
1N1489	300	750 ma
1N1490	400	750 ma
1N1491	500	750 ma
1N1492	600	750 ma
1N1612	50	17.5 A
1N1613	100	17.5 A
1N1614	200	17.5 A
1N1615	400	17.5 A
1N1616	600	17.5 A
1N1692	100	600 ma
1N1693	200	600 ma
1N1694	300	600 ma
1N1695	400	600 ma
1N1696	500	600 ma
1N1697	600	600 ma
USA 1N2135A	500	20 A
1N2154	50	33 A
1N2155	100	33 A
1N2156	200	33 A
1N2157	300	33 A
1N2158	400	33 A
1N2159	500	33 A
1N2160	600	33 A
1N2610	100	850 ma
1N2611	200	850 ma
1N2612	300	850 ma
1N2613	400	850 ma
1N2614	500	850 ma
1N2615	600	850 ma
1N2847	100	1.5 A
1N2848	200	1.5 A
1N2849	300	1.5 A
1N2850	400	1.5 A
1N2851	500	1.5 A
1N2852	600	1.5 A
1N3289-1N3295—See below		
1N3544	100	600 ma
1N3545	200	600 ma
1N3546	300	600 ma
1N3547	400	600 ma
1N3548	500	600 ma
1N3549	600	600 ma
1N3569	100	3.5 A
1N3570	200	3.5 A
1N3571	300	3.5 A
1N3572	400	3.5 A
1N3573	500	3.5 A
1N3574	600	3.5 A
1N3289 (4JA70B)	200	100 A
1N3290 (4JA70C)	300	100 A
1N3291 (4JA70D)	400	100 A
1N3292 (4JA70E)	500	100 A
1N3293 (4JA70M)	600	100 A
1N3294 (4JA70N)	800	100 A
1N3295 (4JA70P)	1000	100 A
*4JA60 series	Up to 400V	85 A
*4JA61 series	Up to 400V	85 A
*4JA62 series	Up to 400V	85 A
*4JA63 series	Up to 400V	85 A
4JA90B	200	250 A
4JA90C	300	250 A
4JA90D	400	250 A
4JA90E	500	250 A
4JA90M	600	250 A
4JA90N	800	250 A

*Obsolete—replaced by 4JA70 types

Appendix B-6
Definitions of Semiconductor Rectifier Terms

Rectifier ratings are always referred to specific ambient air or stud or case temperature conditions. Free convection ratings refer to conditions in which natural air currents are not impeded, and in which no nearby sources of radiant heat exist at a temperature higher than the air. When not otherwise specified, free convection ratings apply up to 10,000 feet altitude without derating.

SEMICONDUCTOR RECTIFIER RATINGS

Ratings are limiting values assigned by the manufacturer, which, if exceeded, may result in permanent impairment of device performance or life.

Terminology	Symbol	Definition
Cyclical peak reverse voltage or Repetitive peak inverse voltage	PRV or PIV	Maximum allowable instantaneous value of reverse voltage that may be applied across the rectifier repetitively under the specified conditions. Voltage may be applied as a sine wave, but it should not be construed to necessarily mean a continuous d-c rating which is defined separately below. While this value of PRV does not represent a "breakdown" voltage, it should never be exceeded except by the transient rating if the device has such a rating.
Transient peak reverse voltage	PRV_{trans}	Maximum allowable instantaneous value of reverse voltage that may be applied on a nonrecurrent basis for the duration and conditions specified.
Continuous reverse d-c (or blocking) voltage	V_{RDC}	Maximum voltage which the rectifier may block on a continuous basis. If this d-c reverse voltage is applied immediately after a forward conducting cycle, other limitations may apply.
Maximum allowable d-c output current	I_F	Maximum d-c current which may be allowed to flow in the forward direction under stated conditions of temperature and reverse voltage. It is the average value of current through a cell when working in a single-phase

circuit feeding a resistive or inductive load. A derating factor is usually applied for other conditions such as three-phase operation or capacitive loading.

Terminology	Symbol	Definition
Peak one-cycle surge (or fault) current	I_{surge}	Maximum allowable non-recurrent peak current of a single forward cycle (8.3 milliseconds duration) in a 60-cps single phase resistive load system. The surge may be preceded and followed by maximum rated voltage, current, and junction temperature conditions.
I-squared t	I^2t	This is a measure of maximum forward nonrecurring overcurrent capability for very short pulses of specified duration. I is in rms amperes and t is pulse duration in seconds. The same conditions as listed above for I_{surge} apply.

SEMICONDUCTOR RECTIFIER CHARACTERISTICS

Characteristics are measurable properties or attributes of a device which are inherent to its design.

Terminology	Symbol	Definition
Forward voltage drop	V_F	Instantaneous forward voltage drop during conduction of load current under stated conditions.
Full-cycle average forward voltage drop	$V_{Favg.}$	Forward voltage drop averaged over one complete cycle at stated temperature and with specified sinusoidal load current flowing in a 60-cps single-phase half-wave rectifier with resistive load.
Reverse (or leakage) current	i_R	Instantaneous value of reverse current at stated conditions of temperature and voltage.
Full-cycle average reverse current	$I_{Ravg.}$	Reverse current averaged over one complete cycle at specified PRV and temperature in a 60-cps sinusoidal single-phase half-wave rectifier with resistive load.

| Thermal resistance | R_T | Steady-state temperature rise per unit power dissipation of the junction above the temperature of the external reference point. For stud mounted cells, thermal resistance is expressed in °C/Watt between junction and the bottom face of stud. |
| Transient thermal resistance | r_T | Apparent thermal resistance defining temperature rise |

per unit power dissipation of junction above reference point for specified period of time after application of step function of heat to junction which was previously at equilibrium with ambient.

Appendix B-7
Military Approved Silicon and Germanium Rectifiers

TYPE	MILITARY SPECIFICATION	SINGLE PHASE MAX. RATINGS	
		PRV	I_{DC} @ TEMP.
GERMANIUM			
USN 1N93	MIL-E-1/895B	300 Volts	75 ma @ 55°C
USAF 1N315	MIL-E-1/1088	100 Volts	100 ma @ 85°C
SILICON			
USA 1N249B	MIL-S-19500/134	125 Volts	20 A @ 150°C case
USA 1N250B	MIL-S-19500/134	250 Volts	20 A @ 150°C case
JAN 1N253	MIL-E-1/1024A	100 Volts	1 A @ 135°C case
JAN 1N254	MIL-E-1/989B	200 Volts	400 ma @ 135°C case
JAN 1N255	MIL-E-1/990B	400 Volts	400 ma @ 135°C case
JAN 1N256	MIL-E-1/991B	600 Volts	200 ma @ 135°C case
JAN 1N538	MIL-E-1/1084A	240 Volts	250 ma @ 150°C amb.
USAF 1N538	MIL-E-1/1089	200 Volts	250 ma @ 150°C amb.
JAN 1N540	MIL-E-1/1085A	480 Volts	250 ma @ 150°C amb.
USAF 1N540	MIL-E-1/1089	400 Volts	250 ma @ 150°C amb.
JAN 1N547	MIL-E-1/1083A	720 Volts	250 ma @ 150°C amb.
USAF 1N547	MIL-E-1/1089	600 Volts	250 ma @ 150°C amb.
USAF 1N645	MIL-E-1/1143	225 Volts	200 ma @ 125°C amb.
USAF 1N646	MIL-E-1/1143	300 Volts	200 ma @ 125°C amb.
USAF 1N647	MIL-E-1/1143	400 Volts	200 ma @ 125°C amb.
USAF 1N648	MIL-E-1/1143	500 Volts	200 ma @ 125°C amb.

TYPE	MILITARY SPECIFICATION	SINGLE PHASE MAX. RATINGS	
		PRV	I_{DC} @ TEMP.
USAF 1N649	MIL-E-1/1143	600 Volts	200 ma @ 125°C amb.
USA 1N1614	MIL-S-19500/162	200	5 A @ 150° stud
USA 1N1615	MIL-S-19500/162	400	5 A @ 150° stud
USA 1N1616	MIL-S-19500/162	600	5 A @ 150° stud
USAF 1N1199	MIL-E-1/1108	50	12 A @ 150° stud
USAF 1N1200	MIL-E-1/1108	100	12 A @ 150° stud
USAF 1N1201	MIL-E-1/1108	150	12 A @ 150° stud
USAF 1N1202	MIL-E-1/1108	200	12 A @ 150° stud
USAF 1N1203	MIL-E-1/1108	300	12 A @ 150° stud
USAF 1N1204	MIL-E-1/1108	400	12 A @ 150° stud
USAF 1N1205	MIL-E-1/1108	500	12 A @ 150° stud
USAF 1N1206	MIL-E-1/1108	600	12 A @ 150° stud
USA 1N2135A	MIL-S-19500/134	500 Volts	20 A @ 150°C case
USN 2N681	MIL-S-19500/108	25	25 A @ 57°C Stud
USN 2N682	MIL-S-19500/108	50	25 A @ 57°C Stud
USN 2N683	MIL-S-19500/108	100	25 A @ 57°C Stud
USN 2N684	MIL-S-19500/108	150	25 A @ 57°C Stud
USN 2N685	MIL-S-19500/108	200	25 A @ 57°C Stud
USN 2N686	MIL-S-19500/108	250	25 A @ 57°C Stud
USN 2N687	MIL-S-19500/108	300	25 A @ 57°C Stud
USN 2N688	MIL-S-19500/108	400	25 A @ 57°C Stud

Appendix B-8
Relay Types and Definitions

General purpose. A general-purpose relay is one which operates upon application of the operating voltage to the coil and has no special features.

Marginal. A marginal relay is one which responds to make or break when the coil voltage or current reaches a predetermined value.

Differential. A differential relay is a multiple-winding relay which operates when the current or voltage difference between the windings reaches a predetermined value.

Time delay. A time delay relay is one in which a delayed action is purposely introduced.

Latch-in. A latch-in relay is one which is designed to lock the contacts in the energized position until the relay is either manually or electrically reset.

Ratchet. A ratchet relay is one which operates in cycles in accordance with a successive or predetermined arrangement of impulses.

Selector. A selector relay is one which permits the selection of one or more circuits from a number of circuits.

High speed. A high speed relay is one which operates within 5 milliseconds.

Sensitive. A sensitive relay is one which is designed to operate on 100 milliwatts or less.

Polarized. A polarized relay is one which is responsive to the direction of current flow.

Interlock. An interlock relay is a relay having two coils with their armatures and associated contacts so arranged that if one of the armatures is actuated, it prevents the other armature from being actuated until the first armature returns to its normal position.

Special purpose. A special purpose is a relay designed for a specific purpose or application that is not covered by any other type of relay defined herein.

Operating frequency. The operating frequency is the rated frequency at which the relay coil is designed to operate.

Rated voltage. Rated voltage is the voltage at which the relay is designed to operate.

Rated coil current. Rated coil current is the current which flows through the coil when rated voltage is applied.

Pick-up voltage (or **current**). Pick-up voltage (or current) is the minimum value of voltage (or current) at which the relay is designed to operate.

Appendix B-9
Preferred Value System and Color Coding in Resistors and Capacitors

PREFERRED VALUES

Composition resistors, mica and ceramic capacitors, and plastic-cased tubular capacitors are most conveniently specified in electronic hardware design and production in terms of preferred values. In this system, each value represents a nearly constant percentage increase over the next lower value, using the base 10.

Thus, only two significant figures are necessary to specify a component and, taking tolerance steps of 20, 10, and 5 percent, we can specify almost any desired component (without going to precision units) by using a group of preferred values as shown in the accompanying table; we need only supply the proper multipliers for any value within a tolerance grouping to designate almost any value of resistor or capacitor.

The system is the result of statistical analysis of the distribution of electrical values most commonly used, or likely to be used, in electronic design. In terms of percentage, by this system and within a decade of numbers (for 20 percent tolerance) over 90 percent of all likely choices can be satisfied using only seven values. This simplifies stockpiling, helps standardization, and reduces the paper work necessary in an otherwise fairly complicated system of values.

Very popular or well-known values which are multiples of 5, 25, or 75 can be added to the preferred list or fitted into the system either directly or by selection of close enough tolerances. For instance, a 500-ohm resistor is well within the 5 percent tolerance of a 510-ohm perferred value.

COLOR CODING

With the two-digit preferred value system, color code marking can, in four dots, completely describe small capacitors and resistors, including the multiplier, tolerance, or voltage rating. The generalized color coding system for marking component part values is summarized in Figs. 5–7 and 5–10, and applies to both capacitors or resistors whether the marking is by painted dots, as in the case of mica capacitors, or by colored bands for plastic-encased tubular or tubular ceramic capacitors.

It should be noted that the color marking system extends further than merely indicating electrical values. We shall see that it can also show case material, voltage rating, tolerance, temperature coefficient, or tolerance on temperature coefficient. Details of interpreting these additional color markings are given in descriptions of individual capacitor types in Chapter 5.

Standard component values

20% tolerance	10% tolerance	5% tolerance
10	10	10
	12	12
15	15	15
		16
	18	18
		20
22	22	22
		24
	27	27
		30
33	33	33
		36
	39	39
		43
47	47	47
		51
	56	56
		62
68	68	68
		75
	82	82
		91
100	100	100

Appendix B-10

Fuse Data

Table 1   Characteristics of fuses in electronic applications

Blowing characteristics	Fuse type	Physical size	Ampere ratings	Max. voltage rating
High speed	8AG	1″ × 1/4″ diam.	1/500–5	32, 125, 250
Medium lag	3AG	1-1/4″ × 1/4″ diam.	1/16–20	32, 125, 250
	5AG	1-1/2″ × 13/32″ diam.	1–50	32, 250
Slo-blo	3AG	1-1/4″ × 1/4″ diam.	1/100–5	32, 125
	5AG	1-1/2″ × 13/32″ diam.	1–30	32, 125

Table 2   Fuse sizes for protection of insulated copper wire

Wire size (B&S)	Fuse rating (amp)
No. 16	10
No. 14	15
No. 12	20–30
No. 10	40
No. 8	50

Table 3   Medium size lag fuses for 115-v power supplies

Power supply rating (watts)	Fuse rating (amp)
40–65	1
65–100	1½
100–150	2
150–250	3
250–350	5
350–450	6

Table 4   Current ratings of fuses for various instrument ranges

Fuse rating (amp)	Max. load (ma)	Voltmeters (ohms per volt)	Milliammeters (all magnetic-type movements)	Milliammeters (thermocouple types)
1/500	2	Over 1,000	Galvanometers	0–0.1 to 0–0.5
1/200	5	Over 1,000	Galvanometers	Up to 0.1
1/100	10	1,000	Up to 0.1	0–5 to 0–10
1/32	25	500–1,000	0–0.1 to 0–10	0–10 to 0–25
1/16	60	100–500	0–10 to 0–25	0–25 to 0–60
1/8	100	20–100	0–25 to 0–75	0–75 to 0–115
1/4	200	10–20	0–75 to 0–150	0–115 to 0–200
3/8	300	5–10	0–150 to 0–250	0–200 to 0–300
1/2	400	3–5	0–250 to 0–350	0–300 to 0–400
3/4	600		0–350 to 0–500	0–400 to 0–600
1	1,000		0–500 to 0–750	0–600 to 0–1,000
1½	1,500		0–750 to 0–1,000	0–1,000 to 0–1,500
2	2,000		0–1,000 to 0–1,500	0–1,500 to 0–2,000
3	3,000		0–1,500 to 0–2,000	0–2,000 to 0–3,000
5	5,000		0–2,000 to 0–4,000	0–3,000 to 0–5,000

Table 5   Fuse wire table

Fusing current, amps.	Copper		Tin		Allo-Tin		Lead	
	Diam., inch	S.W.G. (approx.)	Diam., inch	S.W.G. (approx.)	Diam., inch	S.W.G. (approx.)	Diam., inch	S.W.G. (approx.)
1	.0021	47	.0072	37	.0083	35	.0081	35
2	.0034	43	.0113	31	.0132	29	.0128	30
3	.0044	41	.0149	28	.0173	27	.0168	27
4	.0053	39	.0181	26	.0210	25	.0203	25
5	.0062	38	.0210	25	.0243	23	.0236	23
10	.0098	33	.0334	21	.0386	19	.0375	20
15	.0129	30	.0437	19	.0506	18	.0491	18
20	.0156	28	.0529	17	.0613	16	.0595	17
25	.0181	26	.0614	16	.0711	15	.0690	15
30	.0205	25	.0694	15	.0803	14	.0779	14
40	.0248	23	.0840	14	.0973	13	.0944	13
50	.0288	22	.0975	13	.1129	11	.1095	12
70	.0360	20	.1220	10	.1413	9	.1371	9
100	.0457	18	.1548	8	.1792	7	.1739	7

SYMBOL ELEMENTS

A	Ampere (a-c, r.m.s, or d-c), ambient, anode electrode
a	Ampere (peak or instantaneous)
B, b	Base electrode, breakdown
C, c	Capacitance, collector electrode, cathode electrode
Δ	(Delta) A small change in the value of the indicated variable
E, e	Emitter electrode
F, f	Frequency, forward transfer ratio
G, g	Gain, acceleration of gravity, gate electrode
h	General symbol for hybrid parameter
I, i	Current, input, intrinsic region of device
J, j	Reference electrode
K, k	Unspecified (general) measurement electrode
L	Inductance
N, n	n-region of device
O, o	Output, open circuit
P, p	Power, P-region of device
Q	Charge
R, r	Resistance, reverse transfer ratio
T	Temperature
t	Time
V	Voltage (max, avg, or r.m.s)
v	Volt (peak or instantaneous)
W	Watt (max, avg, or r.m.s)
w	Watt (peak or instantaneous)
X	Unspecified (general) parameter
Y	General symbol for an admittance parameter
θ	(Theta) Thermal resistance
Z, z	General symbol for impedance, impedance parameter

PARAMETER SYMBOLS

BV_{CBO}	*D-c breakdown voltage collector to base junction reverse biased, emitter open-circuited (value of I_C should be specified).
BV_{CEO}	*D-c breakdown voltage, collector to emitter, with base open-circuited. This may be a function of both "m" (the charge carrier multiplication factor) and the h_{fb} of the transistor. Specify I_C.
BV_{CER}	*D-c breakdown voltage, similar to BV_{CEO} except a resistor value "R" between base and emitter.
BV_{CES}	*D-c breakdown voltage, similar to BV_{CEO} but base shorted to emitter.
BV_{CEV}	*D-c breakdown voltage, similar to BV_{CEO} but emitter to base junction reverse biased.
BV_{CEX}	*D-c breakdown voltage, similar to BV_{CEO} but emitter to base junction reverse biased through a specified circuit.
BV_{EBO}	*D-c breakdown voltage, emitter to base junction reverse biased, collector open-circuited. Specify I_E.
BV_R	D-c breakdown voltage, reverse biased diode.
C_c	Barrier capacitance.
C_{eb}	*(Common base) capacitance emitter to base, collector open.
C_{ij}	Input capacitance.
C_{ob}	*(Common base) collector to base — Output capacitance measured across the output terminals.
C_{oe}	*(Common emitter) collector to emitter — Output capacitance measured across the output terminals.
f	Frequency at which measurement is performed.
f_{hfb} (f_{ab})	(Common base) small-signal short-circuit forward current transfer ratio cut-off frequency.
f_{hfe} (f_{ae})	(Common emitter) small-signal short-circuit forward current transfer ratio cut-off frequency.
f_{max} (f_{osc})	Maximum frequency of oscillation
f_t	Gain bandwidth product frequency at which the small signal, common emitter, short-circuit, forward current, transfer ratio (h_{fe}) is unity or zero db
$-g$	Negative conductance
G_{pb}	*(Common base) small-signal power gain
G_{PE}	*(Common emitter) large-signal power gain
G_{pe}	*(Common emitter) small-signal power gain
G_{pe} (CONV.)	*(Common emitter) conversion gain
h_{fb}	(Common base) — Small-signal short-circuit forward current transfer ratio, output a-c short-circuited.
h_{fc}	(Common collector) — Small-signal short-circuit forward current transfer ratio, output a-c short-circuited.
h_{fe}	(Common emitter) — Small-signal short-circuit forward current transfer ratio, output a-c short-circuited.
h_{fj}	(General) — Small-signal short-circuit forward current transfer ratio, output a-c short-circuited.
h_{FE}	*(Common emitter) static value of forward current transfer ratio, $h_{FE} = I_C/I_B$
h_{FE} (inv.)	Inverted h_{FE} (emitter and collector leads switched)
$h_{fb}, h_{fe},$ h_{fc}, h_{ij}	(Common base, common emitter, common collector, general) small-signal input impedance, output ac short-circuited.

h_{IE}	(Common emitter) static value of the input resistance.
h_{fe} (real)	(Common emitter) real part of the small-signal value of the short-circuit input impedance at high frequency.
h_{ob}, h_{oe}, h_{oc}, h_{oj}	(Common base, common emitter, common collector, general) small-signal, output admittance, input ac open-circuited.
h_{rb}, h_{re}, h_{rc}, h_{rj}	(Common base, common emitter, common collector, general) small-signal, reverse voltage transfer ratio, input ac open-circuited.
I, i	Region of a device which is intrinsic and in which neither holes nor electrons predominate.
I_B, I_C, I_E	D-c currents into base, collector, or emitter terminal
I_b	Base current (rms)
i_b	Base current (instantaneous)
I_{BX}	D-c base current with both the emitter and collector junctions reverse biased.
I_c	Collector current (rms)
i_c	Collector current (instantaneous)
I_{CBO} (I_{CO})	*D-c collector current when collector junction is reverse biased and emitter is open-circuited.
I_{CEO}	*D-c collector current with collector junction reverse biased and base open-circuited.
I_{CER}	*D-c collector current with collector junction reverse biased and a resistor of value "R" between base and emitter.
I_{CES}	*D-c collector current with collector junction reverse biased and base shorted to emitter.
I_{CEV}	*D-c collector current with collector junction reverse biased and with a specified base-emitter voltage.
I_{CEX}	*D-c collector current with collector junction reverse biased and with a specified base-emitter circuit connection.
I_e	Emitter current (rms)
i_e	Emitter current (instantaneous)
I_{EBO} (I_{EO})	*D-c emitter current when emitter junction is reverse biased and collector is open-circuited.
I_{ECS}	*D-c emitter current with emitter junction reverse biased and base shorted to collector
I_F	*D-c forward current
i_F	Forward current (instantaneous)
I_P	Peak point current
I_P/I_V	Peak to valley current ratio
I_R	Reverse current (d-c)
i_R	Reverse current (instantaneous)
I_V	Valley point current

L_c	Conversion loss — ratio of available signal power to the available intermediate frequency power.
L_S	Total series inductance.
N, n	Region of a device where electrons are the majority carriers.
η	Intrinsic stand-off ratio (unijunction).
NF	Noise figure
P, p	Region of a device where holes are the majority carriers.
p_t (peak)	Peak collector power dissipation for a specified time duration, duty cycle, and wave shape.
P_C	Average continuous collector power dissipation
P_o	Power output
pt (peak)	Peak total power dissipation for a specified time, duration, duty cycle, and wave shape.
P_T	Average continuous total power dissipation
Q_{SB}	Stored base charge
$r_b{}'$	Base spreading resistance equals h_{ie} (real) when h_{ie} (imaginary) $= 0$.
r_{B1B2O} (r_{BBO})	Device resistance between base 1 and base 2, emitter open-circuited (interbase resistance — unijunction).
$r_{CE(SAT)}$	Device resistance, collector to emitter, under saturation conditions (saturation resistance, steady state).
RE	Rectification efficiency (voltage)
R_{KJ}	Circuit resistance between terminals K and J.
R_L	Load resistance
r_s	Small signal series resistance
T_A	Operating temperature (ambient)
T_J	Junction temperature
T_{STG}	Storage temperature
V_{KJ}	Circuit voltage between terminals K and J
V_P	Peak point voltage
V_R	D-c reverse voltage
V_{RT}	D-c voltage reach-through (formerly called punch-through C_{PT}). At collector voltages above reach-through $V_{RT} = V_{CB} - V_{EB}$. (V_{EB} normally defined as 1 volt).
V_V	Valley point voltage
y_{fj}	Small signal short circuit forward transfer admittance
z_{ij}	Input impedance
z_{oj}	Output impedance

*Test conditions must be specified.

NOTE: D-c voltage and current terminologies (as listed herein) are valid only when measurements are made under non-oscillating conditions. Care must be exercised with avalanche transistors as they may oscillate when making these measurements and give erroneous readings.

ABBREVIATED DEFINITIONS OF TERMS

Absolute max. ratings. The value when so specified is an "absolute limit" and the device is not guaranteed if it is exceeded.

Applied voltage. Voltage applied between a terminal and the reference point.

*Constant current. One that does not produce a parameter value change greater than the required precision of the measurement when the generator impedance is halved.

*Constant voltage. One that does not produce a parameter value change greater than the required precision of the measurement when the generator impedance is doubled.

*Breakdown voltage (BV). That value of applied reverse voltage which remains essentially constant over a considerable range of current values, or where the incremental resistance = 0 at the lowest current in avalanche devices.

Limits. The minimum and maximum values specified.

Noise figure (NF). At a selected input frequency, the noise figure (usually 10 log of base 10 of ratio) is the ratio of the total noise power per unit bandwidth at a corresponding output frequency delivered to the ouput termination, to the portion thereof engendered at the input frequency by the input termination, (whose noise temperature is standard 290°K).

Open circuit. A condition such that halving the magnitude of the terminating impedance does not produce a change in the parameter measured greater than the required precision of the measurement.

Pulse A flow of energy of short duration which conveys intelligence.

Pulse average time (t_w). The time duration from a point on the leading edge which is 50% of the maximum amplitude to a point on the trailing edge which is 50% of the maximum amplitude.

Pulse delay time (t_d). The time interval from a point on the leading edge of the input pulse which is 10% of its maximum amplitude to a point on the leading edge of the output pulse which is 10% of its maximum amplitude.

Pulse fall time (t_f). The time duration during which the amplitude of its trailing edge decreases from 90 to 10% of the maximum amplitude.

Pulse rise time (t_r). The time duration during which the amplitude of its leading edge increases from 10 to 90% of the maximum amplitude.

Pulse storage time (t_s).—the time interval from a point 10% down from the maximum amplitude on the trailing edge of the input pulse to a point 10% down from the maximum amplitude on the trailing edge of the output pulse.

Pulse time (t_p). The time interval from a point on the leading edge which is 90% of the maximum amplitude to a point on the trailing edge which is 90% of the maximum amplitude.

Short circuit. A condition where doubling the magnitude of the terminating impedance does not produce a change in the parameter being measured that is greater than the required precision of the measurement.

Small signal. A signal is considered small when halving its magnitude does not produce a change in the parameter being measured that is greater than required precision of the measurement.

Spike. An unintended flow of electrical energy of short duration.

Supply voltage (V_{BB}, V_{CC}, V_{EE}). The potential of the circuit power source.

Thermal equilibrium. A condition where doubling the test time does not produce a change in the parameter that is greater than the required precision of the measurement.

Thermal resistance (θ). The temperature rise per unit power dissipation of the junction above the device case or ambient temperature under conditions of steady-state operation (where applicable, "case" means device mounting surface).

Thermal response time (γ_r). The time required for the junction temperature to reach 90% of the final value of junction temperature change caused by a step function in power dissipation when the device case or ambient temperature is held constant.

Thermal time constant (γ_t). The time required for the junction temperature to reach 63.2% of the final value of junction temperature change caused by step function in power dissipation when the device case or ambient temperature is held constant.

Base voltage (V_{BJ}) The voltage between the base terminal and the reference point (J).

Collector voltage (V_{CJ}). The voltage between the collector terminal and the reference point (J).

Cut-off current (I_{KJO}, I_{KJR}, I_{KJS}, I_{KJV}, I_{KJX}). The measured value of (K) electrode d-c current when it is reverse-biased by a voltage less than the breakdown voltage and the other electrode(s) is (are) d-c open-circuited (I_{KJO}) or:

1. returned to the reference electrode (J) through a given resistance (I_{KJR})
2. d-c short circuited to the reference electrode (J) (I_{KJS})
3. reverse-biased by a specified voltage (I_{KJV})
4. under a specified set of conditions different from the above (I_{KJX}).

Depletion layer capacitance (C dep). The transition capacitance of a reverse-biased PN junction. (Small signal as well as d-c conditions to be stated).

Diffusion capacitance (C dif). The transition capacitance of a forward biased (with an appreciable current flow) PN junction.

Emitter voltage (V_{EJ}). The voltage between the emitter terminal and the reference point (J).

Floating potential (V_{KJF}. The d-c voltage between the open circuit terminal (K) and the reference point (J) when a d-c voltage is applied to the third terminal and the reference terminal.

Input capacitance (C_{ij}). The shunt capacitance at the input terminals.

Input terminals. The terminals to which input voltage and current are applied.

Inverse electrical characteristics [X_{KJ}(INV)]. Those characteristics obtained when the collector and emitter terminals are interchanged.

Large-signal short circuit forward-current transfer ratio (h_{FJ}). Ratio of the change in output current (ΔI_0) to the corresponding change in input current (ΔI_I).

Large-signal transconductance (G_{MJ}). The ratio of the change in output current (ΔI_0) to the corresponding change in input voltage (ΔV_I).

Large-signal power gain (G_P). The ratio of the a-c output power to the a-c input power under the large signal conditions. Usually expressed in decibels (db). (a-c conditions must be specified).

Maximum frequency of oscillation (f_{osc} or f_{max}). The highest frequency at which a device will oscillate in a particular circuit.

Output capacitance (C_{oj}). The shunt capacitance at the output terminals.

Output terminals. The terminals at which the output voltage and current may be measured.

Power gain cut-off frequency (f_{pj}). That frequency at which the power out-put has dropped 3 db from its value at a reference test frequency ($G_P(f)$ = constant) with constant input power.

Reach-through voltage (V_{RT}) (formerly referred to as "punch-through voltage"). That value of reverse voltage at which the reverse-biased PN junction spreads sufficiently to electrically contact any other junction or contact, and thus act as a short circuit.

Real part of small signal short-circuit input impedance [h_{ij} (real)]. The real part of the ratio of a-c input voltage to the a-c input current with zero a-c output voltage.

Reference point (electrical). The terminal that is common to both the input and output circuits.

Saturation resistance [r_{KJ}(SAT)]. The ratio of saturation voltage to the measurement (K) electrode d-c current.

Saturation Voltage [V_{KJ}(SAT)]. The d-c voltage between the measurement electrode (K) and the reference electrode (J) for the saturation conditions specified.

Small-signal open-circuit forward transfer impedance (z_{fj}). The ratio of the a-c output voltage to the a-c input current with zero a-c output current.

Small-signal open-circuit input impedance (z_{ij}). The ratio of the a-c input voltage to the a-c input current with zero a-c output current.

Small-signal open-circuit output admittance (h_{oj}). The ratio of the a-c output current to the a-c voltage applied to the output terminals with zero a-c input current.

Small-signal open-circuit output impedance (z_{oj}). The ratio of the a-c voltage applied to the output terminals to the a-c output current with zero a-c input current.

Small-signal open-circuit reverse transfer impedance (z_{rj}). The ratio of the a-c input voltage to the a-c output current with zero a-c input current.

Small-signal open-circuit reverse voltage transfer ratio (h_{rj}). The ratio of the a-c input voltage to the a-c output voltage with zero a-c input current.

Small-signal power gain (G_p). The ratio of the a-c output power to the a-c input power. Usually expressed in db.

Small-signal short-circuit forward current transfer ratio (h_{fj}). The ratio of the a-c output current to the a-c input current with zero a-c output voltage.

Small-signal short-circuit forward current transfer ratio cut-off frequency (f_{hfj}). The frequency in cycles per second (cps) at which the absolute value of this ratio is 0.707 times its value at the test frequency specified ($G_p(f)$ = constant).

Small-signal short-circuit forward transfer admittance (y_{fj}). The ratio of the a-c output current to the a-c input voltage with zero a-c output voltage.

Small-signal short-circuit input impedance (h_{ij}). The ratio of the a-c input voltage the a-c input current with zero a-c output voltage.

Forward voltage (V_{FP}). Highest value of positive voltage at which the forward current equals the maximum specified peak point current ($I_F = I_P$).

Peak point current (I_P). Value of the static current flowing at the lowest positive voltage at which $d_I/d_V = 0$.

Peak point voltage (V_P). The lowest positive voltage at which $d_I/d_V = 0$.

Peak to valley ratio (I_P/I_V). The ratio of peak point current to valley point current.

Valley point current (I_V). The value of the static current flowing at the second lowest positive voltage at which $d_I/d_V = 0$.

Valley point voltage (V_V). The second lowest positive voltage at which $d_I/d_V = 0$.

*Test conditions must be specified.

Appendix B-12
Panel Lamp Characteristics

LARGE INCANDESCENT LAMP LISTING

S-6 Bulb
CANDELABRA SCREW Base

← DESIGNATION	RATINGS			DESIGNATION →
	WATTS	VOLTS	HOURS	
6S6—6V	6	6	1500	6S6DC—6V
6S6—12V	6	12	1500	6S6DC—12V
6S6—24V	6	24	1500	6S6DC—24V
6S6—30V	6	30	1500	6S6DC—30V
6S6—48V	6	48	1500	6S6DC—48V
6S6—75V	6	75	1500	6S6DC—75V
6S6—125V	6	125	1500	6S6DC—125V
6S6—135V	6	135	1500	6S6DC—135V
6S6—145V	6	145	1500	6S6DC—145V
10S6—230V	10	230	1500	10S6DC—230V
10S6—250V	10	250	1500	10S6DC—250V

S-6 Bulb
BAYONET BASE
Double Contact

C-7 Bulb BAYONET BASE Double Contact	**C-7 Bulb** BAYONET BASE Double Contact	**C-7 Bulb** CANDELABRA SCREW Base	**T-4½ Bulb** CANDELABRA SCREW Base	**S-6 Bulb** INTERMEDIATE SCREW Base

   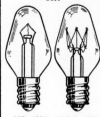  

10C7/DC 10 watts 120 volts 6000 hours	10C7/1DC 10 watts 120 volts 6000 hours	10C7/5DC 10 watts 120 volts 6000 hours	7C7—120V 7 watts 120 volts 1500 hours	10C7/5—120V 10 watts 120 volts 6000 hours	6T 4½/1 6 watts 125 volts 1500 hours	6S6/7 125 volts / 10S6/13 230 V.; 250 V.

MINIATURE INCANDESCENT LAMP LISTING

T-3¼ Bulb, MINIATURE BAYONET Base

NO.	Manufacturer's Rating VOLTS	AMPS	HOURS	VOLTS for 6000 hours
49	2.0	.06	1000	1.7
45	3.2	.35	3000	2.9
47	6.3	.15	3000	6.0
1847	6.3	.15	Long	6.3
44	6.3	.25	3000	6.0
1891	14	.24	500	12.0
1488	14	.15	200	10.5
1813 •	14.4	.10	3000	12.5

NO.	Manufacturer's Rating VOLTS	AMPS	HOURS	VOLTS for 6000 hours
1815	14	.20	3000	13.3
1826	18	.15	250	14.0
1819	28	.04	1000	24.0
1829	28	.07	1000	24.0
1820	28	.10	1000	24.0
313	28	.17	500	21.7
1828	37.5	.05	Long	37.5
1835	55	.05	Long	55.0

T-3¼ Bulb, MINIATURE SCREW Base

NO.	Manufacturer's Rating VOLTS	AMPS	HOURS	VOLTS for 6000 hours
48	2.0	.06	1000	1.7
42	3.2	.35	3000	3.0
40	6.3	.15	3000	6.0
46	6.3	.25	3000	6.0
1481	14	.15	200	10.5
1487	14	.20	3000	13.3
1827	18	.15	250	14.5
1821	28	.17	1000	24.2
1832	37.5	.05	*(L)	37.5

G-3½ Bulb—MINIATURE BAYONET Base—G-4½ Bulb

NO.	Manufacturer's Rating VOLTS	AMPS	HOURS	VOLTS for 6000 hours
51	7.5	.21	1000	6.6
53	14.4	.12	1000	13.5
1445	18	.15	250	13.5
*356	28	.17	500	23.0

*for intermittent service only

| 55 | 7 | .40 | 500 | 5.8 |
| 57 | 14 | .24 | 500 | 11.5 |

G—3½

G—4½

T-2 Bulb, TELEPHONE SLIDE Base

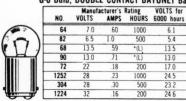

NO.	Manufacturer's Rating VOLTS	Min. (AMPS) Max.		LIFE
6A	6	0.12	0.16	
12C	12	0.17		Indefinite long life— over 6000 hours
24A	24	0.025	0.035	
24E	24	0.032	0.038	
48B	48	0.09	0.0110	
48C	48	0.032	0.038	
55C	55	0.045	0.055	

*(L)—Indefinite long life, over 6000 hours

G-6 Bulb, DOUBLE CONTACT BAYONET Base

NO.	Manufacturer's Rating VOLTS	AMPS	HOURS	VOLTS for 6000 hours
64	7.0	.60	1000	6.1
82	6.5	1.0	500	5.4
68	13.5	.59	*(L)	13.5
90	13.0	.71	*(L)	13.0
72	22	.18	200	17.0
1252	28	.23	1000	24.5
304	28	.30	500	23.2
1224	32	.16	200	24.6

G-6 Bulb, CANDELABRA SCREW Base

NO.	Manufacturer's Rating VOLTS	AMPS	HOURS	VOLTS for 6000 hours
63K	7.0	.60	1000	6.1
81K	6.5	1.0	500	5.4
1471	12	.26	250	10.3
67K	13.5	.59	*(L)	13.5
89K	13	.53	750	11.0
71K	22	.18	200	17.0
530	24	.17	250	18.8
1224K	32	.16	250	24.6

T-1¾ Bulb, MIDGET FLANGE Base

NO.	Manufacturer's Rating VOLTS	AMPS	HOURS
331	1.3	.06	500
343	2.5	40	30
338	2.7	.06	500
328	6.0	.20	500
345	6.0	.04	1000
330	14.0	.08	750
327	28.0	.04	1000

T-3¼ Bulb, ⅓ Watt, MINIATURE BAYONET Base
Types NE-51 and NE-51H (High brightness)

Recommended Resistance Values (Ohms) For NE-51		
Applied Volts	105-125	210-250
Best Light	56,000	180,000
Medium Life	100,000	270,000
Long Life	220,000	680,000

for NE51-H		
Applied Volts	105-125	210-250
Best Light	18,000	56,000
Medium Light	33,000	120,000
Long Life	82,000	220,000

T-4¼ Bulb, ¼ Watt, DOUBLE CONTACT BAYONET Base
Types NE-48, NE-16, and NE-17

Recommended Resistance Values (Ohms)		
Applied Volts	105-125	210-250
Best Light	16,400	44,000
Long Life	30,000	94,000

T-4½ Bulb, ¼ and ½ Watt, CANDELABRA SCREW Base
Types NE-45 and NE-57 (¼ W),
and NE-58 (½ W)

T-2 Bulb, 1/25 Watt, TELEPHONE SLIDE Base
Type NE-3

Recommended Resista..ce Values (Ohms)	
Applied Volts	105-125
Best Light	56,000
Medium Life	100,000
Long Life	220,000

S-7 Bulb, 1 Watt, DOUBLE CONTACT BAYONET Base
Type NE-79

Recommended Resistance Values (Ohms)		
Applied Volts	105-125	210-250
Best Light	3,000	9,400
Long Life	6,000	60,000

T-2 Bulb, MIDGET FLANGE Base
Types NE-2D and NE-2J

Recommended Resistance Values (Ohms) For NE-2D	
Applied Voltage	105-125 AC or DC
Best Light	56,000
Medium Life	100,000
Long Life	220,000

For NE-2J (High Brightness)	
Applied Volts	105-125 AC only
Best Light	18,000
Medium Life	33,000
Long Life	82,000

Appendix B-13
Transistor Parameter Conversion Nomograph

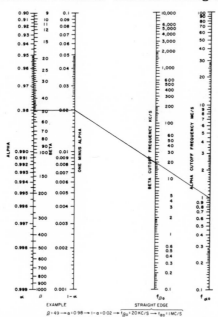

Printed with the permission of *Electronic Design* (Oct. 15, 1956)

Appendix C

Mechanical and Shop Data

Appendix C-1

Decimal Equivalents of Fractions

$\frac{1}{64}$	.015625	$\frac{17}{64}$	.265625	$\frac{33}{64}$	.515625	$\frac{49}{64}$	.765625
$\frac{1}{32}$	.031250	$\frac{9}{32}$	.281250	$\frac{17}{32}$	.531250	$\frac{25}{32}$	.781250
$\frac{3}{64}$	.046875	$\frac{19}{64}$	.296875	$\frac{35}{64}$	.546875	$\frac{51}{64}$	.796875
$\frac{1}{16}$	.062500	$\frac{5}{16}$	.312500	$\frac{9}{16}$	.562500	$\frac{13}{16}$	.812500
$\frac{5}{64}$	.078125	$\frac{21}{64}$	.328125	$\frac{37}{64}$	.578125	$\frac{53}{64}$	.828125
$\frac{3}{32}$	.093750	$\frac{11}{32}$	.343750	$\frac{19}{32}$	.593750	$\frac{27}{32}$	.843750
$\frac{7}{64}$	.109375	$\frac{23}{64}$	.359375	$\frac{39}{64}$	.609375	$\frac{55}{64}$	.859375
$\frac{1}{8}$	.125000	$\frac{3}{8}$	.375000	$\frac{5}{8}$	.625000	$\frac{7}{8}$	.875000
$\frac{9}{64}$	.140625	$\frac{25}{64}$	.390625	$\frac{41}{64}$	.640625	$\frac{57}{64}$	.890625
$\frac{5}{32}$	.156250	$\frac{13}{32}$	.406250	$\frac{21}{32}$	.656250	$\frac{29}{32}$	.906250
$\frac{11}{64}$	.171875	$\frac{27}{64}$	.421875	$\frac{43}{64}$	.671875	$\frac{59}{64}$	.921875
$\frac{3}{16}$	.187500	$\frac{7}{16}$	.437500	$\frac{11}{16}$	.687500	$\frac{15}{16}$	.937500
$\frac{13}{64}$	.203125	$\frac{29}{64}$	.453125	$\frac{45}{64}$	.703125	$\frac{61}{64}$	.953125
$\frac{7}{32}$	.218750	$\frac{15}{32}$	.468750	$\frac{23}{32}$	.718750	$\frac{31}{32}$	.968750
$\frac{15}{64}$	.234375	$\frac{31}{64}$	.484375	$\frac{47}{64}$	.734375	$\frac{63}{64}$	.984375
$\frac{1}{4}$	.250000	$\frac{1}{2}$	.500000	$\frac{3}{4}$	.750000	1	1.000000

Appendix C-2

Machine Screws, Drill Sizes for Clearance, Tap Holes, and Tap Sizes

Screw no.	Threads per inch	Tap size	Drill Number For Tap	Drill Number Clearance
2	48	2 × 48	No. 50	No. 44
2	56	2 × 56	50	44
2	64	2 × 64	50	44
3	40	3 × 40	47	39
3	48	3 × 48	47	39
3	56	3 × 56	45	39
4	32	4 × 32	45	31
4	36	4 × 36	44	31
4	40	4 × 40	43	31
6	32	6 × 32	36	28
6	36	6 × 36	34	28
8	24	8 × 24	30	17
8	32	8 × 32	29	19
10	24	10 × 24	25	10
10	30	10 × 30	22	10
10	32	10 × 32	21	10
12	20	12 × 20	19	2
12	24	12 × 24	16	2
12	28	12 × 28	14	2
14	20	14 × 20	10	1/4
14	24	14 × 24	7	1/4

Note: These are the drill sizes for average use. They vary somewhat with the material being drilled.

Appendix C-3
Insulated and Bare Copper Wire Tables

Table 1   Table of standard annealed bare copper wire using American wire gauge (B&S)

Gauge (AWG) or (B&S)	Diameter, inches			Area	Weight	Length	Resistance at 68° F			Gauge (AWG) or (B&S)
	Min.	Nom.	Max.	Circular mils	Pounds per M′	Feet per lb.	Ohms per M′	Feet per ohm	Ohms per lb.	
0000	.4554	.4600	.4646	211600.	640.5	1.561	.04901	20400.	.00007652	0000
000	.4055	.4096	.4137	167800.	507.9	1.968	.06180	16180.	.0001217	000
00	.3612	.3648	.3684	133100.	402.8	2.482	.07793	12830.	.0001935	00
0	.3217	.3249	.3281	105500.	319.5	3.130	.09827	10180.	.0003076	0
1	.2864	.2893	.2922	83690.	253.3	3.947	.1239	8070.	.0004891	1
2	.2550	.2576	.2602	66370.	200.9	4.977	.1563	6400.	.0007778	2
3	.2271	.2294	.2317	52640.	159.3	6.276	.1970	5075.	.001237	3
4	.2023	.2043	.2063	41740.	126.4	7.914	.2485	4025.	.001966	4
5	.1801	.1819	.1837	33100.	100.2	9.980	.3133	3192.	.003127	5
6	.1604	.1620	.1636	26250.	79.46	12.58	.3951	2531.	.004972	6
7	.1429	.1443	.1457	20820.	63.02	15.87	.4982	2007.	.007905	7
8	.1272	.1285	.1298	16510.	49.98	20.01	.6282	1592.	.01257	8
9	.1133	.1144	.1155	13090.	39.63	25.23	.7921	1262.	.01999	9
10	.1009	.1019	.1029	10380.	31.43	31.82	.9989	1001.	.03178	10
11	.08983	.09074	.09165	8234.	24.92	40.12	1.260	794.	.05053	11
12	.08000	.08081	.08162	6530.	19.77	50.59	1.588	629.6	.08035	12
13	.07124	.07196	.07268	5178.	15.68	63.80	2.003	499.3	.1278	13
14	.06344	.06408	.06472	4107.	12.43	80.44	2.525	396.0	.2032	14
15	.05650	.05707	.05764	3257.	9.858	101.4	3.184	314.0	.3230	15
16	.05031	.05082	.05133	2583.	7.818	127.9	4.016	249.0	.5136	16
17	.04481	.04526	.04571	2048.	6.200	161.3	5.064	197.5	.8167	17
18	.03990	.04030	.04070	1624.	4.917	203.4	6.385	156.5	1.299	18
19	.03553	.03589	.03625	1288.	3.899	256.5	8.051	124.2	2.065	19
20	.03164	.03196	.03228	1022.	3.092	323.4	10.15	98.5	3.283	20
21	.02818	.02846	.02874	810.1	2.452	407.8	12.80	78.11	5.221	21
22	.02510	.02535	.02560	642.4	1.945	514.2	16.14	61.95	8.301	22
23	.02234	.02257	.02280	509.5	1.542	648.4	20.36	49.13	13.20	23
24	.01990	.02010	.02030	404.0	1.223	817.7	25.67	38.96	20.99	24
25	.01770	.01790	.01810	320.4	.9699	1031.	32.37	30.90	33.37	25
26	.01578	.01594	.01610	254.1	.7692	1300.	40.81	24.50	53.06	26
27	.01406	.01420	.01434	201.5	.6100	1639.	51.47	19.43	84.37	27
28	.01251	.01264	.01277	159.8	.4837	2067.	64.90	15.41	134.2	28
29	.01115	.01126	.01137	126.7	.3836	2607.	81.83	12.22	213.3	29
30	.00993	.01003	.01013	100.5	.3042	3287.	103.2	9.691	339.2	30
31	.008828	.008928	.009028	79.7	.2413	4145.	130.1	7.685	539.3	31
32	.007850	.007950	.008050	63.21	.1913	5227.	164.1	6.095	857.6	32
33	.006980	.007080	.007180	50.13	.1517	6591.	206.9	4.833	1364.	33
34	.006205	.006305	.006405	39.75	.1203	8310.	260.9	3.833	2168.	34
35	.005515	.005615	.005715	31.52	.09542	10480.	329.0	3.040	3448.	35
36	.004900	.005000	.005100	25.00	.07568	13210.	414.8	2.411	5482.	36
37	.004353	.004453	.004553	19.83	.06001	16660.	523.1	1.912	8717.	37
38	.003865	.003965	.004065	15.72	.04759	21010.	659.6	1.516	13860.	38
39	.003431	.003531	.003631	12.47	.03774	26500.	831.8	1.202	22040.	39
40	.003045	.003145	.003245	9.888	.02993	33410.	1049.	0.9534	35040.	40
41	.00270	.00280	.00290	7.8400	.02373	42140.	1323.	.7559	55750.	41
42	.00239	.00249	.00259	6.2001	.01877	53270.	1673.	.5977	89120.	42
43	.00212	.00222	.00232	4.9284	.01492	67020.	2104.	.4753	141000.	43
44	.00187	.00197	.00207	3.8809	.01175	85100.	2672.	.3743	227380.	44
45	.00166	.00176	.00186	3.0976	.00938	106600.	3348.	.2987	356890.	45
46	.00147	.00157	.00167	2.4649	.00746	134040.	4207.	.2377	563900.	46

389

Table 2   Insulated Copper Wire Table

AWG of bare copper conductor	Diameter of bare copper conductor		Insulation									
			Enamel & single cotton		Enamel & single silk		Enamel & nylon		Resin & single cotton		Resin & nylon	
			+Diameter over insulation, inches									
	Min.	Max.	Min.	Max.	Min.	Max.	Min.	Max.	Min.	Max.	Min.	Max.
4	.2023	.2063	.2110	.2173	—	—	—	—	.2110	.2173	—	—
5	.1801	.1837	.1888	.1947	—	—	—	—	.1888	.1947	—	—
6	.1604	.1636	.1690	.1745	—	—	—	—	.1690	.1745	—	—
7	.1429	.1457	.1514	.1565	—	—	—	—	.1514	.1565	—	—
8	.1272	.1298	.1356	.1404	*	*	*	*	.1356	.1404	—	—
9	.1133	.1155	.1209	.1251	*	*	*	*	.1208	.1251	—	—
10	.1009	.1029	.1075	.1114	*	*	*	*	.1075	.1114	—	—
11	.0898	.0916	.0960	.0996	*	*	*	*	.0956	.0991	—	—
12	.0800	.0816	.0861	.0895	*	*	*	*	.0857	.0890	—	—
13	.0713	.0727	.0774	.0805	*	*	*	*	.0770	.0800	—	—
14	.0635	.0647	.0696	.0725	*	*	*	*	.0692	.0720	—	—
15	.0565	.0577	.0625	.0654	.0590	.0619	.0591	.0621	.0621	.0649	.0596	.0628
16	.0503	.0513	.0562	.0589	.0527	.0554	.0528	.0556	.0558	.0584	.0533	.0563
17	.0448	.0458	.0507	.0533	.0472	.0498	.0473	.0500	.0503	.0528	.0478	.0507
18	.0399	.0407	.0457	.0481	.0422	.0446	.0423	.0448	.0453	.0476	.0428	.0455
19	.0355	.0363	.0413	.0437	.0378	.0402	.0379	.0404	.0409	.0432	.0384	.0411
20	.0317	.0323	.0374	.0396	.0339	.0361	.0340	.0363	.0370	.0391	.0345	.0370
21	.0282	.0288	.0339	.0361	.0304	.0326	.0305	.0328	.0335	.0356	.0310	.0335
22	.0250	.0256	.0303	.0323	.0272	.0293	.0273	.0295	.0303	.0323	.0278	.0302
23	.0224	.0228	.0276	.0294	.0245	.0264	.0246	.0266	.0276	.0294	.0251	.0273
24	.0199	.0203	.0251	.0268	.0220	.0238	.0221	.0240	.0251	.0268	.0226	.0247
25	.0177	.0181	.0224	.0240	.0198	.0215	.0199	.0217	.0224	.0240	.0204	.0224
26	.0157	.0161	.0203	.0219	.0177	.0194	.0178	.0196	.0203	.0219	.0183	.0203
27	.0141	.0143	.0187	.0201	.0161	.0176	.0162	.0178	.0187	.0201	.0167	.0185
28	.0125	.0127	.0170	.0184	.0144	.0159	.0145	.0161	.0170	.0184	.0150	.0168
29	.0112	.0114	.0157	.0171	.0131	.0146	.0132	.0148	.0157	.0171	.0137	.0155
30	.0099	.0101	.0143	.0157	.0117	.0132	.0118	.0134	.0143	.0157	.0123	.0141
31	.0088	.0090	.0132	.0145	.0106	.0120	.0107	.0122	.0132	.0146	.0112	.0130
32	.0079	.0081	.0123	.0136	.0097	.0111	.0098	.0113	.0123	.0136	.0103	.0120
33	.0070	.0072	.0113	.0126	.0087	.0101	.0088	.0103	.0114	.0127	.0094	.0111
34	.0062	.0064	.0105	.0117	.0079	.0092	.0080	.0094	.0106	.0118	.0086	.0102
35	.0055	.0057	.0097	.0109	.0071	.0084	.0072	.0086	.0098	.0110	.0078	.0094
36	.0049	.0051	.0090	.0101	.0065	.0078	.0066	.0080	.0088	.0099	.0072	.0088
37	.0044	.0046	.0084	.0095	.0059	.0072	.0060	.0074	.0083	.0093	.0067	.0082
38	.0039	.0041	.0079	.0090	.0054	.0067	.0055	.0069	.0077	.0087	.0061	.0076
39	.0034	.0036	.0073	.0084	.0048	.0061	.0049	.0063	.0072	.0082	.0056	.0071
40	.0030	.0032	.0069	.0080	.0044	.0057	.0045	.0059	.0068	.0078	.0052	.0067

*Special construction–not standardized.

Appendix C-4
Twist Drill Sizes

Drill no.	Diam., inch	Drill no.	Diam., inch	Drill no.	Diam., inch	Drill no.	Diam., inch
1	.2280	21	.1590	41	.0960	61	.0390
2	.2210	22	.1570	42	.0935	62	.0380
3	.2130	23	.1540	43	.0890	63	.0370
4	.2090	24	.1520	44	.0860	64	.0360
5	.2055	25	.1495	45	.0820	65	.0350
6	.2040	26	.1470	46	.0810	66	.0330
7	.2010	27	.1440	47	.0785	67	.0320
8	.1990	28	.1405	48	.0760	68	.0310
9	.1960	29	.1360	49	.0730	69	.02925
10	.1935	30	.1285	50	.0700	70	.0280
11	.1910	31	.1200	51	.0670	71	.0260
12	.1890	32	.1160	52	.0635	72	.0250
13	.1850	33	.1130	53	.0595	73	.0240
14	.1820	34	.1110	54	.0550	74	.0225
15	.1800	35	.1100	55	.0520	75	.0210
16	.1770	36	.1065	56	.0465	76	.0200
17	.1730	37	.1040	57	.0430	77	.0180
18	.1695	38	.1015	58	.0420	78	.0160
19	.1660	39	.0995	59	.0410	79	.0145
20	.1610	40	.0980	60	.0400	80	.0135

Appendix C-6
Rod and Pipe Threading Data

Diam., inches	O.D., inches	Number of threads per inch	Total length of threads, inches
1/4	.540	18	5/8
3/8	.675	18	5/8
1/2	.840	14	13/16
3/4	1.050	14	13/16
1	1.315	11-1/2	1
1-1/4	1.660	11-1/2	1
1-1/2	1.900	11-1/2	1
2	2.375	11-1/2	1-1/16
2-1/2	2.875	8	1-9/16
3	3.500	8	1-5/8
4	4.500	8	1-3/4
5	5.563	8	1-13/16
6	6.625	8	1-15/16

Appendix C-5
Head Sizes for Machine Screws

	#0 (.060) Diam.	#0 Ht.	#2 (.086) Diam.	#2 Ht.	#4 (.112) Diam.	#4 Ht.	#6 (.138) Diam.	#6 Ht.	#8 (.164) Diam.	#8 Ht.	#10 (.190) Diam.	#10 Ht.	1/4" (.250) Diam.	1/4" Ht.
Round	.113	.053	.162	.069	.211	.086	.260	.103	.309	.120	.359	.137	.472	.175
Flat (82°)	.119	.035	.172	.051	.225	.067	.279	.083	.332	.100	.385	.116	.507	.153
Flat (100°)	—	—	—	—	.225	.048	.279	.060	.332	.072	.385	.083	.507	.110
Oval	.119	.056	.172	.080	.225	.104	.279	.128	.332	.152	.385	.176	.507	.232
Fillister	.096	.059	.140	.083	.183	.107	.226	.132	.270	.156	.313	.180	.414	.237
Truss	—	—	.194	.053	.257	.069	.321	.086	.384	.102	.448	.118	.573	.150
Binding	—	—	.181	.046	.235	.063	.290	.080	.344	.097	.399	.114	.513	.153
Pan	—	—	.167	.053	.219	.068	.270	.082	.322	.096	.373	.110	.492	.144
Cross recessed	—	—	.167	.062	.219	.080	.270	.097	.322	.115	.373	.133	.492	.175
Hex	—	—	.145	.050	.217	.060	.287	.080	.287	.110	.361	.120	.433	.190

In the case of the Hex Head machine screw the head diameter is actually the across-corners dimension.

Appendix D-1

Glossary of Microwave Terms

Attenuation. Decrease in magnitude of current, voltage, or power of a signal in transmission between points.

Attenuation constant. For a travelling plane wave of a given frequency, the rate of exponential decrease of the amplitude of a field component (or of the voltage or current) in the direction of propagation. Expressed in Nepers or db per unit length.

Attenuator, flap. A device designed to introduce attenuation into a waveguide circuit by means of a resistive material moved into the guide.

Attenuator, rotary vane. A device designed to introduce attenuation into a waveguide circuit by means of varying the angular position of a resistive material in the guide.

Backward-wave tube. A travelling-wave tube in which the electrons travel in a direction opposite to that in which the wave is propagated. A microwave oscillator.

Barretter. A metallic resistor with a positive temperature coefficient of resistivity. Used for detection and power-level measurements.

Bend, E-plane. A bend in a waveguide in the plane of the electric field. ("Easy" bend.)

Bend, H-plane. A bend in a waveguide in the plane of the magnetic field. ("Hard" bend.)

Bolometer. A barretter, a thermistor, or any other device utilizing the temperature coefficient of resistivity of some resistance element.

Choke joint. A type of joint for connecting two sections of waveguide. It is so arranged that there is efficient energy transfer without the necessity of an electrical contact at the insides of the guide.

Coaxial line. A transmission line in which one conductor completely surrounds the other, the two being coaxial and separated by a continuous solid dielectric or by dielectric spacers. Such a line is characterized by no external field and by having no susceptibility to external fields from other sources.

Coupler, directional. A device consisting of two transmission lines coupled together in such a way that a wave travelling in one line in one direction excites a wave in the other guide; ideally, in one direction only.

Coupler, forward. A directional coupler used to sample incident power.

Coupler, reverse. A directional coupler used to sample reflected power.

Coupling coefficient. A ratio between the power entering the main arm of a directional coupler in one direction to the power coupled into the auxiliary arm in the same direction.

Cut-off frquency. The lowest frequency at which lossless waveguide will propagate energy in some particular mode without attenuation.

Cut-off wavelength. The longest wavelength at which lossless waveguide will propagate energy in some particular mode without attenuation.

Demodulator. A device whose output voltage is proportional to the square of its input voltage (i.e., input power).

Detector. An element which reproduces the modulation of an RF wave, usually a semiconductor crystal. Barretters are sometimes used to detect low-frequency modulation.

Directivity. The ratio of (1) power flowing out of the auxiliary arm of a directional coupler when power is flowing in the forward direction in the main arm, to (2) power flowing out of the auxiliary arm of the coupler when power is flowing in the reverse direction in the main arm (both forward and reverse powers in the main arm being equal in magnitude).

Directivity signal. A spurious signal present in the output of a coupler because the directivity of the coupler is not infinite.

Efficiency, bolometer mount. The percentage of net applied power that is absorbed by the RF termination.

EHF. Extremely high frequency. The band of frequencies between 30,000 mc (30 gc) and 300,000 mc (300 gc).

E-H tee. A junction composed of a combination of E and H plane tee junctions having a common point of intersection with the main guide.

E-H tuner. An E-H tee used for impedance transformation, having two arms terminated in adjustable plungers.

Gigacycle. 10^9 cycles (formerly kilomegacycle). Common term for expressing microwave frequencies.

Guide wavelength. The length of waveguide corresponding to one cycle of variation in the axial (transmitted) direction.

Impedance, characteristic (of a rectangular waveguide). For the dominant TE_{10} mode of a lossless rectangular waveguide at a frequency above the cut-off frequency, the ratio of the square of the rms voltage between midpoints of the two conductor faces normal to the electric vector, and the total power flowing when the guide is match-terminated.

Impedance, characteristic (of a two-conductor transmission line). For a travelling, transverse electromagnetic wave, the ratio of the complex voltage between the conductors to the complex current on the conductors.

Impedance, normalized. Any impedance of a system divided by its characteristic impedance.

Incident power or signal. Power flowing from the generator to the load.

Iris. In a waveguide, a conducting plate or plates, of small thickness compared to a wavelength, occupying a part of the cross section of the waveguide. When only a single mode can be supported, an iris acts substantially as a shunt admittance.

Isolator ferrite. A microwave device which allows RF energy to pass through in one direction with very little loss while RF power in the reverse direction is absorbed.

Junction, hybrid. A waveguide arrangement with four branches which, when branches are properly terminated, has the property that energy can be transferred from any one branch into only two of the remaining three. In common usage this energy is equally divided between the two branches.

Magnetron. A high-power microwave oscillator tube with a fixed or limited frequency range. Frequency, efficiency, and power depend on magnetic field strength and anode voltage.

MASER (Microwave Amplification by Stimulated Emission of Radiation). A low-noise, microwave amplifier utilizing a change in energy level of a material to obtain signal amplification. Common materials are gases (ammonia) and crystals (ruby).

Matched termination (waveguide). A termination producing no reflected wave at any transverse section of the waveguide.

Microstrip. A microwave-transmission component utilizing a single conductor supported above a ground plane.

Microwave region. That portion of the electromagnetic spectrum lying between the far infrared and conventional RF portion. Commonly regarded as extending from 1,000 megacycles (30 cm) to 300,000 megacycles (1 mm).

Millimeter waves. The band of frequencies having wavelengths shorter than 1 cm (above 30,000 mc).

Mismatch loss (reflection loss). The ratio, expressed in db, of the incident power to the transmitted power at a discontinuity. A measure of the loss caused by reflection.

Mode (of transmission propagation). A form of propagation of guided waves that is characterized by a particular field pattern in a plane transverse to the direction of propagation. The field pattern is independent of the position along the axis of the waveguide and, for uniconductor waveguide, independent of frequency.

Noise figure. A figure of merit for microwave amplifiers. A ratio in db between actual output noise power, and the output noise power which would come from a noiseless amplifier with identical gain and bandwidth.

Parametric amplifier (MAVAR—Mixer Amplification by Variable Reactance). A microwave amplifier utilizing the nonlinearity of a reactance element to obtain amplification. A low-noise amplifier.

Propagation constant. A transmission characteristic of a line which indicates the effect of the line on the wave being transmitted along the line. It is a complex quantity having a real term, the attenuation constant, and an imaginary term, the phase a constant.

Rat race (hybrid ring). A hybrid junction which consists of a re-entrant line (waveguide) of proper electrical length to sustain standing waves, to which four side arms are connected. Commonly used as an equal power divider.

Reflected power or signal. Power flowing from the load back to the generator.

Reflection coefficient. A numerical ratio between the reflected voltage and the incident voltage.

Reflectometer. A microwave system arranged to measure the incident and reflected voltages and to indicate their ratio (swr).

Reflex klystron. A low-power microwave oscillator tube which depends primarily on the physical size of a cavity resonator for its frequency. Normally has a wider frequency range than a magnetron.

Reike diagram. A polar-coordinate load diagram for microwave oscillators, particularly klystrons and magnetrons.

Return loss. The ratio, expressed in db, between the power incident upon a discontinuity and the power reflected from the discontinuity. (The number of db reflected power is down from incident power.)

Rotator. In waveguides, a means of rotating the plane of polarization. In a rectangular waveguide, rotation is accomplished simply by twisting the guide itself.

SHF. Super high frequency. The band of frequencies between 3,000 and 30,000 mc.

Slotted section. A length of waveguide in the wall of which is cut a nonradiating slot used for standing-wave measurements.

Smith Diagram or Chart. A diagram with polar coordinates; developed to aid in the solution of transmission-line and waveguide problems.

Thermistor. A resistance element made of a semiconducting material which exhibits a high negative temperature coefficient of resistivity.

Travelling-wave tube. A broadband, microwave tube which depends for its characteristics upon the interaction between the field of a wave propagated along a waveguide and the beam of electrons travelling with the wave. A microwave amplifier.

Tuning screw (slide-screw tuner). A screw or probe inserted into the top or bottom of a waveguide (parallel to the E field) to develop susceptance, the magnitude and sign of which is controlled by the depth of penetration of the screw.

UHF. Ultra high frequency, the band of frequencies between 300 and 3,000 mc.

VHF. Very high frequency, the band of frequencies between 30 and 300 mc.

Voltage standing-wave ratio (*VSWR* or *SWR*). The measured ratio of the field strength at a voltage maximum to that at an adjacent minimum.

Wave circuits, slow. A microwave circuit designed to have a phase velocity considerably below the speed of light. The general application for such waves is in travelling-wave tubes.

Wave, dominant. The guided wave having the lowest cut-off frequency. It is the only wave which will carry energy when the excitation is between the lowest cut-off frequency and the next higher frequency of a waveguide.

Waveguide phase shifter. A device for adjusting the phase of a particular field component at the output of the device relative to the phase of that field component at the input.

Waveguide tee. A junction used for the purpose of connecting a branch section of a waveguide in series with or parallel with the main transmission line.

Waveguide tuner. An adjustable device added to a waveguide for the purpose of an impedance transformation.

Waveguide wavelength. For a travelling plane wave at a given frequency, the distance along the waveguide between points at which a field component (or the voltage or current) differs in phase by 2π radians.

Wave, phase velocity. The velocity with which a point of constant phase is propagated in a progressive sinusoidal wave.

Wave, group velocity. The velocity with which the envelope of a group of waves of neighboring frequencies travels in a medium; usually identified with the velocity of energy propagation.

Wave, transverse electric (TE wave). In a homogeneous isotropic medium, an electromagnetic wave in which the electric field vectors are everywhere perpendicular to the direction of propagation.

Wave, transverse electromagnetic (TEM wave). In a homogeneous isotropic medium, an electromagnetic wave in which both the electric and magnetic field vectors are everywhere perpendicular to the direction of propagation. Generally dominant mode of coaxial lines.

Wave, transverse magnetic (TM wave). In a homogeneous istropic medium, an electromagnetic wave in which the magnetic field vector is everywhere perpendicular to the direction of propagation.

Wave, TE_{mn} (in rectangular waveguide). In a hollow, rectangular, metal cylinder, the transverse electric wave for which m is the number of half-period variations of the electric field along the longer transverse dimension, and n is the number of half-period variations of the magnetic field along the shorter transverse dimensions.

Wave, TM_{mn} (in rectangular waveguide). In a hollow, rectangular, metal cylinder, the transverse magnetic wave for which m is the number of half-period variations of the magnetic field along the longer transverse dimension, and n is the number of half-period variations of the magnetic fields along the shorter transverse dimensions.

Wavemeter, absorption. A device which utilizes the characteristics of a resonator, which cause it to absorb maximum energy at its resonant frequency when loosely coupled to a source.

Appendix D-2
Use of Smith Charts in Microwave
Measurements

Some measurements made in transmission lines and waveguides may be interpreted on a Smith Chart. This form of transmission-line chart is a polar plot, consisting of a system of impedance coordinates, superimposed upon which is another system of lines representing loci of constant standing-wave ratio, and constant distance along the line. The chart may be used for the interpretation of the measured values of VSWR and the location of the voltage minima in terms of equivalent input impedance (or admittance) circuits, or in terms of reflection coefficients. It

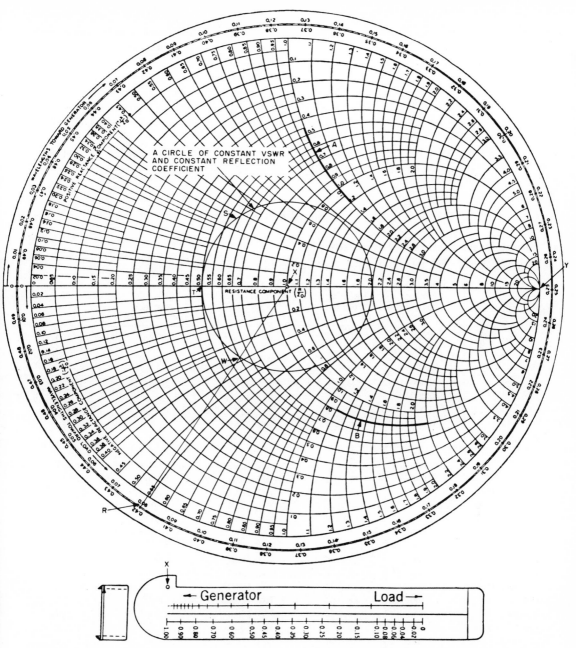

A CIRCLE OF CONSTANT VSWR AND CONSTANT REFLECTION COEFFICIENT

is also useful for determining the effect of a discontinuity or a change in characteristic impedance, and for solving impedance-matching problems.

A Smith Chart is illustrated in the accompanying figure. Point X at the center of the chart is the origin for a polar plot of the reflection coefficient, the angle being indicated on the circular scale around the rim, and the magnitude by the radial distance measured outward from the center on a scale graduated linearly from 0 to 1. Circular arcs such as A extending from point Y

to the outer rim are the loci of all reflection coefficients that correspond to normalized impedances having equal reactive parts; for circle A the impedances have reactance of 1.0. Circles such as B represent reflection coefficients corresponding to normalized impedances having equal resistive parts; for circle B this resistance is .8.

When traversing a standing-wave circle (S) with a standing-wave ratio of 2.0, the resistance axis is crossed at two points, one giving a very high resistance and the other a very low resistance. These correspond to the voltage maxima and minima, respectively, observed on a standing-wave detector. On the basis of this, the Smith Chart can be used in connection with the standing-wave detector to determine unknown load impedances. For example, a standing-wave ratio of 2.0 (circle S) is observed, and the first voltage minimum is .08 wavelength (R) from the load. Starting at point T, which corresponds to

the voltage minimum at a standing-wave ratio of 2.0, travel along this circle S of constant standing-wave ratio toward the load to the point where the line drawn between points R and X intersects circle S. At this point of intersection W, read the coordinates of the load impedance, which in this example are 0.62 and $j0.38$. Multiplying these numbers by the characteristic impedance of the standing-wave detector gives the actual impedance of the terminating load.

Appendix D-3

A. COAXIAL CABLE CHARACTERISTICS (following basic specification MIL-C-17B)

Cable	Minimum dielectric strength (volts, rms)	Impedance (ohms)	Cable	Minimum dielectric strength (volts, rms)	Impedance (ohms)
RG–5B/U	7,000	50 ± 2	RG–81/U	3,000	50 + 4 − 2
RG–6A/U	7,000	75 ± 3	RG–82/U	5,000	50 + 4 − 2
RG–8A/U	10,000	50 ± 2			
RG–9B/U	10,000	50 ± 2	RG–84A/U	22,000	75 ± 3
RG–10A/U	10,000	50 ± 2	RG–85A/U	22,000	75 ± 3
RG–11A/U	10,000	75 ± 3	RG–86/U	10,000	200 ± 10
RG–12A/U	10,000	75 ± 3	RG–87A/U	10,000	50 ± 2
RG–13A/U	10,000	75 ± 3	RG–88B/U	12,000	48 ± 4
RG–14A/U	12,000	50 ± 2	RG–94A/U	12,000	50 ± 2
RG–17A/U	22,000	50 ± 2	RG–108A/U	2,000	78 ± 7
RG–18A/U	11,000	50 ± 2	RG–111A/U	2,000	95 ± 5
RG–19A/U	30,000	50 ± 2	RG–114A/U	5,000	185 ± 10
RG–20A/U	30,000	50 ± 2	RG–115/U	5,000	50 ± 2
RG–21A/U	7,000	50 ± 2	RG–116/U	10,000	50 ± 2
RG–22B/U	2,000	95 ± 5	RG–117/U	10,000	50 ± 2
RG–23A/U	14,500	125 ± 5	RG–118/U	10,000	50 ± 2
RG–24A/U	14,500	125 ± 5	RG–119/U	12,000	50 ± 2
RG–25/U	12,000	48 ± 4	RG–120/U	12,000	50 ± 2
RG–25A/U	12,000	48 ± 4	RG–122/U	5,000	50 ± 2
RG–26/U	12,000	48 ± 4	RG–126/U	7,000	50 ± 2
RG–26A/U	12,000	48 ± 4	RG–130/U	10,000	95 ± 5
RG–27A/U	18,000	48 ± 4	RG–131/U	10,000	95 ± 5
RG–28/U	18,000	48 ± 4	RG–140/U	7,000	75 ± 3
RG–34A/U	15,000	75 ± 3	RG–141/U	5,000	50 ± 2
RG–35A/U	22,000	75 ± 3	RG–142/U	5,000	50 ± 2
RG–55A/U	5,000	50 ± 2	RG–143/U	7,000	50 ± 2
RG–57A/U	10,000	95 ± 5	RG–144/U	10,000	75 ± 3
RG–58C/U	5,000	50 ± 2	RG–146/U	5,000	190 ± 10
RG–59A/U	7,000	75 ± 3	RG–164/U	22,000	75 ± 3
RG–62A/U	3,000	93 ± 5	RG–165/U	10,000	50 ± 2
RG–63B/U	3,000	125 ± 6	RG–166/U	10,000	50 ± 2
RG–64/U	12,000	48 ± 4	RG–177/U	22,000	50 ± 2
RG–64A/U	12,000	48 ± 4	RG–187/U	2,000	75 ± 3
RG–65A/U	3,000	950 ± 50	RG–188/U	2,000	50 ± 2
RG–74A/U	12,000	50 ± 2	RG–195/U	2,000	95 ± 3
RG–79B/U	3,000	125 ± 6	RG–196/U	2,000	50 ± 2

B. TWO-CONDUCTOR SHIELDED CABLES (following basic specification MIL-C-17B)

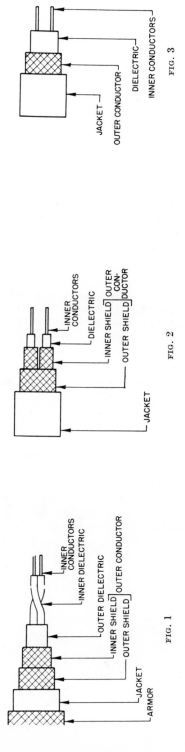

FIG. 1

FIG. 2

FIG. 3

RG-**/U no.	Fig.	Imp., ohms	Cap., μμf/ft	Dielectric strength, volts rms min.	Inner conductor (each)			Dielectric				Outer conductor		Protective coatings			O.D. max., inch
					Strands /AWG	O.D. nom., inch	Mat. (1)	Inner Mat. (2)	Inner O.D. max.	Outer Mat. (2)	Outer O.D. max.	No. of shields	O.D. max., inch	Moisture seal	Jacket mat. (3)	Armor	
22B	1	95±5	16	2,000	7/–	.040	C	A	.092	A	.291	2	.355	—	II a	—	.430
23A	2	125±5	12	14,500	7/–	.0855	C	A	.394	—	—	3	—	—	II a	—	.670 × .965 Oval
24A	2	125±5	12	14,500	7/–	.0855	C	A	.394	—	—	3	—	—	II a	X	.735 × 1.034 Oval
57A	3	95±5	17	10,000	7/–	.0855	C	—	—	A	.487	1	.540	—	II a	—	.640
86	3	200±10	7.8	10,000	7/–	.0855	C	—	—	A	.487	—	—	—	None	—	.665 × .315 Oval
108A	1	78±7	24.5	2,000	7/28	.0456	TC	A	.082	—	—	1	.177	—	II a	—	.245
111A	1	95±5	16	2,000	7/–	.0855	C	A	.092	A	.291	2	.355	—	II a	X	.490
130	1	95±5	—	10,000	7/–	.0855	C	A	.193	A	.487	1	.540	—	I	—	.640
131	1	95±5	—	10,000	7/–	.0855	C	A	.193	A	.487	1	.540	—	I	X	.710

** Insert number listed in column for desired cable.
1. Inner conductor material: C-Copper; TC-Tinned Copper.
2. Dielectric material: A-Polyethylene.
3. Jacket material: I-Black Synthetic Resin; IIa-Black noncontaminating synthetic resin.

397

Appendix D-4
Typical VSWR Measuring Set-up Using the Slotted Line

This is a descriptive summary of a typical slotted-line measuring set-up which aims to augment the description of detailed slotted-line measurement procedures in Chapter 16. The various elements are physically assembled as shown in Fig. 1, demonstrating in this instance the measurement of a newly designed or un-measured piece of waveguide (Item 10). The various pieces of test gear appear as arranged in their correct physical relationships, with numbers keying them to the following decriptions:

1. *Klystron oscillator tube and shield mount.* The *X* band carrier signals generated by the klystron serve as the input power necessary for measured indications.

2. *The klystron power supply* delivers adjustable supply and modulating voltages to the oscillator tube.

3. *The slide screw tuner* provides adjustable tuning so that the klystron output will match the tandem test line; it insures stability and maximum output.

4. *The ferrite isolator* insures that any *changes* or reflections further down the line do not react back to destroy klystron operational stability.

5. *A level set attenuator* delivers variable amounts of power to the rest of the line for steps in measuring.

6. By using a *reaction frequency meter*, dips in the VSWR amplifier indicate adjustment frequency point coincidence with the oscillator frequency. Desired frequency can then be set.

7. *The slotted line* provides the means physically to position the broadband probe.

8. *The broadband probe* provides quantities in terms of dimension and amplitude indicating wave propagation conditions throughout the bench set-up.

9. *The standing-wave amplifier and output indicator* provides detection and amplification of the probe's output.

10. *The unknown section* is the subject of measurement.

11. A proper *waveguide termination* to match the unknown element and correctly to absorb the incident power is necessary.

Figure 2 shows the picture set-up transformed to block-diagrammatic form when arranged to measure a connector, using a variable short circuit for the termination element.

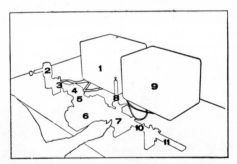

FIG. 1 Pictorial view of VSWR measurement set-up

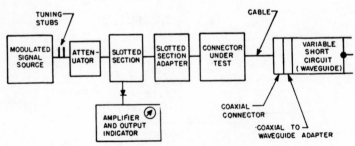

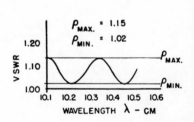

FIG. 2 Frequency variation test set-up

Appendix D-5
Standard Waveguide Characteristics

Band	A-N type	Mates with flange Cover	Choke	Material	Internal dimensions	Frequency kmc/sec	Recommended operating range TE$_{10}$ mode — Wavelength air cm	Wavelength guide cm	Wavelength guide in.	Cut-off Freq. kmc/sec	Cut-off Wave-length cm	Calc atten db/100 ft. Low freq.	High freq.	Calc max c-w power megawatts Low freq.	High freq.
L	RG 69/U	UG-417A/U	UG-417A/U	Brass	6.500 × 3.250	1.12- 1.70	26.766-17.634	45.706-20.857	17.994-8.212	.908	33.020	.424	.284	11.9	17.2
	RG 103/U	UG-417A/U	UG-417A/U	Alum.								.269	.178		
	RG 104/U	UG-435A/U	UG-435A/U	Brass	4.300 × 2.150	1.70- 2.60	17.634-11.530	29.878-13.575	11.763-5.344	1.372	21.844	.788	.516	5.2	7.5
	RG 105/U	UG-437A/U	UG-437A/U	Alum.								.501	.330		
	RG 112/U	UG-553/U	UG-553/U	Brass	3.400 × 1.700	2.20- 3.30	13.629- 9.084	22.175-10.681	8.730-4.205	1.736	17.272	.877	.572	3.5	4.7
	RG 113/U	UG-554/U	UG-554/U	Alum.								.751	.492		
S	RG 48/U	UG-53/U	UG-54A/U	Brass	2.840 × 1.340	2.60- 3.95	11.530- 7.589	19.181- 8.924	7.552-3.513	2.078	14.427	1.48	1.01	2.2	3.2
	RG75/U	UG-584/U	UG-585/U	Alum.								.940	.641		
C	RG 49/U	UG-149A/U	UG-148B/U	Brass	1.872 × 0.872	3.95- 5.85	7.589- 5.124	12.594- 6.083	4.958-2.395	3.152	9.510	2.69	1.93	1.4	2.0
	RG 95/U	UG-407/U	UG-406A/U	Alum.								1.77	1.22		
G	RG 50/U	UG-344/U	UG-343A/U	Brass	1.372 × 0.622	5.85- 8.20	5.124- 3.656	7.560- 4.294	2.976-1.691	4.301	6.970	3.85	3.08	.56	.71
	RG 106/U	UG-441/U	UG-440A/U	Alum.								2.45	1.94		
H	RG 51/U	UG-51/U	UG-52A/U	Brass	1.122 × 0.497	7.05-10.00	4.252- 2.998	6.385- 3.525	2.514-1.388	5.259	5.700	5.51	4.31	.35	.46
	RG 68/U	UG-138/U	UG-137A/U	Alum.								3.50	2.74		
X	RG 52/U	UG-39/U	UG-40A/U	Brass	0.900 × 0.400	8.20-12.40	3.656- 2.418	6.088- 2.848	2.397-1.121	6.557	4.572	8.64	6.02	.20	.29
	RG 67/U	UG-135/U	UG-136A/U	Alum.								5.49	3.83		
U	RG 91/U	UG-419/U	UG-541/U	Brass	0.622 × 0.311	12.40-18.00	2.418- 1.665	3.754- 1.960	1.478- .772	9.487	3.160	12.8	11.2	.12	.16
	RG 107/U	UG-419/U	UG-541/U	Silver								6.14	5.36		
K	RG 53/U	UG-595/U	UG-596/U	Brass	0.420 × 0.170	18.00-26.50	1.665- 1.131	2.664- 1.334	1.049- .525	14.048	2.134	27.7	19.8	.043	.058
	RG 121/U	UG-597/U	UG-598/U	Alum.								17.6	12.6		
	RG 66/U	UG-595/U	UG-596/U	Silver								13.3	9.50		
V	RG 96/U	UG-599/U	UG-600/U	Silver	0.280 × 0.140	26.50-40.00	1.131- .749	1.866- .882	.735- .347	21.075	1.422	21.9	15.0	.022	.031
	RG 97/U	UG-383/U	UG-383/U	Silver	0.224 × 0.112	33.00-50.00	.909- .600	1.508- .705	.549- .278	26.342	1.138	31.0	20.9	.014	.020
	RG 98/U	UG-385/U	UG-385/U	Silver	0.148 × 0.074	50.00-75.00	.600- .400	.994- .472	.391- .186	39.864	.752	52.9	39.1	.0063	.0090
	RG 99/U	UG-387/U	UG-387/U	Silver	0.122 × 0.061	60.00-90.00	.500- .333	.844- .395	.332- .156	48.351	.620	93.3	52.2	.0042	.0063

Courtesy of Sperry Microwave Electronics Co., Div. of Sperry Rand Corp.

Design Data

Appendix E-1
How to Calculate Decibels

The primary fact to be remembered in dealing with decibels is that they express nothing more than a power ratio. Calculations are based on the familiar powers-of-ten method. For example, if an amplifier had a power gain of 10 to 1, this ratio would be expressed as 10 db. A second amplifier with a power gain of 100 to 1 would have its gain expressed as 20 db. A third amplifier with a power gain of 1,000 to 1 would have its gain expressed as 30 db.

In other words, for integral powers of ten the db value corresponds to ten times the exponent. For this conversion we take the following steps:

1. List power gain ratio = 100 to 1
2. Rewrite exponentially = 10^2 to 1
3. Multiply exponent by 10 db = 2×10 db
4. Rewrite in final form = 20 db for any number

An easier way to understand powers of ten is to count the number of zeros or places to the

right of the first digit, write this number down, and multiply it by ten. This procedure is summarized in the ratio conversion chart, Table 1.

Extending this procedure for 10-db steps, our system must be able to express intervening values of decibels in 1-db steps. For this no charts, books, tables, or slide rule are necessary. Only three ratios are used: 1.25, 1.6, and 2.0. These correspond respectively to 1, 2, and 3 db. Next, to use these less-than-10 db figures, we must remember that multiplying numbers is the same as adding exponents or the same as adding db's. Thus 10 (10 db) times 10,000 gives an answer equal to $10^{1+4} = 10^{+5} = 100,000$, or 50 db. Now using these smaller ratios to multiply 1.25 (1 db) by 1.6 (2 db) we see that the product (2) is equal to 3 db. Likewise 2 (3 db) times 2.5 (4 db) = 7 db. These db values between 1 and 10 plus their corresponding ratios are given in Table 2.

Table 1   Ratio conversion chart

Ratio	Decibels
1: 1	0
10: 1	10
100: 1	20
1,000: 1	30
10,000: 1	40
100,000: 1	50
1,000,000: 1	60
10,000,000: 1	70
100,000,000: 1	80

Table 2   Db values from 1 to 10

Ratio	Decibels
1.25 : 1	1
1.6 : 1	2
2.0 : 1	3
2.5 : 1	4
3.2 : 1	5
4.0 : 1	6
5.0 : 1	7
6.4 : 1	8
8.0 : 1	9
10.0 : 1	10

With Tables 1 and 2 we may now calculate the db for any full-number power ratio by (1) factoring the number into integral powers of ten and to nearest digital parts, (2) converting to integral powers, (3) converting to nearest remaining digital factor, and (4) adding the db's corresponding to these two factors.

EXAMPLE 1

A 400-watt amplifier with 1-watt input has a power ratio of 400: 1.

1. Breakdown:	$400 = 100 \times 4$	
	$= 10^2 \times 4$	
2. Converting integral powers:	$100 = 20$ db	
3. Converting digital factors:	$4 = 6$ db	
4. Adding factor db's:	$= 26$ db	
	Total Gain	

DB-TO-RATIO CONVERSION

Reversing the above process—that is, converting from db's into ratios—includes a sequence of events opposite to those above:

1. Break down or factor the db's into their digital (less than ten) and their full-tens parts.
2. Convert digital part to corresponding ratio.
3. Convert full-ten part to its ratio.
4. Multiply the ratios.

EXAMPLE 2

Convert 26 db to power ratio:

1. Break down: 26 db $= 20$ db $+ 6$ db
2. Convert: 20 db $= 10^2: 1$
   $= 100: 1$
3. Convert: 6 db $= 4: 1$
4. Multiply: 26 db $= 100 \times 4 = 400: 1$

EXAMPLE 3

Convert 126 db to power ratio.

Breakdown: 126 db $= 100 + 20 + 6$
   100 db $= 10^{+10}: 1$
   20 db $= 10^{+2}: 1$
   6 db $= 4: 1$
Power ratio: $= 10^{+10} \times 10^{+2} \times 4$
   $= 4 \times 10^{+12}$

DECIMAL DB CALCULATIONS

For applications that require greater accuracy —that is, for tenth-db values—we start with the first of the basic numbers: 1.25, and derive a table in .1-db steps, by setting 1.25 at the top

of the list, and subtracting from each succeeding value the amount in hundredths, as indicated by the following sequence.

1.0 db $= 1.25 - \quad 0 = 1.25: 1$
0.9 db $= 1.25 - .02 = 1.23: 1$
0.8 db $= 1.23 - .03 = 1.20: 1$
0.7 db $= 1.20 - .03 = 1.17: 1$
0.6 db $= 1.17 - .02 = 1.15: 1$
0.5 db $= 1.15 - .03 = 1.12: 1$

Table 3 Full list of tenths of db's

Ratio	Decibels
1.25: 1	1.0
1.23: 1	0.9
1.20: 1	0.8
1.17: 1	0.7
1.15: 1	0.6
1.12: 1	0.5
1.09: 1	0.4
1.07: 1	0.3
1.04: 1	0.2
1.01: 1	0.1

Table 3 is used in conjuction with Tables 1 and 2 following the previous guide to computations, which are exactly the same but with an additional step for decimal db's.

EXAMPLE 4

Find the power ratio that corresponds to 28.4 db.

Factor and convert:	20 db $= 100$ to 1 ratio
Convert digits:	8 db $= 6.4$ to 1 ratio
Convert decimals:	$.4$ db $= 1.09$ to 1 ratio

(add) (mulitply)
28.4 db $= 100 \times 6.4$
$\times 1.09 =$
697.6 to 1 ratio

EXAMPLE 5

Calculate the gain in db of an amplifier having 1 watt input and 697.6 watts output.

1. Ratio is 697.6 to 1 $= 6.976 \times 100$.
2. 100 to 1 $= 20$ db.
3. The smallest number value nearest to 6.976, from Table 2, is 6.4
4. 6.4 to 1 $= 8$ db.
5. To find out how much greater 6.976 is than 6.4, divide 6.976 by 6.4 for a result of 1.09.
6. 1.09 to 1 $= .4$ db
7. 20 db $+ 8$ db $+ .4$ db $= 23.4$db $= 697.6$ to 1 ratio.

Appendix E-2
Chart for Power and Voltage Conversion
to Decibels

Power ratio	Voltage and current ratio	Decibels	Power ratio	Voltage and current ratio	Decibels	Power ratio	Voltage and current ratio	Decibels
1.0233	1.0116	0.1	2.2387	1.4962	3.5	158.49	12.589	22.0
1.0471	1.0233	0.2	2.5119	1.5849	4.0	251.19	15.849	24.0
1.0715	1.0351	0.3	2.8184	1.6788	4.5	398.11	19.953	26.0
1.0965	1.0471	0.4	3.1623	1.7783	5.0	630.96	25.119	28.0
						1000.0	31.623	30.0
1.1220	1.0593	0.5	3.5481	1.8836	5.5	1584.9	39.811	32.0
1.1482	1.0715	0.6	3.9811	1.9953	6.0	2511.9	50.119	34.0
1.1749	1.0839	0.7	5.0119	2.2387	7.0	3981.1	63.096	36.0
1.2023	1.0956	0.8	6.3096	2.5119	8.0	6309.6	79.433	38.0
						10^4	100.000	40.0
1.2303	1.1092	0.9	7.9433	2.8184	9.0	$10^4 \times 1.5849$	125.89	42.0
1.2589	1.1220	1.0	10.0000	3.1623	10.0	$10^4 \times 2.5119$	158.49	44.0
1.3183	1.1482	1.2	12.589	3.5481	11.0	$10^4 \times 3.9811$	199.53	46.0
1.3804	1.1749	1.4	15.849	3.9811	12.0	$10^4 \times 6.3096$	251.19	48.0
						10^5	316.23	50.0
1.4454	1.2023	1.6	19.953	4.4668	13.0	$10^5 \times 1.5849$	398.11	52.0
1.5136	1.2303	1.8	26.119	5.0119	14.0	$10^5 \times 2.5119$	501.19	54.0
1.5849	1.2589	2.0	31.623	5.6234	15.0	$10^5 \times 3.9811$	630.96	56.0
1.6595	1.2882	2.2	39.811	6.3096	16.0	$10^5 \times 6.3096$	794.33	58.0
						10^6	1,000.00	60.0
1.7378	1.3183	2.4	50.119	7.0795	17.0	10^7	3,162.3	70.0
1.8197	1.3490	2.6	63.096	7.9433	18.0	10^8	10,000.0	80.0
1.9055	1.3804	2.8	79.433	8.9125	19.0	10^9	31,623	90.0
1.9953	1.4125	3.0	100.00	10.0000	20.0	10^{10}	100,000	100.0

Appendix E-3
Fahrenheit-Centigrade Temperature
Conversion Tables

FAHRENHEIT TO CENTIGRADE*

Temperature Fahrenheit	0	1	2	3	4	5	6	7	8	9
100	73.33	73.89	74.44	75.00	75.56	76.11	76.67	77.22	77.78	78.33
90	67.78	68.33	68.89	69.44	70.00	70.56	71.11	71.67	72.22	72.78
80	62.22	62.78	63.33	63.89	64.44	65.00	65.56	66.11	66.67	67.22
70	56.67	57.22	57.78	58.33	58.89	59.44	60.00	60.56	61.11	61.67
60	51.11	51.67	52.22	52.78	53.33	53.89	54.44	55.00	55.56	56.11
50	45.56	46.11	46.67	47.22	47.78	48.33	48.89	49.44	50.00	50.56
40	40.00	40.56	41.11	41.67	42.22	42.78	43.33	43.89	44.44	45.00
30	34.44	35.00	35.56	36.11	36.67	37.22	37.78	38.33	38.89	39.44
20	28.89	29.44	30.00	30.56	31.11	31.67	32.22	32.78	33.33	33.89
10	23.33	23.89	24.44	25.00	25.56	26.11	26.67	27.22	27.78	28.33
0	17.78	18.33	18.89	19.44	20.00	20.56	21.11	21.67	22.22	22.78
0	17.78	17.22	16.67	16.11	15.56	15.00	14.44	13.89	13.33	12.78
10	12.22	11.67	11.11	10.56	10.00	9.44	8.89	8.33	7.78	7.22
20	6.67	6.11	5.56	5.00	4.44	3.89	3.33	2.78	2.22	1.67
30	1.11	0.56	0.00	0.56	1.11	1.67	2.22	2.78	3.33	3.89
40	4.44	5.00	5.56	6.11	6.67	7.22	7.78	8.33	8.89	9.44
50	10.00	10.56	11.11	11.67	12.22	12.78	13.33	13.89	14.44	15.00
60	15.56	16.11	16.67	17.22	17.78	18.33	18.89	19.44	20.00	20.56
70	21.11	21.67	22.22	22.78	23.33	23.89	24.44	25.00	25.56	26.11
80	26.67	27.22	27.78	28.33	28.89	29.44	30.00	30.56	31.11	31.67
90	32.22	32.78	33.33	33.89	34.44	35.00	35.56	36.11	36.67	37.22
100	37.78	38.33	38.89	39.44	40.00	40.56	41.11	41.67	42.22	42.78

*Basic formula: $°C = (5/9)(°F - 32)$

Temperature Centigrade	0	1	2	3	4	5	6	7	8	9
100	148.0	149.8	151.6	153.4	155.2	157.0	158.8	160.6	162.4	164.2
90	130.0	131.8	133.6	135.4	137.2	139.0	140.8	142.6	144.4	146.2
80	112.0	113.8	115.6	117.4	119.2	121.0	122.8	124.6	126.4	128.2
70	94.0	95.8	97.6	99.4	101.2	103.0	104.8	106.6	108.4	110.2
60	76.0	77.8	79.6	81.4	83.2	85.0	86.8	88.6	90.4	92.2
50	58.0	59.8	61.6	63.4	65.2	67.0	68.8	70.6	72.4	74.2
40	40.0	41.8	43.6	45.4	47.2	49.0	50.8	52.6	54.4	56.2
30	22.0	23.8	25.6	27.4	29.2	31.0	32.8	34.6	36.4	38.2
20	4.0	5.8	7.6	9.4	11.2	13.0	14.8	16.6	18.4	20.2
10	14.0	12.2	10.4	8.6	6.8	5.0	3.2	1.4	0.4	2.2
0	32.0	30.2	28.4	26.6	24.8	23.0	21.2	19.4	17.6	15.8
0	32.0	33.8	35.6	37.4	39.2	41.0	42.8	44.6	46.4	48.2
10	50.0	51.8	53.6	55.4	57.2	59.0	60.8	62.6	64.4	66.2
20	68.0	69.8	71.6	73.4	75.2	77.0	78.8	80.6	82.4	84.2
30	86.0	87.8	89.6	91.4	93.2	95.0	96.8	98.6	100.4	102.2
40	104.0	105.8	107.6	109.4	111.2	113.0	114.8	116.6	118.4	120.2
50	122.0	123.8	125.6	127.4	129.2	131.0	132.8	134.6	136.4	138.2
60	140.0	141.8	143.6	145.4	147.2	149.0	150.8	152.6	154.4	156.2
70	158.0	159.8	161.6	163.4	165.2	167.0	168.8	170.6	172.4	174.2
80	176.0	177.8	179.6	181.4	183.2	185.0	186.8	188.6	190.4	192.2
90	194.0	195.8	197.6	199.4	201.2	203.0	204.8	206.6	208.4	210.2
100	212.0	213.8	215.6	217.4	219.2	221.0	222.8	224.6	226.4	228.2

*Basic formula: $°F = (9/5)°C + 32$

Appendix E-4
Temperature Coefficient of Resistance

The resistance alloys used for all except the lowest ohmic values show such little change with temperature that in most power circuits the resistance is considered constant. Actually there may be changes at *full load* of -4% to $+8\%$ of the initial resistance. The change is usually referred to in terms of the "temperature coefficient of resistance" which is the change in "ohms-per-ohm-per-degree change in temperature" of the wire.

For special applications which require very constant resistance, it becomes desirable to specify the maximum permissible TC (temperature coefficient of resistance) and the range of temperature; and consequently to use only certain types of resistance alloys. The presently known low TC alloys, in the 800 ohms per circular milfoot class, consist largely of nickel and chromium with small amounts of aluminum and either copper or iron. The low-resistance alloys, 294 ohms per circular milfoot, consist largely of nickel and copper with traces of other metals.

Both of these classes of wire are rated by the wire manufacturers as having a TC of $\pm.00002$ ohm/ohm/°C (also called .002% or 20 parts per million) over a *limited range*, generally $-55°$ to $+150°$C and $+20°$ to $+100°$C, respectively; compared to conventional $+170$ PPM.

Unfortunately, the TC of a completed power resistor is generally different from that of the original wire, as the TC is affected by the materials, heat treatment, methods of construction and the increased temperature range. Without special control, the TC over the range to 300°C rise may increase to as much as ±80 PPM from the original ±20 PPM. Smaller TC's increase the cost of manufacture. Theoretical changes in resistance with temperature are shown in the accompanying figure.

The circuit designer should carefully consider the actual needs of the circuit before specifying limits on the TC of a desired resistor. Wherever possible it is best to select a critical resistor so as to operate at a low temperature rise. This will also provide the maximum stability over a long period.

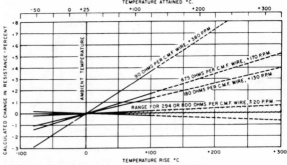

Calculated Change in Resistance with Nominal TC Assumed Constant.

Appendix E-5
Specific Resistance of Conducting Metals

Type of metal	Ohms per circular mil-foot at 20°C	Type of metal	Ohms per circular mil-foot at 20°C
Copper (annealed)	10.35	Mercury	576.
Copper (hard drawn)	10.60	Molybdenum	34.
Aluminum	17.	Monel metal	252.
Brass	42.	Nichrome	675.
Carbon (lampblack)	22,000.	Nickel	60.
German silver (18%)	198.	Platinum	60.
Gold	14.6	Silver	9.56
Graphite	4,300.	Steel (soft, carbon)	96.
Iron (pure, annealed)	61.	Tantalum	93.
Iron (cast)	435.	Tin	69.
Lead	132.35	Tungsten	34.
Manganin	264.	Zinc	35.

Appendix E-6
How to Calculate Temperature Rise from Resistance Measurements

Heat rise (degrees centigrade) in a transformer or copper wire relay winding can be determined accurately by winding-resistance measurement and calculation:

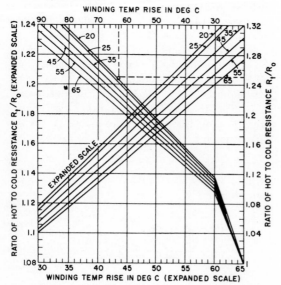

Two scales are presented on chart for greater convenience. Numbers on curves refer to initial winding temperature in degrees C.

1. Measure the winding resistance cold (at room temperature, assumed to be 20°); call it R_0 (say, 16 ohms).

2. Measure the final resistance at the end of the heat run; call this R_t (say, 20 ohms).

3. Calculate the resistance ratio of the hot winding to that of the winding cold:

$$\frac{R_t}{R_0} = \frac{20}{16} = 1.25$$

4. Subtract 1 from this ratio:

$$(1.25 - 1) = .25.$$

5. Divide this figure (.25) by .00393:

$$\frac{.25}{.00393} = 63.20°.$$

Or one may use the accompanying chart as follows:

1. Find the 1.25 ratio point (on right-hand scale).

2. Follow it across to the slanting *cold* temperature line—in this case 20°.

3. At this intersection project directly upward to 63.2° point on top horizontal scale.

404

Appendix E-7
The Metric System

The metric system comprises the meter as the unit of length and the gram as the unit of mass. The unit of fluid capacity, the liter, is the volume of one kilogram of water and is approximately equal to .001 cubic meter. All other metric units are the decimal divisions or multiples of these three basic units and are named by the prefixes below.

The Celsius temperature scale, defined by certain fixed points, is used with the metric system; and the second, defined as $1/31,556,925.9747$ of the tropical year 1900, is taken as the unit of time.

Responsibility for the metric system is with the International Bureau of Weights and Measures, Sevres, France, established by international treaty.

Multiples and Submultiples	Prefixes	Symbols
$1,000,000,000,000 = 10^{12}$	tera	T
$1,000,000,000 = 10^{9}$	giga	G
$1,000,000 = 10^{6}$	mega	M
$1,000 = 10^{3}$	kilo	k
$100 = 10^{2}$	hecto	h
$10 = 10$	deka	dk
$0.1 = 10^{-1}$	deci	d
$0.01 = 10^{-2}$	centi	c
$0.001 = 10^{-3}$	milli	m
$0.000001 = 10^{-6}$	micro	μ*
$0.000000001 = 10^{-9}$	nano	n
$0.000000000001 = 10^{-12}$	pico	p

EXAMPLE: 1000 meters (or 10^3 meters) is called a kilometer, and one millionth of a gram (or 10^{-6} gram) is called a microgram.

*1 millionth of a meter is called a *micron*, and is abbreviated simply μ.

MOST COMMON USES OF PREFIXES

Length

1,000 millimeters mm
100 centimeters cm } = 1 METER
10 decimeters dm (about 40 inches) m

1,000 meters = 1 kilometer
(about 5/8 mile) km

Mass

1,000,000 micrograms μg } = 1 GRAM
1,000 milligrams mg (about 15 grains) g

1,000 grams = 1 kilogram
(about 2 pounds) kg

Capacity

1,000 milliliters ml = 1 LITER
(about 1 quart) l

1,000 liters = 1 kiloliter kl

BASIC CONVERSION FACTORS

Length

Centimeter	=	0.3937 inch
Meter	=	3.28 feet
Meter	=	1.094 yards
Kilometer	=	0.621 statute mile
Kilometer	=	0.5400 nautical mile
Inch	=	2.54 centimeters
Foot	=	0.3048 meter
Yard	=	0.9144 meter
Statute mile	=	1.61 kilometers
Nautical mile	=	1.852 kilometers

Area

Sq centimeter	=	0.155 sq inch
Sq meter	=	10.76 sq feet
Sq meter	=	1.196 sq yards
Hectare	=	2.47 acres
Sq kilometer	=	0.386 sq mile
Sq inch	=	6.45 sq centimeters
Sq foot	=	0.0929 sq meter
Sq yard	=	0.836 sq meter
Acre	=	0.405 hectare
Sq mile	=	2.59 sq kilometers

Volume

Cu centimeter	=	0.0610 cu inch
Cu meter	=	35.3 cu feet
Cu meter	=	1.308 cu yards
Cu inch	=	16.39 cu centimeters
Cu foot	=	0.0283 cu meter
Cu yard	=	0.765 cu meter

Capacity

Milliliter	=	0.0338 U.S. fluid ounce
Liter	=	1.057 U.S. liq quarts
Liter	=	0.908 U.S. dry quart
U.S. fluid ounce	=	29.57 milliliters
U.S. liq quart	=	0.946 liter
U.S. dry quart	=	1.101 liters

Mass or Weight

Gram	=	15.43 grains
Gram	=	0.0353 avdp ounce
Kilogram	=	2.205 avdp pounds
Metric ton	=	1.102 short or net tons
Grain	=	0.0648 gram
Avdp ounce	=	28.35 grams
Avdp pound	=	0.4536 kilogram
Short or net ton	=	0.907 metric ton

Appendix E-8
How to Calculate the Inductance of an Air-core Coil

The self-inductance of an air-core solenoid, in microhenrys, is approximately equal to:

$$L = .0251d^2 n^2 lK$$

where n = the number of turns per inch,

d = the mean diameter of the solenoid in inches,

l = the length of the solenoid when wound (inches),

K = the "form factor" (Nagoaka's correction factor), which depends for its value on the ratio obtained by dividing the diameter by the length of the winding. Values of K for various diameter-length ratios are given in Table 1.

Table 1   Solenoid coil correction factor, K

Diam. length	K	Diam. length	K	Diam. length	K
.00	1.0000	2.00	.5255	7.00	.2584
.10	.9588	2.20	.5025	7.40	.2491
.20	.9201	2.40	.4816	7.80	.2406
.30	.8838	2.60	.4626	8.50	.2272
.40	.8499	2.80	.4452	9.50	.2106
.50	.8181	3.00	.4292	10.00	.2033
.60	.7885	3.20	.4145	12.00	.1790
.70	.7609	3.40	.4008	14.00	.1605
.80	.7351	3.60	.3882	16.00	.1457
.90	.7110	3.80	.3764	18.00	.1336
1.00	.6884	4.00	.3654	20.00	.1236
1.10	.6673	4.20	.3551	24.00	.1078
1.20	.6475	4.40	.3455	28.00	.0959
1.30	.6290	4.60	.3364	35.00	.0808
1.40	.6115	4.80	.3279	45.00	.0664
1.50	.5950	5.00	.3198	60.00	.0528
1.60	.5795	5.40	.3050	80.00	.0419
1.70	.5649	5.80	.2916	00.00	.0350
1.80	.5511	6.20	.2795	—	—
1.90	.5379	6.60	.2685	—	—

Appendix E-9
Glossary of Servo Terms

Acceleration at stall (theoretical). Computed value of servo motor angular acceleration calculated from motor stall torque and rotor moment of inertia. Sometimes called torque-to-inertia ratio.

Ambient temperature. Temperature of the immediate surroundings of a component excluding its own effect.

Backlash. A position error between gears where the relative position of the output with respect to the input varies with direction of rotation.

Block diagram. Simplified system diagram reducing each element to its transfer function and schematically representing it as a block.

Breadboarding. Construction of a system or portion of a system for the purpose of studying characteristics without any regard for size or appearance.

Carrier frequency. Constant frequency upon which usable data are superimposed.

Chopper. Switch designed to operate at carrier frequency for the purpose of converting d-c data to square-wave a-c data at the carrier frequency.

Closed loop. A system where the output is fed back to the input for constant comparison.

Controller. The element or group of elements which

receive data proportional to the difference between input and output and convert these data into power capable of restoring agreement between input and output.

Corner frequency. Frequency where the open-loop plot of gain versus frequency changes slope. For a servo motor, the product of this frequency in radians per second and the motor time constant equals unity.

Critical damping. The point at which system damping is great enough to overcome all tendencies to oscillate.

Damping coefficient. Ratio of actual damping to critical damping.

Data element. Element which converts desired function into a signal of usable form.

Dead space. Maximum deviation on either side of the point of agreement between input and output for which no corrective action will take place.

Drag cup. Nonmagnetic metal rotated in a magnetic field for generation of torque or voltage proportional to speed.

Electrical zero. A standard synchro position where electrical outputs are at defined amplitudes and time phase.

Environmental testing. Controlled testing of a component or system under each of the conditions which tend to affect its operation or life.

Error. Difference between output and input.

Error detector. The element or group of elements which convert the difference between output and input of a system into usable form.

Error-rate damping. Method of damping in which an additional signal proportional to the rate of change of error is introduced and added to the error signal for anticipatory purposes.

Free speed. The angular speed of an energized motor under no-load conditions.

Frequency response. Practical or mathematical observation of the ability of the output to follow the input, when the input is varied sinusoidally over a given frequency range.

Gain crossover frequency. Frequency at which the open-loop system gain is unity or zero db.

Harmonics. Signals at some exact multiple of the fundamental carrier frequency.

Hunting. Condition where the output of a system oscillates back and forth from the position of agreement between output and input.

Linearity. The maximum deviation of any curve from the best straight line which can be drawn over its limits.

Moment of inertia. Proportionality constant between applied torque and angular acceleration.

Negative feedback. Subtracting some or all of an output from the input for desirable effects.

Null, error detector. Condition where zero in-phase signal appears as an output from an error detector or error detectors.

Null, generator. Output of generator when its rotating element is stationary.

Open loop. Condition where efforts are made to make an output agree with an input without any direct comparison.

Phase crossover frequency. Frequency at which the open-loop phase shift is a full 180 degrees.

Potentiometer. A resistive data element used to transform angular position into proportional voltage.

Quadrature. Any signal, or portion of a signal, 90 electrical degrees away from a signal in question.

Rate generator. Proportional element which converts angular speed into constant frequency output voltage.

Reversing time. Time required for a servo motor when fully powered to change from free speed in one direction to 63.2 per cent of speed in the opposite direction.

Rotor. Member of any inductive device free to rotate.

Sensitivity. Maximum possible difference between output and input for which no corrective action will take place.

Servo amplifier. Linear amplifier specifically designed to link error-detector voltage to motor control phase at some higher voltage and power level.

Servo motor. (a) Any motor used in a servomechanism to physically correct differences between input and output. (b) Two-phase motor specifically designed for servo applications and having low torque-to-inertia ratio, sloping speed-torque curve, and torque proportional to product of the voltages on each phase.

Servomechanism. A system in which the output is mechanically driven by the difference between the input and the output for the purpose of making the output agree with the input.

Slip clutch. Protective device used in gear trains which isolates the load when it exceeds a predetermined value.

Split gears. Technique used in gear-train design for minimizing backlash. Consists of splitting one gear of a pair in mesh and connecting a spring between the two halves in such a way that pressure is exerted upon both sides of the driving teeth of the meshing gear.

Stall torque. The torque produced at the rotor of an energized motor when the rotor is restrained from any motion.

Stator. Stationary member of any inductive device.

Synchro. An inductive device capable of transforming an angular position input into an electrical output or an electrical input into an angular output.

Synchronous Motor. A motor which is specifically designed for its rotor to follow exactly its rotating electrical stator field.

Time Constant. Time required for a function increasing at an exponential rate to reach 63.2 per cent of its final value.

Torque constant. Constant of proportionality between motor stall torque and control phase voltage, with motor fixed phase fully powered.

Transfer function. The ratio between the output and the input of a single element or a group of elements in a system.

Transformation ratio. Exact ratio between electrical output and electrical input under defined conditions.

Undamped natural frequency. System oscillatory frequency when all damping is removed.

Velocity lag error. Lag between input and output proportional to the rate at which the input is varying.

Viscous damping. Utilization of reactive torque or force proportional to speed for braking action.

Viscous friction. Friction proportional to angular or linear speed.

Reprinted by permission of the Daystrom Trans. Division.

Appendix E-10
Physical and Electrical Conversion Factors

To convert	Into	Multiply by	Conversely multiply by
Ampere-hours	Coulombs	3,600	2.778×10^{-4}
Amperes per sq. cm	Amperes per sq. inch	6.452	.155
Ampere turns	Gilberts	1.257	.7958
Ampere turns per cm	Ampere turns per inch	2.54	.3937
Btu (British thermal unit)	Foot-pounds	778.3	1.285×10^{-3}
Btu	Joules	1,054.8	9.48×10^{-4}
Btu	Kilogram-calories	.252	3.969
Btu	Horsepower-hours	3.929×10^{-4}	2,545
Centigrade	Fahrenheit	$(C° \times 9/5) + 32$	$(F° - 32) \times 5/9.$
Circular mils	Square centimeters	5.067×10^{-6}	1.973×10^{5}
Circular mils	Square mils	.7854	1.273.
Cubic inches	Cubic centimeters	16.39	6.102×10^{-2}
Cubic inches	Cubic feet	5.785×10^{-4}	1,728
Cubic inches	Cubic meters	1.639×10^{-5}	6.102×10^{4}
Cubic meters	Cubic feet	35.31	2.832×10^{-2}
Cubic meters	Cubic yards	1.308	.7646.
Degrees (angle)	Radians	1.745×10^{-2}	57.3
Dynes	Pounds	2.248×10^{-6}	4.448×10^{5}
Ergs	Foot-pounds	7.367×10^{-8}	1.356×10^{7}
Feet	Centimeters	30.48	3.281×10^{-2}
Foot-pounds	Horsepower-hours	5.05×10^{-7}	1.98×10^{6}
Foot-pounds	Kilogram-meters	.1383	7.233
Foot-pounds	Kilowatt-hours	3.766×10^{-7}	2.655×10^{6}
Gauss	Lines per sq. inch	6.452	.155
Grams	Dynes	980.7	1.02×10^{-3}
Grams	Ounces (avoirdupois)	3.527×10^{-2}	28.35
Grams per cm	Pounds per inch	5.6×10^{-3}	178.6
Grams per cubic cm	Pounds per cu. inch	3.613×10^{-2}	27.68
Grams per sq. cm	Pounds per sq. foot	2.0481	.4883
Horsepower (550 ft.-lb. per sec.)	Foot-lb. per minute	3.3×10^{4}	3.03×10^{-5}
Horsepower (550 ft.-lb. per sec.)	Btu per minute	42.41	2.357×10^{-2}
Horsepower (550 ft.-lb. per sec.)	Kg-calories per minute	10.69	9.355×10^{-2}
Horsepower (Metric) (542.5 ft.-lb. per sec.)	Horsepower (550 ft.-lb. per sec.)	.9863	1.014
Inches	Centimeters	2.54	.3937
Inches	Mils	1,000	.001
Joules	Foot-pounds	.7376	1.356.
Joules	Ergs	10^{7}	10^{-7}
Kilogram-calories	Kilojoules	4.186	.2389
Kilograms	Pounds (avoirdupois)	2.205	.4536
Kg per sq. meter	Pounds per sq. foot	.2048	4.882
Kilometers	Feet	3,281	3.048×10^{-4}
Kilowatt-hours	Btu	3,413	2.93×10^{-4}
Kilowatt-hours	Foot-pounds	2.655×10^{6}	3.766×10^{-7}
Kilowatt-hours	Joules	3.6×10^{6}	2.778×10^{-7}
Kilowatt-hours	Kilogram-calories	860	1.163×10^{-3}
Kilowatt-hours	Kilogram-meters	3.671×10^{5}	2.724×10^{-6}
Liters	Cubic meters	.001	1,000
Liters	Cubic inches	61.02	1.639×10^{-2}
Liters	Gallons (liq. US)	.2642	3.785
Liters	Pints (liq. US)	2.113	.4732
Meters	Yards	1.094	.9144

To convert	Into	Multiply by	Conversely multiply by
Meters per min	Feet per min	3.281	.3048
Meters per min	Kilometers per hr	.06	16.67
Miles (nautical)	Kilometers	1.853	.5396
Miles (statute)	Kilometers	1.609	.6214
Miles per hr	Kilometers per min	2.682×10^{-2}	37.28
Miles per hr	Feet per minute	88	1.136×10^{-2}
Miles per hr	Kilometers per hr	1.609	.6214
Poundals	Dynes	1.383×10^4	7.233×10^{-5}
Poundals	Pounds (avoirdupois)	3.108×10^{-2}	32.17
Sq inches	Circular mils	1.273×10^6	7.854×10^{-7}
Sq inches	Sq centimeters	6.452	.155
Sq feet	Sq meters	9.29×10^{-2}	10.76
Sq miles	Sq yards	3.098×10^6	3.228×10^{-7}
Sq miles	Sq kilometers	2.59	.3861
Sq millimeters	Circular mils	1,973	5.067×10^{-4}
Tons, short (avoir 2,000 lb.)	Tonnes (1,000 Kg.)	.9072	1.102
Tons, long (avoir 2,240 lb.)	Tonnes (1,000 Kg.)	1.016	.9842
Tons, long (avoir 2,240 lb.)	Tons, short (avoir 2,000 lb)	1.120	.8929
Watts	Btu per min	5.689×10^{-2}	17.58
Watts	Ergs per sec	10^7	10^{-7}
Watts	Ft-lb per minute	44.26	2.26×10^{-2}
Watts	Horsepower (550 ft-lb per sec.)	1.341×10^{-3}	745.7
Watts	Horsepower (metric) (542.5 ft-lb per sec.)	1.36×10^{-3}	735.5
Watts	Kg-calories per min	1.433×10^{-2}	69.77

Appendix F-1

GREEK ALPHABET

Name	Capital	Lower case	Designates
Alpha	A	α	Angles
Beta	B	β	Angles, flux density
Gamma	Γ	γ	Conductivity
Delta	Δ	δ	Variation of a quantity, increment
Epsilon	E	ϵ	Base of natural logarithms (2.71828)
Zeta	Z	ζ	Impedance, coefficients, coordinates
Eta	H	η	Hysteresis coefficient, efficiency
Theta	Θ	θ	Phase angle
Iota	I	ι	
Kappa	K	κ	Dielectric constant, coupling coefficient, susceptibility
Lambda	Λ	λ	Wavelength
Mu	M	μ	Permeability, micro, amplification factor
Nu	N	ν	Reluctivity
Xi	Ξ	ξ	
Omicron	O	o	
Pi	Π	π	3.1416
Rho	P	ρ	Resistivity
Sigma	Σ	σ	
Tau	T	τ	Time constant, time-phase displacement
Upsilon	$\dot{T}$	υ	
Phi	Φ	ϕ	Angles, magnetic flux
Chi	X	χ	
Psi	Ψ	ψ	Dielectric flux, phase difference
Omega	Ω	ω	Ohms (capital), angular velocity $(2\pi f)$

COMMON PREFIXES (see Appendix E-7)

Metric prefix	Meaning		Associated with
Mega	Million	(1,000,000)	Volt, ohms, cycles, amperes
Kilo	Thousand	(1,000)	Volts, watts, cycles, meters, amperes
Hecto	Hundred	(100)	Meters
Deka	Ten	(10)	Meters
Deci	One-tenth	(0.1)	Meters
Centi	One-hundredth	(0.01)	Meters
Milli	One-thousandth	(0.001)	Volts, amperes, meters, henrys, watts, ohms
Micro	One-millionth	(0.0000001)	Volts, amperes, farads, henrys, mhos, ohms
Micromicro	One-millionth of one-millionth	(0.000,000,000,001)	Volts, amperes, farads, coulombs

Appendix F-2
Table of Number Functions, 1-99

No.	Square	Cube	Square root	Cube root	No. = Diam. Circum.	No. = Diam. Area	No.
1	1	1	1.0000	1.0000	3.142	0.7854	1
2	4	8	1.4142	1.2599	6.283	3.1416	2
3	9	27	1.7321	1.4423	9.425	7.0686	3
4	16	64	2.0000	1.5874	12.566	12.5664	4
5	25	125	2.2361	1.7100	15.708	19.6350	5
6	36	216	2.4495	1.8171	18.850	28.2743	6
7	49	343	2.6458	1.9129	21.991	38.4845	7
8	64	512	2.8284	2.0000	25.133	50.2655	8
9	81	729	3.0000	2.0801	28.274	63.6173	9
10	100	1000	3.1623	2.1544	31.416	78.5398	10
11	121	1331	3.3166	2.2240	34.558	95.0332	11
12	144	1728	3.4641	2.2894	37.699	113.097	12
13	169	2197	3.6056	2.3513	40.841	132.732	13
14	196	2744	3.7417	2.4101	43.982	153.938	14
15	225	3375	3.8730	2.4662	47.124	176.715	15
16	256	4096	4.0000	2.5198	50.265	201.062	16
17	289	4913	4.1231	2.5713	53.407	226.980	17
18	324	5832	4.2426	2.6207	56.549	254.469	18
19	361	6859	4.3589	2.6684	59.690	283.529	19
20	400	8000	4.4721	2.7144	62.832	314.159	20
21	441	9261	4.5826	2.7589	65.973	346.361	21
22	484	10648	4.6904	2.8020	69.115	380.133	22
23	529	12167	4.7958	2.8439	72.257	415.476	23
24	576	13824	4.8990	2.8845	75.398	452.389	24
25	625	15625	5.0000	2.9240	78.540	490.874	25
26	676	17576	5.0990	2.9625	81.681	530.929	26
27	729	19683	5.1962	3.0000	84.823	572.555	27
28	784	21952	5.2915	3.0366	87.965	615.752	28
29	841	24389	5.3852	3.0723	91.106	660.520	29
30	900	27000	5.4772	3.1072	94.248	706.858	30
31	961	29791	5.5678	3.1414	97.389	754.768	31
32	1024	32768	5.6569	3.1748	100.531	804.248	32
33	1089	35937	5.7446	3.2075	103.673	855.299	33
34	1156	39304	5.8310	3.2396	106.814	907.920	34
35	1225	42875	5.9161	3.2711	109.956	962.113	35
36	1296	46656	6.0000	3.3019	113.097	1017.88	36
37	1369	50653	6.0828	3.3322	116.239	1075.21	37
38	1444	54872	6.1644	3.3620	119.381	1134.11	38
39	1521	59319	6.2450	3.3912	122.522	1194.59	39
40	1600	64000	6.3246	3.4200	125.66	1256.64	40
41	1681	68921	6.4031	3.4482	128.81	1320.25	41
42	1764	74088	6.4807	3.4760	131.95	1385.44	42
43	1849	79507	6.5574	3.5034	135.09	1452.20	43
44	1936	85184	6.6332	3.5303	138.23	1520.53	44
45	2025	91125	6.7082	3.5569	141.37	1590.43	45
46	2116	97336	6.7823	3.5830	144.51	1661.90	46
47	2209	103823	6.8557	3.6088	147.65	1734.94	47
48	2304	110592	6.9282	3.6342	150.80	1809.56	48
49	2401	117649	7.0000	3.6593	153.94	1885.74	49

No.	Square	Cube	Square root	Cube root	No. = Diam.		No.
					Circum.	Area	
50	2500	125000	7.0711	3.6840	157.08	1963.50	50
51	2601	132651	7.1414	3.7084	160.22	2042.82	51
52	2704	140608	7.2111	3.8325	163.36	2123.72	52
53	2809	148877	7.2801	3.7563	166.50	2206.18	53
54	2916	157464	7.3485	3.7798	169.65	2290.22	54
55	3025	166375	7.4162	3.8030	172.79	2375.83	55
56	3136	175616	7.4833	3.8259	175.93	2463.01	56
57	3249	185193	7.5498	3.8485	179.07	2551.76	57
58	3364	195112	7.6158	3.8709	182.21	2642.08	58
59	3481	205379	7.6811	3.8930	185.35	2733.97	59
60	3600	216000	7.7460	3.9149	188.50	2827.43	60
61	3721	226981	7.8102	3.9365	191.64	2922.47	61
62	3844	238328	7.8740	3.9579	194.78	3019.07	62
63	3969	250047	7.9373	3.9791	197.92	3117.25	63
64	4096	262114	8.0000	4.0000	201.06	3216.99	64
65	4225	274625	8.0623	4.0207	204.20	3318.31	65
66	4356	287496	8.1240	4.0412	207.35	3421.19	66
67	4489	300763	8.1854	4.0615	210.49	3525.65	67
68	4624	314432	8.2462	4.0817	213.63	3631.68	68
69	4761	328509	8.3066	4.1016	216.77	3739.28	69
70	4900	343000	8.3666	4.1213	219.91	3848.45	70
71	5041	357911	8.4261	4.1408	223.05	3959.19	71
72	5184	373248	8.4853	4.1602	226.19	4071.50	72
73	5329	389017	8.5440	4.1793	229.34	4185.39	73
74	5476	405224	8.6023	4.1983	232.48	4300.84	74
75	5625	421875	8.6603	4.2172	235.62	4417.86	75
76	5776	438976	8.7178	4.2358	238.76	4536.46	76
77	5929	456533	8.7750	4.2543	241.90	4656.63	77
78	6084	474552	8.8318	4.2727	245.04	4778.36	78
79	6241	493039	8.8882	4.2908	248.19	4901.67	79
80	6400	512000	8.9443	4.3089	251.33	5026.55	80
81	6561	531441	9.0000	4.3267	254.47	5153.00	81
82	6724	551368	9.0554	4.3445	257.61	5281.02	82
83	6889	571787	9.1104	4.3621	260.75	5410.61	83
84	7056	592704	9.1652	4.3795	263.89	5541.77	84
85	7225	614125	9.2195	4.3968	267.04	5674.50	85
86	7396	636056	9.2736	4.4140	270.18	5808.80	86
87	7569	658503	9.3274	4.4310	273.32	5944.68	87
88	7744	681472	9.3808	4.4480	276.46	6082.12	88
89	7921	704969	9.4340	4.4647	279.60	6221.14	89
90	8100	729000	9.4868	4.4814	282.74	6361.73	90
91	8281	753571	9.5394	4.4979	285.88	6503.88	91
92	8464	778688	9.5917	4.5144	289.03	6647.61	92
93	8649	804357	9.6437	4.5307	292.17	6792.91	93
94	8836	830584	9.6954	4.5468	295.31	6939.78	94
95	9025	857375	9.7468	4.5629	298.45	7088.22	95
96	9216	884736	9.7980	4.5789	301.59	7238.23	96
97	9409	912673	9.4889	4.5947	304.73	7389.81	97
98	9604	941192	9.8995	4.6104	307.88	7542.96	98
99	9801	970299	9.9499	4.6261	311.02	7697.69	99

Appendix F-3
Table of Sines, Cosines, and Tangents

Angle	Radians	Sine	Cosine	Tangent	Angle	Radians	Sine	Cosine	Tangent
0°	.0000	.0000	1.0000	.0000	45°	.7854	.7071	.7071	1.0000
1	.0175	.0175	.9998	.0175	46	.8029	.7193	.6947	1.0355
2	.0349	.0349	.9994	.0349	47	.8203	.7314	.6820	1.0724
3	.0524	.0523	.9986	.0524	48	.8378	.7431	.6691	1.1106
4	.0698	.0698	.9976	.0699	49	.8552	.7547	.6561	1.1504
5	.0873	.0872	.9962	.0875	50	.8727	.7660	.6428	1.1918
6	.1047	.1045	.9945	.1051	51	.8901	.7771	.6293	1.2349
7	.1222	.1219	.9925	.1228	52	.9076	.7880	.6157	1.2799
8	.1396	.1392	.9903	.1405	53	.9250	.7986	.6018	1.3270
9	.1571	.1564	.9877	.1584	54	.9425	.8090	.5878	1.3764
10	.1745	.1736	.9848	.1763	55	.9599	.8192	.5736	1.4281
11	.1920	.1908	.9816	.1944	56	.9774	.8290	.5592	1.4826
12	.2094	.2079	.9781	.2126	57	.9948	.8387	.5446	1.5399
13	.2269	.2250	.9744	.2309	58	1.0123	.8480	.5299	1.6003
14	.2443	.2419	.9703	.2493	59	1.0297	.8572	.5150	1.6643
15	.2618	.2588	.9659	.2679	60	1.0472	.8660	.5000	1.7321
16	.2793	.2756	.9613	.2867	61	1.0647	.8746	.4848	1.8040
17	.2967	.2924	.9563	.3057	62	1.0821	.8829	.4695	1.8807
18	.3142	.3090	.9511	.3249	63	1.0996	.8910	.4540	1.9626
19	.3316	.3256	.9455	.3443	64	1.1170	.8988	.4384	2.0503
20	.3491	.3420	.9397	.3640	65	1.1345	.9063	.4226	2.1445
21	.3665	.3584	.9336	.3839	66	1.1519	.9135	.4067	2.2460
22	.3840	.3746	.9272	.4040	67	1.1694	.9205	.3907	2.3559
23	.4014	.3907	.9205	.4245	68	1.1868	.9272	.3746	2.4751
24	.4189	.4067	.9135	.4452	69	1.2043	.9336	.3584	2.6051
25	.4363	.4226	.9063	.4663	70	1.2217	.9397	.3420	2.7475
26	.4538	.4384	.8988	.4877	71	1.2392	.9455	.3256	2.9042
27	.4712	.4540	.8910	.5095	72	1.2566	.9511	.3090	3.0777
28	.4887	.4695	.8829	.5317	73	1.2741	.9563	.2924	3.2709
29	.5061	.4848	.8746	.5543	74	1.2915	.9613	.2756	3.4874
30	.5236	.5000	.8660	.5774	75	1.3090	.9659	.2588	3.7321
31	.5411	.5150	.8572	.6009	76	1.3265	.9703	.2419	4.0108
32	.5585	.5299	.8480	.6249	77	1.3439	.9744	.2250	4.3315
33	.5760	.5446	.8387	.6494	78	1.3614	.9781	.2079	4.7046
34	.5934	.5592	.8290	.6745	79	1.3788	.9816	.1908	5.1446
35	.6109	.5736	.8192	.7002	80	1.3963	.9848	.1736	5.6713
36	.6283	.5878	.8090	.7265	81	1.4137	.9877	.1564	6.3138
37	.6458	.6018	.7986	.7536	82	1.4312	.9903	.1392	7.1154
38	.6632	.6157	.7880	.7813	83	1.4486	.9925	.1219	8.1443
39	.6807	.6293	.7771	.8098	84	1.4661	.9945	.1045	9.5144
40	.6981	.6428	.7660	.8391	85	1.4835	.9962	.0872	11.43
41	.7156	.6561	.7547	.8693	86	1.5010	.9976	.0698	14.30
42	.7330	.6691	.7431	.9004	87	1.5184	.9986	.0523	19.08
43	.7505	.6820	.7314	.9325	88	1.5359	.9994	.0349	28.64
44	.7679	.6947	.7193	.9657	89	1.5533	.9998	.0175	57.29

Appendix F-4
Four-place Log Tables

N	0	1	2	3	4	5	6	7	8	9	u. d.
10	0000	0043	0086	0128	0170	0212	0253	0294	0334	0374	4.2
11	0414	0453	0492	0531	0569	0607	0645	0682	0719	0755	3.8
12	0792	0828	0864	0899	0934	0969	1004	1038	1072	1106	3.5
13	1139	1173	1206	1239	1271	1303	1335	1367	1399	1430	3.2
14	1461	1492	1523	1553	1584	1614	1644	1673	1703	1732	3.0
15	1761	1790	1818	1847	1875	1903	1931	1959	1987	2014	2.8
16	2041	2068	2095	2122	2148	2175	2201	2227	2253	2279	2.6
17	2304	2330	2355	2380	2405	2430	2455	2480	2504	2529	2.5
18	2553	2577	2601	2625	2648	2672	2695	2718	2742	2765	2.4
19	2788	2810	2833	2856	2878	2900	2923	2945	2967	2989	2.2
20	3010	3032	3054	3075	3096	3118	3139	3160	3181	3201	2.1
21	3222	3243	3263	3284	3304	3324	3345	3365	3385	3404	2.0
22	3424	3444	3464	3483	3502	3522	3541	3560	3579	3598	1.9
23	3617	3636	3655	3674	3692	3711	3729	3747	3766	3784	1.8
24	3802	3820	3838	3856	3874	3892	3909	3927	3945	3962	1.8
25	3979	3997	4014	4031	4048	4065	4082	4099	4116	4133	1.7
26	4150	4166	4183	4200	4216	4232	4249	4265	4281	4298	1.6
27	4314	4330	4346	4362	4378	4393	4409	4425	4440	4456	1.6
28	4472	4487	4502	4518	4533	4548	4564	4579	4594	4609	1.5
29	4624	4639	4654	4669	4683	4698	4713	4728	4742	4757	1.5
30	4771	4786	4800	4814	4829	4843	4857	4871	4886	4900	1.4
31	4914	4928	4942	4955	4969	4983	4997	5011	5024	5038	1.4
32	5051	5065	5079	5092	5105	5119	5132	5145	5159	5172	1.3
33	5185	5198	5211	5224	5237	5250	5263	5276	5289	5302	1.3
34	5315	5328	5340	5353	5366	5378	5391	5403	5416	5428	1.3
35	5441	5453	5465	5478	5490	5502	5514	5527	5539	5551	1.2
36	5563	5575	5587	5599	5611	5623	5635	5647	5658	5670	1.2
37	5682	5694	5705	5717	5729	5740	5752	5763	5775	5786	1.2
38	5798	5809	5821	5832	5843	5855	5866	5877	5888	5899	1.1
39	5911	5922	5933	5944	5955	5966	5977	5988	5999	6010	1.1
40	6021	6031	6042	6053	6064	6075	6085	6096	6107	6117	1.1
41	6128	6138	6149	6160	6170	6180	6191	6201	6212	6222	1.0
42	6232	6243	6253	6263	6274	6284	6294	6304	6314	6325	1.0
43	6335	6345	6355	6365	6375	6385	6395	6405	6415	6425	1.0
44	6435	6444	6454	6464	6474	6484	6493	6503	6513	6522	1.0
45	6532	6542	6551	6561	6571	6580	6590	6599	6609	6618	1.0
46	6628	6637	6646	6656	6665	6675	6684	6693	6702	6712	.9
47	6721	6730	6739	6749	6758	6767	6776	6785	6794	6803	.9
48	6812	6821	6830	6839	6848	6857	6866	6875	6884	6893	.9
49	6902	6911	6920	6928	6937	6946	6955	6964	6972	6981	.9
50	6990	6998	7007	7016	7024	7033	7042	7050	7059	7067	.9
51	7076	7084	7093	7101	7110	7118	7126	7135	7143	7152	.8
52	7160	7168	7177	7185	7193	7202	7210	7218	7226	7235	.8
53	7243	7251	7259	7267	7275	7284	7292	7300	7308	7316	.8
54	7324	7332	7340	7348	7356	7364	7372	7380	7388	7396	.8

N	0	1	2	3	4	5	6	7	8	9	u. d.
55	7404	7412	7419	7427	7435	7443	7451	7459	7466	7474	.8
56	7482	7490	7497	7505	7513	7520	7528	7536	7543	7551	.8
57	7559	7566	7574	7582	7589	7597	7604	7612	7619	7627	.8
58	7634	7642	7649	7657	7664	7672	7679	7686	7694	7701	.7
59	7709	7716	7723	7731	7738	7745	7752	7760	7767	7774	.7
60	7782	7789	7796	7803	7810	7818	7825	7832	7839	7846	.7
61	7853	7860	7868	7875	7882	7889	7896	7903	7910	7917	.7
62	7924	7931	7938	7945	7952	7959	7966	7973	7980	7987	.7
63	7993	8000	8007	8014	8021	8028	8035	8041	8048	8055	.7
64	8062	8069	8075	8082	8089	8096	8102	8109	8116	8122	.7
65	8129	8136	8142	8149	8156	8162	8169	8176	8182	8189	.7
66	8195	8202	8209	8215	8222	8228	8235	8241	8248	8254	.7
67	8261	8267	8274	8280	8287	8293	8299	8306	8312	8319	.6
68	8325	8331	8338	8344	8351	8357	8363	8370	8376	8382	.6
69	8388	8395	8401	8407	8414	8420	8426	8432	8439	8445	.6
70	8451	8457	8463	8470	8476	8482	8488	8494	8500	8506	.6
71	8513	8519	8525	8531	8537	8543	8549	8555	8561	8567	.6
72	8573	8579	8585	8591	8597	8603	8609	8615	8621	8627	.6
73	8633	8639	8645	8651	8657	8663	8669	8675	8681	8686	.6
74	8692	8698	8704	8710	8716	8722	8727	8733	8739	8745	.6
75	8751	8756	8762	8768	8774	8779	8785	8791	8797	8802	.6
76	8808	8814	8820	8825	8831	8837	8842	8848	8854	8859	.6
77	8865	8871	8876	8882	8887	8893	8899	8904	8910	8915	.6
78	8921	8927	8932	8938	8943	8949	8954	8960	8965	8971	.6
79	8976	8982	8987	8993	8998	9004	9009	9015	9020	9025	.5
80	9031	9036	9042	9047	9053	9058	9063	9069	9074	9079	.5
81	9085	9090	9096	9101	9106	9112	9117	9122	9128	9133	.5
82	9138	9143	9149	9154	9159	9165	9170	9175	9180	9186	.5
83	9191	9196	9201	9206	9212	9217	9222	9227	9232	9238	.5
84	9243	9248	9253	9258	9263	9269	9274	9279	9284	9289	.5
85	9294	9299	9304	9309	9315	9320	9325	9330	9335	9340	.5
86	9345	9350	9355	9360	9365	9370	9375	9380	9385	9390	.5
87	9395	9400	9405	9410	9415	9420	9425	9430	9435	9440	.5
88	9445	9450	9455	9460	9465	9469	9474	9479	9484	9489	.5
89	9494	9499	9504	9509	9513	9518	9523	9528	9533	9538	.5
90	9542	9547	9552	9557	9562	9566	9571	9576	9581	9586	.5
91	9590	9595	9600	9605	9609	9614	9619	9624	9628	9633	.5
92	9638	9643	9647	9652	9657	9661	9666	9671	9675	9680	.5
93	9685	9689	9694	9699	9703	9708	9713	9717	9722	9727	.5
94	9731	9736	9741	9745	9750	9754	9759	9763	9768	9773	.5
95	9777	9782	9786	9791	9795	9800	9805	9809	9814	9818	.5
96	9823	9827	9832	9836	9841	9845	9850	9854	9859	9863	.5
97	9868	9872	9877	9881	9886	9890	9894	9899	9903	9908	.4
98	9912	9917	9921	9926	9930	9934	9939	9943	9948	9952	.4
99	9956	9961	9965	9969	9974	9978	9983	9987	9991	9996	.4

Appendix F-5
Summary of Exponents in Calculations

It is very convenient to express very large or very small quantities by means of whole numbers with suitable exponents. For instance, the rather cumbersome number 350,000,000 may be written as 3.5×10^8, which really means that 3.5 is multiplied by *ten*, eight times. The small number above and to the side of the figure 10 is called the *exponent*. In this case the exponent is 8. Numbers less than 1 have *negative* exponents. Thus five ten-thousandths may be expressed in the following ways:

$$.0005, \quad \text{or} \quad 5 \times 10^{-4}, \quad \text{or} \quad \frac{5}{10,000}, \quad \text{or} \quad \frac{5}{10^4}.$$

This representation is really a shorthand method of working with inconveniently large or small quantities, and the student should become thoroughly familiar with it, as it is used extensively in technical work. The table below will be found helpful in making clear how the proper exponent is found.

$$
\begin{aligned}
1 &= 10^0 &&= \text{units} \\
10 &= 10^1 &&= \text{tens} \\
100 &= 10^2 &&= \text{hundreds} \\
1,000 &= 10^3 &&= \text{thousands (kilo.)} \\
1,000,000 &= 10^6 &&= \text{millions} \quad \text{(mega.)} \\
1 &= 10^0 &&= \text{units} \\
.1 &= 10^{-1} &&= \text{tenths} \\
.01 &= 10^{-2} &&= \text{hundredths} \\
.001 &= 10^{-3} &&= \text{thousandths (milli.)} \\
.000001 &= 10^{-6} &&= \text{millionths} \quad \text{(micro.)}
\end{aligned}
$$

The following rules, when mastered, provide an exceptionally easy method of handling large numbers:

When multiplying numbers, *add* the exponents.

When dividing numbers, *subtract* the exponents.

When squaring a number, *double* its exponent.

When obtaining a square root, *halve* the exponent.

When transferring an exponent across the dividing line, *change its sign.*

EXAMPLE:

Express the following quantities in simple numbers by the use of exponents. (a) 342,000,000,000. (b) 9,653,000. (c) .0000084. (d) .000432.

Answers: (a) 3.42×10^{11}. (b) 9.653×10^6. (c) 8.4×10^{-6}. (d) 4.32×10^{-4}.

EXAMPLE:

6.28×10^{18} electrons flowing past a given point in a second consitute a current of 1 ampere. How many electrons flow past a given point in a second when the number of amperes is (a) 600? (b) 0.002?

Solutions: (a) $6.28 \times 10^{18} \times 6 \times 10^2 = 37.68 \times 10^{20}$ or 3.768×10^{21}. (b) $6.28 \times 10^{18} \times 2 \times 10^{-3} = 12.56 \times 10^{15}$ or 1.256×10^{16}.

Appendix F-6
Frequently Used Angles and Their Functions

Angle	sin A	cos A	tan A	cot A	sec A	csc A
0°	0	1	0	∞	1	∞
30°	$\dfrac{1}{2}$	$\dfrac{\sqrt{3}}{2}$	$\dfrac{\sqrt{3}}{3}$	$\sqrt{3}$	$\dfrac{2\sqrt{3}}{3}$	2
45°	$\dfrac{\sqrt{2}}{2}$	$\dfrac{\sqrt{2}}{2}$	1	1	$\sqrt{2}$	$\sqrt{2}$
60°	$\dfrac{\sqrt{3}}{2}$	$\dfrac{1}{2}$	$\sqrt{3}$	$\dfrac{\sqrt{3}}{3}$	2	$\dfrac{2\sqrt{3}}{3}$
90°	1	0	∞	0	∞	1
120°	$\dfrac{\sqrt{3}}{2}$	$-\dfrac{1}{2}$	$-\sqrt{3}$	$-\dfrac{\sqrt{3}}{3}$	-2	$\dfrac{2\sqrt{3}}{3}$
180°	0	-1	0	∞	-1	∞
270°	-1	0	∞	0	∞	-1
360°	0	1	0	∞	1	∞

Appendix F-7
Mathematical Symbols and Abbreviations

SYMBOLS

$+$	plus (addition)
$-$	minus (subtraction)
$\pm$ $\mp$	plus or minus, (minus or plus)
$\times$	times, by (multiplication)
$\div, /$	divided by
$:$	is to (ratio)
$::$	equals, as, so is
$\therefore$	therefore
$=$	equals
$\sim$ $\approx$	approximately equals
$>$	greater than
$<$	less than
$\geqq$	greater than or equals
$\leqq$	less than or equals
$\neq$	not equal to
$\doteq$	approaches
∞	varies as
∞	infinity
$\parallel$	parallel to
$\circ$	degrees (arc or thermometer)
$'$	minutes or feet
$''$	seconds or inches
( ), [ ], { }	parentheses, brackets, braces
$\angle, \perp$	angle, perpendicular to
Σ	summation of
Δ	difference

ABBREVIATIONS

a-c	alternating-current
a-f	audio-frequency
B	flux density
C	capacitance
cemf	instantaneous counter electromotive force
cm	centimeters
cps	cycles per second
C_T	total capacitance
d	distance between points
d-c	direct-current
de	change in voltage
di	change in current
dq	change in charge
dt	change in time
E	voltage
e	instantaneous voltage
E_c	capacitive voltage
e_c	instantaneous capacitive voltage
E_L	inductive voltage
e_L	instantaneous inductive voltage
E_m	maximum voltage
E_{max}	maximum voltage
emf	electromotive force
E_p	primary voltage
E_s	secondary voltage

f	frequency
f_r	frequency at resonance
H	magnetizing flux
h	henry
I	current
i	instantaneous current
I_c	capacitive current
i_c	instantaneous capacitive current
I_{eff}	effective current
IF	intermediate-frequency
I_L	inductive current
i_L	instantaneous inductive current
I_m	maximum current
I_{max}	maximum current
I_p	plate current
I_R	current through resistance
i_R	instaneous current through resistance
I_s	secondary current
I_T	total current
$I\phi$	phase current
K	coefficient of coupling
kc	kilocycle
L	inductance
L-C	inductance-capacitance
L-C-R	inductance-capacitance-resistance
L_T	total inductance
mh	millihenry
N	revolutions per minute
N_p	primary turns
N_s	secondary turns
P	power
p	instantaneous power
P_{ap}	apparent power
P_{av}	average power
P_p	primary power
P_s	secondary power
Q	charge or quality
q	instantaneous charge
RF	radio-frequency
R_G	grid resistance
R_0	load resistance
rpm	revolutions per minute
sq cm	square centimeters
t	time constant
t	time (seconds)
μf	microfarad
$\mu\mu f$	micromicrofarad
V, v	volt
X_c	capacitive reactance
X_L	inductive reactance
Z	impedance
Z_0	load impedance
Z_p	primary impedance
Z_s	secondary impedance
Z_T	total impedance

Appendix F-8
Electrical and Physical Symbols

Quantity	Symbol	Equation	Practical unit	Subrationalized mks.
Length	l		centimeter	Meter
Distance	d		centimeter	Meter
Mass	m			Kilogram
Time	t		second	Second
Velocity	v	$v = l/t$	cm/sec	Meter/sec
Acceleration	α	$\alpha = v/t$	cm/sec^2	Meter/sec^2
Force	F	$F = \eta\alpha$		$\dfrac{joule}{meter} = $ newton
Work	W	$W = Fl$	joule	Joule
Power	P	$P = w/t$	watt	Watt
Permittivity of medium	ϵ		$\dfrac{1}{(9 \times 10^{N})}$ farad/cm	$\dfrac{1}{(36\pi \times 10^{9})}$ farad/meter
Charge	q	$F = q_1 q_2/E r^2$	coulomb	Coulomb
Capacitance	C	$C = q/v$	farad	Farad
Potential difference	V or E	$V = \dfrac{W}{q}$	volt	Volt
e. m. f	e	$e = -d\phi/dt$	volt	Volt
Current	I	$I = dq/dt$	ampere	Ampere
Resistance	R	$R = V/I$	ohm	ohm
Resistivity	ρ		ohm/cm	Ohm/meter
Conductance	G	$G = 1/R$	mho	mho
Conductivity	γ	$\gamma = 1/\mu$	mho/cm	mho/meter
Permeability	μ		10^{-9} henry/cm	$\dfrac{4\pi \times 10^{-7} \text{ henry}}{meter}$
Reluctivity	ν	$\nu = 1/\mu$		
Pole strength	m	$F = m_1 m_2/\mu\tau^2$		Weber
Magnetomotive force	F		$\frac{1}{4}\pi$ ampere turn	Ampere turn
Magnetizing force	H	$H = F/I$	$\frac{1}{4}\pi$ ampere turn	Ampere turn/m
Magnetic flux density	B	$B = \mu H$	weber/cm^2	Weber/meter^2
Magnetic flux	ϕ	$\phi = BA$	weber or volt-sec	Weber = volt-sec
Reluctance	R	$R = F/\phi$	$\dfrac{\frac{1}{4}\pi \text{ ampere turn}}{weber}$	$\dfrac{ampere\ turn}{weber}$
Inductance	L	$L = e/(dI/dt)$	henry	Henry

Appendix F-9
Electrical Multiples and Submultiples

Multiply reading in	By	To obtain reading in	Multiply reading in	By	To obtain reading in
Amperes	1,000,000,000,000	micromicro-amperes	Mhos	1,000	millimhos
			Microamperes	.000,001	amperes
Amperes	1,000,000	microamperes	Microfarads	.000,001	farads
Amperes	1,000	milliamperes	Microhenrys	.000,001	henrys
Cycles	.000,001	megacycles	Micromhos	.000,001	mhos
Cycles	.001	kilocycles	Microvolts	.000,001	volts
Farads	1,000,000,000,000	micromicro-farads	Micromicro-farads	.000,000,000,001	farads
Farads	1,000,000	microfarads	Milliamperes	.001	amperes
Farads	1,000	millifarads	Millihenrys	.001	henrys
Henrys	1,000,000	microhenrys	Millimhos	.001	mhos
Henrys	1,000	millihenrys	Millivolts	.001	volts
Kilocycles	1,000	cycles	Milliwatts	.001	watts
Kilowatts	1,000	watts	Volts	1,000,000	microvolts
Megacycles	1,000,000	cycles	Volts	1,000	millivolts
Mhos	1,000,000	micromhos	Watts	1,000	milliwatts

Appendix F-10
Trigonometric Solution of Triangles

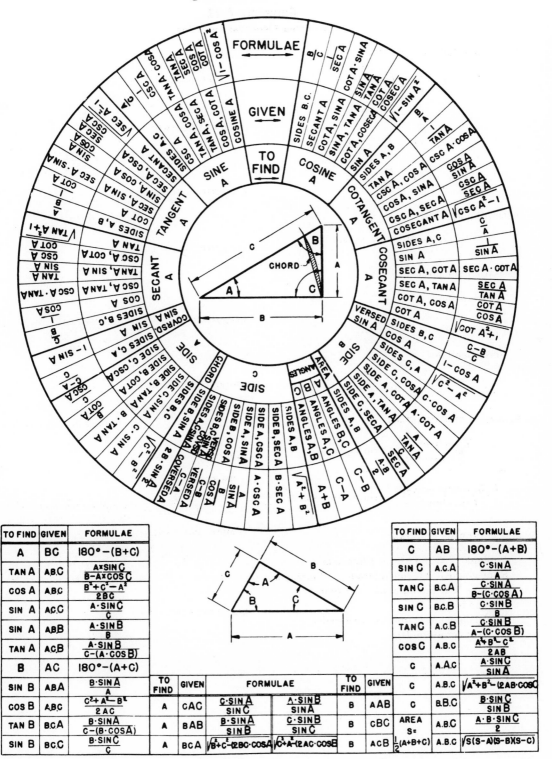

TO FIND	GIVEN	FORMULAE
A	BC	$180° - (B+C)$
TAN A	A,B,C	$\dfrac{A \times \sin C}{B - A \times \cos C}$
COS A	A,B,C	$\dfrac{B^2 + C^2 - A^2}{2BC}$
SIN A	A,C,C	$\dfrac{A \cdot \sin C}{C}$
SIN A	A,B,B	$\dfrac{A \cdot \sin B}{B}$
TAN A	A,C,B	$\dfrac{A \cdot \sin B}{C - (A \cdot \cos B)}$
B	AC	$180° - (A+C)$
SIN B	A,B,A	$\dfrac{B \cdot \sin A}{A}$
COS B	A,B,C	$\dfrac{C^2 + A^2 - B^2}{2AC}$
TAN B	B,C,A	$\dfrac{B \cdot \sin A}{C - (B \cdot \cos A)}$
SIN B	B,C,C	$\dfrac{B \cdot \sin C}{C}$

TO FIND	GIVEN	FORMULAE		TO FIND	GIVEN	FORMULAE
A	C,A,C	$\dfrac{C \cdot \sin A}{\sin C}$	$\dfrac{A \cdot \sin B}{\sin A}$	B	A,A,B	
A	B,A,B	$\dfrac{B \cdot \sin A}{\sin B}$	$\dfrac{C \cdot \sin B}{\sin C}$	B	C,B,C	AREA $S=$
A	B,C,A	$\sqrt{B^2 + C^2 - (2BC \cdot \cos A)}$	$\sqrt{C^2 + A^2 - (2AC \cdot \cos B)}$	B	A,C,B	$\tfrac{1}{2}(A+B+C)$

TO FIND	GIVEN	FORMULAE
C	AB	$180° - (A+B)$
SIN C	A,C,A	$\dfrac{C \cdot \sin A}{A}$
TAN C	B,C,A	$\dfrac{C \cdot \sin A}{B - (C \cdot \cos A)}$
SIN C	B,C,B	$\dfrac{C \cdot \sin B}{B}$
TAN C	A,C,B	$\dfrac{C \cdot \sin B}{A - (C \cdot \cos B)}$
COS C	A,B,C	$\dfrac{A^2 + B^2 - C^2}{2AB}$
C	A,A,C	$\dfrac{A \cdot \sin C}{\sin A}$
C	A,B,C	$\sqrt{A^2 + B^2 - (2AB \cdot \cos C)}$
C	B,B,C	$\dfrac{B \cdot \sin C}{\sin B}$
C	A,B,C	$\dfrac{A \cdot B \cdot \sin C}{2}$
C	A,B,C	$\sqrt{S(S-A)(S-B)(S-C)}$

Appendix F-11
Common Electrical Formulas

OHM'S LAW FOR D-C CIRCUITS

$$I = \frac{E}{R} = \frac{P}{E} = \sqrt{\frac{P}{R}}$$

$$R = \frac{E}{I} = \frac{P}{I^2} = \frac{E^2}{P}$$

$$E = IR = \frac{P}{I} = \sqrt{PR}$$

$$P = EI = \frac{E^2}{R} = I^2 R$$

RESISTORS IN SERIES

$$R_T = R_1 + R_2 + \cdots$$

RESISTORS IN PARALLEL

Two resistors:

$$R_T = \frac{R_1 R_2}{R_1 + R_2}$$

More than two:

$$\frac{1}{R_T} = \frac{1}{R_1} + \frac{1}{R_2} + \frac{1}{R_3} + \cdots$$

RL CIRCUIT TIME CONSTANT

$$\frac{L \text{ (in henrys)}}{R \text{ (in ohms)}} = t \text{ (in seconds)}$$

or

$$\frac{L \text{ (in microhenrys)}}{R \text{ (in ohms)}} = t \text{ (in microseconds)}$$

RC CIRCUIT TIME CONSTANT

R (ohms) $\times$ C (farads) $= t$ (seconds)

R (megohms) $\times$ C (microfarads) $= t$ (seconds)

R (ohms $\times$ C (microfarads) $= t$ (micro-seconds)

R (megohms) $\times$ C (micromicrofarads) $= t$ (microseconds)

CAPACITORS IN SERIES

Two capacitors:

$$C_T = \frac{C_1 C_2}{C_1 + C_2}$$

More than two:

$$\frac{1}{C_T} = \frac{1}{C_1} + \frac{1}{C_2} + \frac{1}{C_3} + \cdots$$

CAPACITORS IN PARALLEL

$$C_T = C_1 + C_2 + \cdots$$

CAPACITIVE REACTANCE

$$X_C = \frac{1}{2\pi f C}$$

IMPEDANCE IN AN RC CIRCUIT (SERIES)

$$Z = \sqrt{R^2 + X_C^2}$$

INDUCTORS IN SERIES

$$L_T = L_1 + L_2 + \cdots$$

(no coupling between coils)

INDUCTORS IN PARALLEL

Two inductors:

$$L_T = \frac{L_1 L_2}{L_1 + L_2} \quad \text{(no coupling between coils)}$$

More than two:

$$\frac{1}{L_T} = \frac{1}{L_1} + \frac{1}{L_2} + \frac{1}{L_3} + \cdots$$

(no coupling between coils)

INDUCTIVE REACTANCE

$$X_L = 2\pi f L$$

Appendix F-12
Ohm's-law Formulas for D-c and A-c Circuits

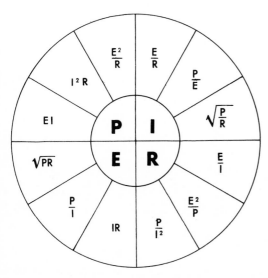
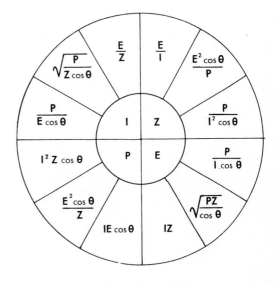

The fundamental Ohm's-law formulas for d-c circuits are given by

$$E = IR, \quad I = \frac{E}{R}, \quad R = \frac{E}{I}, \quad P = EI$$

where I = current in amperes,
R = resistance in ohms,
E = potential across R in volts,
P = power in watts.

Solution for quantities printed in boldface type (center section) is calculated by substituting known values in the formulas adjoining the respective center sections.

The fundamental Ohm's-law formulas for a-c circuits are given by

$$I = \frac{E}{Z}, \quad Z = \frac{E}{I}, \quad E = IZ, \quad P = EI \cos \theta$$

where I = current in amperes,
Z = impedance in ohms,
E = potential across Z in volts,
P = powers in watts,
θ = phase angle in degrees.

Solution for quantities printed in boldface type (center section) is calculated by substituting known values in the formulas adjoining the respective center sections.

Index